The New Naturalist 1

A SURVEY OF IRISH NATU

IRELAND

A NATURAL HISTORY

Editors

Sarah A. Corbet

S.M.Walters, ScD, VMH

Prof. Richard West, ScD, FRS, FGS

David Streeter, FIBiol

Derek A. Ratcliffe

The aim of this series is to interest the general reader
in the wildlife of Britain and Ireland by recapturing
the enquiring spirit of the old naturalists. The editors
believe that the natural pride of the public in the
native flora and fauna, to which must be added
concern for their conservation, is best fostered by
maintaining a high standard of accuracy combined
with clarity of exposition in presenting the results of
modern scientific research.

Ireland

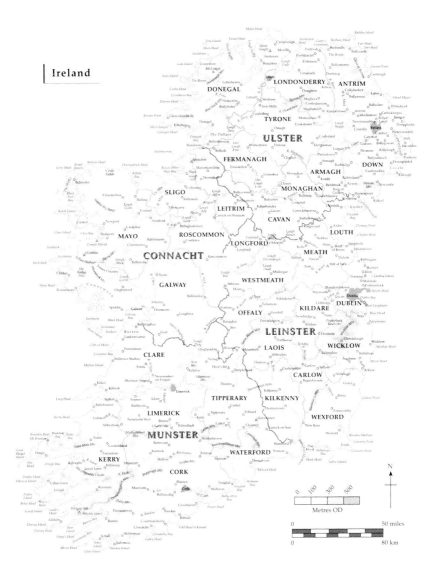

From F.H.A. Aalen, K. Whelan & M. Stout (eds) (1997) *Atlas of the Irish Rural Landscape.*
Cork University Press.

The New Naturalist

IRELAND

David Cabot

With 8 colour plates and over 230 black and white photographs and line drawings

HarperCollins*Publishers*

HarperCollinsPublishers
London Glasgow Sydney Auckland
Toronto Johannesburg

For my parents, Isabel & Sid.

First published 1999

ISBN 000 220079 1(Hardback)
ISBN 000 220080 5 (Paperback)
Printed and bound in England by The Bath Press Plc
Colour reproduction by Colourscan, Singapore

Contents

List of Plates

Plate 1
Remains of a sixth century monastery, including a later twelfth century round tower, Devenish Island, Lower Lough Erne, Co. Fermanagh
Crucifixion slab, early Christian hermitage, Duvillaun More, Co. Mayo
Mweelrea Mountain with Killary Harbour and Maumturk Mountains in the distance
Red deer stag and hind

Plate 2
Part of the northeast facing cliffs, Benbulbin mountain range, Co. Sligo
Lowland blanket bog with characteristic surface pools. Glenamoy, Co. Mayo
Bank of hand cut blanket bog, Co. Galway
Irish heath in April. Bellacragher Bay, Co. Mayo

Plate 3
Colony of naturalised pitcher plants on Derrychashel raised bog, Co. Westmeath
The River Suck below Ballinasloe before joining the River Shannon
Lough Neagh, the largest lake in Ireland. A view to the southwest, overlooking Toome and the eel traps
The otter is more widespread and abundant in Ireland than in any other European country

Plate 4
A Connemara river in flood, acidic in nature, rich in oxygen, and conduit for sea trout from the nearby sea to freshwater lakes
Mullagh More with slumped beds of carboniferous limestone. The tree in the foreground would hardly support a hanging man
Spring gentians, one of the glories of the Burren, Co. Clare
Rahasane Turlough, Co. Galway, one of Ireland's most celebrated wintering wildfowl wetlands

Plate 5
Glen Inchiquin, Co. Kerry, with Lough Inchiquin and Uragh Wood in the distance
Willow and alder carr woodland, near Newport, Co. Mayo
Uragh Wood. Co. Kerry – an ancient sessile oak woodland
Silver birch woodland, Killadangan, near Westport, Co. Mayo

Plate 6

Abandoned farmland in west Mayo. The 'fossilised' lazy beds or old potato ridges testify to the former importance of these lands

Greenland white-fronted geese, formerly confined to raised and blanket bog-lands but now found principally on improved grasslands as here on the North Slob, Co. Wexford, their most important habitat in Ireland

A mosaic of farmland with intact hedgerow systems, Co. Fermanagh

Ballydavid Head, Co. Kerry, with Smerwick Harbour in the distance. One of the wildest stretches of coastline where the Atlantic waves have eaten back the rocks to create dramatic cliff scenery. A favoured habitat of the chough

Plate 7

Inner Galway Bay where long sea inlets penetrate the land providing excellent conditions for the cultivation of oysters

Cliffs of Moher, Co. Clare, where the horizontally bedded sandstone cliffs provide breeding sites for an abundance of seabirds

Banna Strand, Co. Kerry, with the Dingle peninsula in the distance. One of the many fine beaches and associated sand dune systems found along the Irish coastline

Great Blasket island, Co. Kerry. Occupied until 1952, the island is now an important haul-out area for Atlantic grey seals

Plate 8

Increasing numbers of barnacle geese are wintering in northwestern and western coastal areas

Tory Island, Co. Donegal, one of the remotest and bleakest of inhabited islands of Ireland. It is an important observation point for migratory seabirds

The gannet is the largest seabird in Ireland, and numbered some 24,700 breeding pairs in five colonies during 1984–8

The power of the Atlantic is slowly sculpting and forming new coastal land-scapes along the western seaboard

Editors' Preface

Ireland has a long and proud tradition of natural history, and some of its leading figures have made outstanding contributions to the knowledge and understanding of its important segment of the European flora and fauna. Some of its most distinctive features have achieved fame as gems of the international scene of natural wonders: the fantastic limestone pavements of the Burren with their unique plant assemblage; the desolate blanket bogs and rocky heaths of Mayo and Connemara; the magnificent mossy oak woods of Kerry and Cork; the spectacular seabird islands and headlands; and the greatly varied series of lakes and fens among both lowlands and mountains.

There is a large literature on all this, yet few Irish natural historians have tackled the subject as a whole. Geraldus Cambrensis ambitiously had a shot within his all-embracing work on Ireland *Topographia Hiberniae* around 1188, but it was not until 1944 that the doyen of Irish naturalists, Robert Lloyd Praeger, tried again with his *Natural History of Ireland*. This is, as its sub-title said, 'a sketch of its flora and fauna', and though valuable as a summary, it still left a need for something much more comprehensive. The New Naturalist Editors were mindful of the scope for a modern treatment of the subject within the series, but it seemed to require such a breadth and depth of knowledge and insight that a suitable author was not easily to be found.

Happily, David Cabot proved to be just the person for the task. He has applied his unrivalled all-round personal experience of Ireland, its wildlife and physical features, and his assiduous literature research, to the compilation of this volume. Since plants and animals know no political frontiers, it has the particular merit of dealing with Ireland as a geographical and ecological whole. Little escapes the author's breadth of grasp, and enthusiasts for all the main groups of plants and animals will find much to excite and inform their interest. The main habitats are all comprehensively explored, and the mysteries of the special Irish features – such as turloughs, slobs and callows – revealed. For those craving further knowledge, a very full list of references is given. David Cabot's book does justice to the rich variety of Irish wildlife, and its illustrations convey the similarly diverse beauty of the country it inhabits.

As well as providing an in-depth treatment of the fascinating Irish flora and fauna, their habitats and their history, *Ireland* examines the topical concerns of nature conservation and human impact. We are delighted to present it as a much-needed and worthy addition to the other regional works in the series, and as a tribute to the many generations of Irish naturalists whose labours have helped the author to paint this portrait.

Author's Foreword

My endeavours for this book began in 1959 when I 'fell out of the sky' into County Wexford, in a sort of horizontal manner from the Fishguard-Rosslare Ferry, one warm, sunny August afternoon. Making my way northwards, the first arresting ornithological surprise was a hooded crow frisking some rubbish on a heap of refuse outside New Ross. They were a rarity where I had just come from.

That innocent encounter set me thinking. Why were these crows so numerous and living so far south in Ireland, while Britain was bereft of them at the same latitudes? Their only claw-hold was in Scotland, a more northerly territory than the most northern extremity of Ireland. What extra inducements were on offer in this low green island, some 80 kilometres west of Wales? Not only did these grey crows buck the code of 'conventional' distribution behaviour, but other birds and some mammals were at it too, and so were plants. Straight away I was intrigued by the natural history questions posed by islands.

Islands, because of their remoteness, beg scores of difficult questions from biologists. How and when did they acquire their flora and fauna? How many times did the ice wipe out the incipient growth in Ireland and northwestern Europe to produce a clean slate? Was the slate entirely clean or were there species lurking in a concealed spot, dormant, quiescent, and waiting for conditions to be right again? Or did they all travel from the Continent at various stages in time, attempting a new onslaught every time the climate allowed a move? What delayed the absentees – nowhere to be seen in Ireland today, but present on the larger, nearby land mass? Have any of the island dwellers turned into new species or varieties in their cloistered gene pool? Do island plants and animals practice a different ecology from that of their brothers and sisters elsewhere? And if so, why?

While continuing to tread the hot road I pondered these questions. Eventually a bruised Renault 4, answering my thumb, stopped. The owner, profusely apologetic for the agglomeration of dirty nappies adrift on the back seat, displayed such a virtuoso performance of wild words and images that I was seduced into the domain of supreme significance in Ireland: the world of imagination. The crows flapped out of my head. Eventually, after an unexpected three week digression – I was only to have stayed for two nights as a guest with a farming family deep in the lush Carlow countryside – I arrived at Trinity College, Dublin, to pursue my studies in Natural Sciences. The crow came back to nag me. It was the beginning of an enduring fascination for the country I went on to adopt as my home. In other words, I fell in love with Ireland under the unlikely sign of the crow, stayed on, married her, and never ceased to be enraptured.

The intention of this book is to provide a descriptive overview of the natural history of Ireland. Such a book involves choices and judgement concerning what to include and what to leave out. My aim throughout has been to present a balanced view.

First came the question of the structure of the book. Perhaps it would be helpful to explain my philosophy of approach on this point. The first chapter is about earlier naturalists, and sets in place the basic natural history rubrics of Ireland. Some knowledge of these naturalists and their works provides a background to what follows in the subsequent chapters. The second chapter gives an explanation of Ireland's biological history.

The narrative strategy adopted in the rest of the book is simple. It is based on the configuration of the Irish landscape. We start high up with mountains and uplands, then come down to lower levels in subsequent chapters before moving out towards the sea. The journey across the lower altitudes takes us in and out of the vast expanses of peatlands and the great lakes and rivers that play such a dominant role in the landscape. The Burren and turloughs, internationally famous treasures of Ireland and Europe, deserve a special chapter to themselves. The small remnants of ancient broadleaved woodlands make up the following chapter. Farmland, replacing ancient woodlands, commands most of the land area of the country and is discussed next. As a modified ecosystem it provides many opportunities for wildlife. Then we move on to the coastline, the islands and finally the sea.

The final chapter, conservation of nature, explores the developments and milestones in our efforts to protect and manage the natural environment in Ireland. The chapter concludes with a forward look at what contribution Ireland has to offer Europe with regard to its natural heritage.

Thus the book has been structured on nine major habitats or what might be better called 'eco-zones' of Ireland and concludes with a review of what care is taken of them today. I have tried to explain the principal ecological characteristics of each habitat before moving on to particular issues, or sometimes key species, which are highlighted and treated in greater detail. The selection of specific issues was a difficult task, but it had to be done if the book was to stay within sensible limits. I have also taken a 'gazetteer' approach to each habitat, mentioning as many sites of interest as possible in the hope that people will visit and enjoy them.

Throughout the preparation of the book I have been conscious of the imbalance of information on Ireland's natural history. I have drawn extensively upon a sometimes thin and scattered literature, not always as up-to-date as I would have wished it to be. I have also dug deep into my own experience, gained over almost 40 years' field work and fortified by three trips to Greenland in pursuit of one of my special interests, the barnacle goose. However, it will be clear that it has been impossible for a single person in one book to deal with every facet of Ireland's natural history in great detail. One would have to write a series of monographs to do the subject justice. So there are many caveats and limitations to the book and I hope that these will be clearly understood.

I have tried to write in a simple, easily understood language for the non-specialist. I would have preferred to use scientific names alongside common names throughout the text. However, in the interests of reducing the text length, scientific names may be found in the index. In several instances their use cannot be avoided when dealing with subspecies or derivations of common names. Also where ordinary names do not exist, as in the case of most mosses, liverworts, insects, marine invertebrates and numerous other organisms, there is no alternative but to use their scientific names. Place names have been taken from the maps of the *Discovery Series* of the Ordnance Survey of Ireland 1:50,000 published by the Government of Ireland and, where not available, from the 1:126,720 series. Following this reference source some hallowed names have been changed, e.g. 'Ben Bulben', Co. Sligo, becomes 'Benbulbin' and so on. However, concerning Connemara I have used 'Twelve Bens' in preference to the Ordnance Survey 'Twelve Pins'. I have used the second edition of *The Census Catalogue of the Flora of Ireland* by Scannell & Synnott, published by the Stationary Office, Dublin, 1987, for all the common and scientific names of pteridophytes, gymnosperms and angiosperms. For other scientific and common names I have used the following Collins guides: *Freshwater Life of Britain and North-West Europe* (1986) by Fitter & Manuel; *Sea Shore of Britain and Northern Europe* (1996) by Hayward, Nelson-Smith & Shields; *Insects of Britain and Western Europe* (1986 and 1993) by Chinery; *Butterflies and Day-flying Moths of Britain and Europe* (1989) by Chinery; *Mammals of Britain and Europe* (1993) by Macdonald & Barrett; *Ferns, Mosses and Lichens of Britain, Northern and Central Europe* (1983) by Jahns; *Fish of Britain and Europe* (1997) by Miller & Loates and *Birds of Britain and Europe* (1993) by Peterson, Mountfort & Hollom. The following have also been used as references: *The Flora and Fauna of Exmoor National Park – a natural history checklist* (1996) by Giddens, Robbins & Allen (Exmoor Books, Dulverton), *Handbook of the Marine Fauna of North-West Europe* (1991) by Hayward & Ryland (OUP, Oxford), *Atlas of the Bryophytes of Britain and Ireland* by Hill, Preston & Smith (Harley Books, Colchester), *Marine Algae of Northern Ireland* (1994) by Morton (Ulster Museum, Belfast), Charophytes of Great Britain and Ireland *BSBI Handbook No 5* by Moore (BSBI, London), *A portable dictionary of the higher plants* (1990) by Mabberley (CUP, Cambridge) and *New Flora of the British Isles* (2nd ed. 1997) by Stace (CUP, Cambridge).

I should also explain that the frequent comparisons between the natural history of Ireland and the larger island of Britain are necessary to set Ireland in its ecological context alongside its nearest neighbour. These two islands have much in common but there are also many differences between them. Britain harbours a much more diverse natural inheritance, firstly because it is bigger with a wider range of habitats, and secondly because it was more closely and more recently connected with the Continent and thus inherited more plants and animals than Ireland.

Whilst writing this book I have always tried to keep in mind the curiosity, enlightenment and pleasure of the reader and hope that this work will provide an inspiration to whoever comes across it. I was inspired by a series of people who had an abiding interest in nature; I would like this book to perform a similar function.

Acknowledgements

I am indebted to many people for encouraging my early interest in natural history. Firstly my parents, Isabel and Sid, who brought me to nature in the woods and long grass of Vermont where as a family we spent several summer vacations. Later they gave me the space and support to pursue my growing interests. On moving to England in 1946, Leonard Elmhirst, one of the founders of the pioneering social experiment at Dartington Hall, South Devon, became an important mentor. Hugh Boyd, formerly of the Wildfowl and Wetlands Trust, Slimbridge, and later of the Canadian Wildlife Service, provided me with many occasions to develop my field craft, especially with waterfowl, often casting his inimitable critical eye on my work.

As a wild young thing I spent an inordinate amount of time wandering the woods and fields at Dartington Hall studying woodlarks and cirl buntings at a time when they were relatively common. My often despairing biology teacher, Dr Margarita Camps, was tireless yet generally unsuccessful in her attempts to focus my attention on academic work. Over the intervening years I studied waders while living on the tip of Dawlish Warren, Exe Estuary, before it was gobbled up by the sea; boated up and down the River Dart counting duck; explored the South Devon coastline; made my first residential visit to Skokholm Bird Observatory at the very tender age of 15; roamed the wilder corners of Ireland during all my free moments as a student at Trinity College, Dublin, and later working in Dublin at An Foras Forbartha (The National Institute for Physical Planning and Construction Research); spent three summers in northeast Greenland and one in Iceland; roved the Brittany coastline for two summers, and visited many interesting wild spots in Europe from Greece to Portugal, Norway to the Camargue and eastwards to Lithuania, Hungary, Bulgaria and Slovenia. And yet there remains so much more to do and see.

At Trinity College, Dublin, I was taken under the wing of Professor David Webb and joined him on many expeditions to the Burren, Co. Clare. Professor Bill Watts introduced us to the mysteries of the auger, that long steely tube capable of 'stinging' a bog or fen to ten metres deep to reveal the secrets of 10,000 years of vegetational history. These and many other botanical adventures were important and formative: although primarily an ornithologist I have kept up a near specialist interest in botany. Later, when teaching and doing my postgraduate research in the Zoology Department, University College, Galway, I had many opportunities for field work along the western seaboard and its islands. At this time and later both Miriam Rothschild and John Barlee were great sources of inspiration and encouragement. John let me pick some of his best photographs for this book. Fiona Guinness also kindly allowed me to use some of her excellent pictures. Alyn Walsh, of The National Parks and Wildlife Service, also generously provided photographs from his collection.

Over the years I have drawn upon many helpers and co-workers in my long-term ornithological projects on seabirds and barnacle geese. In this context I would like to thank in particular fellow naturalists Dr Brian West, Maurice Cassidy, Michael Viney and Richard Nairn.

I would like to thank the following for reading the book in draft: Jim Hurley of Grange, Co. Wexford, Dr Jim O'Connor, Natural History Museum, Dublin and Maura Scannell, formerly of the National Botanic Gardens, Dublin. They provided many helpful comments and important improvements. The following read specific chapters or excerpts: Ciaran Crummey, formerly of Bord Iascaigh Mhara (The Sea; Islands), Simon Delany, BirdWatch Ireland, Dublin (wetland bird extracts), Dr Paddy Fitzmaurice and Joe Caffrey, Central Fisheries Board, Dublin, (Lakes and Rivers), Oliver Kiely and Dr Emer Rogan, University College, Cork, (Islands; The Sea), Dr Daniel Kelly, Trinity College, Dublin (Broadleaved Woodlands), Professor Brendan Keegan, University College Galway (The Coastline), Michael Canny and colleagues in Dúchas – The Heritage Service (Conservation of Nature) and Dr John Whittow (geological excerpts). All these readers provided helpful comments which improved the text. Any lingering errors or mistakes that might remain are solely my responsibility. Stephen Heery provided additional data on the Shannon callows. Emer Rogan kindly prepared the maps of all the cetacean strandings and Dúchas – The Heritage Service, Dublin, supplied me with information on protected areas for the final chapter. Alison McCloy of the RSPB, Belfast, assisted with information on nature reserves in Northern Ireland. Finbarr Crowley and Catherine Casey provided information on seed-eating finches and corncrake numbers in Ireland respectively. Howard Fox, Donal Synnott and Matthew Jebb of the National Botanic Gardens, Dublin, helped with the checking of botanical names and other queries.

With regard to other contributors, Redmond Cabot was not only a most efficient gatherer and dispatcher of papers and publications whilst I was abroad in Slovenia but also helped with the photographs. Tim Cabot also acted as a reference hunter. Hugh Shields, Royal Irish Academy, was most responsive to my gargantuan quest for publications. Pauric Dempsey, also of the Academy, rounded up some bibliographic material for me. Ken Perry and William McDowell kindly supplied some bibliographic information on some Irish naturalists. I also wish to thank all the listed publishers and individuals for their permissions for reproduction of the illustrations.

Myles Archibald at HarperCollins was most encouraging and helpful throughout the execution of the project while Isobel Smales provided much positive and invaluable editorial assistance. The manuscript also greatly benefited from comments and observations from Dr Derek Ratcliffe.

This book was written during the past two years as I moved around, like an itinerant, whilst working full time on administrative assignments in Central and Eastern Europe. While in Slovenia my good friend Bojc Jermanj, from Ljubljana, provided me with a peaceful working environment over many weekends in his house at Karigador, Croatia, where between my writing bouts we did battle on the table tennis table, each struggling to conquer the other. However, it was the book that nearly conquered me.

My family have had to tolerate numerous absences over many years when I was away on field trips. However, they have always given valuable back-up and support over the years and some help with field work. So thank you Penny, Liam, Tim and Redmond.

Finally, I owe a very special debt of acknowledgement to Véronique Alexandre who was my editorial assistant throughout the writing of the book. Without her help I am sure the text would have been much more ragged and incomprehensible.

David Cabot
October 1998

1

Naturalists and their Works

Ireland has a distinguished tradition of natural historians, stretching back to early Christian times. Charting their contributions here reveals remarkable achievements which prepare the reader for the chapters to follow. Living Irish naturalists, whose work is unfinished, will not be discussed, but many of their accomplishments are quoted in subsequent chapters. Our purpose here is to salute those early pioneers who unravelled much of the rich pageant of Ireland's natural world.

The trail begins with early Christian monks, living close to nature and its moods, who set down their observations of the changing seasons. Their perceptions of the flora and fauna were recorded in poetry that was at first oral before being written down several centuries later as alliterative verse – much of which was botched by antiquarians and modified not inconsiderably by scribes.[1] Emerging from this first wave of nature watchers was a perspicacious monk, Augustin, reckoned by Praeger to have been *the* first Irish naturalist.[2] Augustin flourished around AD 655, when he wrote *Liber de Mirabilibus Sanctae Scripturae*, and his ideas pre-empted by 1,200 years many fundamental concepts about animal distribution expounded by Charles Darwin and others.

During the thirteenth century, Giraldus Cambrensis (*c.*1146–*c.*1223), a Welsh ecclesiastic and travel writer, produced *Topographia Hiberniae*,[3] a vivid

Remains of a sixth or early seventh century monastic settlement perched on the summit of the Bailey Mór, Inishkea North, Co. Mayo.

and robust sketch of Ireland's natural history. Yet another visitor, Gerard Boate (1604–49), a medical doctor from Holland, followed many years later with *Irelands Naturall History* (1652),[4] a popular handbook for 'adventurers' and land investors at the time of Oliver Cromwell. Both the Cambrensis and Boate texts provide the earliest framework for natural history in Ireland. Thereafter Ireland remained a scientific backwater until towards the close of the seventeenth century when a small group of Dublin-based natural philosophers, belonging to the age of new learning and enlightenment, brought a rational approach to the study of natural history. Subsequently many amateurs, divines, members of the landed gentry, businessmen and ordinary folk, together with academics, bore the torch of knowledge. Natural history societies bloomed in Ireland, especially in Belfast, during the heady industrial atmosphere of the Victorian era. These developments triggered off a surge of natural history investigations that gathered momentum throughout the present century.

Early Christian monks and their nature poetry AD 600–800

From their austere and silent cells and monasteries the early Christian monks spoke eloquently of a love for the natural world. These men, scattered throughout the countryside, had plenty of time at their disposal to become the first observers of natural patterns, rhythms and cycles, and of a wide variety of living creatures, all of which had God for a cause. As well as being uplifting, their poetry yields to us today information regarding the natural surroundings with which they were familiar.

One of the better known poems from this period is *Tánic sam* on the coming of summer, taken from a Bodleian Library manuscript dating from the twelfth century but considered by James Carney to have originally been composed in the mid-ninth century or possibly earlier, and published by the Irish scholar Kuno Meyer.[5,6] The version here was translated by Greene & O'Connor.[1]

'Summer's come, healthy free, that bows down the dark wood;
The slim, spry deer jumps and the seal's path is smooth.
The cuckoo sings sweet music, and there is smooth, soft sleep.
Birds skim the quiet hill and the swift grey stags.

The deer's lair is too hot, and active packs cry pleasantly;
The white stretch of strand smiles and the swift sea grows rough.

There is a noise of wanton winds in the palace of the oakwood of Drumdell;
The fine clipped horses who shelter in Cuan Wood are rushing about.

Green bursts out from every plant; leafy is the shoot of the green oakwood.
Summer has come, winter gone, twisted hollies hurt the stag.

The hardy blackbird who owns the thorny wood sings a bass;
The wild, weary sea reposes and the speckled salmon leaps.

Over every land the sun smiles for me a parting greeting to bad weather.
Hounds bark, stags gather, ravens flourish, summer's come.'

Above: Carvings (*c.* seventh to eighth centuries) on slabs, Inishkeel, Co. Donegal. Below: Hunting scene (*c.* 790 AD), Bealin Cross, Co. Westmeath. From F. Henry (1965) *Irish Art in the Early Christian Period (to 800 AD)*. Methuen & Co. Ltd., London.

A limited analysis of some ten of these early nature poems published by Jackson[7] and Greene & O'Connor[1] revealed that of 33 references to mammals, 19 were of (red) deer, stags, hinds and fawns, with many references to the stag's roaring and bellowing.[8] Next in occurrence were swine and boars (five mentions each) followed by three for badgers, two each for wolves and foxes and one each for the otter and seal (grey or common). Of the feathered creatures, the blackbird is cited most frequently (nine mentions) followed by four for the cuckoo and three each for the crane, heron and ducks. There are two references to a 'woodpecker', a species no longer resident in Ireland. Trees feature prominently with most citations being of the oak (six mentions), followed by yew (four) and three each for hazel, rowan and apple. Birch and ash carry two references. Hazel nuts were obviously of great significance, judging by the frequent references to them. Acorns and sloes were the next most noted. Of the plants and wildflowers mentioned, water-cress was the most prominent, followed by ivy, bracken, cottongrass, yellow iris, honeysuckle, marsh pennywort and saxifrage. The monk's culinary interests were reflected by references to wild garlic, fresh leeks and wild onions.

What do these early nature poems tell us about the natural world of Ireland as seen by the monks about 1,150 years ago? Firstly, the location of the observers determined their commentary and, contrary to the general impression that they lived in the fastness of remote islands off the west coast, most monks resided in monasteries located in the Midlands. Their poetry conjures up an auspicious mix of woodlands, pastures, lakes and rivers. Those religious men dwelled in a much richer and more biologically diverse environment than today's, populated by several large mammals and bird species which subsequently became extinct. Red deer were clearly widespread and frequent due to more extensive deciduous woodland cover (of which the Irish red deer makes a greater use than its European counterparts). Also present in these woods were wolves and wild boars, not yet exterminated by man.

The descendants of the wolves from the early Christian period had mostly disappeared by 1700 but struggled on until 1786, when the last specimen was exterminated in Co. Carlow. Wild boar were formerly the most abundant of wild animals of Ireland. Their bones were found associated with the first known human settlers in Ireland some 9,000 years ago.

Eagle. Book of Durrow (late eighth or early ninth century). (The Board of Trinity College, Dublin).

According to Thompson[9] they continued to be plentiful down to the seventeenth century, but their date of extinction is not known nor is it recorded when they were last seen. Robert Francis Scharff (1858–1934), Keeper of the Natural History Museum, Dublin, from 1890 until 1921, believed that the degenerate wild pigs seen by Giraldus Cambrensis during the late twelfth century were descended from domesticated stock introduced by the first Neolithic farmers some 6,000 years ago, but that also present with these feral pigs were descendants of the old European wild boar which he claimed had been present in prehistoric Ireland.

The corncrake and wild swans, distinguished by their striking and unmistakable calls, impressed the monks as summer and winter visitors respectively to earn several citations in the early poetry. Eagles in those days bred on the cliffs in remote areas: the white-tailed eagle survived in coastal regions in decreasing numbers until the early twentieth century, when it completely died out, and the golden eagle hung on until 1926 then remained extinct apart from a pair from the Mull of Kintyre in Scotland that bred on the Antrim coast from 1953–60. Remains of the great spotted woodpecker found in two separate caves in Co. Clare indicate that they were present in the primeval woods. They may have persisted to the ninth century, as suggested by several references to them in the nature poems, but by the twelfth century they would appear to have become extinct. They too fell foul of the shrinking woodlands. In contrast to these unfortunate species, the descendants of the badger and otter, also featuring in the monks' observations, have maintained thriving populations and remained symbols of the countryside.

Augustin, the first naturalist

One Irish monk living in the seventh century, known as Augustin, composed an interesting text in 655 which, unlike many others, survived because of a superficial confusion between him and his virtual namesake, St Augustine,

Principal monastic and other sites of AD 650–800. From F. Henry (1965) *Irish Art in the Early Christian Period (to 800 AD)*. Methuen & Co. Ltd., London.

Bishop of Hippo (354–430), the founding father of the Christian Church. The Hibernian Augustin was fortunate – and so are we – to have his text *Liber de Mirabilibus Sanctae Scripturae* embedded in the third volume of most editions of the great St Augustine's works, notwithstanding the 200 years separating the two men. Without such an occurrence of editorial laxity it is doubtful whether the writings of the lesser Augustin would have survived for posterity.[10]

The central thesis of Augustin's work was that God rested on the seventh day after all his work was done but that once *creatio* was completed the *gubernatio* of the Deity never ceased. The monk believed that *mirabilia* or miracles were not new creations but only certain unusual developments of the secrets of nature. He wrote of the miracles of the Bible, and questioned why terrestrial animals, unlike their aquatic relatives, were made to bear the brunt of the Deluge (they drowned whereas fish did not) and how the life of amphibious creatures such as otters and seals could be maintained during the same period when they needed dry land to sleep and rest on. In the chapter *De recussu aquarum diluvii* he wondered where the Deluge waters came from and went to. He observed the fluctuations of the sea, the *inundationes et recessus Oceani*, noting the daily tides, the fortnightly neap tides and spring tides that suggested to him the waxing and waning of the Deluge waters. He observed that the changes in sea level were so great that what were islands may have been part of the mainland at some stage and that these changes were of considerable significance regarding the animals found on islands.

Augustin reasoned that if the mainland and islands shared a common fauna they must have had former connections. Thus, some 1,200 years before eminent naturalists such as Alfred Wallace and Charles Darwin tackled the same issues, the monk had the first intuition of a land bridge between countries. St Augustine of Hippo had himself earlier pondered in *De Cicitate Dei* whether the remotest islands had been granted their animals from the stocks preserved throughout the Deluge in the Ark or whether those animals had sprung to life on the spot:

> 'It might indeed be said that they crossed to the island by swimming, but this could only be true of those islands which lie very near the mainland, while there are others so distant that we fancy no animal could ever swim to them... At the same time it cannot be denied that by the intervention of angels they might be transported thither, by order and permission of God. If however they are produced out of the earth as at their first Creation, when God said "Let the earth bring forth the living creatures", this makes it more evident that all kinds of animals were preserved in the ark not so much for the sake of renewing the stock as prefiguring the various nations which were to be saved by the Church; this, I say, is more evident if the earth brought forth many animals to islands to which they could not cross over.'[11]

The Irish Augustin focused the argument closer to home. Being familiar with the fauna of Ireland and knowing that much of it was common to Britain he asked the following question: '*Quis enim, verbi gratia, lupos, cervos, et sylvaticos porcos, et vulpes, taxones, et lepusculos et sesquivolos in Hiberniam deveheret?*'[12] 'Who indeed could have brought wolves, deer, wild (wood) swine, foxes, badgers, little hares and squirrels to Ireland?' His statement is the first known written record of some of the quadrupeds present in the country during the mid-seventh century.

Giraldus Cambrensis: *Topographia Hiberniae* 1185

The next important text on Irish natural history came some 530 years later. The author was Giraldus de Barri, alias Giraldus Cambrensis, the grandson of

Henry I. His family on his mother's side were FitzGeralds, active in the Norman invasions of Ireland. Maurice FitzGerald, his uncle, was one of the principal leaders. Cambrensis's first excursion to Hibernia was in 1183, a visit lasting less than a year. According to his treatise *Expungnatio Hiberniae,* the reason for his travel was 'to help my uncle and brother by my council, and diligently to explore the site and nature of the island and primitive origin of its race'.

Topographia Hiberniae, which received its inaugural reading at Oxford in or around 1188,[3] provides a remarkably interesting account of twelfth century Ireland, although the accuracy of its natural history has been questioned and dismissed by one naturalist as 'an amalgam of fact, fibs and fantasy and much of it patently absurd. It is undoubtedly of much use but, from the scientific point of view, so apocryphal a document is not to be relied upon without supporting evidence.'[13] Other naturalists have concentrated on the miracles and strange beliefs recounted, using them to discredit the whole text. For instance, Cambrensis talks about barnacle geese hatching from goose barnacles found clinging to floating logs in the sea. 'They take their food and nourishment from the juice of wood and water during their mysterious and remarkable generation. I myself have seen many times with my own eyes more than a thousand of the small bird-like creatures hanging from a single log upon the sea-shore.' Such miracles were in vogue, a convenient way of explaining mysterious phenomena and the substance of bestiaries. What about, for instance, the bended leg of the crane? Cambrensis explained that when on watch duty, the crane stood on one leg while clutching a stone in the other which would drop when the bird went to sleep, so that it would be awakened on the spot and could resume its watch. Not all of Cambrensis is as blatantly fantastical as this. Praeger sums it up when he says that Cambrensis 'was a careful recorder, but credulous; and from his statements it often requires care and ingenuity to extract the truth'.[2] Thus the reader has to disentangle strands of truth from strands of fiction, and make intelligent guesses – whereupon certain important points emerge.

In defence of Cambrensis's flights of fancy, many writers on natural history, even well into the second millennium, also traded some equally extraordinary beliefs and myths. Another typical story is that of the vanishing birds, or 'birds that do not appear in the winter-time'. To Cambrensis they '... seem ... to be seized up into a long ecstasy and some middle state between life and death. They receive no support from food ... and are wakened up from sleep, return with the "zephyr" and the first swallow.' This is close to the misconceptions, persisting many centuries later, concerning the hibernation of swallows, which, it was postulated, spent the winter in estuarine muds. The large pre-migratory flocks congregating in the autumn, their wheeling over reed beds, their subsequent disappearance and mysterious re-emergence the following spring led many naturalists to believe that at some stage they buried themselves in the soft ooze. Such stories were trotted out into the late eighteenth century, even by such writers as Gilbert White (1720–93).[14] If White could agree to such absurdities then Cambrensis will be partly forgiven for seeing birds in shellfish and slumberous cranes holding stones.

Topographia Hiberniae is presented in three parts: the position and topography of Ireland, including its natural history; the wonders and miracles of Ireland, and the inhabitants of the country. Cambrensis claimed that he used no written sources for the first two parts and so must have drawn mostly upon his own observations and notes, together with information provided by other people. As shown by his text, Cambrensis did not venture outside the neighbourhoods of Waterford or Cork on his first visit. On his second trip he travelled from Waterford to Dublin, possibly by the coastal route, and he probably visited Arklow and Wicklow. He saw both Kildare and Meath and almost certainly the River Shannon at Athlone, as well as Loughs Ree and Derg.[15] In short, Cambrensis remained within the Norman-occupied areas where he would always be granted protection and succour. His commentary is thus biased towards the more fertile and amenable landscapes of Ireland.

The following analysis of the fauna of the time is based on the first version of the three known manuscripts copied from the original work by Cambrensis. This version dates from the twelfth century and is a copy in Latin, translated here by O'Meara.[15] For Cambrensis, Ireland was a land 'fruitful and rich in its fertile soil and plentiful harvests. Crops abound in the fields, flocks on the mountain and wild animals in the woods.' However, the island was 'richer in pastures than in crops, and in grass rather than grain'. As to the grass, it was 'green in the fields in winter just the same as in summer. Consequently the meadows are not cut for fodder, nor do they ever build stalls for their beasts.'

Cambrensis went on to describe the soil, 'soft and watery, and there are many woods and marshes. Even at the tops of high and steep mountains you will find pools and swamps. Still there are, here and there, some fine plains, but in comparison with the woods they are small.' Swarms of bees 'would be much more plentiful if they were not frightened off by the yew trees that are poisonous and bitter, and with which the island woods are flourishing.' The rivers and lakes were rich in fish, especially salmon, trout and eels, and there were sea lamprey in the River Shannon. Three fish were present in Ireland that were 'not found anywhere else' – pollan, shad and charr – but other freshwater fish were 'wanting' – pike, perch, roach, gardon (chubb) and gudgeon. The same applied to minnows, loach and bullheads, and 'nearly all that do not have their seminal origin in tidal rivers...'. They were nowhere to be seen.

Amongst the birds, Cambrensis noted that sparrowhawks and peregrine falcons were abundant, together with ospreys. He pondered why the hawks and falcons never increased their numbers as he observed that many young were born each year but few seemed to survive to adulthood, perhaps a hasty observation as he was hardly there long enough to pay close attention to population dynamics: 'There is one remarkable thing about these birds, and that is, that no more of them build nests now than did many generations ago. And although their offspring increases every year, nevertheless the number of nest-builders does not increase; but if one pair of birds is destroyed, another takes its place.' Eagles were as numerous as kites (harriers were often called 'kites' in ancient times), quail were plentiful, corncrakes innumerable, capercaillie nested in the woods (by 1800 they had become extinct) and only a few red grouse occupied the hills. 'Cranes' were recorded as being so

Floral motifs on cross (c. twelfth century) at Glendalough, Co. Wicklow. From F. Henry (1970) *Irish Art in the Romanesque Period 1020-1170 AD*. Methuen & Co. Ltd., London

numerous that one flock would contain a 'hundred or about that number'. Barnacle geese were seen on the coastline while rivers had dippers, described by Cambrensis as a kind of kingfisher: 'they are smaller than the blackbird, and are found on rivers. They are short like quails.' True kingfishers were also present on the waterways. Swans (almost certainly whooper or Bewick's) were very plentiful in the northern part of Ireland. Storks were seldom observed and were the 'black kind', but were in fact almost certainly the white or common stork, in view of the extreme scarcity of the black stork in Ireland. There were no black (carrion) crows, or 'very few'. Crows that were present were 'of different colours' – i.e. hooded crows – and were seen dropping shells from the air onto stones, a behaviour often witnessed today. Partridges and pheasants (introduced during Elizabethan times) were absent, as were nightingales (the first Irish record was a migrant at Great Saltee, Co. Wexford, in 1953) and magpies. The historian Richard Stanihurst also observed in 1577 that 'They lack the Bird called the Pye.'[16] All magpies in Ireland today have descended from a 'parcel of magpies' that suddenly appeared in Co. Wexford about 1676.[17]

Corroborative evidence for some of Cambrensis's bird records comes from the remains of bird bones found in a lake dwelling, or crannóg, on a small island in the middle of a shallow lake at Lagore, near Dunshaughlin, Co. Meath. The crannóg dates from AD 700–900 with no evidence of occupancy after the Norman invasion of the twelfth century. Over one thousand bird bones were found during an excavation of the site and most were identified by Stelfox of the Natural History Museum, Dublin.[18] The following species, relevant to Cambrensis's text, were recorded: sea-eagle (four bones), barnacle goose (202 bones or fragments), whooper swan (19 bones), Bewick's swan (9 bones), corncrake (one bone), crane (25 bones or portions of bones representing cranes of three different sizes) and heron (one skull and one beak). From these last two findings it might be concluded that Cambrensis was right about the abundance of cranes in Ireland, and that he was not confusing them with herons.

While now long extinct, cranes abounded in Ireland during the fourteenth century according to the text *Polychronicon* written by Ranulphus Higden (*c.*1299–*c.*1364), a monk from Chester, England.[19] Their bones have been found in the Catacomb (five bones in the lower stratum of cave material, indicating the antiquity of the material) and Newhall Caves (one bone in the upper stratum), Co. Clare, dating back to prehistoric times.[20] They were also a dietary item for the Late Bronze Age people of Ballycotton, Co. Cork.[21]

Animal bone evidence from earlier human settlement sites has shown wild boar, pigeons, duck, grouse, capercaillie and goshawk – another woodland species – at Mount Sandel, over looking the lower reaches of the River Bann, Co. Derry, and dating from some 9,000 years ago. Goshawk bones have also been found at a later Mesolithic site on Dalkey Island, Co. Dublin, and at the Early Bronze age site of Newgrange, Co. Meath. Further south at Boora Bog, near Tullamore, Co. Offaly, human food remains, contemporary with Mount Sandel, included pig, red deer and hare.[22]

Red deer stags were noted by Cambrensis as 'not able to escape because of their too great fatness' whereas the wild boars 'were small, badly formed and inclined to run away'. Hares were present: 'but rather small, and very like rabbits both in size and in the softness of their fur'. When put up by dogs 'they always try to make their escape in cover, as does the fox – in hidden country, and not in the open'. However, when talking about 'hares', Cambrensis may have been describing wild rabbits – the behaviour reported is more typical of rabbits than hares – which were introduced by the Normans at about the time of Cambrensis's visits. Pine martens occurred commonly in the woods, where they were hunted day and night, and badgers, according to the Welshman, frequented 'rocky and mountainous places'. Cambrensis states that the following were absent from Ireland: moles, wild goats, deer, hedgehogs (later recorded by the historian Roderic O'Flaherty in 1684), beavers and polecats. Mice, on the other hand, were 'infinite in numbers and consume much more grain than anywhere else'. There were no 'poisonous reptiles', nor 'snakes, toads or frogs, tortoises or scorpions'.

This last statement has repeatedly been taken by naturalists as evidence that there were no native frogs in Ireland, leading to much debate about the status of the species. The controversy concerning the history of the frog is discussed in Chapter 2. Cambrensis also came across lizards, presumably viviparous lizards, the only lizard in Ireland. This was a politically injudicious observation, for St Patrick was supposed to have done a thorough job in banishing not only all snakes but also all reptiles. Cambrensis was, in fact, blunt in dismissing St Patrick's alleged role. 'Some indulge in the pleasant conjecture that St Patrick and other saints of the land purged the island of all harmful animals. But it is more probable that from the earliest times, and long before the laying of the foundations of the Faith, the island was naturally without these as well as other things.' Already in the third century, before St Patrick is supposed to have wielded the crozier, Caius Julius Solinus, the Roman compiler of the early third century, had commented in *Polyhistor* – which drew from the work of Pliny the Elder – on the absence of snakes:[23]

'*Illic* [in Hibernia] *nullus anguis, avis rara, gens inhospita et bellicosa.*'

'In that land there are no snakes, birds are few and the people are inhospitable and war-like.'

Gerard Boate: *Irelands Naturall History* 1652

Irelands Naturall History was the first regional natural history in the English language, written essentially for the benefit of adventurers and planters who were thinking of settling in Ireland during the mid-seventeenth century. Its compiler and author was a Dutchman by the name of Gerald Boate (1604–49). He and his brother Arnold were involved with the formation in the summer of 1646 of the Invisible College, a body of Anglo-Irish intellectuals revolving around the Boyle family of Lismore Castle, Co. Cork. The formation of the College was initiated in London by the scientist Benjamin Worsley and his brilliant 19 year-old intellectual friend Robert Boyle as a means to propagate their conception of experimental philosophy amongst their immediate friends and colleagues. These included the Boates and Samuel Hartlib, a Pole and puritan intellectual resident in London – later the publisher of *Irelands Naturall History*.[24] Gerard Boate was a physician and he attended to the health of Robert Boyle and his sister Katherine, later Lady Ranelagh, herself a patron and driving force behind the Invisible College.[24] The Boates were anti-authoritarian both in natural philosophy and medicine (they had several conflicts

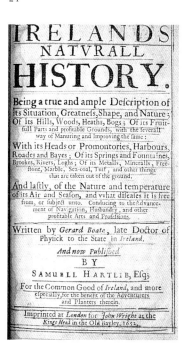

IRELANDS NATVRALL HISTORY.

Being a true and ample Description of its Situation, Greatnes, Shape, and Nature; Of its Hills, Woods, Heaths, Bogs; Of its Fruit-full Parts and profitable Grounds, with the severall way of Manuring and Improving the same:

With its Heads or Promontories, Harbours, Roades and Bayes; Of its Springs and Fountaines, Brookes, Rivers, Loghs; Of its Metalls, Mineralls, Free-stone, Marble, Sea-coal, Tuif, and other things that are taken out of the ground.

And lastly, of the Nature and temperature of its Air and Season, and what diseases it is free from, or subject unto. Conducing to the Advancement of Navigation, Husbandry, and other profitable Arts and Professions.

Written by *Gerard Boate*, late Doctor of Physick to the State in *Ireland*.

And now Published

B Y

S A M U E L L H A R T L I B, Esq;

For the Common Good of *Ireland*, and more especially, for the benefit of the Adventurers and Planters therein.

Imprinted at *London* for *John Wright* at the *Kings Head* in the Old Bayley, 1652.

Title page of the first edition of Boate's *Irelands Naturall History* (1652).

with the College of Physicians) and were keen supporters of Baconian natural history – both good recommendations for membership of the Invisible College.

The College played an important role in ushering into Ireland the new natural philosophy that was arising in Europe in the wake of work by Galileo, Mersenne and Descartes.[25] It was an assembly of 'learned and curious gentlemen, who after breaking out of the civil wars, in order to divert themselves from those melancholy scenes, applied themselves to experimental inquiries, and the study of nature, which was then called the new philosophy, and at length gave birth to the Royal Society.'[26] The Royal Society was formed in London during 1662.

Gerard Boate, a medical graduate of Leyden University, Holland, settled in London in 1630 where he was appointed Royal Physician to King Charles I. He subscribed to the fund established for the reduction of the Irish in Ireland, opened to the Dutch by a special Act of Parliament in 1642. He invested £180 in expectation of a reward of 847 acres in Co. Tipperary.[27] That was about the time that Boate the physician became Boate the promoter of Ireland, working entirely from England: he 'begun to write that work at the beginning of the year of our Lord 1645 and made an end of it long before the end of the same year: wheras he went not to Ireland untill the latter end of the year 1649' as explained by his brother Arnold in the section in *Irelands Naturall History* entitled 'To the Reader'. In 1647 Boate was appointed physician to the Army of Ireland but was unable for unknown reasons to take up his position until 1649.[28] He died a few months after arriving in Dublin and his widow was left to claim the grant to the lands in Tipperary. Gerard's manuscript was published by Samuel Hartlib in 1652.

Most of the knowledge in the book came from Arnold Boate, who had spent eight years in Ireland as Physician-General to the Army in Leinster, during which time he had gathered a large amount of information about the country. Much of it was probably obtained from surveyors, judging by the amount of topographic material in the book, especially concerning the coastline. Arnold 'made very many journeys into the countrie and by meanes therof saw a great part of it, especially the provinces of Leinster and Ulster'. Before Gerard started writing the book Arnold went to London to spend six months with him 'reasoning about Ireland ... chiefly about the Natural History of the same'. Gerard set down what he heard and then conferred afterwards with various gentlemen including the Irish scientists William and Richard Parsons, who were exiles in London because of civil unrest in the colony. It is thought that the Parsons contributed a lot of the information, especially on geology and minerals.

The approach adopted by Boate in his book was one of scientific pragmatism, following the Baconian New Philosophy of utilitarianism which advocated taking advantage of the accumulated experience of artisans, gardeners, husbandmen, etc., to compile exhaustive 'Histories of Trade and Nature'. Because of this new method, *Irelands Naturall History* was a major triumph over the antiquarian, anecdotal and chorographical tradition embodied in previous descriptive texts. The chorographical approach was not much more than a bare listing of natural history features whereas the artisans and others drew upon many years of practical management of the environment and were wont to make enlightening comments. Most of their statements were based on observation and in many cases verifiable facts – sometimes through scientific experimentation. The book went a long way to remedying many of the 'chief defects for which the Truths of Naturall Philosophie and the products thereof....are so imperfectly known'.[29] Regrettably, Gerald Boate's plan to write a threefold sequel dealing with plants, other living creatures, and 'old Fashions, Lawes and customs' never came about because of his premature death.

Irelands Naturall History is divided into 25 chapters and written in a direct, unconvoluted style. After describing the situation and shape of Ireland, Boate turns to the provinces, the counties of the English Pale (an area around Dublin bounded by a palisade, to keep out the 'barbarous' Irish) and the principal cities and towns of Ireland. Almost one third of the book is devoted to a very detailed descriptive analysis of the coastline – its headlands, bays, sandbanks, harbours and anchorages. In this part Boate reveals himself as one of the earliest geomorphologists, with an interest in the coastal erosion produced by wave action. He was also clearly following Bacon's advocacy that information should be gathered about the ebb and flow of the sea, currents, salinity, subterranean features, etc. Minerals and mining receive much attention, while the property of Lough Neagh's waters to turn wood into stone was personally investigated by Arnold Boate (see p.160).

It was the bogs that fascinated Gerard, especially their potential for agricultural development. He thought they were of recent origin, only requiring drainage to make them available to agriculture – for pasture or good tillage land. He provided the first classification of bogs which were arranged as 'grassy, watry, muddy and hassocky'. He thought that very few of the wet bogs were a 'natural property or of a primitive constitution' but arose through superfluous moisture gathering over time, arising from springs that had no easy run off for their water. The result was 'rottenness and springiness, which nevertheless is not a little increased through the rain water coming to that of the Springs'.

The lack of woodland over the greater part of Ireland was noted by Boate who quotes that the area between Dublin, Drogheda, Dundalk, Newry, and as far as Dromore was bereft of woodlands 'worth speaking of' and without a single tree in most parts. Some great woods still persisted in Kerry and Tipperary, despite the depredations of the Earl of Cork, a well-known enemy of anything leafy and tall. The country had been well stocked with woods at the time of the Norman invasions:

> 'In ancient times, and as long as the land was in the full possession of the Irish themselves, all Ireland was very full of woods on every side, as evidently appeareth by the writings of

Giraldus Cambrensis.... But the English having settled themselves in the land, did by degrees greatly diminish the woods in
all places where they were masters, partly to deprive the thieves
and rogues, who used to lurk in the woods in great numbers, of
their refuge and starting-holes, and partly to gain the greater
scope of profitable lands. For the trees being cut down, the
roots stubbed up, and the land used and tilled according to exi-
gency, the woods in most places of Ireland may be reduced not
only to very good pastures, but also to excellent arable and
meadow.'

Boate went on to say that most of the woodland remaining after the initial
English onslaught was destroyed for the manufacture of charcoal used in the
smelting of iron, an industry started by the New English who had been in
Ireland since the Elizabethan wars. Another aspect that Boate commented on
was the nature of the soil in Ireland. He noticed that the surface deposits were
varied – as the last Ice Age would have ordained them to be – but he did not
speculate as to their origin: 'The fertile soil is in some places a blackish earth,
in others clay, and in many parts mixt of both together; as likewise there be
sundry places, where the ground is mixt of earth and sand, sand and clay, gravel and clay, or earth; but the chalk ground and the red earth, which both are
very plentiful and common in many parts of England, are no where to be
found in Ireland.'

Perhaps the most interesting feature of Ireland for Boate was its suitability
for agriculture. Emphasising the potential to make profits as a planter, he
expounded various possibilities for the improvement of the land by drainage,
the laying down of special manures, and the reclamation of bogs. He went to
great technical length to make the prospect of tillage in Ireland an attractive
one: 'the best and richest soils, if but half a foot deep, and if lying upon a stiff
clay or hard stone, is not so fertile, as a leaner soil of greater depth, and lying
upon sand and gravel, through which the superfluous moisture may descend,
and not standing still, as upon the clay and stone, make cold the roots of grass,
or corn, and so hurt the whole.'

Other early endeavours

In 1633, 12 years before Boate was busy writing his book from his London
quarters, a real field naturalist, Richard Heaton (c.1604–c.1666), born in
England, first arrived in Dublin to become rector of Kilrush, Co. Clare, and
later Birr, Co. Offaly, before returning to England after the outbreak of the
Confederate War in 1641. He came back to Birr in 1660 and was appointed
Dean of Clonfert later that year. It was only during his first sojourn that he
botanised, exploring the landscape, discovering new plant records and passing
them on to other botanists such as William How who published them in
Phytologia Britannica (1650).[30] Heaton, credited by the botanical scholar
Charles Nelson to be the first person to have carried out a systematic study of
the Irish flora, probably prepared a manuscript sometime before 1641. What
became of it is unknown but it was certainly used by Caleb Threlkeld
(1676–1728) in the formation of his own comprehensive study *Synopsis Stirpium
Hibernicarum*, published in 1726.[31]

Another early traveller to Ireland was Gédéon Bonnivert (fl.1673–1703), born at Sedan in Champagne, France, who came as one of a 'troop of horse' to join King William III's army in Ireland for seven weeks in the summer of 1690. Bonnivert, a highly educated man, an enthusiastic scientist and eager botanist, corresponded with the eminent botanists Hans Sloane and Leonard Plukenet. Sloane (1660–1753), born in Killyleagh, Co. Down, founded the Chelsea Botanic Garden whose collections went on to form the nucleus of the future British Museum. In a letter dated 5 August 1703, Bonnivert wrote to Sloane:

> '... Near this Town [Limerick] in a bog call'd by ye name of Douglass grow aboundance of Plants, and amongst 'em a *Pentaphyllum rubrum* out of those bogs as I have seen firr trees wth their boughs and roots very sound timber, and wch is most admirable is that none of those trees grow in Ireland...'.[32]

Bonnivert sent Sloane and Plukenet plant specimens that he had gathered in Limerick, Cork, and elsewhere. These specimens, now residing in the Sloane Herbarium in the British Museum, represent the oldest known herbarium material of Irish origin.[30]

In 1682, some 30 years after Boate's *Irelands Naturall History* was published, the London book publisher Moses Pitt proposed to put together an English Atlas which would include natural history of the regions. William Molyneux (1656–98), elder brother of the famous Thomas Molyneux (1661–1733) and ardent Baconian, was approached by Pitt to write the natural history of Ireland. Upon accepting, Molyneux sent out questionnaires, or *Quareries*, listing 16 questions to his contacts throughout Ireland. Unfortunately, the project collapsed in 1685 on the arrest of Pitt for non payment of debts and Molyneux burnt all that he had written himself, only sparing some rough notes which found their way into the Library of Trinity College, Dublin.

One of Molyneux's correspondents was the scholar and antiquarian Roderic O'Flaherty (1629–1718) who lived in west Galway and had written in 1684 a fine text about his region *A Chorographical Description of West or H-Iar Connaught*, which for unknown reasons had to wait for 162 years before it was edited by James Hardiman and then published by the Irish Archaeological Society in 1846.[33] O'Flaherty was an accurate recorder and while his observations were generally restricted to Connemara they provide an important source of information to supplement the writings of Boate which covered a much broader geographical area.

> 'The country is generally coarse, moorish, and mountanous, full of high rocky hills, large valleys, great bogs, some woods, whereof it had abundance before they were cut. It is replenished with rivers, brooks, lakes, and standing waters, even on the tops of the highest mountains. On the sea side there are many excellent large and safe harbours for ships to ride on anchor; the climate is wholsome, soe as divers attain to the age of ninety years, a hundred and upwards. The land produces wild beasts, as wolves, deere, foxes, badgers, hedgehogs, hares, rabbets, squirrells, martins, weesles and the amphibious otter, of which kind the white-faced otter is very rare. It is never killed, they say, but with loss of man or dog, and its skin is mighty precious. It admits no rats to live anywhere within it, except the Isles of Aran, and the district of the west liberties of Galway.'

The other section of O'Flaherty's text directly relevant to the natural history of Ireland concerned the creatures and birds in the coastal waters off Connemara.

'It now and then casts ashore great whales, gramps [dolphins], por-cupisses, thunies [tuna]. Both sea and land have their severall kinds of birds. Here is a kind of black eagle, which kills the deere by grappling him with his claw, and forcing him to run headlong into precipices. Here the ganet soares high into the sky to espy his prey in the sea under him, at which he casts himself headlong into the sea, and swal-lows up whole herrings in a moresell. This bird flys through the ship's sailes, piercing them with his beak. Here is the bird engendered by the sea out of timber long lying in the sea. Some call them clakes and soland-geese, some puffins, other bernacles, because they resemble them. We call them "girrinn".'

Here we find again the enduring theory that some birds were descended from floating planks of wood, i.e. from the attached shellfish – something already encountered in the work of Cambrensis.

In the early 1680s, when O'Flaherty was writing his text, Ireland was in a sci-entific and intellectual torpor. Social and financial power were rooted in London with few benefits spreading westwards. A notable exception, from the first part of the century was the scholar James Ussher (1581–1656), who became Bishop of Meath in 1621 and four years later Archbishop of Armagh. His main contribution to natural history was to provide some scope for the belief in evolutionary theory rather than a catastrophic vision of the creation of the world. After careful study of the Old Testament he concluded that the world had begun 'upon the entrance of the night preceding Sunday 23 October' in the year 4004 BC.[34] His chronology was incorporated into one of the Authorised Versions of the Bible in 1701 and henceforth was known as 'The Received Chronology' or 'Bible Chronology'.[35] That the world had existed for some 6,000 years posed many problems for those that believed in cataclysms. Apart from the sparkle of Usher and a few others there was little happening in the field of science in Ireland at that time. Indeed, K. Theodore Hoppen concluded that 'the scientific scene in pre-restoration Ireland was one in which inertia, rather than movement, was quite clearly the dominant factor'.[36]

By the turn of the eighteenth century the trend set by Gerard Boate of recording Irish natural history more by direct observation than by hearsay was well established. Edward Lhwyd (1670–1709), the eminent Welsh natural his-torian and Keeper of the Ashmolean Museum in Oxford, visited Ireland briefly in 1699 in search of antiquities and natural history. He toured places which many present-day naturalists would put high on their visiting list: the moun-tains of Sligo, Mayo, Galway and Kerry; the Aran Islands, Co. Galway; the Burren, Co. Clare, and Co. Antrim. He recorded several new plants and reported his visit in a letter dated 25 August 1700 to his friend Tancred Robinson, Fellow of the Royal Society. It was printed in the *Philosophical Transactions* of the Royal Society somewhat late in 1712.[37]

But the claim for writing the first original book on botany published in Ireland – *Methodus plantarum, in horto medico collegii Dubinensis, jam jam dispo-*

nendarum; In dua partes divisa; quarum prima de plantis, altera de fruiticibus &
arboribus agit – must go to the first Professor of Botany at Trinity College
Dublin, Henry Nicholson (*c.*1681–*c.*1721). Published in 1712, it is a catalogue
of plants growing in the Physic Garden at Trinity; hardly a natural history treatise, but a step in the right direction.

Two years later appeared a remarkable work written by the naturalist-game-
keeper Arthur Stringer (*c.*1664–*c.*1728), who was employed by the Conway
family on their estate east of Lough Neagh. *The Experienc'd Huntsman* was the
first reliable text on the wild mammals of either Ireland or Britain. Strangely,
it remained 'undiscovered' until James Fairley, whose attention had been
brought to it by C. Douglas Deane (1914–92), Deputy Director of the Ulster
Museum 1957–77 and ornithologist, encouraged its republication in 1977.[38]
Stringer had a genuine naturalist's eye for the behaviour and habits of the wild
mammals of his concern – deer, hares, foxes, badgers, martens and otters. All
his observations ring true today despite his somewhat florid descriptions such
as the entry for the badger, which he observed 'is a very melancholy fat
Creature, Sleeps incessantly, and naturally (when in Season) very Lecherous'.

Caleb Threlkeld: *Synopsis stirpium Hibernicarum* 1726

The appearance in 1726 of Caleb Threlkeld's *Synopsis stirpium Hibernicarum*,
the earliest Irish flora, represented a turning point in the history of natural history in Ireland.[39] Threlkeld (1676–1728), an English Dissenting minister and
physician, settled in Dublin in 1713, and compiled his flora from several
sources, which he tapped to some varying and unclear degree. He probably
used the Heaton manuscript men-
tioned earlier, but he also harnessed
records from other naturalists such as
William Sherard, founder of the Chair
of Botany at Oxford University, who
was based in Co. Down for four years.
Sherard's plant records were published in the second edition of John
Ray's *Synopsis Methodica stirpium
Britannicarum* (1696),[40] and then
extracted by Threlkeld for his own
work. Other information was gathered
from William How's work mentioned
above, and finally Threlkeld used his
own observations. Opinions differ as
to the extent of Threlkeld's personal
input. Was he 'A candid Author and
plain Dealer' as suggested by
Nathaniel Colgan, author of the *Flora
of County Dublin*,[41] or just the opposite,
i.e. a plagiariser, as suggested by
Mitchell?[42] Nelson contends that the
bulk of the information in the book
was generated by Threlkeld.[43] The
recent discovery of 22 sheets holding
plant specimens in the Herbarium in

Caleb Threlkeld's *Synopsis stirpium
Hibernicarum* (1726), the earliest Irish flora.

Synopsis Stirpium
HIBERNICARUM
ALPHABETICE DISPOSITARUM,
SIVE
. Commentatio de Plantis Indigenis
præfertim *Dublinenſibus* inſtituta,
BEING
A Short Treatiſe of Native Plants, eſpecially
ſuch as grow ſpontaneouſly in the Vicinity
of *Dublin*; with their *Latin*, *Engliſh*, and
Iriſh Names: And an Abridgment of their
Vertues, With ſeveral new Diſcoverys.
WITH
An APPENDIX of Obſervations made upon Plants. By
Dr. *Molyneux*, Phyſician to the State in *Ireland*.

The firſt ESSAY *of this Kind in the Kingdom of* Ireland,

Auctore CALEB THRELKELD, M. D.

Eſt quiddam prodire tenus, ſi non datur ultra,
Hor. Ep. 1. Lib. 1,

DUBLIN:
Printed by S. POWELL, for F. DAVYS in *Roſs-lane*;
RICHARD NORRIS in *Eſſex-ſtreet*, at the Corner of
Crane-lane, and JOSIAH WORRALL oppoſite to the
Swan-tavern on the *Blind-key*, MDCCXXVII.

Trinity College, Dublin, and very likely to have been the minister's own collection from his *Hortus Siccus*, would support the latter's hypothesis.[44] The
author's preface in the *Synopsis* is clear about his own field work:

> 'During the Summer Months I used to perambulate in
> Company of ingenious Men, both of the Clergy and Laity, to
> have ocular Demonstration of the Plants themselves in their
> native Soil, where Nature regaled our Senses with her Gaiety
> and Garnishes, which makes some resemblance of the paradisi-
> acal State. From twelve Years Observations I collected
> Specimens for an Hortus Siccus, and set down Places where
> they grew, besides I made Inquiries of Ingenious Men, and now
> I have reduced our Plants into the Model you here see.'

An Irish Herbal

Following the appearance in 1525 of *Bancks' Herbal*,[45] the first printed herbal
in English, named after the printer Richard Bancks, there was a succession of
other herbals acting as vehicles for botanical information. But the herbalist's
era came to an end in 1735 when Linnaeus published *Systema Naturae*, the
book that ushered in modern botany.[46] The very same year, Ireland's first
herbal *Botanalogia Universalis Hibernica* by John K'Eogh (1681?–1754) was published in the city of Cork.[47] Probably born in Co. Roscommon, K'Eogh was
appointed Chaplain to James King, fourth Lord Kingston, and later obtained
the living of Mitchelstown, Co. Cork. K'Eogh's reason for writing the herbal
was the daily viewing of his master's gardens in which grew nearly 200 different species of herbs and trees. 'I was
not acquainted with any Garden,
which could show so many, this was
no small advantage, or Conveniency
to forward this Undertaking.'
However, K'Eogh's vision extended
beyond the garden walls and comments on Irish localities and habitats of some of the listed plants are
included in the herbal. A similar
treatise followed in 1739 – *Zoologia
Medicinalis Hibernica* – on the medicinal properties of animals.[48] In his
preface, K'Eogh stated 'My principal
intention in publishing these treatis-
es on vegetables and animals, was to
contrive to cure all the diseases,
which the natives of kingdom are
afflicted with, by simple, easy, and
safe methods, prepared either by
pulverisation, decoction, infusion,
distillation, etc.'. The frequent eating of the brains of sparrows 'excite
venery and clear the sight'. Powered
otter testicles drunk in a liquid 'help

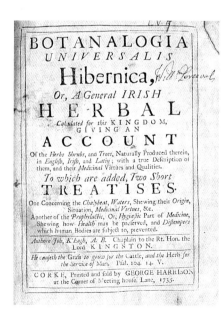

Keogh's *Botanalogia Universalis Hibernica*
(1735) – a late herbal.

to cure the Epilepsy'; the fat of a heron, mixed with oil of amber, 'being dropt warm into the ears, cures deafness'. K'Eogh acknowledges his debit to Horace (65 BC–AD 8), Pliny (d. AD 79), Avicenna (980–1037) Albertus Magnus (c.1280) and others for the preparation of the listed prescriptions. Unfortunately no natural history information is included along with the animals listed in the *Zoologia.*

County natural histories and botanical works

The year 1744 marked the formation of the Physico-Historical Society of Ireland, some 13 years after the founding of the Dublin Society (later Royal Dublin Society). The learned gentlemen of the PHSI decided to prepare a series of monographs on the 'ancient and present state' of the counties. These contained lists of plants and often animals, essays on agriculture and descriptions of minerals, woodlands, etc. They can be considered harbingers of the county natural histories that blossomed in the later half of the nineteenth century.

John Rutty's (1697–1775) *An Essay Towards a Natural History of the County Dublin*, published in 1772, was the first real county natural history in Ireland and dealt extensively with the flora, fauna, geology, meteorology, agriculture, water, minerals, air and soils of Dublin as well as the mortality of Dubliners.[49] He ignored the Linnean system of binomial classification which was in the process of being widely adopted in England. Under international agreement the year 1758 was taken as the start date of this new nomenclature – first unveiled by Linnaeus in *Species Plantarum* in 1753 – whereby each species of plant or animal is described by two, sometimes three, Latin names. The Linnean system simplified matters. Thus Rutty's long-winded scientific name for water mint – *Mentha rotundifolia palustris seu aquatica major* – would simply have been *Mentha aquatica* under the Linnean system. The binomial system meant that space was saved on paper at a time when printing costs were prohibitively high, and that names were easier to remember. Moreover, it provided a strong logical framework for all future advancement in the study of biology.

Soon after the adoption of the Linnean system some interesting early botanical investigations were undertaken by Patrick Browne (1720–90), from Woodstock, Co. Mayo, who attended Leyden University and became friendly with Linnaeus. He settled in Jamaica, practised as a medical doctor, and wrote *The Civil and Natural History of Jamaica*.[50] His important manuscript, *Fasciculus Plantarum Hiberniae*, containing records of his botanical findings during 1788, made principally in Mayo (although he also investigated Co. Galway), lay dormant for about two centuries in the cupboards of the Linnean Society, London, before being published in 1996 as *The Flowers of Mayo* together with a commentary and extensive notes by Nelson and illustrations by Walsh.[51] Browne also published important catalogues of the birds and fishes of Ireland in the *Gentleman's and London Magazine* in 1774.[52,53]

Despite the advent of regional natural histories, Ireland still lagged behind in scientific matters. Progress was, of course, impeded by a lack of wealth, a poor institutional infrastructure, and often hazardous and difficult travel through the countryside. But towards the close of the century things were warming up in Dublin. One driving force behind the foundation of the National Botanic Gardens, Glasnevin, in 1795 was Walter Wade (fl.1770?–1825) who, a year earlier, had published *Catalogus Systematicus*

Plantarum Indigenarum in Comitatu Dublinensi Inventarum. Pars Prima – a flora of
Co. Dublin, the first Irish flora to be arranged according to the Linnean classification.[54] Wade insisted on personally viewing each species before listing it.
He also wrote several other texts including one on rare plants in Co. Galway,
with a particular emphasis on Connemara, and he claimed to be the first serious visiting botanist there. His subsequent *Plantae Rariores in Hibernia Inventae*
(1804) was a more ambitious cataloguing of flowering plants, including 55 new
additions to his Dublin flora.[55] Interest was now spreading beyond flowering
plants, a point highlighted by the appearance in 1804 of Dawson Turner's
(1775–1858) *Muscologiae Hibernicae Spicilegium*,[56] entirely devoted to the mosses of Ireland, all of which had either been seen by him growing *in situ* or had
been sent to him by Irish correspondents including John Templeton from
Cranmore, near Belfast, one of Ireland's outstanding naturalists.

The now flourishing Royal Dublin Society was encouraging economic development of the country through agricultural improvement. Naturalists and scientists rose to the occasion. John White (d. before 1845), one of the gardeners
to the Society, published *An Essay on the Indigenous Grasses of Ireland* in 1808.[57]
Wade came forward with *Sketch of Lectures on Meadow and Pasture Grasses*,[58] which
he delivered in Glasnevin at the beginning of the nineteenth century. William
Richardson (1740–1820), rector of Moy and Clonfeacle, Co. Antrim, and a
writer on geology and agriculture, engaged in a vigorous and eccentric campaign to promote creeping bent grass and brought out a *Memoir on Fiorin Grass*,
published in 1808 as a Select Paper of the Belfast Literary Society. Another util-
itarian natural history contribution was Wade's most substantial book: *Salices or
an Essay towards a General History of Sallows, Willows & Osiers, their Uses and Best
Methods of Propagating and Cultivating Them* (1811).[59]

The scientific study of botany came of age before that of zoology. Plants were
not elusive; they stayed put and lent themselves to scrutiny, whereas animals
were much more difficult to observe, so botanical discoveries were continuing
at an even pace. Belfastman John Templeton, (1766–1825) who furthered the
cause of Irish botany more than any other, and was described by Praeger as the
most eminent naturalist that Ireland ever produced, completed his manuscript
Catalogue of the Native Plants of Ireland in 1801 – now in the Royal Irish Academy,
Dublin. Unfortunately, he failed to realise his ambition of producing an elab-
orate *Hibernian Flora* that would have drawn from his *Catalogue* and embodied
new records together with colour illustrations. The remaining manuscript,
including some fine watercolour drawings by Templeton himself, is little more
than a skeleton with some volumes now missing. It resides in the Ulster
Museum, Belfast.

Templeton was quite content to live in Northern Ireland, working diligently
on both the flora and fauna, with little ambition to travel abroad despite a
tempting offer from the British botanist Sir Joseph Banks to go to New
Holland (Australia), 'with a good salary and a large grant of land'.[2] Templeton
published very little but maintained an active correspondence with many eminent British naturalists such as William Hooker, Dawson Turner, James
Sowerby and Lewis Dillwyn (who also visited Ireland), many of whom published his records.

The first national flora was *The Irish Flora Comprising the Phaenogramous Plants
and Ferns*, published anonymously in 1833.[60] Katherine Sophia Baily
(1811–86), later Lady Kane and wife of Sir Robert Kane, was the reputed

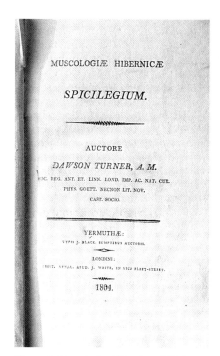

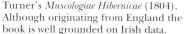

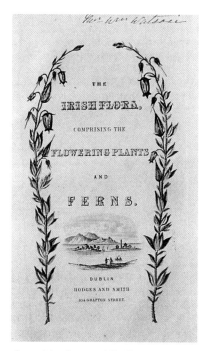

Turner's *Muscologiae Hibernicae* (1804). Although originating from England the book is well grounded on Irish data.

One of the few specially illustrated title pages for Baily's *Irish Flora* (1833).

author at the tender age of 22. John White of the National Botanic Gardens is acknowledged in the preface as having supplied the localities for plants. Three years later James Townsend Mackay (1775?–1862), a Scot who had been appointed Curator of the Trinity College Botanic Garden at Ball's Bridge in 1806, brought forth *Flora Hibernica*,[61] a much more substantial and scholarly work which ambitiously encompassed both phanerogams (seed-bearing plants) and cryptogams (those that do not produce seeds) of the entire island in one work. The book was a joint effort, despite no acknowledgement on the title page – the other contributors are acknowledged later in the text – between William Henry Harvey (1811–66) who was responsible for the section on algae and Thomas Taylor (d.1848) who wrote the sections on mosses, liverworts and lichens while Mackay dealt with the flowering plants, ferns and stoneworts.

The British Association for the Advancement of Science, founded in 1831, was based, in the words of social historian David Allen, 'ostensibly on the model of a similar perambulatory body started nine years before in Germany'. Apart from providing the natural history world as a whole with a usual annual meeting ground and forum, the B.A. helped these studies in a more practical way by making grants-in-aid.[62] The B.A. provided enormous stimulus to the development of regional and local natural histories by holding its regional meetings throughout Britain and Ireland. The 1843 Association meeting was held in Cork and to mark the event the Cuvierian Society of Cork published a small volume of 'communications' entitled *Contributions Towards a Fauna and Flora of the County of Cork*.[63] John D. Humphreys (fl. 1843) prepared the lists of molluscs, crustaceans and echinoderms; J.R. Harvey (fl. 1843) wrote on the vertebrates while Thomas Power (fl. 1845) was responsible for the section 'The Botanist's Guide for the County of Cork' – one of the first local floras in Ireland.

Twenty years after the publication of the Cork regional flora came *Flora Belfastiensis* in 1863.[64] Its author, Ralph Tate (1840–1901), hoped that it might be of use to the botanical members of the Belfast Naturalists' Field Club which had been founded as an enthusiastic response to his series of lectures delivered at the Belfast School of Science. Tate, born in Britain, was only resident in Belfast for three years after which he travelled widely, ending up as Professor of geology at Adelaide, Australia. Another similar product was the small, slim volume *A Flora of Ulster*,[65] published the following year by George Dickie (1812–82), and offered as a 'Collectanea' towards a more comprehensive flora of the North of Ireland. Dickie's view of Ulster was definitely expansionist for he included parts of Connacht in the surveyed localities. Both *Flora Belfastiensis* and *A Flora of Ulster* consisted of a list of species accompanied with notes on their habitats and distribution.

A departure from the presentation of traditional floras came with the publication in 1866 of *Cybele Hibernica*[66] by David Moore (1807–79) and Alexander Goodman More (1830–95). When living in England, More had worked with H.C. Watson who devised, for *Cybele Britannica* (1847–59)[67] a scheme of 18 'provinces' that were later split into 112 'vice-counties', a first move towards the recording of plant distribution on a quantitative basis. This was the ancestor of the dot distribution maps showing the presence or absence of a species within a grid of 10 km squares, now the internationally accepted grid recording system.

The division of Ireland into 12 'districts' (based mostly on county boundaries) and 37 'vice-counties' was originally proposed by Charles Babington (1808–95), Professor of Botany at Cambridge, in a paper presented to the Dublin University Zoological and Botanical Association in 1859.[68] More, quick to see the advantages of such a scheme, adopted the 12 'districts' for Ireland for his compilation of *Cybele Hibernica*. Plants now had a framework in which they could be recorded; their distribution could be compared region for region over time.

Such was the success of *Cybele Hibernica* that a supplement followed in 1872 and a second edition of the book in 1898.[69] In 1896, shortly before the second edition, Robert Lloyd Praeger (see p.43) proposed an even more fine-grained recording net of 40 'divisions' or 'vice-counties' (each an average 813 km^2) based on the 32 administrative counties that comprised all Ireland.[70] The new divisions were used in his monumental *Irish Topographical Botany*,[71] published in 1900, the product of 35 years of active botanising, and have been adopted, subject to minor modifications, as the standard botanical recording units of Ireland. The distribution of plant records in the most recent 1987 *Census Catalogue of the Flora of Ireland* by Scannell & Synnott are referenced on Praeger's 40 botanical 'divisions'.[72]

The Rev. Thomas Allin (d?1909) served in several parishes in Ireland – Cork, Galway and Carlow – but apparently 'botanised' only in Co. Cork, when he possibly had more available time, and where he gathered his records for the

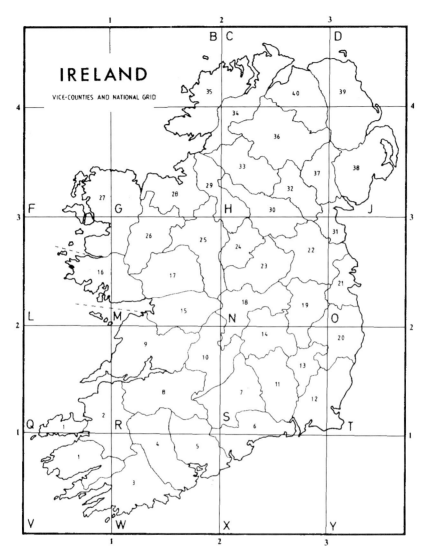

Botanical sub-divisions of Ireland based on vice-counties with the 100 km lines of the
National Grid. The sub-zone letters are also given; each sub-zone is a particular 100 km
square of the National Grid: B=14, C=24, D=34, F=03, G=13, H =23, J=33, L=02, M=12,
N=22, O=32, Q=01, R=11, S=21, T=31, V=00, W=10, X=20, Y=30. From Scannell & Synnott[72].

Flowering Plants and Ferns of the County Cork (1883).[73] He divided the county
into two parts, shown on the book's coloured frontispiece, which bore no correspondence to the system adopted in *Cybele Hibernica*. Allin was a careful
recorder and listed 700 flowering plants and ferns together with notes on their
distribution. In his preface he pays tribute to Isaac Carroll (1828–80), one of
the best botanists in the county at the time. The extent of Carroll's contribu-

tion to Allin's flora is not known but it may have been substantial. The amount of information Allin published was a marked advance on Power's earlier flora of Cork.

From the bubbling crucible of Northern Ireland arose *A Flora of the North-east of Ireland* (1888)[74] by Samuel Alexander Stewart (1826–1910) and Thomas Corry (1860–83). Stewart, an errand boy at 11 and later a trunk maker, played the leading role in founding the Belfast Naturalists' Field Club in 1863. He was one of a select band of 'working-men naturalists' who transcended the social barriers and joined in with middle class hunters of flowers and plants. In 1891 he gave up trunk-making to become Curator of the museum of the Belfast Natural History and Philosophical Society. His colleague Corry was a brilliant and diligent botanist and a poet, who tragically drowned in Lough Gill, Co. Sligo, aged 23. Although the geographic scope of flora of northeast of Ireland is restricted to three counties (Down, Antrim and Derry) the book has been updated, revised and added to numerous times, the most recent edition being 1992.

One of the botanical 'giants' of Victorian Ireland was Henry Chichester Hart (1847–1908) who, according to Praeger, was 'a man of magnificent physique, a daring climber and a tireless worker, and though his pace was usually too fast for exhaustive work, he missed little, and penetrated to places where very few have followed him'.[2] Although Hart did not know any Irish he gathered the names and folklore of plants from country people, the results of which remained in manuscript form until 1953 when they were published by M. Traynor as *The English Dialect of Donegal.*[75,76] Born in Dublin, where his father was Vice-Provost of Trinity College, Hart was of a Donegal landed gentry family and started work on *Flora of the County Donegal* (1898)[77] when aged 17, having been inspired by *Cybele Hibernica*. It was the beginning of a 35 year task which took him on innumerable walks and hikes during which he collected more than half the many hundreds of records that were to enter his book – a remarkable achievement. In 1887 he published a more modest volume on the *Flora of Howth.*[78] Like many before him, Hart was a naturalist of independent means working on a private basis and not affiliated to any state body.

Zoological natural history

Naturalists have historically focused more attention on Irish botany than on zoology, a fact reflected by the discrepancy between the two bodies of literature corresponding to the two areas. Animals are, however, catching up fast, as naturalists and scientists are spurred on by conservation requirements to discover more about endangered and threatened species. New resources for field studies together with advanced technologies are facilitating their task.

Some of the earliest and most original zoological investigations in Ireland were carried out by John Vaughan Thompson (1779–1847) who was born in Berwick-on-Tweed, England, and stationed at Cork in 1816 as Surgeon to the Forces, later Deputy Inspector-General of Hospitals, before going on to Australia in 1835. He was a specialist in planktonic larvae. It had been widely believed at the time that the fundamental difference between crustaceans and insects was that the crustaceans did not pass through different stages or forms in their development from egg to adult. Working almost alone, Thompson discovered that the edible crab did in fact undergo a metamorphosis and developed from a larval form called a zoea which had, until then, been classified as

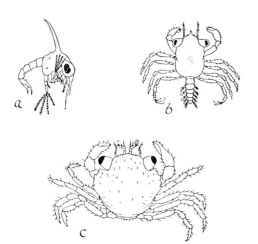

Stages (a–c) in the development of the shore crab. The discovery of the zoea larva (a) by zoologist John Thompson showed that the crab went thorough metamorphosis in its development from egg to adult, sharing this feature with the insects and uniting both as belonging to the Phylum Arthropoda. From C.M. Yonge (1961). *The New Naturalist: The Sea Shore.* Collins, London.

a species unrelated to the crab. Thompson was also responsible for the reclassification of acorn barnacles – the small symmetrical sessile barnacles exposed on rocks at low tide – from the Mollusca to the Crustacea, a major break with the accepted Cuvierian system of the classification of animals in force at the time. Cuvier and other contemporary zoologists believed, on the basis of external similarities, that barnacles were aberrant molluscs. Most of Thompson's work was privately published in Cork in an obscure series of six memoirs bearing the – similarly obscure – title *Zoological Researches, and Illustrations; or, Natural History of Nondescript or Imperfectly Known Animals in a Series of Memoirs,* issued between 1828 and 1834.[79]

West Mayo, and especially the Erris peninsula, was the '*ultima Thule*' of Ireland where William Hamilton Maxwell (1792–1850) retreated in 1819 from holding the curacy at Clonallon, near Newry, Co. Down, after disgracing himself by riding through his parish naked on horseback following an early morning dip in Carlingford Lough. The wayward curate then became a canon of the Tuam diocese and was appointed to three parishes. He befriended the Marquis of Sligo who gave him the use of his shooting lodge at Ballycroy on the edge of Blacksod Bay where he appears to have spent more time shooting, fishing and writing than administering his parishes. The stories of his adventures and encounters with eagles, otters, seals, grouse and wild geese make *Wild Sports of the West, with Legendary Tales and Local Sketches* (1832) a vivid read.[80] It is an obligatory text, written along semi-fictional lines with many 'ripping' yarns which tell a lot about western Ireland, its wildlife and local lore during the early nineteenth century. His capability as a lively raconteur and his easy social manner gave him access to and accommodation with the British garrison in Castlebar, Co. Mayo, whenever he wanted it: 'Maxwell introduced the officers to capital shooting, dined at their mess; and while draining their decanters drained their memories of those stirring recollections which he turned to account in *Stories of Waterloo*.'[81] In between his fishing, hunting, drinking and socialising, Maxwell mustered enough energy to write 20 books. His ambition in *Wild Sports* was to 'record the wild features and wilder associations of that romantic and untouched country' – a goal he certainly honoured. Amongst his numerous observations, he recorded some of the last indigenous red deer of Mayo which were persecuted almost to extinction during his time with the aid of muskets abandoned by the French in 1798. He lost his 'living' of Balla in 1844 through absenteeism which, combined with a self-indulgent lifestyle and increasing debts, forced him into exile in Scotland where, as an alcoholic, he died of broken health aged 58.

In contrast to the wild Maxwell, naturalists in Northern Ireland were a more sedate and collected lot, reflecting a society steeped in Protestant ethics and moral sternness. However, Northern Ireland was about to experience a period of great excitement and ebullience: the golden age of natural history, dominated by the zoologist William Thompson, was just behind the door.

Born into one of the famous Belfast families of linen-makers, Thompson (1805–52) devoted his life to zoology, spurning the loom and the spinning jenny. Thompson's magnum opus was *The Natural History of Ireland*.[9] The first three volumes were on birds and were published in 1849, 1850 and 1851, before his untimely death in 1852, aged 47. He had intended to produce several more volumes to include all the remaining fauna, but only left a very incomplete manuscript. In accordance with Thompson's will it fell upon Robert Patterson (1802–72), another eminent Belfast naturalist from a mill furnishing family, and James R. Garrett (1818–55), a Belfast solicitor and keen naturalist, to edit and publish this manuscript, which came out as a fourth variegated volume in 1856. Garrett was responsible for the mammals, fish and reptiles while Patterson handled all other groups. The production of the work must have been fated, for Garrett died before the book was printed. The information contained in the first three bird volumes is of such high standard – due to the accuracy of Thompson's observations and those of a network of correspondents – that it is still interesting and valuable today.

One of the greatest tragedies of Irish natural history was the premature death of Belfast naturalist William Thompson aged 47.

While Thompson had been labouring away on his bird volumes he realised the need for a much smaller and inexpensive book for the general reader. The necessity was met by *The Natural History of the Birds of Ireland* (1853)[82], written by his friend John Watters (fl. 1850s). A small, almost whimsical, Victorian production, laced with occasional romantic poems, it also contains hard facts on the habits, migrations and occurrences of the 261 listed species – a good antidote to Thompson's weighty tomes.

Another fine zoologist from Northern Ireland, considered to be one of Europe's greatest entomologists, was Alexander Henry Haliday (1806–70), a contemporary and friend of Thompson.[83] A graduate in law, he never practised and managed the family's estates in Co. Down, but he was more interested in entomology. He was highly cultured and an able linguist, a facility that allowed fruitful intercourse with continental entomologists. He published 75 entomological papers, including descriptions of several species new to science. He also contributed to Curtis's *British Entomology* (1827–40) and other books.[83]

The Patterson family of Belfast were another force in the study of natural history. The first Robert Patterson (1802–72) was an accomplished naturalist who was elected a Fellow of the Royal Society in recognition of this services to zoology. He authored the offbeat *Letters on the Natural History of Insects Mentioned in Shakespeare's Plays with Incidental Notes on the Insects of Ireland* (1838), as well as several more traditional books including *Introduction to Zoology for the Use of Schools* (1845) and *First Steps in Zoology* (1848).[84,85,86] His second son, Robert Lloyd Patterson (1836–1906), a keen student of all the zoological facets of Belfast Lough, wrote *Birds, Fishes and Cetacea commonly frequenting Belfast Lough* (1880)[87], which drew upon a series of papers he read to the Belfast Natural History and Philosophical Society (BNHPS). Another Robert Patterson (1863–1931), grandson of the first one, specialised in ornithology but wrote very little, concentrating his natural history interests in playing a leading role in the Belfast Naturalists' Field Club and the BNHPS.

Interest in birds was gathering momentum, though not always benevolent in spirit. Shooting and killing was much in vogue in the 1850s and Ralph Payne-Gallwey's *The Fowler in Ireland* (1882)[88] was a practitioner's guide on how to shoot and trap wildfowl. It contained advice on how one could massacre birds by the hundreds by slowly paddling a punt equipped with a gun, mounted like a horizontal artillery piece, across muddy estuarine ooze towards unsuspecting flocks. Netting of plovers and other bird-catching tricks were described together with natural history accounts of the more valued quarry species. A more gentle bird book, with an evangelical flavour, produced by a school teacher, the Rev. Charles Benson (1883–1919) was *Our Irish Song Birds* (1886)[89], which, according to Praeger, was 'written with charm and understanding, worthy of a true naturalist'.

The migration of birds had long fascinated ornithologists. Despite a call by J. D. Salmon in 1834 for a chain of coastal observatories in Britain the initia-

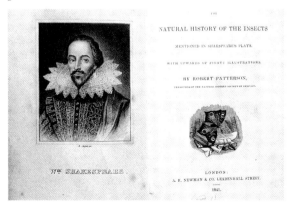

Robert Patterson successfully quarried the zoological curiosities of the insects mentioned by Shakespeare and turned his endeavours into a charming and erudite book.

tive came from the Continent. In 1842 the Belgians attempted the observation of 'periodic phenomena', of which birds were a small part; then in 1875 the German bird watchers were organised into a massive scheme for recording the seasonal movements of migrating birds. In 1879 a pilot scheme was put into operation in Britain by the naturalists J. A. Harvie-Brown and John Cordeaux who had the bright idea of relying on the ready-made network of lighthouses and lighthouse keepers. Special recording forms were despatched to over 100 such coastal beacons and the experiment was a success.

The following year, under the sponsorship of the British Association for the Advancement of Science, the scheme was refined and extended to Ireland. The Irish naturalist Richard Manliffe Barrington (1849–1915) set up the project, enlisting single-handedly all the lighthouse keepers in the country. Another member of the landed gentry and a contemporary of Henry Chichester Hart, Barrington was born and lived at the family property at Fassaroe, Co. Wicklow. He possessed remarkable energy and enthusiasm for natural history. With the encouragement of his mentor, Alexander Goodman More, Barrington undertook several botanical expeditions to west coast islands, Midland lakes and Benbulbin, Co. Sligo and for the purpose of his ornithological work he visited most Irish islands. He is probably best-known for his work on bird migration. From the observations of the lighthouse keepers, Barrington gathered a vast amount of information on bird migrations and movements, much of it new and exciting (see p.363). He painstakingly compiled all the raw data and brought them together into a fat, information-packed tome *The Migration of Birds as observed at Irish Lighthouses and Lightships* (1900). The book is a particularly important reference source for Irish ornithologists as, unlike most other bird books, all the raw data is published in full, turning the book into a rich ornithological database.[90]

Barrington, Richard John Ussher (1841–1913) and Robert Warren (1829–1915) comprised an ornithological triumvirate of probably the most gifted bird watchers ever seen in Ireland. In 1890 the three had planned together with More to write a much needed sequel to Thompson's great work on birds published nearly 50 years earlier. New data had been gathered, especially on species in the process of becoming extinct or undergoing distributional changes, and it was clearly time for a new work. But Barrington was over-committed to his migration studies and unable to assist, More was suffering from ill health – he died in 1895 – and Robert Warren, in the words of Praeger 'did not feel himself sufficiently equipped for so wide an undertaking' so the task fell upon Ussher who became the 'real' author of *The Birds of Ireland* (1900).[91]

Ussher, born and based in Co. Waterford, was, according to Praeger, *facile princeps* among Irish ornithologists. He was a quiet, courteous man with blue eyes and a red bushy beard. His almost over-modest bearing conveyed little impression of the determination, fearlessness, and contempt for discomfort he harboured inside. His expeditions, whether ornithological or speleological, necessitated descending the most dangerous cliffs and working underground for weeks amid rocks and mud. There were indeed very few cliffs, hills, loughs, woods and other places in Ireland that did not receive the imprint of Ussher's foot. He was an oologist and for many years relentlessly persecuted the eyries of his favourite species, the peregrine falcon. He gave up egg collecting later in life. Warren was less robust. Born in Cork, he later settled on the Moy Estuary, Co. Mayo, an excellent location for birds. A regular correspondent with Thompson, he supplied the latter with plenty of information to be used in the *Natural History of Ireland*.

The Birds of Ireland proved worthy of its predecessor of 50 years earlier. It is probably the finest avifauna of its time from any European country with accurate and detailed information on the status and distribution of all species recorded in Ireland. Much of the data was gathered in the field by Ussher, to which were added Barrington's results from the migration studies, and Warren's steady contributions. Like Thompson, Ussher also drew upon an extensive network of gifted bird watchers scattered throughout the country who provided, by correspondence, detail of local occurrences. The quality of the information in *The Birds of Ireland*, as in Thompson's three volumes on birds, is irreproachable, making it an invaluable historical text, regularly quoted by ornithologists today.

The Victorian natural history clubs

One particularly important development of the Victorian period was the field club which has been described by Allen as a masterpiece of social mechanism.[62] These clubs were founded in most large British towns and cities during the 1820s and 1830s. The meeting rooms were the focus of intellectual debates on natural history with much exchanging and sharing of views. Special displays, or 'cabinets of curiosity', which were essentially miniature museums, flourished in association with these clubs. Field excursions were all the rage. The day was spent, often after a group breakfast – improved by a few stiffening drinks for the more hardy members – collecting specimens of flowers and rocks and perhaps some insects. Women were very much present on the outings as shown by group photographs. A grand picnic punctuated midday, adding further to the fortification of the participants, followed by more hunting of 'specimens' before the group dispersed to change gear and boots – the excursionists wore what would be seen today as the most inappropriate attire for active field work. They later reassembled for dinner and afterwards continued to be enlightened on the subject of natural history by 'addresses' and speeches from the luminaries. Most clubs were patronised by a single social class, the privileged one. But a few were more open and democratic.

The Belfast Natural History Society came into existence in 1821 – one of the first societies within Ireland and Britain. It was formed for the 'cultivation of Zoology, Botany and Mineralogy in all their branches, more especially the investigation of the Natural History and Antiquities of Ireland'. The word 'Philosophical' was added in 1842 to the Society's name which then became The Belfast Natural History and Philosophical Society to allow scope for a broader interaction between science and ideas. Robert Templeton and William Thompson, two of Ireland's most distinguished naturalists, were members of the BNHPS. So was Robert Patterson, author of several zoological text books and, following the death of his friend Thompson, editor of the fourth volume of *The Natural History of Ireland*. In the words of John Wilson Foster, the Society was an 'impressive intellectual consortium' that bridged the arts and science.[92]

Partly as a result of a series of very successful public lectures on geology by Joseph Beete Jukes (1811–69) and on natural history by Ralph Tate (1840–1901), organised by the Department of Science and Art in Belfast in 1862–3, demand arose for a specialist natural history society. This led to the

Eminent Victorian naturalists Samuel Alexander Stewart, Ralph Tate, William Gray and Joseph Wright at a meeting of the Belfast Naturalists' Field Club in the early 1860s.

creation of the Belfast Naturalists' Field Club (BNFC) in 1863, a society much more narrowly focused on natural history than its predecessor, the BNHPS. However, both these organisations shared many common members, up to 500, most of whom were of the Protestant middle classes from the ship-owning and linen-manufacturing families of Belfast – a good number of them were women. Further south, in the less industrial parts of the country, the development of societies and clubs was slower: the Natural History Society of Dublin started in 1838 and ended *c*.1871; the Cuvierian Society of Cork fl.1845–55; the Dublin Microscopical Club in 1849–1924; the Dublin Naturalists' Field Club in 1885–present day; the Cork Naturalists' Field Club 1892–1923, and the Limerick Naturalists' Field Club 1892–1912.

The Dublin Naturalists' Field Club was founded by Alfred Cort Haddon (1855–1940), who started his scientific career as a marine zoologist engaged in deep water dredging expeditions off the southwest coast in 1885 and 1886. But, on taking up a Fellowship at Cambridge in 1901, it was his interest in anthropology that consumed the remainder of his professional life. Towards the end of his stay in Ireland he published several papers on the cranial measurements of west coast islanders where he was affectionately known as 'Haddon the head hunter'. In the words of Praeger, 'after a brief period of decline following a very successful start, the Club settled down, and with some fluctuations has reached a gratifying success'.[2] Initially the Club apparently felt no need to establish its own journal as there already existed other publication outlets that could be used. But the Club's great achievement was the founding, in 1892, of the *Irish Naturalist*, an independent monthly journal for all aspects of Irish natural history. For 33 years the *Irish Naturalist* was the main outlet for Irish natural history publications. As rightly pointed out by Patrick and Peter Wyse-Jackson in their review of the journal 'it is one of the major sources for scientific research today and provides a valuable insight into the countryside, nature, environment and attitudes of the 1890s to 1920s'.[93] The last issue was December 1924. Its demise was due mainly to financial mismanagement and other circumstances of the early 1920s, exacerbated by the wider economic and political uncertainties facing the country. Almost immediately after its death another publication, *The Irish Naturalists' Journal*, sprung forth from Belfast in September 1925. The new *Journal* was born, at the insistence of the Belfast Naturalists' Field Club, under the aegis of a committee, representing various natural history societies and institutions from both parts of Ireland. Today, after 73 vigorous years, *The Irish Naturalists' Journal* is the main organ for Irish naturalists to reveal their discoveries and findings.

Another institution pivotal to the development of Irish natural history was the Dublin Natural History Museum. In 1792 the Royal Dublin Society (founded in 1731 for improving 'Husbandry, Manufactures and other useful Arts and Sciences') bought 'the natural history museum' of the German Nathaniel Gottfried Lesk (1752–86), known as the Leskean collection, of minerals, shells and insects – at least 2,500 species of the latter. Later, in June 1795, William Higgins was appointed Professor of Chemistry and Mineralogy and put in charge of the special cabinet, designed to host this collection, placed in a spacious apartment in Hawkins Street and open to students. Thus the Dublin Natural History Museum was born. Now located in its own building in Merrion Street, it attracts over a quarter of million visitors each year. The Museum has one of the world's finest and fullest collections in the old cabinet style, reminiscent of former times. To enter it is to set foot in another world, so much so that it could be described as 'the museum of a museum'. Over the years many distinguished Irish naturalists and zoologists have served in the institution, making significant contributions to Irish natural history.

Back in Northern Ireland the BNFC served as a valuable nursery for young naturalists who were given their first organised encounters with nature and had opportunities for brushing their minds against their more learned and experienced elders. Praeger's father enrolled the young Robert aged 11 as a member. Praeger recounts that he formed many friendships with the older members who 'one by one crept silently into the grave'. Praeger acquired, along with many others, a knowledge of field-lore – botanical, zoological and geological – which stood him in good stead throughout his life. To Praeger the Field Club was a 'second university in which I formed friendships which, despite disparity of age, remained warm and intimate'. Some Field Club excursions into the countryside aroused wry comments from locals. On one such occasion Praeger was leader of the group and overheard two locals: 'Where d'you think they've come from?' asked one. 'O'ch, they're from the asylum', came the answer from the other, and pointing his finger at Praeger 'That one there is the keeper.'

Natural history in the twentieth century

Robert Lloyd Praeger (1865–1953) was one of the indomitable class of naturalists who were robust in physique and driven by continuous energy. Together with John Templeton and William Thompson, Praeger was probably the most significant naturalist to have come out of the Province of Ulster. Praeger was born near Belfast. His father was from the Hague, Holland, and his mother was Maria, daughter of Robert Patterson F.R.S. (1863–1931), of three generations of Belfast naturalists and from whom Praeger claims to have inherited 'a taste for natural science'.[94] His masterpiece was *Irish Topographical Botany*, published in 1901 as Volume VII of the *Proceedings of the Royal Irish Academy*.[71] A peak in Irish botanical research, it represents five years of intensive field work and the collation of thousands of records arranged systematically with notes on their distribution throughout the 40 botanical divisions of Ireland. The book was effectively the equivalent of 40 'county' floras! Praeger updated it by publishing a series of three special supplements that included new discoveries for the periods 1900–1905, 1906–28 and 1929–34, also in the *Proceedings of the Royal Irish Academy*.[95,96,97] A monument of knowledge, *Irish Topographical Botany* provides a feast of information for the specialist, but it is not a book that accommodates the general reader. Praeger corrected this with *A Tourist's Flora of the West of Ireland* (1909)[98] covering 11 of the western botanical 'Divisions' and later by *The Botanist in Ireland* (1934)[99] which embraced the whole country. The charm of these two popular books rests on Praeger's succinct and concise style when dealing with the topographical, geological and botanical features of the best-known sites. In his preface to *The Botanist in Ireland* he writes: 'All that I have to say at the conclusion of fifty years' field-work in Ireland, during which I have explored the flora of every country, of every important mountain-range, lake, river and island, is embodied in condensed form in the present work.' Neither *A Tourist's Flora* nor *The Botanist in Ireland* are obsolete today. They contain fine photographs of the countryside and close-ups by Robert Welch (1859–1936), a Belfast-based professional photographer and a naturalist in his own right.

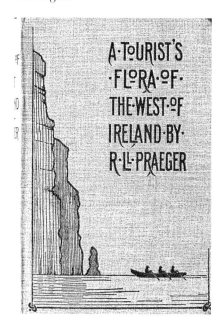

Although published some 89 years ago, Praeger's *A Tourist's Flora* remains a practicable guide.

Robert Lloyd Praeger (1865–1953), the doyen of Irish botany.

Praeger was extremely prolific, producing a vast body of scientific papers as well as three other books, for educational use, which were illustrated by his sister Rosamond (1867–1954): *Open-Air Studies in Botany: Sketches of British Wildflowers in Their Homes* (1897), *Weeds: Simple Lessons for Children* (1913) and *Aspects of Plant Life with Special Reference to the British Flora* (1921).[100,101,102] His readiness to synthesise scientific information in order to make it more accessible to ordinary people was a direct consequence of his involvement with the Belfast Naturalists' Field Club, whose purpose was to enlighten and educate.

Two other lesser known Irish natural history texts that combine similar concerns deal with the etymology of *Plant Names* (1923)[103] by Thomas Somerville Lindsay (1854–1933), who was also Archdeacon of Dublin, and *A Student's Illustrated Irish Flora Being a Guide to the Indigenous Seed-plants of Ireland* (1931)[104] by John Adams (1872–1950). Adams also published several papers on algae, lichen and fungi. He left Ireland and became Dominion Botanist in Canada.

Following encouragement from Alexander Goodman More, Nathaniel Colgan (1851–1919) put together and published *Flora of the County Dublin*[41] in 1904 – a botanical study considered by Praeger to be a model in its painstaking accuracy and careful detail. Much later on in the century the Dublin Naturalists' Field Club prepared a supplement to it which came out under the aegis of the National Museum of Ireland in 1961. A new edition was prepared by the DNFC for publication in 1998. Provisions in More's will made Colgan and Reginald W. Scully editors of the second edition of *Cybele Hibernica,* an enormous task which they completed within three years. Scully (1858–1935), a man of retiring disposition, not unlike Colgan, was also indebted to More for providing him with inspiration. His own endeavours came to fruition in *The Flora of County Kerry* (1916)[105], an additional county flora noted for its fullness and accuracy. Scully passed the torch on to James Ponsonby Brunker (1885–1970) who admitted that *Flora of the County Wicklow* (1950)[106] was initiated by his 'blundering' upon some clovers growing near Wicklow town which he took to Scully for identification. Thereafter Scully 'schooled' him in field craft.

Cynthia Longfield (1896–1991) was a gifted entomologist whose landed family were from Cloyne, Co. Cork. She was a member of the St George Scientific Expedition to the Pacific in 1924 and undertook many other expeditions at a time when it was considered not quite correct for young women to be going off by themselves. She was a world authority on the Odonata — the damselflies and dragonflies. Her *Dragonflies of the British Isles* (1937)[107] was the standard text for many years and she collaborated with Philip Corbet and Norman Moore to produce the New Naturalist volume on *Dragonflies* (1960).[108]

James Parsons Burkitt (1870–1959) made a major and generally unappreciated contribution to the science of ornithology.[109] Working by himself in the 1920s he unravelled some previously misinterpreted behaviour of the robin as well as contributing new insights into the population dynamics of birds. He was the County Surveyor for Fermanagh between 1900 and 1940 but in his spare time, working alone in his back garden, he trapped robins and by marking them individually with metal bands of different shapes – colour rings were precluded as he was colour-blind – he followed the fortunes of each bird. Burkitt was probably the first to use this technique; he also introduced age identification through ring recovery, something which then became standard practice and an important aspect of ornithological field work.

Cecil Robert Vesey Stoney (1878–1952), ornithologist and Donegal squire, was one of the finest field ornithologists Ireland has ever produced. His greatest discovery in 1930, together with G.R. Humphreys, was the large breeding colony of black-necked grebes at Lough Funshinagh, Co. Roscommon. Stoney was known for his delightful sense of humour, puckish wit, buoyant enthusiasm and the gift of teaching and inspiring others. C.J. Carroll (fl. 1920), another squire from Co. Tipperary, shared Stoney's enthusiasm for egg-collecting. Apart from contributing much information on the distribution of the peregrine falcon in Ireland, Carroll built up perhaps the best private collection of birds displaying albinism and melanism.

Another remarkable naturalist who worked mostly by himself in Northern Ireland for many years was the Rev. Edward Allworthy Armstrong (1900–78). He was born in Belfast, ordained a deacon in 1921 in Cambridge, England, and eventually returned to Cambridge in 1944 as vicar of St Mark's, Newnham, until his retirement in 1966. He had a prodigious output of natural history works. His intensive study of the wren, based on his own careful and rigorous field work, chronicled the behaviour and breeding biology of this diminutive bird. The resultant treatise *The Wren* (1955) is one of the finest bird monographs ever published.[110] His previous book *The Birds of the Grey Wind* (1940) is a prize-winning classic of regional natural history, mostly about birds, full of erudition and exuding a deep love for Northern Ireland's countryside.[111] He published many other original natural history classics, blending scholarship with his passion for nature. These include the *Folklore of Birds* (1952), still the best text today on this subject.[112]

Amongst other Northern Ireland naturalists of note, C. Douglas 'Jimmy' Deane played an important role in publicising natural history and conservation issues through his writings over 37 years in the *Belfast Telegraph* and then the *Belfast Newsletter*. He wrote several books, the most important being the *Handbook of the Birds of Northern Ireland* (1954).[113] He was an accomplished film maker – *Birds of the Grey Wind* (1958) being his best – and was active in setting up the Ulster Society for the Protection of Birds.

Arnold Benington (1904–82) was another important Northern Ireland naturalist. His studies on peregrines and sparrowhawk populations in the 1940s–1960s provided important baseline information while he was, like Deane, a populariser of natural history through lecturing, writing and broadcasting. He was also instrumental in the founding of Ulster's only bird observatory, on the Copeland Islands.

The 1930s was also the time for the birth of perhaps the finest and most accessible book on the Irish countryside. In Robert Lloyd Praeger's *The Way That I Went* (1937) the richness of Ireland's landscape and its flora and fauna are effortlessly intermingled with other strands of archaeology, folklore, etymology and history to form a complete narrative.[114] The book could best be described as a prolonged love poem of the country, its landscape and its life. No text published since has rivalled it. Before embarking on this title, Praeger had a trial flight with *Beyond Soundings* (1930),[115] also aimed at the general public, but it lacked the force and excitement of *The Way That I Went*. In 1941 he brought out *A Populous Solitude* but again it did not match up to his masterpiece.[116] One of Praeger's most important works for the natural history bibliographer was *Some Irish Naturalists* (1949), an indispensable source of information on earlier Irish naturalists.[2]

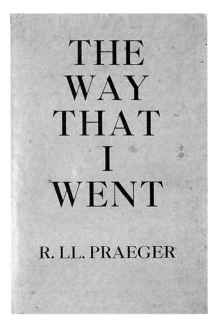

The Way That I Went, Praeger's general natural history, topographical and cultural account of Ireland, remains the best account of the country for natural historians and the general reader.

Praeger's *A Populous Solitude* was less successful than *The Way That I Went* but nevertheless satisfied the public demand for such works.

Father Patrick G. Kennedy (1881–1966), a Jesuit priest based in Dublin, emerged during the 1930s as a gifted bird watcher, writer and campaigner for bird conservation. He was invited to take on the preparation of the 1961 edition of the *List of Irish Birds* which had been published by the National Museum at infrequent intervals since the first issue was compiled by More in 1885. What had started life as a somewhat stark and lifeless catalogue of birds bearing the title *A List of Irish Birds showing the species contained in the Science and Art Museum, Dublin*[117] became, under Kennedy's pen, generous, excellent and the most fulsome of all the Museum lists. It still stands today as an exhaustive text.[118] Kennedy also championed the conservation of North Bull Island, Dublin, an extensive sand dune system surrounded by intertidal mud flats in the northern part of Dublin Bay, one of the best places in the country to watch waders and wildfowl at unbelievably close quarters. Several mad schemes had been hatched to transform the area into a major recreation playground by damming the intertidal mud flats at either end of the landward side of the island, turning the impounded area into a massive permanent water lagoon. But it was obvious that the so-called 'blue lagoon' could turn into a putrefying mass of stagnating water laced with seaweed growth. Such a development would have destroyed the wader and wildfowl feeding habitats and driven the birds away. Kennedy fought all the schemes and eventually persuaded the authorities to declare the area Ireland's first bird sanctuary under the *Protection of Birds Act, 1930* – something Kennedy also had a hand in promoting through his friend Senator S. Brown. Kennedy's *An Irish Sanctuary* (1953) tells of the ecology of the birds at North Bull as well as relating the story of the battles to save the area from development.[119]

The impending Second World War had the effect of dampening down the growth of interest in natural history in Ireland although the country was not engaged in hostilities. One vitally important project fell as an unfortunate victim of this period of astringency. It was Praeger's *Natural History of Ireland: a Sketch of its Flora and Fauna,* written in 1944 when Praeger was aged 79.[120] The War and consequent delays prevented the book's publication until 1950 by which time its format, style and much of the information it contained was 'dated'. Echoes of long species lists with little interpretation or analysis, as was customary in earlier works, reverberated throughout the book. In fact, Praeger admitted in his preface that only a limited amount of emendation to the 1944 text had been possible prior to its publication. The book also suffered greatly from the absence of any illustrations apart from three stark graphs.

In the early 1950s Kennedy teamed up with Robert Francis Ruttledge (b.1899) and Charles F. Scroope (1876–1975) with assistance from George Rayner Humphreys (1886–1980) to produce *The Birds of Ireland* (1954), an updated version of Ussher and Warren's 1900 exemplar.[121] Each of the three primary authors undertook to write the entry for the species or group of species with which they were most familiar. They were helped by an extensive network of correspondents who diligently sent in information from the fastnesses of estate walls, rectories, or retiring cottages, for traditionally the amateur study of birds was favoured by the Protestant fringe of the population – something no longer true. The 1954 vintage of *The Birds of Ireland* maintained the high standards set in 1900. It was the third in a series of major national ornithological works, each appearing at almost 50 year intervals since 1850. When is the fourth due to hatch? Ruttledge's *Ireland's Birds* appeared in 1966 and was a somewhat abbreviated work, drawing heavily upon the many discoveries and observations made by an enthusiastic band of bird watchers during the late 1950s and early 1960s.[122] Clive Hutchinson's (1949–98) *Birds in Ireland* (1989) is a more comprehensive and satisfactory work, approximating the style, detail and grandness expected of an enduring national work.[123]

David Allardice Webb (1912–95), the doyen of modern Irish botanists, first published *An Irish Flora* in 1943 (now in its seventh revised edition 1996),[124] a small and innocuous-looking volume but full of plant identification tips as well as notes on the habitats and distribution of all Irish species, written in the author's characteristic taut style. Webb was an outstanding field botanist as well as a brilliant conversationalist.

John J. Moore was the doyen of the Irish school of plant sociologists following the vegetation description methods of Braun-Blanquet. He was also a champion of the conservation of Ireland's vanishing peatlands, as well as an inspired field worker. Both Moore and Webb represented the finest scientific traditions of the two main cultural strands of Ireland.

Integrated ecological studies of a region are now generally *de rigueur,* making it difficult for the more traditional floras to survive. However, the past 18 years have seen the publication of *The Flora of County Carlow* (1979) by Booth (1897–1988) assisted by Scannell;[125] *Flora of Connemara and the Burren* (1983) by Webb & Scannell;[126] *The Flora of Inner Dublin* (1984) by Wyse-Jackson & Sheehy-Skeffington;[127] *Flora of Lough Neagh* (1986) by Harron[128] and Synnott's slim but valuable volume *County Louth Wildflowers* (1970).[129]

One of the greatest polymath naturalists of this century was Frank Mitchell (1912–98). Equipped with a brilliant and creative mind, he was primarily a geologist who branched off into many different fields of natural history. The Chair of Quaternary Studies in Trinity College was especially created to both honour him and capture his talents for the University. His early work on the vegetation history of Ireland was inspired by the Dane Knud Jessen, whom he assisted on Jessen's first Irish visit in 1934. Mitchell's many talents culminated in his remarkable book *The Irish Landscape* (1986)[130] which was recently republished for the third time as *Reading the Irish Landscape* (1997)[22] with the archaeologist Michael Ryan as co-author. The critic and writer Eileen Battersby summed up the book as 'an extraordinary achievement in that this essentially geologically-based text offers a multi-faceted and complete view of Ireland. It is a feat no other single narrative has matched.'[131]

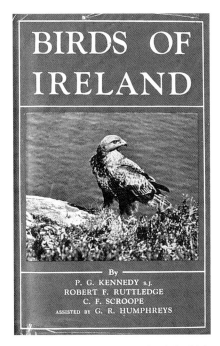

Birds of Ireland maintained the high standard set by its predecessor of 1900 and drew upon the combined experience of the four best field ornithologists of the time.

The past 25 years have witnessed a remarkable upsurge in both professional and amateur natural history activity in Ireland. The literature generated by this new generation of naturalists has become increasingly sophisticated, and natural historians, once objects of some curiosity and derision, have at last achieved their just recognition in a rapidly evolving Irish society.[13,20,51,123,126,132-142]

2

Biological History

Approximately two million years ago, severe cold conditions developed in northwestern Europe marking the onset of the Pleistocene or Ice Age. At the height of this period, ice sheets smothered Ireland and much of the European Continent, eliminating plants and animals that had evolved throughout the preceding era. When the ice relented it gave way to alternating cycles of warmth and cold spread over the last 750,000 years. The effects were profound. The development of flora and fauna was periodically encouraged only to be inhibited and largely eliminated later, with the result that the plants and animals found in Ireland today are the outcome of a most complex and not fully understood sequence of survival and migration, driven by the climatic oscillations of the Pleistocene.

It was only some 13,000 years ago, at the close of the Ice Age, that the cold began to lift, allowing a progressive development of vegetation and fauna which has continued through to the present day. The activities of the Neolithic farmers commencing some 6,000 years ago inaugurated the first anthropogenic modifications of Ireland's biotic inheritance. Woodland clearance, initiated by those farmers, brought about many long-term ecological changes including the elimination of some species, redistribution of others and the introduction of alien flora and fauna. This chapter will explore the history and sequencing of Ireland's vegetational history while detailing what is known about the origins of Ireland's mammalian fauna and, in particular, highlighting the history of red and sika deer and the wolf. The pedigree of the frog and natterjack toad in Ireland, subject to much speculation, will be explored, along with the history of Ireland's freshwater fish. Finally the many unresolved questions concerning the origin of some Lusitanian or Mediterranean–Atlantic flora will be considered, as well as the curious geographical distribution of certain plant species, especially in parts of western Ireland.

The Pleistocene or Ice Age

The latter part of the Ice Age, from about 750,000 years ago, has been characterised by a series of alternating warm phases – known as 'interstadial' if minor and without the development of closed woodland and 'interglacial' when full woodland cover developed – followed by colder phases. The interglacials and interstadials are thought to have been relatively short, in the order of 10,000–15,000 years, with temperatures close to today's levels which allowed a rich flora to emerge before it was expunged by the next cold phase. The vegetation which developed during these warm periods was generally similar to that found in other parts of Europe, although the record from Ireland is far from complete.[1] The cold periods were longer in duration, lasting some 50,000–100,000 years, and ushered in arctic and tundra floras. During the most severe conditions the landscape was covered by ice in varying amounts making it difficult for living things to survive.

This chapter will follow the tentative chronological and stratigraphical sequence of the cold and warm stages of the Quaternary deposits over the past 500,000 years as proposed by Mitchell & Ryan.[2]

Years Ago	Proposed tentative stratigraphical sequence
13,000–10,000	Late glacial
35,000–13,000	Midlandian (Drumlin) cold
65,000–35,000	Aghnadarraghian mild
79,000–65,000	Midlandian (Main) cold
122,000–100,000	Fenitian mild
132,000–122,000	Eemian warm
302,000–132,000	Munsterian cold
428,000–302,000	Gortian warm
500,000–480,000	Ballylinian warm

Pollen remains from interglacial deposits

The Ballylinian warm (500,000–480,000 years ago) takes its name from an area south of Castlecomer, Co. Kilkenny, where fossil pollen remains in a 25 m thick deposit of lacustrine clay show that the warm climate allowed the development of open forest containing most of the trees present in Ireland today including fir, spruce, hornbeam, oak, alder, wing-nut (found today in Turkey and present in Ireland from an earlier period) and yew. In the open areas there were grasses and heaths, where rhododendron and many herbs grew.[3]

The most famous interglacial deposit in Ireland is of peat and mud lying underneath glacial deposits cut by the Boleyneendorrish River near Gort, Co. Galway. It was first discovered and described by Kinahan in 1865 and was re-examined in 1949 by Jessen, Anderson & Farrington. They investigated the pollen remains in the muds and peat and named this warm interglacial stage the Gortian.[4,5] The Gortian interglacial has been uncertainly dated as occurring some 428,000–302,000 years ago.[2] About 12 other similarly aged deposits have been so far investigated in Ireland, some of whose results have been reviewed by Coxon, Mitchell & Ryan and Watts.[1,2,6] The first plant species to appear at the onset of the Gortian interglacial phase, as summarised by Coxon, were the pioneering willow, juniper and buckthorn as well as many herbs and birch scrub. As the weather became milder the extent of pine and birch woodland grew while many other species – oak, elm, holly and hazel – are thought to have migrated into Ireland from other European ice-free areas. Unlike other interglacial sites examined in Britain, these Irish woodlands did not develop into a mature mixed oak forest but into heath, as increasing wet conditions fostered the growth of heather together with alder, yew, spruce and fir

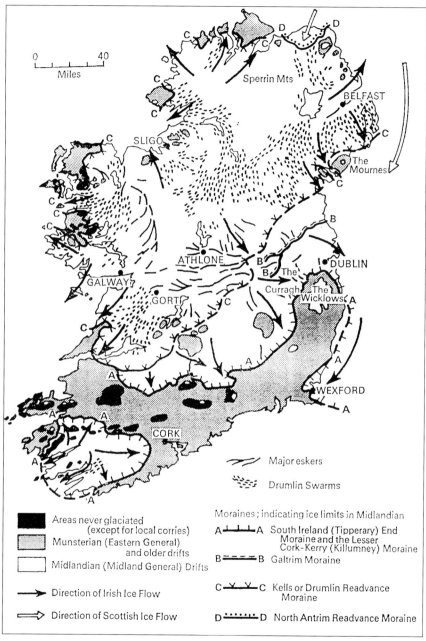

The Pliestocene geology of Ireland showing the areas considered never glaciated and the extent of the older Munsterian glaciation (302,000–132,000 years ago) and more recent two cold phases of the Midlandian: Main: 79,000–65,000 years ago and Midlandian Drumlin: 35,000–13,000 years ago. From J.B. Whittow (1974). *Geology and Scenery of Ireland.* Penguin Books, London.

trees. The end result was a crowberry wet heath – to be replaced by tundra again when the Gortian period came to an abrupt end as temperatures plummeted. The next cold stage, the Munsterian, persisted from 302,000–132,000 years ago.

The Gortian floral assemblage contains several species whose history in Ireland is a matter of much conjecture. The occurrence of pollen from Mackay's heath, Dorset heath and St Dabeoc's heath opens up the possibility of their survival through the subsequent cold phases rather than a more recent postglacial arrival on land bridges from their southern headquarters in Portugal, Spain and France. Rhododendron, another Gortian species, possibly moved into Ireland to escape declining temperatures elsewhere in Europe at the time but is generally considered to have become extinct in Ireland at the end of the Gortian phase. Its reintroduction came during the eighteenth century and it has since spread into many habitats, especially deciduous woodland and peatlands. Two further species, considered north American in their current distribution – the slender naiad and pipewort – were also present in Gortian deposits. They, like the heaths and heathers above, could possibly have continued their tenure in the country through the subsequent Munsterian cold stage in areas not subjected to intense coldness, having arrived before the glacial period by migration through Greenland and Iceland when the water barriers were not so great. This would make the need for other explanations unnecessary – such as their arrival on the feet of migratory waders and geese from western Greenland and northern Canada and perhaps America from the end of the late glacial period onwards.

Palaeobotanists have found it difficult to correlate the Gortian interglacial deposits with other such deposits in Britain and Europe but Mitchell & Ryan believe that the closest fit is with the Hoxonian period in Britain and the Holsteinian period in Germany. Whatever the correlation, the Gortian interglacial is considered by some scientists to have been the last warm interglacial before the onset of the very cold Munsterian stage.[7] The Gortian period provided the opportunity for the development of some 100 taxa of higher plants of which some 20 are not native of Ireland today.

Before the Munsterian ice was fully in place, the low ground turned into a polar desert. Only the toughest species of the Gortian vegetation could have survived these conditions while others migrated southwards to avoid the falling temperatures. Jessen was of the opinion that many of the species that migrated southwards before the advancing cold in Europe ended up in the Black Sea area. During the Munsterian glacial period large masses of ice flowed into Ireland from the Scottish Highlands and probably covered much of Ireland during its maximum extent. Limited areas of high land in the west and south probably remained ice-free. Low-lying areas, even along the Atlantic coastline, were characterised by a cold polar desert climate. Only the hardiest forms of flora and flora could have survived in Ireland when the Munsterian cold stage was at its maximum extent.

Mitchell & Ryan have put forward some evidence for the occurrence of two warm or mild phases (the Eemian and Fenitian) which followed the Munsterian cold stage and lasted from approximately 132,000–100,000 years ago, but more research is needed to establish the full nature of these interludes before the onset of the next cold phase, the Midlandian (Main) cold stage. Around 79,000 years ago it became severely cold with arctic and dry conditions until ice sheets formed and spread out from their two main centres located in an area from Donegal to Belfast and in the Midlands. A tongue of Scottish ice also passed down the Irish Sea. There were also ice caps in the Wicklow Mountains and the Cork and Kerry mountains. There were, however, substantial areas south of a line approximately between Askeaton, Co. Limerick, and the Wicklow Mountains that remained ice-free, and it was in this very cold region that many plants and animals would have had the opportunity to survive to then recolonise Ireland with the onset of warmer conditions commencing some 13,000 years ago.

During the Aghnadarraghian period, approximately 65,000–35,000 years ago, mild conditions set in. Remains of fossil beetles indicate summer and winter temperatures similar to those of today. The relatively warm conditions encouraged the development of temperate cool woodlands with hazel and yew. The earliest mammalian remains in Ireland, molar teeth, tusks and broken bones of woolly mammoth and musk ox bones (but see below), were found in gravel deposited on top of a band of lignite (brown coal) and date from over 50,000 years ago. The warm Aghnadarraghian mild phase was brought to an end with the onset of dry cold conditions which persisted for some 8,000 years before the development of more ice marking the Drumlin phase of the Midlandian cold stage, but conditions were sufficiently mild to allow the development of open grasslands with scattered birch and willow woodlands. It was in this environment that many mammals flourished, evidence of their occupation provided by bone remains in caves. The renewed ice possibly peaked around 25,000 years ago and then lasted until about 15,000 years ago when it started to melt, a process that took about 2,000 years.

Grass covered eskers, sinuous ridges composed of glacial outwash gravel.

The late glacial period and the development of woodlands

By the end of the late glacial phase some 13,000 years ago the ice sheets had melted and the final ordering of the rocky skeleton and cosmetic adjustments to the skin of the Irish landscape were complete. Mountains, hills and rocks had been scraped, scoured and polished by the flowing ice. Soil and boulders had been lifted up, moved over huge distances and dumped as rude morainic material and glacial till: sinuous ridges of outwash gravels or eskers, some extending over several kilometres and reaching 20 m in height, had established their presence in the Midlands. Miniature hilly landscapes made of drumlins or small hilly lumps of glacial drift, possibly formed underneath the melting ice sheets or dropped as dollops of material, had appeared. Lake basins were scooped out, valleys were formed.

As it emerged from the cold, Ireland entered what is known as the Woodgrange interstadial phase; a sort of mini-interglacial period without the full development of woodlands. The name comes from the shallow lake basin lying between drumlins at Woodgrange, Co. Down, where pollen was blown, settled, and remained preserved in the organic muds. Originally described by Singh,[8] the Woodgrange pollen signatures were later recounted by Mitchell & Ryan. They chronicle the succession of plants that settled and spread in this area over a period of 3,000 years.

The first plants to emerge and fix themselves in the bare soil were sorrels, grasses and the dwarf willow. This initial growth is known as the grass/sorrel phase. Five hundred years later juniper and birch flourished while other pollen deposits showed crowberry growing close to the Atlantic coastline near Roundstone, Co. Galway. In those days the Irish landscape must have approximated that of arctic tundra with a smattering of birch woodland and juniper scattered over the ground. However, this initial growth was brought to an abrupt end as a renewed drop in temperature killed off the pioneering species.

Pollen diagram from Woodgrange, Co. Down. From Singh[8].

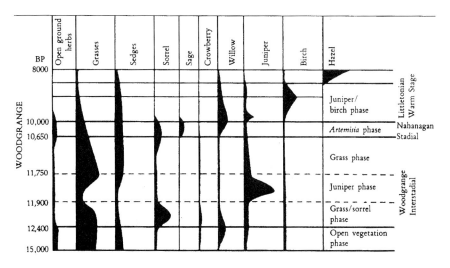

A cold snap, triggered by a southerly movement of arctic waters down the Atlantic coast of Europe around 10,600 years ago, suppressed the birch and juniper development and opened up bare patches of soil only suitable for the more resistant grasses. This period, lasting some 600 years, is named the Nahanagan stadial by Mitchell & Ryan, after Lough Nahanagan in the Wicklow Mountains where glacier ice reformed as it did in other mountain corries under the renewed influence of freezing temperatures. Such extreme conditions only allowed the emergence of a sporadic plant cover, mainly of arctic-alpine species, growing at low altitudes and also at sea level along the western seaboard – as shown by pollen remains from Achill Island, Co. Mayo, and Waterville and Killarney, Co. Kerry. There was permafrost on the lowlands with a scattered plant cover, much of it made up of dwarf willow and other arctic species. The initial vegetation cover of the Irish lowland landscape was a succession of different plant communities consisting of grasses, mugwort and low scrub with juniper and crowberry. Open grasslands later developed, characterised by docks and sedges. The mugwort, *Artemisia* sp. was also common, as evidenced by the pollen remains, thus giving rise to the description of this period as the Artemisia phase. These grasslands endured for some 1,000 years as large herbivores – giant deer and reindeer – stalked and munched their way through the lush pastures. The Nahanagan cold snap snuffed out much of the start of postglacial life in Ireland and the process had to commence all over again – from a generally bare soil to grasses to shrubs to dwarf trees and eventually to mature woodlands.

During the next 4,900 years, from 10,000–5,100 years ago, the Irish landscape evolved from open tundra to a country almost totally swaddled by woodlands. Only the mountains, poking above the green canopy, and the rivers, lakes and bogs in the lowlands differed from their surroundings. Temperatures continued to rise, more than doubling the July mean temperature from about 7°C to 15°C, approximately the same as today. Because of these new climatic conditions, Ireland became available for colonisation by the flora and fauna that had survived on the ice-free and warmer European mainland and also possibly in parts of Ireland.

How Ireland acquired its flora and fauna is a continuing and unresolved saga. There are three principal scenarios. Firstly, many plants and animals may have entered the country before the Ice Age or during interglacial periods and survived in ice-free areas. The flora and fauna then colonised the landscape at the end of the Ice Age. Forbes first championed this preglacial survival hypothesis in 1846.[9] It received support from Praeger in 1932 and Beirne in 1952.[10,11] Secondly, there may have been no Ice Age or interglacial survivors, and Ireland's flora and fauna mostly arrived during the postglacial period, migrating from Britain and southern Europe when sea levels were some 130 m lower than present. This hypothesis was supported by Charlesworth in 1930, Godwin in 1975 and most recently by Mitchell & Ryan in 1997.[2,12,13] Finally, postglacial arrival may have been by aerial dispersion, chance methods, and introduction, deliberate or accidental, by early man. This hypothesis was postulated by Reid in 1899 and more recently by Corbet in 1961.[14,15]

The most probable explanation is likely to be a combination of the three possibilities. Thus it would seem quite plausible for many species to have survived the Midlandian glaciation in the southern ice-free zones, and possibly earlier episodes of extreme coldness, while many other species may have arrived in

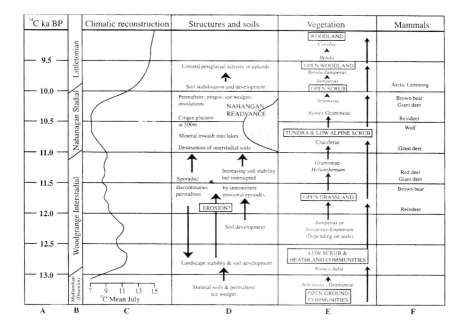

Late glacial Ireland. Column A gives the timescale for the last 13,000 radiocarbon years. Column B gives the names of the Irish type sites. Column C shows temperature trends, largely based on information from fossil animals and plants rather than instrumental measurements. Column D shows geomorphological and soil developments. Column E outlines vegetational developments. Column F lists mammalian records. From Mitchell & Ryan[2].

Ireland during the postglacial period. The postglacial land bridge migration of flora and fauna has been strongly argued by Mitchell & Ryan. They postulated that land bridges between Ireland and Britain existed when the sea level fell to about 130 m below today's levels exposing dry ridges of land, thus making it possible to cross dry-shod from the Lancashire–Cumbria area to Dublin, from north Wales to Co. Wicklow and from Cornwall to southeast Ireland. Ireland also had an Atlantic coastal 'pathway' linking it with southwest England, France and northern Spain. The sea fell to its lowest level some 15,000 years ago. By 10,000 years ago it was back to present day levels. Despite the appeal of the land bridge routes, the country could well have been repopulated from a reservoir of flora and fauna that had survived in the southern ice-free areas of Limerick, Cork and Waterford.

In support of their land bridge concept, Mitchell & Ryan explain the process whereby the retreat northwards of the large wedge of ice that filled the area now occupied by the Irish Sea created a land bridge which was 'pulled' northwards with the withdrawal of the glacier. It is argued that the great weight of the ice depressed the land underneath which was squeezed out laterally and at the front of the glacier. Pushing down a fist into a ball of dough would produce a similar effect with the dough squeezed out laterally and rising up around the edges. The squeezed-out land moved out sideways and in front of the ice as a sort of bow of land as the ice pushed southwards. On the retreat of the ice northwards up the Irish Sea area the forebulge of land also retreated. Mitchell

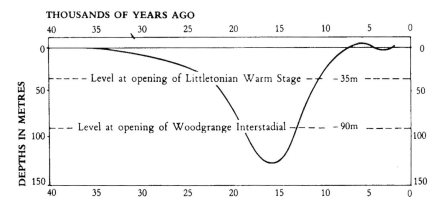

Outline curve to indicate possible course of sea level around Ireland during the last 40,000 years. From Mitchell & Ryan[2].

& Ryan, drawing upon a detailed study by Wingfield of the British Geological Survey,[16] postulated that the fore-bulge moved or was pushed into the south end of the Irish Sea area about 11,000 years ago, when it provided a land bridge link between Devon and Carnsore Point, Co. Wexford. As the glacier melted and retreated northwards up the Irish Sea so the fore-bulge followed, providing a sort of moving land bridge link, of a continually diminishing height, across which plants and animals were able to migrate into Ireland from west Wales. About 9,500 years ago the bridge was enveloped and submerged by the rising waters of the Irish Sea.

A land bridge also spanned what is now the English Channel, remaining open for business for approximately 2,500 years longer than the Irish–Welsh bridge. It was along this route that the plants and animals almost certainly moved from southern Europe to Ireland. They had about 1,500 years to travel across a 'dry' Irish Sea from Britain, having already trekked from the Continent into Britain over a 'dry' English Channel. It may seem a long time but in fact the colonisation process was a race against time as the immigration routes were being rapidly cut off by the rising waters, first in the Irish Sea and subsequently in the English Channel. Many species failing to cross the last bridge remained circumscribed to Britain, and the paucity of the Irish flora and fauna today is mainly – albeit not entirely – attributable to that late phenomenon. There remains, however, much conjecture and many difficult unanswered questions about the ways and means by which many animals and plants may have moved back into Ireland over the land bridges.[17,18]

Many of the plants and animals involved in the migration process would have travelled a distance of at least 1,000 km by direct line, say, for example, from Luxembourg to Dublin. The time allocated for the trip (about 2,500 years including the 1,500 years when the Irish land bridge was open) would have allowed a rate of migration of 400 m per annum, a not unrealistic rate of progress. The pace of settlement was fast indeed as oaks were already growing in the south of Ireland 9,000 years ago while wild boars were being hunted near Coleraine, Co. Derry, by the first men on record. Wild deer too, had already established their presence in the Midlands some 8,400 years ago.

However, opponents of the land bridge hypothesis would argue that these species were already present in the country and their populations expanded their range with rising temperatures.

Ten thousand years ago, pollen deposits were being laid down in a raised bog near Littleton, Co. Tipperary, starting an important historical archive and providing one of the most important chronologies of vegetational development in Ireland from 10,000 years ago to the present time.[19] It tells the story of rich meadows of grasses, docks and meadowsweet which were quickly replaced by a juniper scrub mixed with willow trees. These low-growing species were subsequently overtaken by the taller downy birch forming the first real woodlands. Hazel then established itself with a patchy distribution of sometimes quite dense stands, while Scots pine also started expanding from about 9,000–8,500 years ago to produce a pine–hazel wooded landscape.

The oak first put in an appearance around 9,000 years ago and quickly expanded its range together with the wych elm to form a high forest. As a result of this woodland expansion, the pine was pushed off the better Midland soils onto the poorer regions of the west. Alder also extended its cover but remained confined to the wetter areas, while the drier limestone soils attracted the ash. By then yew was already in Ireland.

Schematic pollen-diagram to illustrate the early development of the Littletonian woodlands in Ireland. From Mitchell & Ryan[2].

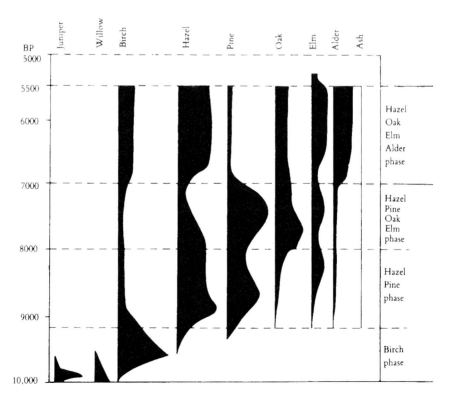

The deciduous woodland climax phase, dominated by a high forest of hazel–oak–elm–alder lasted for almost 2,000 years between 7,000 and 5,100 years ago. With the onset of wetter climatic conditions, alder had spread considerably and joined the dense forest of oaks and elms. Pine was very much restricted to the poorer soils of the west or other upland areas where birch was also competing for some ground.

These were the finest years of Ireland's woodlands. Vast areas of the country were covered by a continuous mantle of trees. It was the time of the proverbial tree top walking squirrels, which travelled the length of Ireland from Malin Head, Co. Donegal, to Cape Clear, Co. Cork, without touching the ground.

Many trees such as the limes, hornbeam, beech, service, all the elms except wych elm, the field maple and the sycamore failed to reach Ireland and become established as native species. The black poplar, together with the grey poplar, was formerly considered by Praeger to be rare and an introduced species.[20] However, recent surveys, initiated by the Botanical Society of the British Isles, have discovered large numbers of black poplar on the River Shannon system as far north as Lough Allen, Co. Leitrim, and in the damp plains that form the headwaters of the Rivers Liffey, Co. Wicklow, and Barrow, Co. Laois, which are thought to be remnants of native woodlands. The population is reported to have a well-balanced age structure and is regenerating, especially on the shore of Loughs Allen and Ree. There is a young population on the east shore of Lough Allen which is thought to be unique.[21] Slightly over half of all the trees examined had smooth trunks and lower branches, without bosses, or burrs – a feature distinguishing the Irish population from that growing in England where only 0.3% are without bosses.[22]

All except the sycamore managed to set foot in Britain where, however, they remained restricted to the south and east. Limes, hornbeam, beech, service, all the elms except wych elm, the field maple and the sycamore were subsequently introduced to Ireland by man. Beech and sycamore perhaps arrived with the Normans during the twelfth century – although archaeologists have identified fragments of beech dating from a period between AD 600 and 1000, possibly imported – while lime species and hornbeam only came in the seventeenth or eighteenth centuries. Despite their non-native pedigree, both beech and sycamore have adapted and flourished in Ireland as if they were native. On the other hand, Ireland can claim one native tree that is missing from Britain, the strawberry-tree. This belongs to a small group of so-called Mediterranean–Atlantic species and is found in Portugal, northern Spain and western France but not in Britain, probably because it travelled up the western European coast and bypassed Britain.

When the woodland reached its zenith about 5,250 years ago, elm was the commonest tree on the good soils in the drier areas of the Midlands and eastern Ireland.[23] Hazel, formerly common all over the country, was now concentrated in the north-central areas while pine was most abundant along the western seaboard. This woodland tranquillity was, however, to be interrupted by a dramatic decline in the production of elm pollen some 5,100 years ago. Debate has raged as to the causes of this phenomenon: was it man-induced or the result of natural causes? Mitchell & Ryan put it down to a disease – a fungal pathogen *Ceratocystis ulmi* (Dutch elm fungus) – a situation re-enacted this century with devastating consequences. While no figures are available for Ireland, over 90% of the British elms died, involving an estimated 25 million trees, dur-

Early plantations of beech woodlands.

ing the late 1960s and 1970s.

The decline of the elm followed soon after the arrival of the first Neolithic farmers about 6,000 years ago, together with their cereal crops and domestic animals. They landed on the shores of Ireland with polished stone axes that had sharp cutting edges and they opened up the first woodland clearances by chopping down the trees, as well as killing them by ring-barking, in order to grow crops. The natural collapse of elm must have come as a gift to them for they did not have to exert so much effort to get at the good soil. The forests were progressively reduced over the next 1,500 years and replaced by extensive grassland and heathland. This commitment to tree cutting and removal was intensified as new waves of Neolithic immigrants arrived, later followed by the Celtic invasions, the Vikings, the Normans and then the English planters. All of them took a bite at the woods, which were soon cleared for purposes other than agriculture, such as charcoal production for the smelting of iron ore, the construction of ships, barrels and houses and the curing and preservation of cattle hides with tannins derived from oak bark. All this went on with such vigour that by the end of the Tudor period, virtually all of Ireland's native woodlands had been reduced to a miserable rag bag of scrappy and uneconomic patches in steep and rocky places that were not attractive for agriculture or any other purpose. The grass pollen that was now swirling in the air was deposited in lake water where it descended into soft mud sediments to remain unaltered. Ireland's new grasslands – visible under the microscope today – had arrived. Today, grassland dominates, accounting for 93% of all the land used for agricultural purposes.

The early fauna of Ireland and cave explorations

Towards the end of the nineteenth century, a small and enthusiastic band of Irish naturalists led by the ornithologist Richard John Ussher was deeply preoccupied with the exploration of caves which they thought must contain the bones of animals, and possibly early man, that once roamed through and flew over the Irish landscape. The caves in the limestone areas of Ireland were probed and excavated with such dedication and energy that the movement could almost have been dubbed the 'Victorian bone craze'. The hard core cave naturalists included Praeger, Scharff and Ussher. Their publications on the findings from Kesh, Co. Sligo, Castlepook, Co. Cork, and at several sites in Clare are a source of endless fascination.[24,25,26] They were quick to realise that the bones provided incontrovertible evidence of the prehistoric fauna. But the circumstances in which the deposition of bones had occurred clearly varied. Some animals adopted the caves as their homes while others occasionally sought refuge there. Many bones were the remnants of prey dragged into the caves by the larger carnivores such as spotted hyenas, bears and wolves.

The Midlandian cold stage as described above was not as severe as the Munsterian cold stage. It is named after the elongated ice dome that was located between Galway City and Castlerea, Co. Roscommon, which sent ice sheets southwards through the Midlands which petered out along a line from Kilrush in the Shannon estuary to Tipperary town and then northeastwards to the Wicklow hills. There were also local ice caps to the mountains together with valley glaciers in Donegal, Wicklow, Cork and Kerry. Temperatures in the ice-free zones were possibly similar to cold Continental conditions, approximating parts of Siberia today. The landscape, out of reach from the glaciers, was probably open grassland with scattered woods of dwarf birch and least willow with only small amounts of bare tundra.[2] It was in this environment that many of the prehistoric animals existed.

The earliest known remains of animal bones in Ireland come from the east shore of Lough Neagh at Aghnadarragh, near the village of Glenavy, where lignite deposits date from about 55,000 years ago. A number of teeth and bones of the woolly mammoth together with bones of the musk ox were found in the thin glacial covering sitting on top of the lignite and probably dating from over 50,000 years ago.[27] The bones of bison have also been reported at this site but may be the result of misidentification – bison are close relatives of the musk ox.[2] Plant and beetle fossils from the area suggest temperatures very similar to those of today, giving the period the characteristics of a warm interstadial. Two tree species – yew and hazel – grew in scattered woodlands. During this period it is likely but not proven by the discovery of bone remains that there were other large mammals in the Irish countryside such as Irish giant deer, reindeer, brown bear and spotted hyena. Some of these were to become extinct with the resurgence of ice during the Drumlin phase of the Midlandian cold stage (35,000–13,000 years ago).

The Drumlin phase opened as cool interstadial with massive ice developing later and peaking at 25,000 years ago.[2] As the temperatures nose-dived, many animals took refuge in nearby caves where their bones lay dormant until discovered by the cave explorers. Ussher's, Praeger's and Scharff's findings included woolly mammoth, red deer, giant Irish deer, reindeer, brown bear, wild boar, mountain hare, Arctic fox, spotted hyena, Norway lemming and Arctic or Greenland lemming.

Interpretation of the historical sequence and associations of the species was beset by problems of shifting soil horizons due to water movements in the caves, much of which was caused by melting ice from the glaciers. Additional problems were created by badgers entering the caves much later, and disturbing the bones embedded in the soil when excavating their setts. There were also cases of collapsing ceilings bringing in intruders from the strata above the caves. Radiocarbon dating was not available to Praeger, Ussher and Scharff at the beginning of the century, hence the difficulty of disentangling the muddle of bones. It is only very recently, in last 25 years, that cave explorers have been able to place their finds accurately within a chronology.

In 1993 a selection of some 30 samples of known bones, recovered from caves by early investigators and entrusted to the quiet security of museums, had small extracts of collagen removed for radiocarbon dating at the Oxford University Accelerator Unit. The programme was devised by Woodman & Monaghan.[27] The project had three aims: to discover (i) which mammals were in Ireland before the final glaciers of the Midlandian cold stage; (ii) which animals were present afterwards in the late glacial period and (iii) which were present in the postglacial period from some 10,000 years ago.

The radiocarbon results (given as median dates in years ago and rounded to the nearest 100), based on bones from Castlepook and Foley's caves in Co. Cork and Shandon cave, Co. Waterford, showed that in the ice-free zones in Cork and Waterford giant Irish deer (32,100), reindeer (28,000), Norway lemming (27,900), woolly mammoth (27,200), brown bear (26,300), red deer (26,100) Arctic lemming (20,300) and Arctic fox (20,000) were present. During the late glacial period the following species were found in caves in Cork, Sligo, Clare and Limerick: reindeer (12,500 and 10,900), brown bear, (11,900 and 10,700), red deer (11,800), giant Irish deer (11,800), wolf (11,200) and Arctic lemming (10,000), showing that the first four species soldiered on into the late glacial period (13,000–10,000 years ago). The gradual warming up of the landscape was rudely interrupted by the Nahanagan stadial, during which the mean annual summer temperatures may have been less than 5°C. Many questions remain as to the impact of this sudden temperature reversal on flora and fauna. However, it should be remembered that Arctic foxes, Greenland lemmings, Arctic hares, ermines, wolves and musk ox as well as hundreds of insect and flowering plant species are able to survive Greenland winters when temperature drop as low as -20°C with summer temperatures higher than experienced during the Nahanagan stadial. The question applies to all the previous cold periods. If some animals and plants were able to survive the Drumlin phase of the Midlandian and subsequent Nahanagan stadial then the need to argue for their land bridge arrival in Ireland is considerably weakened. Many of the large herbivores disappeared, together with their carnivore predators, with the decline of their important grasslands.

Without further information from a large scale radiocarbon dating programme it will remain a moot point whether the known early mammals such as Arctic hares, red deer and wolf, and species such as stoats, otters, pine martens, etc., for which there is no evidence yet of their early occupancy, achieved a continuous presence in Ireland through to the postglacial period, when a warmer and a more environmentally friendly landscape re-emerged, or whether they re-entered Ireland as immigrants across the land bridge. All that can be said is that Woodman & Monaghan dated red deer bones from 4,200 years ago at Stonestown, Co. Westmeath and to 2,020 years ago at Sydenham, Co. Down and that brown bears were present in Ireland as recently as 8,900 years ago – as testified by remains at Derrykeel Bog, Co. Offaly. They were con-

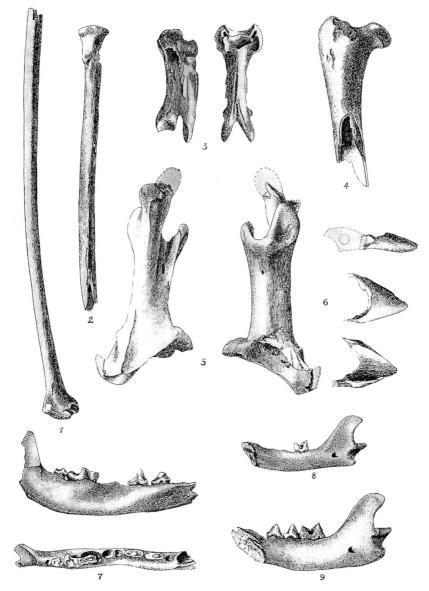

Animal bones recovered from County Clare caves. 1-5 Crane bones; 6 Hawfinch? 7 Arctic fox; 8 Domestic cat; 9 Irish wild cat. From Scharff *et. al.*[26]

temporary with the first human settlers at Mount Sandel on the lower reaches of the River Bann, just south of Coleraine, Co. Derry.

Lynch & Hayden have argued that the range contraction of the Arctic hare and stoat, both present in the Castlepook interstadial (35,000 years ago[28]), before the Drumlin phase of the Midlandian period, into an ice-free southern

Co. Cork, together with their genetic isolation from their assumed British and Continental mother stock, may have been sufficient time for both the stoat and hare to develop their subspecific characteristics.[29] They tested morphological differences by multivariate analysis of cranial measurements between Irish, English and Scottish carnivores – badger, mink, otter and stoat. Significant differences between English, Scottish and Irish badgers, otters, mink and stoat populations were demonstrated – the greatest were between the Irish stoat and its English counterpart, thus strengthening the argument for the stoat being a glacial relict species. Little evidence was found for musteline colonisation of Ireland via a land bridge between northeast Ireland and Scotland. The evolution of established subspecific differences which separate Irish hares and otters from their English relations would also have been facilitated by their genetic isolation provided by their presence in Ireland some 35,000 years ago.

Woodman & Monaghan also attempted to unravel the history of the horse in Ireland.[27] Was it introduced around 4,000 years ago or was it a survivor, in its wild form, from the late glacial to the postglacial period – as is the case in Britain? The subject is still open to debate as one horse bone, recovered from Shandon Cave, near Dungarvan, Co. Waterford, gave a radiocarbon date indicating that it was more than 40,000 years old.[2] This places the wild horse in Ireland long before a series of horse bones from five widely separated caves from Antrim to Clare, which gave a range of dates from 1,675–120 years ago. These latter datings would support the idea that the horse was introduced late to Ireland.

Red deer

Red deer were part of the rich mammalian fauna during the Midlandian stage prior to the Drumlin cold phase. Radiocarbon dating shows them present in Co. Waterford from at least 26,100 years ago with more recent records from 11,800 (Co. Sligo) and 4,200–2,000 years ago (Westmeath, Kerry, Clare and Down).[27] It would appear that they survived the Drumlin phase of the Midlandian cold stage, possibly along with other mammals whose bones have not yet been found, to earn 'native' status in the Killarney Valley, Co. Kerry. However, the degree to which the Killarney deer are unadulterated descendants of the original native stock is a complex and unresolved issue.

Scharff wrote of 'red deer which still survives in a semi-domesticated and not entirely pure strain in the forests of Killarney.'[30] Moffat stated in 1938 that 'These Deer cannot be claimed as a perfectly pure breed, for inter-breeding has occurred with imported animals, and the extent to which this has prevailed is not easily estimated. The Red Deer at Muckross have, however, at least a fair claim to represent in the main the old native stock that is known to have been abundant throughout Ireland in early historic and pre-historic times.'[31] Finally, Whitehead declared in 1964: 'Of the three established herds, only the Kerry deer can claim descent from the original wild stock, but even these cannot be considered as being perfectly pure bred.'[32] Whitehead has produced the only evidence questioning the status of the deer. He reported that during the nineteenth century both Lord Kenmare and Mr Herbert of Muckross, Co. Kerry, brought in fresh blood which included five stags from Co. Roscommon – presumably from the herd at Croghan House Park, Boyle, where a small herd existed until 1939. Around 1900 Lord Kenmare brought in a stag from Windsor Great Park, England, which was liberated in Derrycunihy wood. Also

A recently born red deer calf
(F. Guinness).

at this time some stags from Muckross were rounded up and sent to Scotland in exchange for Scottish stags. Since the latter arrived, occasional bald-faced deer have been seen in Derrycunihy. They may be the descendants of deer from the Glenlyon area of Perthshire possibly included in the exchange.[32] The red deer in Kerry today are confined to the Mangerton and Torc mountain ranges and number about 600.

At the National Park at Glenveagh, Co. Donegal, the red deer herd was established in 1891, when two stags and four hinds were brought in from Glenartney deer forest in Perthshire, followed in 1892 by a stag and nine hinds from Langwell deer forest in Caithness. Subsequently, whenever fresh blood was required it was introduced from either England or from other parks in Ireland such as Colebrooke, Co. Fermanagh (1910), and Slane, Co. Meath (1947–9).[32]

Sika deer

In 1860, Lord Powerscourt introduced four sika deer from Japan to his demesne in Co. Wicklow. Ireland was the first country in Europe in which these deer were bred successfully.[33] Within 24 years, numbers had increased to 100 – not taking into account individuals shot or sent to other parks – and reached 500–600 strong by the early 1930s. Many slipped out into the Wicklow hills and its woodlands where they flourished. Lord Powerscourt mated red with sika deer and produced fertile offspring which was indicative of their close biological relationship. Once started, the hybridisation process spread outside the demesne into the Wicklow Mountains, uplands and forests, where it is unlikely that there is any true red deer left today. In other words, this particular tampering with nature brought about the extinction of a species, albeit only the Wicklow population of red deer. The lessons learnt will hopefully discourage other potential Noahs from introducing non-native species and dabbling in cross-breeding experiments.

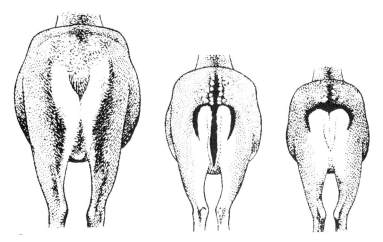

Rump patterns of the red (left), fallow (centre) and sika deer (right). From G.B. Corbet & N.H. Southern (1977) *The Handbook of British Mammals*. Blackwells, Oxford.

Lord Powerscourt, however, was not the first. The Normans had done it before him, bringing both the rabbit and fallow deer into Ireland during the twelfth century. Rabbits became pests, successfully competing with other herbivores for grass, but at least they did not interbreed with other species. Fallow deer provided sport, food and ornament and could be considered as an ecologically benign species although they may cause damage to forestry, agriculture and horticulture.

Lord Powerscourt was a prominent member and one of the vice-presidents of The Society for the Acclimatisation of Animals, Birds, Fishes, Insects and Vegetables within the United Kingdom, founded in 1860 and disbanded in 1865. Its purpose was to 'acclimatise and cultivate those animals, birds etc., which will be useful and suitable to the park, the moorland, the plain, the woodland, the farm, the poultry yard, as well as those which will increase the resources of our seashores, rivers, ponds and gardens'.[34] Apart from the sika he brought in other foreign creatures to Ireland: axis deer, Sardinian mouflon (wild sheep), sambar deer and several colour varieties of the red deer including the wapiti or Canadian deer. Fortunately none of these 'took' or became acclimatised to Ireland. He also introduced roe deer but nothing is known of the results apart from the fact that they never survived at Powerscourt or elsewhere in Wicklow. Henry Gore-Booth was more successful in the early 1870s and established a small feral population of roe deer on his estate at Lissadell, Co. Sligo. They survived, apparently restricted to the estate, for about 50 years before being shot out.

In 1865, some of the Powerscourt sika deer were sent to the deer park at Killarney. Some 20 years later, they successfully spread throughout the surrounding woodlands, opening up the possibilities of hybridisation with the reds. In the face of this threat, a small number of Killarney red deer was transported during the 1970s to Inishvickillane, a remote and privately owned island off the Kerry coast. They settled down well and are self-sustaining today in a herd of over 50 individuals. Another small group of red deer from

Lissadell House and estate, Co. Sligo, the site of roe deer introduction in the early 1870s.

Killarney has been established within the Connemara National Park, Co. Galway, where there is no prospect of them interbreeding with sika deer.

Wolves

Like the red deer, the wolf is an ancient Irish mammal, and one of the several species that became extinct in Ireland in historic times. It was predominant in Irish woods until the end of the seventeenth century, but man, under instruction from the English authorities, soon got the better of it. What organised hunting could not do, wood clearances perfected, and the bulk of the furry marauders was quickly extinguished. A few straggling remnants survived through the eighteenth century and it would appear that the last of the wolves was killed in Co. Carlow in 1786.[31]

Wolves were present in Ireland from prehistoric times, as shown by remains found in caves in Waterford, Sligo and Cork.[35] In those Arcadian days the hungry lupines did not have to cover kilometres to find prey, as the countryside was teeming with giant deer and reindeer. Later, when the giant deer became extinct and man appeared, the beginning of farming meant a renewed diet of cattle and sheep. Fortified settlements such as raths or ring forts dating between 500 BC and AD 1000 are evidence of the necessity to protect domestic animals from thieves and wolves during the night.

From the early days of colonisation, the English authorities were concerned that if Ireland were to be fully civilised, the wolves had to be eradicated. The species had disappeared from England and Wales around 1500 and Scotland was in the process of being rid of it (the last Scottish wolf died in 1740). There is no doubt, however, that, prior to English rule, it had been a sport of the Irish chieftains to hunt the wolf – known as *fael* or *bréach* and sometimes occurring under the name 'son of the country' (*mac-tíre*).[36] For that purpose they were

Wolf from the
Book of Kells
(*c*.800 AD).
(The Board
of Trinity
College,
Dublin).

assisted by dogs of gigantic proportion, great swiftness and indomitable courage, variously called 'Wolf-dogs' or 'Wolf-hounds' and not to be confused with greyhounds – although historical research is vague on the origin of the wolfhound as a specific breed and confusion is often noticeable.

The habit was to kill the wolves by trailing a dead horse through the woods before dropping it in a clearing. When the wolves came to feed at night, the hounds were let slip and quickly dealt with the famished guests. As farming developed and more of the country was put under pasture, the wolf became an increasing nuisance and hunting was promoted through various edicts and bills. In a 'Book of Information' compiled in 1584 it was recommended that 'some order might be had, as when the lease is granted to put in some clause that the tenant endeavour himself to spoil and kill Wolves with traps, snares, or such devices as he may devise'.[37] No doubt, the species in the sixteenth century was still very widespread and numerous. An entry in the diary of William Russell, Lord-Deputy of Ireland, in 1596 indicates that there were wolves in the woods just outside Dublin. Further action was encouraged under James I and in 1611 it was decided that an 'Act for killing Wolves and other vermin' was necessary – though it was never passed. The text of the proposed Bill cautioned the Lord Deputy or Principal Governor to call off the hunt if they thought that the hunters (requisitioned peasants mostly) were using it as a ploy to get armed – a clear case of wolves in sheep's clothing.

In a subsequent attempt to civilise Ireland, Cromwell brought out a Bill in 1653 spelling out the necessity to hunt and destroy the plunderers he called 'doggie wolves'. Some organisation was required – 'daies and tymes for hunting the Wolfe' had to be appointed – and money was to be paid on presentation of the heads of male, female or infant wolves, a different rate applying to each specimen. Settlers and natives therefore actively engaged in a renewed bout of destruction, which in 1683 enabled an observer to say about Co. Leitrim: 'The wolves, which were very numerous, are now very scarce...'. By the close of the seventeenth century the battle was nearly won and Ireland's reputation as 'Wolf-land' could no longer be literally sustained. But the saga of the 'last' wolf continued through the eighteenth century with some counties being entirely cleared while in others, like Kerry, more hunting was required. But as the woods dwindled the wolf was left with straggly pockets of trees, which made it even more vulnerable. Eventually silence fell: there was no more 'panting, lolling, vapouring'[38] outside farmyards and no more howling.

European frogs and natterjack toads

The history of the European frog in Ireland has perplexed biologists for several centuries. Was it introduced in 1699, or does its lineage stretch back into the mists of time, to the postglacial period at least 10,000 years ago? The story begins with early categoric statements regarding the frog's absence. Donatus, the ninth century Irish monk, appears to have been the first to speak:[39]

> *Nulla venena nocent, nec serpens serpit in herba*
> *Nec conquesta canit garrula rana lacu.*

> No poison there infects, no scaly snake,
> Creeps through the grass; nor croaking frog annoys the lake.

Cambrensis echoed these sentiments in *Topographia Hiberniae*, written in the 1180s:[43] 'Of all kinds of reptiles, only those that are not harmful are found in Ireland. It has no poisonous reptiles. It has no serpents or snakes, toads or frogs, tortoises or scorpions.' But Cambrensis contradicts himself a few pages later when he speaks of the discovery of at least one European frog, found near Waterford: 'Nevertheless in our days a frog was found near Waterford in some grassy land, and was brought to Robert Poer...'. It was seen by many people including Duvenaldus (Domhnall), King of Ossory, 'who happened to be there at the time, with a great shaking of his head and great sorrow in his heart at last said (and he was a man of great wisdom among his people and loyal to them): "that reptile brings very bad news to Ireland".' So what are we to make of this? What is the real truth about the frog's pedigree in Ireland?

Noxious animals and their evil associations were an obsession of early Christian commentators who placed the frog in the same category as toads, snakes and lizards because of a superficial similarity. Thus when St Patrick, in one generous swing of the crozier, drove all the pernicious creatures away, the frog left the country – or so Christian mythology claims. Another story concerns a certain Dr Gwithers, Fellow of Trinity College, Dublin, labelled 'frog introducer to Ireland' who is supposed to have performed his sly deed in 1699.[40] One snag is that there is no Dr Gwithers recorded on the books of Trinity College, although there was a Dr Gwithers who was one of William Molyneux's network of correspondents gathering information for the *English Atlas*, an ambitious and ill-fated project launched by the London bookseller Moses Pitt in 1682 (see p.27). Dr Gwithers, in his notes supplied to Molyneux, now lodged in the library of Trinity College, Dublin, categorically states that the frog was absent from Ireland. But his zoological credentials were seriously compromised when he noted that both the stag and otter were also absent which, of course, was not true.[41]

Another chapter in the mystery of the frog's antiquity was unravelled some 355 m up on the side of Keishcorran Hill as the present century dawned. Here, at one of the southern outposts of the limestone region in Sligo and Leitrim, at about 90 m above the base of the hill, on the southwestern side, is a line of low cliffs some 15–30 m high punctured by a series of cave entrances. The caves provided refuge and shelter to many animals during the late glacial period some 12,000 years ago. Bones of brown bear, red deer and wolf from this period have been found buried in the earthen floors under more recent material. Other animals came as prey brought by others. During the excavation of one of these caves, the Plunkett Cave, in 1901, a large number of frog bones were found in the upper stratum of soil extending to a depth of some 30 cm on the cave floor. No doubt this stratum was of recent origin, but below were much older layers of soil that revealed more frog bones, associated with Arctic lemmings. Lemmings were present in the Irish landscape some 10,000 years ago as evidenced by the radiocarbon dating of bones found in the Edenvale Cave, Co. Cork, but probably not much longer after that as the rise in temperatures made habitats unsuitable for them. In other words, if frogs were contemporary with the lemmings they had to date back about 10,000 years.

Some of the fossilised frog bones recovered from Plunkett Cave lay in the clay stratum nearly 2 m below the surface layers. Such depth ruled out any likelihood that frogs from more recent times had burrowed down through this overburden, or were deposited there by other animals digging up holes, or had been displaced by soil shifts caused by running water coursing through the cave systems. Moreover the bones were blackened and filled with clay showing that they had not arrived recently. The evidence was enough to convince Scharff that the frog was indeed a member of the ancient fauna of Ireland.[24,42] But there are other opinions about the bones' antiquity and the argument can only be settled with a radiocarbon date. That this task has not yet been undertaken is quite astonishing. As the European frog lives quite happily throughout Europe and within the Arctic Circle there is no reason why low temperatures in Ireland, at the end of the last glacial phase some 10,000 years ago, would have cramped their style or inhibited their spread throughout the country.

The natterjack toad's history in Ireland is equally controversial without any definitive conclusion as to its antiquity. However, the somewhat slender evi-

View from Keishcorran Cave, Co. Sligo, where ancient frog bones were discovered.

dence would point to it being a more recent arrival in the country than the frog.

Although Cambrensis observed that there were no toads in Ireland in the twelfth century[43] there is no evidence in his texts that he went to west Kerry or had any informants from the region. There was no written reference to toads until 1836, when J.T. Mackay, botanist and author of *Flora Hibernica*, reported seeing them in 1805 in Callanafersy, a large district between the lower parts of the Rivers Laune and Maine adjacent to the eastern end of Castlemaine Harbour.[44]

How did these toads come to Ireland and why are they restricted to a relatively small sandy coastal area in west Kerry? Are they relics of a once more widely spread population from a warmer and drier period? What do we make of Chute, writing from Blennerville on 31 March 1846, to Thompson, author of *The Natural History of Ireland*, 'I believe the Natter-jack is indigenous to Kerry, though there is an old tradition that a ship at one time brought a lot of them and let them go at the head of Dingle Bay. This is born out by the fact that this is the only part of Kerry that they are met in: a district extending from the sandhills at Inch at Rosbegh at the head of the bay (where they are most numerous) to Carrignaferay, about ten miles in length in low marshy ground, and about the same number in breadth.'[45] A century later, Praeger spoke contemptuously of this invasion hypothesis: 'Could misdirected ingenuity go further than to suggest the importation or shipwreck of a cargo of toads on that lonely and harbourless coast!'[20]

Beebee says of natterjack toads in Ireland: 'It seems much more likely that they are truly indigenous' and he argues that they are part of the Lusitanian biota of the Iberian peninsula which is well known in southwest Ireland.[46] However, the natterjack can hardly be considered Lusitanian with a European distribution stretching northwards to southern Sweden and into western Russia.

Their indigenous status is also supported by Praeger who wrote 'There is no doubt that in spite of its extremely restricted range the animal is indigenous in Kerry – a relict species like some of the Kerry plants.'[20] The only real evidence to support the indigenous status of the toad comes from the discovery of their bones from a megalithic cemetery at Carrowmore, Co. Sligo, during the 1970s.[47] But the status of these bones is not clear. Were they contemporary with Neolithic man or did they arrive much later and end up buried in the soil at the same spot? Whatever the explanation, this would be the first evidence of the natterjack existing outside its very restricted Kerry range.

In fact, there are two flies in the indigenous ointment. First, the natterjack's restricted distribution and its failure over its presumed long period of residence to colonise other available habitats and second, the lack of place names incorporating the Irish for 'toad'.[36] Both would argue against its native status. On the other hand, it would be wrong to dismiss completely the possibility of their arrival from a ship at the head of Dingle Bay for two reasons. First, local stories in Ireland are more than often grounded in fact and there is no reason to disbelieve this one. Smith, in his survey of Kerry published in 1756, wrote about Castlemaine Harbour in the mid-eighteenth century: 'Deep enough for vessels of 50 tons or upwards to sail up to the bridge at high water where they may lie on soft oozy ground to discharge. Some vessels are unloaded here on the bankside which serves as a wharf. These are generally freighted with rock salt from England, and others are laden with iron ore which is carried on horses to the iron foundries.'[48] Some toads could have been caught up in sand ballast, brought from European ports, and dumped on the shore at any point of the operations described above. The dumping of ballast on both sides of the Dingle Peninsula would explain the toad's presence at Castlegregory and Castlemaine sites. Secondly, toads would have almost certainly been noticed and commented upon prior to their first recording in 1805 had they been present in the area over the centuries. Also, how could such an astute recorder as Smith overlook them in the 1750s? Finally, the non-indigenous hypothesis is strengthened by the absence in Ireland of the common toad whose European distribution is even more widespread than the natterjack's, with populations extending much further north and east. It might therefore be suggested that the factors operating against the common toad's spread westwards were also operating against the natterjack: both were probably prevented from hopping across land bridges connecting Britain and Ireland because those had already been drowned.

The hypothesis of the natterjack's arrival by boat is also supported by some comments by Cambrensis. When discussing the fate of poisonous reptiles when they arrive in Ireland he states 'I have heard merchants that ply their trade on the seas say that sometimes, when they unloaded their cargoes at Irish port, they found toads brought in by chance in the bottom of the holds. They threw them out still living on to the land...'. [43] One way of throwing more light onto the natterjack's status would be to investigate biochemical and genetic divergence between the Irish, British and European populations by electrophoresis or more sophisticated genetic techniques. Some historical research into the traffic of boats and the way their ballast and cargoes were handled in Dingle and Tralee Bays might also be helpful. The occurrence of jettisoned ballast on Irish shores is well known: it has been accepted that the large erratics of flint on the foreshore at Kilmore Quay, Co. Wexford, came by boat, while the many small boulders of brown granite found near the entrance of Lough Hyne, Co. Cork, close to a rough disused landing place were the same rocks used to build the lighthouse works on Clear Island, Co. Cork – they came from Cornwall. In Broadstrand Bay, on the west side of Courtmacsherry Bay, Co. Cork, a variety of igneous pebbles and boulders, most of them granite with coloured feldspars, were found in the clefts of an early glacial rock platform as well as in the gullies of small beaches. Farrington was in no doubt, having examined all likely local sources, that the boulders and pebbles in question were ballast, probably deposited 60 years before he recorded his observations in 1965.[49]

Freshwater fish

The first fish to come back to Ireland after the last Ice Age were the euryhaline species (those that can tolerate a wide range of salinity and are encountered in both salt and fresh water). These fish are able to maintain the concentration of chemical salts in their blood and body fluids regardless of the changes in the water around them. Thousands of years ago they almost certainly cruised around the coastline, following the northwards retreat of the glaciers, exploring the unfolding and warming aquatic systems, and penetrating the ice-free rivers and lakes. Maitland considered that the following 12 euryhaline fish colonised the freshwater systems of Ireland in early postglacial times:[50] sea lamprey, river lamprey, Allis shad, Twaite shad, Atlantic salmon, brown trout, Arctic charr, pollan, smelt, European eel, three-spined stickleback and ten-spined stickleback. The latter, however, is considered by some to have been introduced (see below).

As to the stenohaline species (those that can tolerate only a narrow range of salinity), a question mark prevails over their provenance. The issue is twofold. Firstly, they are non-migratory although some, like the pike, have a capacity to spread rapidly across the land through interconnecting lakes and rivers. Secondly, they were not suited to the salt waters that surrounded all Irish shores from postglacial or earlier times. The four possible explanations for their presence are that they were already present during the last interglacial period and survived the final phase of the Ice Age in sheltered ice-free ponds; that they swam into Ireland, using the waterways in the land bridges between Ireland, Britain and the Continent; that they were once able to tolerate salt water and swam into Ireland across the sea, or that they were introduced by man or by some other agent.

The following species are generally considered to have been introduced to Ireland by man:[51] brook lamprey, pike, carp, gudgeon, tench, bream, minnow, rudd, roach, dace, stone loach, perch and ten-spined stickleback. When were these first brought into Ireland? The weight of expert opinion is that probably most, if not all, were introduced sometime between the Norman invasions and the late nineteenth century. An examination of the Irish names for fish provides some corroborative insights: salmon or brown trout, not in the above list, have at least 30 different Irish names – including many local variants – authenticating their ancient presence in Ireland. By contrast, the dace and tench, both relatively recent arrivals, have only one and two Irish names respectively.[52] However, this is subject to caution, as the Arctic charr and pollan, both prehistoric but rather scarce species, and not known to many, only carry a few names.

Cambrensis provides clues as to the origin of certain fish. The following translation, quoted by Went, is by Forester from Wright's *The Historical Works of Giraldus Cambrensis*.[53,54]

> 'Sea-fishes are found in considerable abundance on all the coasts. The rivers and lakes, also, are plentifully stored with the sorts of fish peculiar *to* those waters, and especially three species: *salmon* and *trout*, muddy *eels* and oily *shad*. The Shannon abounds in *lampreys,* a dangerous delicacy indulged in by the wealthy.
>
> This country, however, does not produce some fine fishes found in other countries, and some excellent fresh-water fishes, such as the *pike*, the *perch*, the *roach*, the *barbel*, the *gardon* [chub], and the *gudgeon*. *Minnows*, also, *bullheads*, and *verones* [minnows] are not found there, also no *loches*, or they are very rare.
>
> On the other hand, the lakes of this country contain three species of fish which are found nowhere else. One is a sort of trout, called the *salares*, which are longer and rounder than

trout, and which are white, close grained and good flavoured. The *tymal*, commonly called the *umber*, resembles the former kind of fishes, except that it is distinguished by a larger head. There are others which very much resemble the sea herring, both in shape and quality and in colour and taste. A third sort, exactly resembles the trout, except that it has no spots. The first sort is called *Glassans*, the second *Cates*, and third *Brits*. These three fish make their appearance in the summer only, and are never seen in the winter'.

It would appear from this text that the freshwater fish present in Ireland during the twelfth century included salmon, brown trout, eel, shad (probably both Twaite and Allis), sea and river lampreys, and almost certainly the brook lamprey, as the habitats of the three overlap. Amongst these early settlers, the sea and river lampreys, Atlantic salmon and the brown trout are anadromous, i.e. spend most of their lives in the sea but migrate to fresh water to spawn.

Other anadromous species arrived in Ireland from more southerly seas at the end of the last glaciation. They were the Allis and Twaite shads. Resembling herrings and found in shallow coastal waters and estuaries in western Europe, they run up the lower reaches of the larger rivers during the spawning season. In Ireland, however, the Allis shad has no known spawning site left. In fact, it is not certain whether the species is still here, as its presence is only supported by a few post-1960 records – in the Foyle estuary, Co. Derry, at two north Mayo sites, in the River Corrib, Co. Galway, and at one site in Cork. The Twaite shad shares the same coastal distribution and probably still breeds in a few Irish rivers such as the Nore, Suir and Barrow, all flowing into Waterford Harbour and the Cork Blackwater. When locked away in remote lakes, it developed into different subspecies, the Killarney shad, *Alosa fallax killarnensis*, being one of the most celebrated. Known locally as the 'goureen', it is restricted to Lough Leane and Muckross Lake, Co. Kerry, where it has been preserved for several thousand years. The smelt, also a coastal dweller in western Europe, imitates the anadromous behaviour of the shads. In Ireland it spawns in the rivers Shannon, Fergus and Foyle and perhaps at various sites in rivers Suir, Nore and Barrow. The remaining native euryhaline fish to arrive after the last Ice Age was the European eel, a catadromous species (one that migrates from rivers to the sea to spawn). Eels live in lakes and rivers and spawn in the Sargasso sea, after which the baby eels return to Ireland.

Once in Ireland the brown trout evolved a series of varieties, some of which are collectively known as sea trout (sometimes ascribed subspecific status as *Salmo trutta trutta* but not fully accepted by all scientists) with anadromous habits, and the darker, landlocked non-anadromous brown trout (sometimes ascribed the subspecific status *Salmo trutta fario*, again not fully accepted by all scientists). The latter have given rise to many other different varieties. For instance in Lough Melvin, Co. Leitrim, there are three clearly distinct stocks of brown trout: the ferox (*Salmo trutta ferox*), the gillaroo (*Salmo trutta stomachius*) and the sonaghan (*Salmo trutta nigripannis*). They are genetically different and spawning takes place in different parts of the lake.

Arthur Went who, apart from being the scientific advisor on fisheries to the Irish Government, was a specialist in questions concerning the history of fish in Ireland, believed that the pike was an introduced species, basing his arguments on an examination of historical documents including the statement by Cambrensis (see p.74). Cambrensis had a reasonable knowledge of Irish lakes and rivers. He mentions the pike as absent from Ireland. A further clue as to the late introduction of the species is supplied by the great historian Roderic O'Flaherty, who clearly ascertained that in 1684 the pike was absent from Connacht when he wrote:

> 'The water streames, besides lampreys, roches, and the like of no value, breed salmons (where there is recourse to the sea), eels and divers sorts of trouts. There was never a pike or bream as yet engendered in all this countrey, nor in the adjacent parts of Mayo or Galway counteys.'[55]

The pike must have been brought into Ireland some time before 1682, for historical records state the presence of weirs for eels and pike on the River Camoge at the Abbey of Monasternenagh, near Croom, Co. Limerick, at the time of the Abbey's dissolution.[56] The *Civil Survey of Ireland* (1654–6) also noted the River Camoge as well as other tributaries of the River Maigue had pike.[57] Its widespread distribution today should not be mistaken for a sign of long-lasting presence in the country. As a rapid coloniser, the species was able, once introduced, to spread throughout freshwater systems over a short period of time.[53]

Went stated that there was no evidence as to whether the perch was a native species or not. However, since the remark by Young in *Tour in Ireland* that perch first 'swarmed in the Shannon' in about the year 1770, the geographic distribution of the species and its numbers have increased considerably.[58] The roach, often confused with the rudd, was introduced to the River Blackwater, Co. Cork, in 1889. The barbel and 'gardon' – almost certainly the chub – referred to by Cambrensis are not present in Ireland today. The gudgeon, how-ever, which the Welshman reported absent in the twelfth century, is now claimed to be a native species as are minnows – also called 'verones' by Cambrensis – and the stone loach.

The 'salares' of Cambrensis is almost certainly one of the pollan or whitefish species, restricted to five of the largest Irish lakes – Lough Neagh, Upper Lough Erne (no records this century), Lower Lough Erne (small but precari-ous population[59]), Lough Derg and Lough Ree (no recent records). Absent from Britain and elsewhere in western Europe, its presence in Ireland is out-landish, and it is possibly a relict from a once wider distribution. Today it is only found in the coastal areas and lower reaches of arctic rivers in eastern Europe, Asia and western North America. Once thought to be an intermedi-ate between the powan and the vendace – both absent from Ireland – it has the status of an endemic Irish subspecies of the Arctic cisco which lives in Alaska, *Coregonus autumnalis pollan*. These two 'conspecifics', the Arctic cisco and Irish pollan, have probably been separated for about 10,000 years since the first pol-lan – a cold water species able to withstand life at the edge of ice sheets – are thought to have entered Ireland through the Shannon system at the start of the postglacial period.[60] Although the pollan are anadromous throughout most of their northern range, in Ireland they are virtually non-migratory, and restricted to fresh waters. The species named the 'tymal' by Cambrensis is the grayling which, in fact, is absent from Ireland. Was it ever present or did the observer misidentify the species? It is impossible to say.

The 'spotless' fish referred to by Cambrensis is the Arctic charr, whose name is derived from the Gaelic '*tarr*', meaning belly. The male belly colour ranges from pink to bright vermilion, as pointed out in two Irish names, *tarr-dhearg*, meaning 'red-bellied', and *ruadh bhreac*, meaning 'red trout'.[52] The female is drabber than her male counterpart whose bright red colour plays an important role both in courtship and defence of the breeding territory. Charr, more than most other freshwater fish, excite the imagination of naturalists who know them as 'glacial, or Ice Age relicts', i.e. survivors of the Ice Age. They inhabit the deep dark, oligotrophic (nutrient-poor) formerly glaciated lakes which they invariably share with brown trout – although in Ireland, they often break from their austere habitats and are found in shallow and eutrophic (nutrient-rich) waters. The Arctic charr is distributed throughout the northern hemisphere with both anadromous and non-anadromous populations. In Ireland, it is non-anadromous. Like the smelt and Twaite shad, it is classified as an 'endangered and vulnerable' species – the pollan, Killarney shad and Allis shad are 'endangered' species while the sea lamprey, river lamprey and brook lamprey are 'threatened' species.[61]

In an exercise of species-splitting much practised once, Regan examined various charr from Ireland and identified six 'species' living in different Irish lakes.[62] They were: Cole's charr, *Salvelinus colii*, (Loughs Eske and Derg, Co. Donegal, Lough Conn, Co. Mayo, Loughs Mask and Inagh, Co. Galway, Counties Clare and Kerry); Grey's charr, *S. grayi*, (Lough Melvin, Co. Fermanagh); Trevelyan's charr, *S. trevelyani*, (Lough Finn, Co. Donegal); Scharff's charr, *S. scharffii*, (Loughs Owel and Ennell, Co. Westmeath); Coomasaharn charr, *S. fimbriatus*, (Coomasaharn Lake, Co. Kerry) and blunt-nosed charr, *S. obtusus*, (Loughs Tay and Dan, Co. Wicklow, and Loughs Leane and Acoose, Co. Kerry). Today these are regarded as different local forms of the single species Arctic charr.[63] Since 1930, the Arctic charr has been recorded in 32 lakes in western Ireland ranging from Lough Fad, Co. Donegal, to Lough Inchiquin, Co. Kerry, together with Lough Dan, Co. Wicklow. Several other lakes, especially those suffering from eutrophication, have lost their populations of this pollution-sensitive salmonid.[61]

The freshwater fish that have been indisputably introduced to Ireland, and for which there are reasonably good historical records, include the following five species.

1. RAINBOW TROUT
Introduced to Ireland from western North America in 1888 when eggs were sent to hatcheries at Inishshannon and the River Bandon, Co. Cork, and Ballymena, Co. Antrim.[64] Spawning takes place at about 40 sites in Britain and Ireland but the populations are self-sustaining at only six, including three in Ireland. One site was at Lough Shure, Aran Island, Co. Donegal, where they were recorded present in 1940, and the second was at White Lough, Co. Westmeath, where they were introduced by the Inland Fisheries Trust in 1955.[64] Breeding was recorded at the third site, Lough na Leibe, Ballymote, Co. Sligo, in 1971 (originally stocked in 1955 by the Inland Fisheries Trust). In all cases their present status is unknown.[65,66] Elsewhere most populations are maintained by the continued introduction of hatchery-reared fish.

Rainbow trout. There are only
two self-sustaining populations
in Ireland (J. Barlee).

2. CARP

Originally a central Asian species, carp was brought to England in the first
quarter of the sixteenth century and to Ireland some time around 1634 on
account of its potential as a food fish. Originally introduced to Ireland by
Richard Boyle, Earl of Cork, as announced by his son Robert to the Royal
Society in April 1663.[67] Diary entries in the autumns of 1640 and 1643 record
orders given by the Earl to send both carp and tench to his friends.[68] Smith
claims that both carp and tench were in the River Awbeg, Co. Cork, during the
reign of James I (1603–25).[69] Like tench, carp can live in stagnant waters with
very low oxygen levels (down to 0.7 mg/l) but require a water temperature of
at least 18°C before they can spawn either in spring or late summer.

3. TENCH

Since its introduction in the seventeenth century noted above there have been
selective introductions to Ireland during the past 40 years.

4. ROACH

Accidentally introduced to the River Blackwater, Co. Cork, in 1889, then introduced to a small ornamental lake on the River Foyle system in the mid 1920s,
from where it soon escaped to colonise the river system. In the early 1970s it
was illegally introduced to the Erne waterways and within ten years had
colonised this large river system up to its headwaters. Since then it has been
introduced to the rivers Boyne, Shannon, Corrib, Liffey, Barrow and
Nore.[70,71]

5. DACE
Accidentally introduced to the River Blackwater at the same time as the roach.
Apparently two tins of each species were brought over from England as pike
bait and were washed away in a flood.[65] In the late 1980s and early 1990s they
were illegally introduced to Doon Lake, Co. Clare and to the lower end of the
River Nore.[72]

Many of these introductions have upset the ecology of rivers and lakes, and led
to the displacement of native species such as trout. The roach, one of the most
recent interlopers and a prolific breeder, has rapidly spread from its initial area
of introduction in Co. Cork some hundred years ago to colonise many river systems. It has displaced the rudd and hybridised with it, and also with bream.
Apart from interspecific competition for food resources, introduced fish can
bring with them fungal, viral, bacterial and other diseases. Cross-breeding with
closely related species will cause genetic disruption to the disadvantage of resident species. However, fish, like other animals, are able to share out food and
habitat resources. As a general ecological principle, coarse fish tend to occupy
warmer, calmer and muddier waters, leaving the more turbulent, oxygen-rich
and cooler areas to the native salmon and sea trout.

The heathers

The Ericales or heathers are to many people the most typical and interesting
group of peatland plants in Ireland. They are pretty and colourful, and five
species are of particular biogeographical and botanical interest. Not only do
they have a restricted distribution in Ireland but they exhibit a discontinuous
or relict distribution in Europe, suggesting a more widespread earlier dispersion. Such issues raise many difficult questions such as when and how did they
travel to Ireland, or have they been resident here since Gortian times? Why are
four of the species concentrated in a relatively restricted bogland area of west
Galway and Mayo? Together with five other plant species – large-flowered butterwort, St Patrick's cabbage, kidney saxifrage, the strawberry-tree and the Irish
orchid – they form the central core of the so-called Mediterranean–Atlantic
element of the Irish flora. These are the species found generally in the west and
southwest of Ireland, western France, Spain, Portugal and in some western
Mediterranean locations. The presence of the five heaths in Ireland, and how
they accomplished and survived the transition from quite different ecological
circumstances are puzzling questions. If they entered Ireland on a land bridge
from north Spain during an interglacial period, why did none of them lodge
in Cork and Kerry? Why did they all congregate in western Galway and Mayo?
   As the five species of heath are such special members of the Irish flora, additional information is presented on their discoveries and general ecology.

1. DORSET HEATH
Originally discovered in 1846 by Thomas Bergin at one very small site, close to
a bog road, some 6 km southeast of Clifden, Co. Galway. Bergin presented an
annotated herbarium specimen to Trinity College Dublin.[73] It was reported
again from the same location in 1852 and then remained elusive until it was
rediscovered by Lambert in 1965. Its site is a damp hollow, close to the road,
and it has been suggested that the location indicates introduction by the
agency of man.[74] Its growth is low and straggly, and seems at a disadvantage in

relation to the nearby and taller vegetation of purple moor-grass and soft rush. The site extends no more than a few square metres with approximately five plants.[74] Its bell-like deep pink flowers are large, up to 8–10 mm, with leaves in whorls of three. The population here is unique in that there are no glands on the tips of the stout marginal hairs of the leaf.[75] It is sterile, never setting any seed of its own, but a hybrid with cross-leaved heath has been found here by Scannell. Outside Connemara it only occurs in Cornwall, Devon and further east in Dorset. In Britain it hybridises with cross-leaved heath. On the Continent it occurs in central France, Spain, Portugal and in heathy woodland in northwest Morocco. Dorset heath was present and growing in Ireland during the warm interglacial Gortian period some 428,000–302,000 years ago (see below).[1]

2. MACKAY'S HEATH

Confined to Counties Donegal and Galway until it was recently discovered in northwestern Mayo in 1990 by van Doorslaer in a small area of raised bog near Bellacorick. The natural hybrid *Erica mackaiana* x *tetralix* (a cross between Mackay's and cross-leaved heath) was growing nearby. In Donegal, Mackay's heath grows on blanket bog on the shore of Lough Nacung Upper near Dunlewy, while in west Galway there are two stations – one small colony 1.5 km southeast of Carna and the other, more extensive (about 3 km²), around Lough Nalawney on the lowland blanket bog stretching southeast from Clifden to Errisbeg. The species was first discovered, prior to 1835, by schoolmaster William McAlla, who was born at Roundstone. It has shorter, broader, darker green leaves than Dorset heath, but like the latter it is sterile, for reasons not yet understood. It spreads vegetatively and the population would

Mackay's heath at Lough Nacung Upper, near Dunlewy, Co. Donegal. Very similar to cross-leaved heather but has a stronger and bushier habit.

therefore seem to consist of a single clone from the original plant or plants. It hybridises with cross-leaved heath. The hybrid is now known as *E.* x *stuartii*. Outside Ireland it is found only in the province of Oviedo in northwest Spain, in the mountains of Castile and Asturia. Remains of leaves of *E. mackaiana* have been recorded in postglacial deposits from a blanket bog near Roundstone, Co. Galway[76] and from the much earlier interglacial Gortian deposit. Remains of Mackay's, Dorset and Cornish heath have all been found in the Gort deposits as they have been in other interglacial deposits raising the possibility that they may have survived the final stages of the Ice Age and that they may not be of recent origin.[2,77]

St. Dabeoc's heath with its urn-shaped corolla.

3. St Dabeoc's heath

Confined to but very numerous in some locations in west Galway and in south and west Mayo from near Cong and Partry to the Killary Harbour and Croagh Patrick, and at Corraun on Achill Island. It was first unwittingly discovered by Edward Lhwyd, the great Welsh naturalist and antiquarian, who found it growing in most of the mountains of Galway and Mayo during a visit, probably mid May 1700. At the time he did not know it was St Dabeoc's heath, describing it as '...an elegant sort of Heath, bearing large Thyme-leaves, a spike of fair purple Flowers, like some Campanula, and various stalk...'. He brought his specimens back to London and presented several to his friends there, including the botanist Petiver who later identified and described it in 1703.[78] It is a small undershrub with straggly branches, often growing up through heather or gorse. Its leaves are narrow, elliptical, shiny green on top and whitish underneath. The large purplish corolla is about three times the size of those of bell heather. It is absent in Britain but found in southwest France as far north as the River Loire, and especially in the Cantabrian mountains, in the Spanish peninsula and the Azores. In the Pyrenees it survives quite happily under a snow covering for five months each year, belying the notion that it is a tender Mediterranean plant.

4. Irish heath

First found by Mackay in 1830 on Errisbeg, near Roundstone, Co. Galway, and later in other localities in west Co. Galway. In Co. Mayo it is present at the mouth of Killary Harbour, on Clare Island, at Bellacragher Bay (north of Mallaranny), northwards to the Mullet peninsula and eastwards to Lough Conn (west and eastern shores). It is absent from Britain. The single station northwest of Bordeaux in southwest France is probably extinct.[75] It occurs in good quantity in Portugal and in northwest Spain. Unlike the other heaths in Ireland, it may start flowering in January with the blooms at their finest in

April, producing one of most magnificent botanical sights in the country. This hairless shrub forms dense stands, sometimes as high as 3 m, both at sea level (Praeger once observed it adorned with seaweed thrown up during storms) and on the mountainside (up to at least 155 m) rising up from the head of Bellacragher Bay. The sight of it here in early spring is a truly remarkable botanical feast.[79] On the Bellacragher Bay mountainside the heather tracks the snaking pathways of small streams and rivulets that provide the plant with extra nutrients and moisture. Irish heath is also found further south, in the remarkable area of lowland blanket bog between Roundstone and Clifden, Co. Galway, that was covered with woods in the aftermath of the last glaciation. Jessen showed from the analysis of pollen remains found in the muds that Irish heath was growing in those woods, as it does in northwest Spain today.[77] How it successfully survived the transition from a protective woodland environment to the barren, bleak and windswept blanket bog habitats in the west of Ireland is a tribute to its adaptive capabilities. Unlike the two other rare heaths, Dorset heath and Mackay's heath, it is fertile and reproduces by seed. It has been argued by Foss & Doyle that it could have been introduced to Ireland by man some 500 years ago, at a time when there were direct trade links between Ireland, Spain and Portugal. Irish heath is found growing close to many pilgrimage shrines and abbeys in Portugal, Spain and France and it is postulated that it could have been carried by pilgrims.[80]

5. CORNISH HEATH

Originally found by Major Dickie of Enniskillen, but first reported by Praeger in 1938.[81] It was growing on an isolated blanket bog near Belcoo, Co. Fermanagh, with white flowers (normally lilac-pink), and Praeger sided with those who considered the plant indigenous in a native habitat. Webb visited the bog in 1954 and reckoned that 'the force of arguments were in favour of regarding it as native'.[82] The site, close to a mineral flush, was visited in 1965 and 1966 by McClintock when about 1,000 plants were recorded.[83] Another historical site was reported by Robert Burkitt in the 1850s, on the cliffs of Islandikane townland, west of Tramore, Co. Waterford, but the species has not been seen there since, despite repeated searches. It was naturalised on the

Irish heath with western gorse at Ballacragher Bay, Co. Mayo.

sand hills at Dundrum, Co. Down, where it was discovered by Swanston in 1899, and was still present in 1978.[84] It also grows on the rocky shore at Shane's Castle, Co. Antrim. Outside Ireland it occurs in heaths in south Cornwall, and elsewhere in western Europe. It is a short to medium hairless undershrub with flowers ranging from white to pink to lilac. No evidence has yet been produced to show that Irish heath was a member of the Irish inter-glacial flora. Their seeds are consistently larger (*c*.0.7 mm) compared with *c*. 0.5 mm of other *Erica* species, so it would have been difficult to overlook them in samples of interglacial deposits.[85]

The Connemara and Burren plant assemblages

The congregation of the above ericaceous species in western Connemara is one example of apparent geographical plant madness, but the eclectic agglom-eration of rare flowers in the Burren, Co. Clare, with representatives of arctic, alpine and Mediterranean floras also begs explanations. What could be the ori-gin of such an unlikely association?

One interpretation postulates that these species originally had a more wide-spread range in Ireland. Although the Pleistocene glaciers probably wiped much of the landscape clean of living resources, some plants may have been able to avoid the ice blanket by moving up to the highest mountain peaks or sheltering in other refugia. Others, however, possibly shifted westwards to ice-free offshore islands and peninsulas. The sea level started to drop around 35,000 years ago, reaching its maximum fall of some 130 m below present day levels around 15,000 years ago. The west Clare and Connemara coastlines could then have extended perhaps some 45 and 10 km respectively west of today's shorelines.[2] Admiralty charts show commodious areas off the Burren coast stretching beyond the Aran Islands which would have been uncovered and well above water during the Ice Age. Assuming that the North Atlantic Current exercised some warming influence, the glaciers could not have impacted those areas. It is therefore possible that the plants may have survived in isolation on mist-shrouded, ice-free banks. As the glaciers withdrew and the sea started to rise again, the plants would have had to move back to the main-land. Despite the vegetative reproduction of most alpine species and presumed slow migration rates, the long time spans associated with the waxing and wan-ing of the glaciers would have been sufficient to permit the relatively short migrations from the Burren and Connemara to those western tips and back again. Survival of plants during the first glacial epochs of the Ice Age on the summits of the Burren hills can probably be ruled out as all of them are too low to have escaped a scouring of the ice sheets (the highest is Slieve Elva at 344 m). However, several Burren hills were glacier-free during the last Midlandian glacial phase, towards the end of the Ice Age.

An alternative hypothesis regarding the survival of plants put forward by Mitchell & Ryan envisages a general migration of the various Burren and Connemara curiosities as well as other Lusitanian plant species up and down the western Atlantic seaboard from the Irish west coast to the shores of Spain and Portugal. In support of their western seaboard migration route hypothe-sis they quote the present known distribution of the shore-living bug *Aepophilus bonnairei* in Ireland, southern England, west Wales and the Isle of Man. Its modern day distribution centre is the Atlantic coast from Morocco to Portugal. If the bugs had been present in Ireland historically, they would not have sur-

Western Connemara, Co. Galway, the location of rare plant assemblages.

vived the cold Nahanagan snap and must have 'marched' up along a western seaboard land bridge as temperatures rose some 10,000 years ago. Additional support for the southern route to Ireland for Lusitanian species comes from detailed pollen studies carried out by Fraser Mitchell,[2] which show that pine, oak and alder followed the proposed route taken by *Aepophilus* across the 'dry' Bay of Biscay to the Celtic Sea and then into southern Ireland. However, the question of sea barriers and the long distances involved make this hypothesis less convincing. The introduction of seeds by migrating birds travelling northwards from Spain and Portugal is also improbable as most seeds of the Burren and Connemara curiosities are not eaten by birds.

Devoy has discussed five possible land bridge connections between Ireland and Britain, including the Continental shelf, across which flora and fauna could have moved into Ireland when the country was released from the grip of ice during the late Ice Age.[86] Devoy considered that the route from the south, across the Continental shelf, along which the southern Lusitanian species would have travelled, would have been problematical. An interconnected series of channels and troughs off the south coast of Ireland led west and southwest into canyons lying at a greater depth than 100 m below today's sea level. The movement of meltwaters and sediments over this area at the time even when sea levels were much lower than today would have created adverse conditions (pools, channels, rivers, etc.) for species sensitive to water, and made it very difficult, if not impossible, for plants to move dry-shod from Portugal, northern Spain and western France into Ireland. Thus the southern entry route for the so-called Lusitanian and other Mediterranean species now present in the Burren and in Connemara seems to be ruled out. Entry into Ireland of these species across the other four land bridges traversing what is now the Irish Sea is not supported by any historic or present day evidence. Survival of these species, many of which were already present in Ireland, in ice-free areas or refugia (off the west coast) thus appears to provide the most plausible explanation to account for the curiosities of Clare and Connemara.

The oceanic flora

The lowlier plants – ferns, mosses, liverworts and lichens – reproducing by minute, wind-blown spores, have less difficulty in crossing expanses of sea, and the mild, oceanic climate of Ireland has been particularly favourable to their colonisation. Especially in the extremely humid west, the profusion and luxuriance of these plants is a striking and important feature of the vegetation. In many of the western woods, communities of filmy-ferns, mosses and liverworts cover the rocky woodland floor and lower tree trunks, while lichens are most conspicuous on the upper trunks and branches. Many of these species have an extremely restricted European and even world distribution, confined to the far western seaboard and the Atlantic Isles of the Azores, Madeira and the Canaries (Macaronesia).

The most famous is the Killarney fern, much the largest and finest of our three filmy-ferns, once locally abundant along the rocky streams and in the lower corries of the southwestern mountains, but reduced to rarity by indiscriminate collecting. The moss-like Tunbridge and Wilson's filmy-ferns are in amazing quantity in many rocky woodlands and shady block screes, while the hay-scented buckler-fern, with its distinctive crinkly fronds, grows large and in unusual quantity. Visitors from Britain are struck by the general abundance in western Ireland of the royal fern, often to be seen in great dense patches on peaty ground. The fern collectors made less impression on it here than in western Britain, where it was once also abundant in places. The Irish spleenwort is a very rare and beautiful fern of exposed dry rocks and banks in southern Ireland and is unknown in Britain, but another Mediterranean–Atlantic fern of similar habitats, the lanceolate spleenwort, is more frequent in western Britain than Ireland. The delicate maidenhair fern, a widespread species in warmer parts of the world, grows luxuriantly on limestone, especially in crevices of the Burren pavements. Also of interest are the liverworts *Cephalozia hibernica*, *Lejeunea flava*, *L. hibernica* and *Radula holtii*, found in Ireland but not in Britain (see Appendix 1).

The profusion of ferns, mosses and liverworts, including many oceanic species, extends up the mountains. In the extreme west, the shady corries and slopes facing between north and east have communities of leafy liverworts amongst or below heather or other dwarf shrubs and on rock ledges. These are virtually identical to liverwort carpets in similar situations on the equally wet mountains of the western Scottish Highlands. They contain species notable for their highly discontinuous world distribution in humid mountain regions as far apart as southwest Norway, British Columbia, Alaska, the Himalayas and Yünnan (e.g. *Mastigophora woodsii*, *Herbertus aduncus* and *Pleurozia purpurea*). The abundance of the woolly fringe-moss on stable block screes, bog hummocks and peat hags, and its dominance on many high mountain tops, is another feature of the oceanic climate.

Many plant introductions from warmer regions have flourished in the mild Irish climate. The luxuriant and colourful hedges of fuchsia are one of the most distinctive features of the west, while the invasion of woodland by rhododendron has created a conservation problem. The southwest, with lowest incidence of frost, has well-established growths of escallonia, New Zealand flax, giant rhubarb, the hedge veronica *Hebe elliptica* and the cabbage palm tree.

3

Mountains and Uplands

Nothing more sharply exemplifies relativity than a mountain. A 100 metre-high hill in a flat landscape assumes mountainous proportions, but a normal arctic-alpine plant, casting a cold eye for a frosty north-facing cliff, would pass it by. Compared with their cousins in Wales, Northern England and Scotland, Irish mountains are not only generally lower but also cover a smaller proportion of the landscape and, as a consequence, offer fewer opportunities for a rich mountain, alpine or arctic-alpine flora and fauna.

Raven & Walters[1] define a mountain as land over 2,000 ft or 610 m – in practice any height above 600 m is generally accepted as mountain land – which puts only about 0.3% or some 240 km^2 of Ireland in the 'mountain' category with approximately 190 peaks penetrating the 600 m limit. 'Upland' is a more difficult issue and is taken to include all land between 300 and 600 m and as such would embrace some 4,100 km^2 of Ireland. Together, mountains and uplands occupy 5% of the country's surface. Most elevations are located in the coastal counties with the notable exception of the Galty Mountains rising up from the south Tipperary lowlands to reach 919 m.

The great Irish botanist Nathaniel Colgan was the first person to point out that of the 67 species comprising the so-called Watsonian 'highland' group of plants found in Britain (named after the British botanist H.C.Watson), only 42 occurred in Ireland.[2] However, as Praeger has said, Watson's definition of highland plants – 'species chiefly seen about mountains' – does not fit well in Ireland, where many of these plants are found in more places than just the mountains. Sixteen of them occur as far down as sea level.[3] In the 1950s Raven & Walters provided a much more rigorous list of 150 'mountain' species recorded in Britain and Ireland.[1] The vast majority of these fall into the 'arctic-alpine' category, i.e. plants that occur both in the Arctic and on some or all of the main European mountain ranges. If one ignores the taxonomically complicated and controversial dandelion-like hawkweeds (*Hieraciums*) and the real dandelions (*Taraxacums*), only 58 species or 39% of the Raven & Walters list are found in Ireland.

Despite the impoverished representation of the 'highland' and 'mountain' plants in Ireland, Colgan made some interesting discoveries in the Mayo and Galway Highlands. 'It may sound like a paradox to say that the botanical survey of an Irish mountain region derives a peculiar zest from the very poverty of our flora in alpine species. Yet the assertion may be made with perfect truthfulness. That the rapture of discovery varies directly with the rarity of the object sought for, that the value of the thing attained is measured by the labour of attainment – these are time-honoured truisms in every system of proverbial philosophy; and their essential truth is daily borne in upon the mind of the botanist who devotes himself to the exploration of any of the mountain groups in Ireland.'

The natural history interest of Irish mountains and uplands derives primari-

|Relief

Relief of
Ireland.From
F.H.A. Aalen,
K. Whelan &
M. Stout (eds)
(1997) *Atlas of
the Irish Rural
Landscape.*
Cork
University
Press.

0   100   300   500

Metres OD

N

0   50 miles

0   80 km

ly from their extreme ecological conditions and their possible role as refugia
for flora and fauna during the Ice Age. Some of the present day plants and
insects may be relict species, survivors of these earlier days. The astringency
brought about by poor soil conditions, few nutrients, high rainfall, searing
winds, low temperatures, cold and short summers, frost and intense sunlight
underpins the existence of a remarkable assemblage of mountain lichens,
mosses, ferns, flowering plants, invertebrates and vertebrates that are at home
in and, in many cases, restricted to, the mountain environment. Plant and animal species that live in such conditions are particularly interesting ecologically because to meet the prerogatives of survival and reproduction requires a
strategy of adaptive responses.

But what about the physical framework of Irish mountains? What about their
environmental conditions – the soils and climate? And finally, what kind of
mountain flora and fauna characterises Irish eminences and where are the
best places to encounter it?

Physical frameworks

Most Irish mountains and uplands are formed of the older and harder rocks, the most ancient dating from the Precambrian period some 600 million years ago. These are the schists and gneisses (formed mainly of quartz, feldspar and mica, differing from granite in the size, colour and configuration of the crystals) that were originally laid down as sediments in the seas prior to severe alteration by pressure and heat. The effects of these processes were to change radically the character of the minerals and particles that made up the sedimentary rocks. Also included amongst the oldest rocks are the granites, originating in the molten material spewed out from deeper sources some 400 million years ago and injected into the surface layers. Mountains built of these earliest rocks are found mainly in Donegal, west Mayo, west Galway and in the Leinster region – especially the Wicklow uplands. The granites of the Mourne Mountains, Co. Down, were formed 350 million years later. During the Cambrian period, slates and quartzites were born out of sedimentary marine muds and sands. These rocks are found mainly in north Wicklow, Wexford and at Howth in Dublin. More recently still, in the Ordovician period, shaly rocks with some sandstones and limestones, including some molten rocks that have flowed into them, formed in the sea as sedimentary depositions. These amalgams of rocks are found mainly in the southeast of Ireland.

The Devonian grits and sandstones, often called 'Old Red Sandstones', and principally made up of fresh or marine water deposits, form the bulk of the Cork and Kerry highlands. Closer to us still, Carboniferous limestones, the result of deposition of millions of tiny calcareous shells and marine creatures in warm tropical seas around 300 million years ago, line the floor of the Central Plain, while in the Burren, Co. Clare, these limestones thrust up to produce grey rounded hills. In Co. Sligo the Benbulbin mountain range has been carved from great thicknesses of such limestones. As to the most recent Irish mountains, the extensive upland plateau in Co. Antrim and eastern Derry, they are the result of outpourings of lava belched up from underground sources some 65 million years ago.

The largest continuous upland area in Ireland is in Co. Wicklow where the granite hills higher than 300 m range over 520 km^2 and peak at 925 m on Lugnaquillia Mountain, which, unlike most of the other parts of the Wicklow uplands, has retained its Old Red Sandstone capping. The original body of the Wicklow Hills consisted of sandstones, grits and conglomerates that were laid down in an ancient sea during the Ordovician period. About 400 million years ago a large mass of hot molten granite was extruded from the earth's belly. This heaving mass pushed the overlaying rocks upwards and humped them into a southwesterly aligned dome. Later on the sandstones and other slatey rocks were eroded away, a few lingering as marginal flanks to the hills, exposing the granite core that now forms the greatest area of granite in Ireland or Britain.

Further south in Cork and Kerry it is the hard Old Red Sandstone rocks that have endured. Their limestone covering was stripped off after all the rock layers were thrust up by a gigantic lateral earth movement some 300 million years ago, and folded in a series of ridges, aligned west-east. The intervening valleys, however, retain some of the surviving limestone. Towards the western side of this mountain mass are the Macgillycuddy's Reeks, Co. Kerry. These host amongst a cluster of tall conical peaks, Ireland's highest mountain,

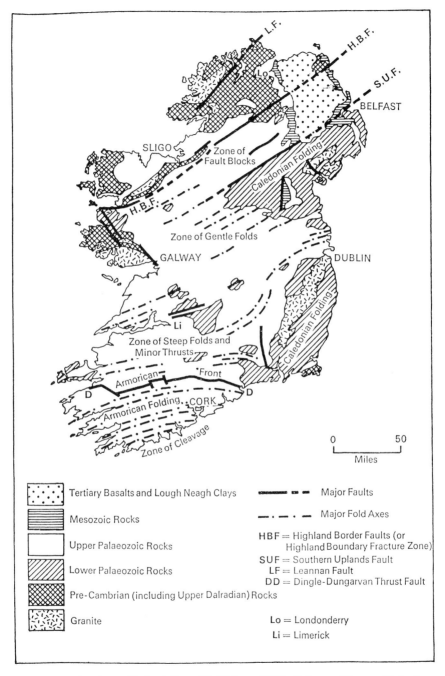

The structural geology of Ireland. From J.B. Whittow (1974) *Geology and Scenery of Ireland.*
Penguin Books, London.

Era	Period	Epoch	Absolute timescale (BP = Before Present)	Events in Ireland
CAINOZOIC	QUATERNARY	Holocene	12,000 BP	Postglacial. Growth of peat bogs. Appearance of Man in Ireland.
			Millions BP	
		Pleistocene	c. 1.5	The Ice Age. Deposition of glacial drifts.
	TERTIARY	Pliocene	c. 7	Widespread erosion and drainage development.
		Miocene	26	Widespread uplift. Possible folding in Munster.
		Oligocene	38	Lough Neagh clays. Ballymacadam clays, Tipperary.
		Eocene	54	Vulcanicity in NE Ireland. Intrusion of plutonics of the
		Palaeocene	65	Mournes, Carlingford and Slieve Gullion.
MESOZOIC	CRETACEOUS	Chalk	100	Upper Chalk of NE Ireland. Tiny outcrop near Killarney.
		Upper Greensand and Gault	105	Thin sandstones and marls in SE Antrim.
		Lower Greensand	112	Not represented in Ireland.
		Wealden	136	Not represented in Ireland.
	JURASSIC	Upper (Portlandian etc.)	162	Not represented in Ireland.
		Middle (Oolites)	172	Not represented in Ireland.
		Lower (Lias)	195	Shales and clays in NE Ireland
	TRIASSIC	Keuper		Marls and sandstones in NE Ireland. Salt deposits.
		Bunter — New Red Sandstone	225	Marls, sandstones, gypsum in Antrim and Kingscourt.
PALAEOZOIC	PERMIAN	including Magnesian Limestone	280	Magnesium limestone at Cultra, marls at Kingscourt
				Mineralization. Amorican or Hercynian orogeny - a period of mountain building and folding
	CARBONIFEROUS	Upper: Ammanian Namurian	325	Major coal measures formed in Ireland. Widespread grit and shale formation.
		Lower: Visean		Ballycastle coals and sandstones. Limerick vulcanicity. Widespread limestone formation (including reefs).
		Tournaisian	345	'Carboniferous slates' of South Munster (Culm facies).
	DEVONIAN	Kiltorcan beds	350	Widespread deposition of 'continental' conglomerates, sandstones and flagstones.
		Old Red Sandstone	c.370	No marine deposits known in Ireland. Vulcanicity at Killarney, Cushendall and Curlew Mts.
		Dingle Beds	c.390	Intrusion of major granite plutons of Donegal, Galway, Newry and Leinster.
	SILURIAN		440	Mineralization. Caledonian orogeny - a period of mountain-building and folding.
	ORDOVICIAN	Generally referred to as Lower Palaeozoic	500	Ordovician vulcanicity in Connaught, Tyrone and East Leinster
	CAMBRIAN		570	Widespread formation of grits, sandstones, shales, mudstones and limestones
PROTEROZOIC	PRE-CAMBRIAN OR ARCHAEAN	Including Dalradian (Upper Dalradian is probably of Lower Palaeozoic Age)	Pre-600	Dalradian rocks of Ulster and Connaught - highly metamorphosed and folded. Moinian rocks of Donegal and Connaught. Torridonian of Scotland unrepresented in Ireland. Lewisian igneous rocks of Donegal, Connaught and Wexford. This period may have lasted some 3,000 million years

Table 3.1. Sequence of events and dates for the geological history of Ireland. From J.B. Whittow (1974) *Geology and Scenery of Ireland*. Penguin Books, London.

Carrauntoohil, rising to 1,039 m, to the east of which are the famous lakes and mountains of the Killarney National Park.

The Galway and Mayo highlands are also the result of convulsions that took place during the Caledonian mountain-building period some 400 million years ago. Hard granites in the south of Connemara and quartzites, gneiss, Silurian slates and shales in the north were pushed upwards to create hills and mountains. The Twelve Bens are made up of quartzite surrounded by Silurian schists and separated by valleys covered with blanket bog. Further north, over the Killary fjord, Co. Mayo, lies Mweelrea, the highest mountain in the west of Ireland (814 m), north of Brandon, Co. Kerry. The coastal cliffs at Slieve League, Co. Donegal, the highest sea cliffs within Ireland and Europe, plunge into the Atlantic from a height of 595 m. On the steep northeastern and landward face, one of the richest assemblages of alpine flora in Ireland looks out over blanket bogland and the cold, desolate Lough Agh below.

Rainfall, soil and environmental conditions

Levels of rainfall and humidity are much elevated on Irish mountains. The prevailing westerly winds are moisture-laden as they hit the west coast after travelling across several thousand kilometres of Atlantic Ocean, hence the often substantial and persistent falls of rain. Published figures from the highest recording station, set at 308 m at Ballaghbeama, Co. Kerry, show 396.5 cm of rain for the year 1960. At another station in Co. Kerry, at the Cummeragh River, 540 m above sea level, a total of 68.6 cm of rain was logged for just the *month* of December 1959, more than the average *annual* fall on the east coast. Further up the west coast at Kylemore, Co. Galway, close to sea level, the average over a 16 year period was 207.7 cm per year. At nearby Delphi, Co. Mayo, on the lee side of Mweelrea, rainfall of 254 cm per annum is not unusual, while in the wettest spots of Kerry and Galway precipitation can be as high as 250 cm per year.[3] Such high rainfall encourages the development of boggy wet acidic soil and induces the leaching of nutrients. Still more important is the *frequency* of precipitation. The mountains of Donegal, Mayo–Galway and Kerry–Cork experience over 220 'wet days' each year (a wet day is a period of 24 hours with precipitation of at least 1 mm).

Unfortunately no temperature readings are available from Irish mountains. However, for every 150 m rise in altitude the temperature decreases by approximately 1°C, so temperatures at any altitude may be estimated from isotherm maps corrected to sea level. For instance, at a height of 1,000 m the air will be at least 6.7°C colder than at sea level. The increased wind speed at the top of mountains will drop the temperature even further – a phenomenon known as the wind chill factor. Below freezing temperatures are encountered in winter as a thin white mantle covers the summits. On the country's highest mountain, Carrauntoohil, snow can fall and lie for six months of the year, from November to early May[4], while on Mweelrea there may be snow around the summit for at least 20 days each winter.

Despite some extremes, the Irish climate is essentially mild, especially in the southwest. The mean daily air temperature recorded at Valentia Observatory, Co. Kerry, 1951–80 was 10.5°C, the highest figure from eight stations throughout Ireland. The coldest months were December (mean 7.7°C), January (6.6°C), February (6.5°C) and March (7.8°C). The mean annual number of days on which ground frost was recorded at Valentia Observatory 1960–84 (grass minimum temperature less than 0.0°C) was 38.6, approximately one third the number of days recorded at eight other stations throughout Ireland.[5]

Wherever drainage is poor in the uplands or on the mountains, acid peat bog develops. This is one of the three main vegetation types typical of Irish high ground, the others being grassland and heath. On the exposed mountain summits, a more montane community is often present. Within the mountain environment there are many habitats hosting different groups of liverworts, mosses, ferns and flowering plants. Boulder screes, gullies, streams, vertical cliff faces, ridges and even snow fields that persist for several months each year provide specialist niches for the 58 species that are characteristic of Irish mountains and uplands.

Average annual rainfall 1951–1980. From Rohan[5].

    The occurrence of calcareous outcrops, pockets of base-rich rocks such as mica schists, or out-flushings of mineral rich waters from deeper below, have dramatic impacts on the mountain flora, allowing many species to flourish profusely in an otherwise acidic environment. The largest limestone outcrop and mountain range in Ireland is Benbulbin, Co. Sligo. Benbulbin ascends vertically in the upper parts to a blanket bog-covered plateau with a maximum altitude of 526 m. On first sight this smothering of peat appears to defy ecological good manners, sitting on top of limestone rock which should, according to conventional rules, be supporting a community of calcicole or lime-loving plants. Peatland communities, made up of more astringent calcifuge or lime-fleeing species are normally found in lime poor habitats. The dramatic cliff walls, hanging over the lowlands below, are where most of Benbulbin's renowned arctic-alpine flora is to be found.

Burning and grazing are traditional agricultural practices that have moulded and shaped the upland and mountain plant communities for centuries. However, since Ireland joined the European Union in 1973 the number of sheep grazing the mountains has increased dramatically, prompted by generous subsidies and premiums from Brussels and the government. Numbers nearly trebled from 3.3 million in 1980 to 8.9 million in June 1991. The heavy grazing intensity steadily eradicates the dwarf shrubs, such as heather and other ericales, and allows their replacement by grasses and, in dry places, bracken. Under high densities of animals, peat also suffers compaction which alters its oxygenation, leading to a premature death of the vegetation skin. The mechanical trampling leads to the disappearance of peat mosses, *Sphagnum* spp., whose water absorbency is crucial for the ecology of the bog. Tussock-forming sedges are the most resistant to the sheep's aggression. The compaction of peat and the loss of *Sphagnum*, compounded by the removal of vegetation by incessant grazing, leads to a faster runoff of water down the mountain slopes.[6] During a limited ecological survey in Co. Mayo, conducted nearly eight years ago, a total of 66 selected blanket bog sites were visited with the objective of identifying the more intact areas for conservation. Twenty-five, or 38%, of the sites, covering some 12,500 ha, contained significant areas that were overgrazed. Several sites among the 25 were completely destroyed. Indeed, it is estimated that in the case of very eroded blanket bog, rock-bare in places, it would take between 5,000 and 10,000 years for just 2.5 cm of soil to be regenerated.[6]

How the precious alpine and arctic flora has fared under this new regime of unabated encroachment is not known. It is easier to assess the declining populations of moorland breeding birds such as the red grouse, merlin, hen harrier, and even of the Irish hare. Other impacts on upland and mountain flora

Erriff Valley, Co. Mayo. Excessive grazing by sheep (A. Walsh).

come from burning, reclamation of moorland through drainage, afforestation and the application of a wide range of chemical fertilisers, often by air.

The arctic-alpine flora

David Webb, doyen of modern Irish botanists, in a critical review of the flora of Ireland in its European context, concluded that there were 16 genuine arctic-alpines in the Irish flora.[7] His criteria were that the plant 'must be fairly widespread in the arctic and sub-arctic regions of Europe and must reappear at high altitudes (at least up to 2,000 m) in the Alps (often also in the Pyrenees). But it must be scarce or absent in the intervening areas for otherwise it becomes merged in the main mass of northern continental species.' He excluded any species that was found at low altitudes south of about 54°–55°N and any occurring in Central Europe at altitudes below 800 m in the immediate neighbourhood of high mountains. Using these criteria he excluded the following species often described by many different authorities as arctic-alpines: alpine saxifrage, marsh saxifrage, northern rock-cress, stiff sedge, spring sandwort, bearberry, cowberry and spring gentian. While all the these species are arctic they do not fulfil Webb's other arctic-alpine criteria. According to Webb the spring gentian is a well-known example of incorrect geographic placement. It is often assumed – because of its association with mountain avens in the Burren, Co. Clare, and in the high Alps – to have an identical geographic distribution to mountain avens which is a true arctic-alpine. However, the spring gentian is common in central and southern Germany below 800 m and also present in the karst country of Slovenia. Moreover, its representation in the Arctic is extremely meagre, being confined to a few locations in arctic Russia.

The arctic-alpine species occurring in Ireland, according to Webb's criteria, are alpine lady's-mantle, fringed sandwort, hoary whitlowgrass, mountain avens, chickweed willowherb, mountain sorrel, alpine meadow-grass, alpine bistort, roseroot, dwarf willow, alpine saw-wort, yellow saxifrage, purple saxifrage, starry saxifrage, moss campion and alpine meadow-rue. Webb also identified the following seven 'alpine' and 'arctic-sub-arctic' species, some with reservations: *alpine*: recurved sandwort; *alpine* (with reservations): large-flowered butterwort and Irish eyebright; *arctic-sub-arctic*: Scots lovage and oyster-plant; *arctic-sub-arctic* (marginal): water sedge and alpine saxifrage.

The cloudberry, which has one station in Ireland on the Tyrone side of the Tyrone/Derry county boundary in the Sperrin Mountains, is usually thought to deserve in other texts the appellation 'arctic-sub-arctic' but, according to Webb, it is too widespread south of the Baltic, in north Germany and Poland, to qualify for that status. Therefore it is not included in any of the above categories. All the seven 'marginal' species listed above are presumed to be arctic in origin, and to have spread southwards in front of the glaciers without going far enough to get up high in the Alps, Pyrenees or Carpathians.

In his seminal paper 'On the range of flowering plants and ferns on the mountains of Ireland' the great Irish botanist Henry Chichester Hart considered that 13 species qualified as 'alpines' but without giving precise criteria. Hart was perhaps the most intrepid and adventurous of all explorers of Irish mountains with an unrivalled knowledge of Irish mountain flora. His list of alpines is important as a tool for comparing the floras of various mountains throughout Ireland: cloudberry, northern bedstraw, the hawkweed *Hieracium anglicum*, bearberry, cowberry, juniper, stiff sedge, blue moor-grass, parsley fern, holly fern, green spleenwort, lesser clubmoss and quillwort. None meet the Webb criteria of arctic-alpines.[8]

Alpine and arctic-alpine species are both rare and thinly spread throughout the country. Concentrations occur principally in the coastal counties, where most mountain ranges are found, with more species in the northern than in the southern parts of the island. The elevation at which they occur increases from the north to south as temperatures are higher in the south and thus more elevation is required to find a suitable cold spot. Of 17 species analysed by Praeger that were common to the Donegal–Derry and Kerry–Cork mountains, the mean lower limit in the north was 168 m while in the south it was approximately double that, illustrating one of the few impacts of latitude on the Irish flora. A similar comparison for 12 species found in western and eastern Ireland, showed that the mean lower limit was 326 m in Down–Wicklow compared with 219 m for Mayo–Galway, a reaction thought to be due to the wet and windy conditions along the western seaboard which effectively lower the temperatures.[3]

One of the curious features of alpine plants in Ireland is that many of them do not remain perched high up on the mountains but descend down to sea level and into the countryside, sometimes well away from their *alma mater*. In fact, even when on the mountains they prefer reasonable to dizzy heights. Praeger looked at their distribution in relation to elevation in Ireland and found that the number of species increased steadily as one travelled towards the summit with a maximum number of 19 species at 300 m above sea level. Thereafter their numbers decreased equally steadily.[9] Praeger also noted that 16 of the 42 so-called Watsonian 'highland' plants (including arctic-alpines and alpines) occur down to sea level. In fact, most Irish summits have a paltry flora, generally almost devoid of alpines and arctic-alpines. These are happier growing at lower levels, in more favourable habitats where, for instance, there are outcrops of mineral-rich rocks, and the ground is free from tall vegetation.

A few of the alpines do not give in to this 'erratic' behaviour but, as Hart observed, they are not numerous: 'Of those more thoroughly alpine plants which never descended to sea level in these mountains (or elsewhere in

Juniper is common on some mountains, where the sub-species *Juniperus communis* subsp. *nana* is mainly found on siliceous rocks, always growing prostrate.

Ireland), only three are ever met with on the exposed summits or outer ridges.'[8] They were alpine clubmoss, dwarf willow and stiff sedge. As to the species that will occur very high up, Praeger listed eight that persisted above 914 m on the Macgillycuddy's Reeks, Co. Kerry.[3] The species, with their maximum recorded altitudes in Ireland were: starry saxifrage (1,036 m), alpine hair-grass (1,027 m), stiff sedge (1,006 m), green spleenwort (960 m), mountain sorrel (960 m), roseroot (960 m), alpine meadow-grass (945 m) and dwarf willow (930 m). These, together with the alpine clubmoss, could be taken as the hard core of the Irish alpine and arctic-alpine flora.

Most Irish summits – generally covered by thin peat or just bare soil and stones – make drab spots for flowers, whether or not of the alpine kind. One wishing to find 'summit' flowers might well have to abseil down along the north-facing cliffs and scarps in order to peruse the nooks and crannies and the rock overhangs. Praeger – himself a fearless cliffhanger – listed 13 of these core 'summit' plants, based on an analysis of the flora of the seven highest Irish peaks. They were tormentil, heath bedstraw, bilberry, heather, sheep's sorrel, crowberry, heath rush, great wood-rush, hare's-tail cottongrass, tufted hair-grass, sweet vernal-grass, sheep's fescue and fir clubmoss.

Four maritime plants, which could be considered 'sea-loving', are frequently encountered growing on mountains at high altitudes in the company of alpine species. The first, thrift, a common coastal species, occurs on most of the highest mountains in Ireland. Hart encountered it at or close to the summits of the Mayo and Galway mountains – on Nephin and Mweelrea, Co. Mayo, both at 805 m, Croagh Patrick, Co. Mayo, at 675 m, and in the Twelve Bens, Co. Galway, up to 686 m. At Corraun, Achill Island, Co. Mayo, thrift grows abundantly on siliceous rocks at sea level, but then appears only above 366 m. It also grows at the summit of Carrauntoohil, Co. Kerry, at 1,039 m. Thrift adopts different shapes according to environmental stress. In its mountain habitat, subjected to grazing or particularly dry conditions it contracts into a dense cushion with short leaves and stems. Without stress, especially flourishing at sea level, it takes on a more straggly, less defensive aspect.

The sea plantain grows on the highest Galway and Mayo mountains up to 792 m. A curiously stunted variety, with broad leaves and a stem 3.8 cm high, was found by Hart at 701 m on the Askaheeraun ridge, Mweelrea, and on the summit of Ben Creggan (693 m), Co. Mayo. In the Twelve Bens the species ascends to 518 m. On Achill Island, Co. Mayo, it occurs continuously from the summit of Slievemore (671 m) to the sea-drenched cliffs below. This plantain also grows inland at low altitude levels, breaking with convention when it occurs around the shores of Lough Derg – some 40 km from the coast. It is also on the limestone pavements around Loughs Corrib, Mask, Carra, and Conn, Co. Mayo.

There are also outposts of maritime plants, including the two already mentioned and the following species, at the Killarney lakes, Co. Kerry, and around the shore of Lough Neagh in Northern Ireland. The white-flowered sea campion, normally found growing on sea cliffs, islands and coastal shingle, occurs on most of the Galway and Mayo mountains – on Croagh Patrick at 764 m, Mweelrea and Benlettery, Connemara, at 580 m and Birreencorragh, Co. Mayo, at 610 m. The common scurvygrass, common in dry salt marshes and coastal areas is also found in its subspecific form *Cochlearia officinalis* subsp. *alpina* in the Galty Mountains, Co. Tipperary, as well as joining the other three

Sea campion in its more natural lowland and coastal habitat, Little Saltee Island, Co. Wexford.

species already mentioned on the Binevenagh cliffs, Co. Derry. Finally, Hart also mentions a fifth species, the English stonecrop, as a member of the group which displays such aberrant distribution. A plant of rocky places, very frequently near the sea and rarely inland, this stonecrop is found on the Cork and Kerry mountains up to 801 m while in Wicklow it occurs up to 594 m and in Donegal up to 259 m.

A plausible explanation for the mountain ascent of these maritime plants was put forward over 100 years ago by the Scottish naturalist Buchanan White who argued that they were part of the late glacial flora that was forced to migrate ahead of the expanding woodland cover during the Atlantic period. As the upper parts of the mountains were generally the only tree-free areas this is where the plants retreated to and survived until today.[10] Work carried out by Watts on the flora of the Quaternary period in Ireland has shown that several species – likely candidates for migration up the mountain slopes – could be identified from the interglacial deposits at Kilbeg, Co. Waterford.[11] The records included alpine meadow-rue (fruits), alpine clubmoss (spores), juniper (pollen, seed, needle), lesser clubmoss (micro and megaspores) and the sea plantain (pollen). Once established on mountain tops these, and many other species, found themselves safe from the re-advancing glaciers when another cold spell clamped down on the Irish landscape.

Principal locations for alpine and arctic-alpine species

The Wicklow Mountains and uplands

The Wicklow Mountains and uplands are the most extensive area of granite in Ireland and greater than any in Britain. The region is of considerable natural beauty and topographical diversity, where glacier-scoured river valleys and glens clothed in broadleaved woods host enchanting lakes; where large tracts of blanket bog are presided over by granite summits and dominated by Lugnaquillia Mountain (925 m); where there is a swaddling coverage of coniferous plantations, and where cliffs and corries are frequent. The vegetation found there is characteristic of the upland and mountain habitats of many other sections of Ireland.

During the winter of 1901–2 George H. Pethybridge, a young English plant physiologist, teamed up with Praeger to start a survey of the vegetation lying south of Dublin, including the Wicklow uplands.[12] According to White this was the start of the modern investigations of Irish vegetation.[13] Pethybridge & Praeger distinguished four zones: (i) the lowest, or the littoral zone which is of little or no interest to botanists; (ii) farmland, that merged into (iii) hill pasture at about 275 m (with gorse to begin with and western gorse at higher altitudes) before giving way to (iv) heather moorland which developed at around 380 m and continued upwards to the highest – flora-poor – summits.

The dry heath of the hill pasture, dominated by western gorse, heather and bell heather, is typically found in Counties Dublin and Wicklow from about 70 m to 400 m. The dry heath community was not described in detail and had to wait for its first precise description by Clark in 1968.[14] Where the heath had been burnt about four years previously, Clark found that western gorse formed a mat of vegetation 20–30 cm tall. In areas untouched by fire for more than ten years the gorse was taller – 30–50 cm – and often more open, leaving room for bell heather, heather and a sparse herb layer of mainly sheep's fescue and some common bent.

Western gorse, abundant in eastern Ireland and more local in the west, is characteristically found in coastal, lowland and sub-montane habitats, especially in the Wicklow Mountains where it occurs typically in the upper hill pasture areas before the vegetation changes to heather moorland at about 400 m. The somewhat similar but much taller gorse (also known as furze or whin) occurs typically at lower altitudes in the Wicklow hills and elsewhere in Ireland.

Higher up in the heather moorland Pethybridge & Praeger described areas, especially on the flat summits, dominated by deergrass and common cotton-grass. On the flat summit of Lugnaquillia Mountain they found a thin skin of vegetation, dominated by the woolly fringe-moss, bilberry, heath bedstraw, heath rush, stiff sedge, the moss *Polytrichum commune* and colonies of the alpine clubmoss.

The Wicklow uplands are a disappointment for mountain plants when compared with some of the highland sites in the northern and western counties. Both the arctic-alpine roseroot and the mossy saxifrage, first reported in 1897 and 1927 respectively, have not been found recently and are feared to be extinct.[15] St Patrick's cabbage and fir clubmoss are found on the mountain itself. The occurrence of St Patrick's cabbage is an oddity because Lugnaquillia Mountain is very much an outlying station, far away from the main centre of distribution in Cork and Kerry. Some 13.5 km northeast of Lugnaquillia Mountain a rocky escarpment at 557 m overlooking Lough Ouler, near Tonelagee, hosts alpine lady's-mantle and, together with a site on the Brandon Mountains, Co. Kerry, these are the only localities where the species has been seen in Ireland since 1970. Alpine lady's-mantle is tall for an arctic-alpine, reaching up to 20 cm. Its leaves, unlike those of its close relative lady's-mantle,

Gorse, furze or whin, characteristic of the rough grassland or heaths of the lower parts of the Wicklow Mountains.

are divided to the base and underneath are silvery grey with hairs. The flowers are small (3 mm) and pale green. Also growing on the Lough Ouler escarpment is alpine saw-wort which belongs to the daisy family. It is a short, stout perennial that looks somewhat like a thistle with fragrant purple flowers in August–September. Both alpine lady's-mantle and alpine saw-wort were first recorded in Ireland from the mountains of 'Keri' by the Welsh antiquarian and naturalist Edward Lhwyd in 1699. Alpine saw-wort has now been reported from 26 sites in Ireland, at altitudes over 300 m. It is thought to be declining. [16]

A re-survey of the area studied by Pethybridge & Praeger was carried out 50 years later by John J. Moore, champion in Ireland of the study of plant communities using the mathematical and quantitative phytosociological methods of the German botanist Braun-Blanquet.[17] Moore redefined the plant communities and found that they had remained remarkably stable over the years, the main changes being an advance of bracken, extending its range by a maximum distance of 150 m, and to a lesser extent of western gorse, into abandoned farmland. A widespread reduction in the frequency of the woolly fringe-moss in the high land was also observed.

The Galway and Mayo highlands

The great metamorphic rock masses of west Galway and Mayo stretch some 120 km from south Connemara to north Erris in one of the wildest and most beautiful parts of Ireland. In the south, the Twelve Bens stand out as rugged steep-sided mountains with quartzite peaks, many of which are higher than 600 m. Although the region is described as the Twelve Bens, there are, as pointed out by Hart, 17 more or less detached peaks from about 457–731 m.[8] Mica schists appear in the western peaks and through weathering break down to provide

Irish mountains and uplands are invariably bleak, generally bereft of woody vegetation
above 300 m. Here, in the neighbourhood of the Killary Harbour, Co. Mayo, the siliceous
soils, derived from Silurian slates and shales, offer little opportunity for a diverse vegetation.

the more attractive calcareous soils on which many mountain species thrive in
an abundance rarely attained elsewhere in Ireland. To the east of Lough
Inagh, defining the eastern boundary of the Twelve Bens, lie the Maumturk
Mountains, a large ridge of quartzite, peaking at 702 m. Blanket bogland, characterised by purple moor-grass which grows with extreme luxuriance, dominates the Connemara slopes to about 300 m before giving way to vegetation in
which heather is the key species.

Bengower is one of the most southerly peaks of the Twelve Bens and its summit reaches 666 m. The vegetation of the north-facing slope at 550 m was
examined in the early 1960s by Ratcliffe, the first to give a detailed description
of the flora of that particular stretch.[18] No remarkable specimens were found
apart from the liverwort *Adelanthus lindenbergianus*, a southern hemisphere
species first discovered at Slievemore, Achill Island, Co. Mayo, in 1903 by H. W.
Lett – when it was mistakenly named as an endemic, *A. dugortiensis* – and only
known from these two stations and from Errigal and Muckish Mountains, Co.
Donegal.

Praeger wrote that the best ground for the botanist is Muckanaght (654 m)
in the centre of the Twelve Bens, where 'an oasis of schist in a Sahara of quartz'
encourages a 'very pretty colony of alpine plants'.[3] Alpine meadow-rue, purple
saxifrage, mountain sorrel, alpine saw-wort, dwarf willow and holly fern grow
here. Ever since Wade first published a list, albeit slender, of the flora of
Connemara – in which he recorded the first discovery in Ireland of the
American species pipewort[19] – Connemara has attracted a continuous proces-

Slievemore, Achill Island, Co. Mayo, in the distance.

sion of distinguished botanists and naturalists. The most extensive botanical investigations of the Connemara mountains were carried out by Hart, whose 1883 paper remains a standard text today.[8] Colgan followed soon afterwards with a less ambitious work[2] and Praeger was also a frequent visitor from the early part of this century.[3] More recent investigations on mountain plants have been published by Roden[20], while Webb & Scannell provide an account of all Connemara plants in *Flora of Connemara and the Burren*.[21]

Mweelrea Mountain, Co. Mayo

The Irish name of this highest mountain in Connacht – *An maol riabhach*: 'the grey bald mountain top' – fits it perfectly. Built of Silurian slates and shales chiefly with sandstones, schists and conglomerates, it presides boldly over a remote corner of southwestern Mayo, overlooking Killary Harbour. To the north are the islands of Clare and Achill; to the east the more stark grey mountain of Ben Gorm (700 m) and the Sheeffry Hills (highest point 762 m). Whilst in many respects a smooth and accessible mountain, Mweelrea has high vertical cliffs on the inland side. As observed by Hart when he visited the summit (814 m) in the summer of 1882, the prospects for alpine plants are raised but not completely fulfilled by 'the long ranges of precipices, ridges and gullies ending in ravines with sheer sides and dangerous nooks'. Once he got to the top he found the following, amongst other species: St Patrick's cabbage, starry saxifrage, roseroot, the hawkweeds *Hieracium anglicum* and *H. iricum*, bearberry, mountain sorrel, dwarf willow, stiff sedge, tufted hair-grass, alpine clubmoss, lesser clubmoss and quillwort.

During a visit in September 1961, while examining the cliffs at the head of the great north corrie at nearly 790 m on the east spur of Mweelrea, Ratcliffe discovered the liverwort *Jamesoniella carringtonii*, widespread in the Scottish

Mweelrea Mountain, Co. Mayo. The scree slopes support little vegetation.

Highlands but never previously recorded in Ireland. On Mweelrea it was found growing sparingly on broken cliffs and ledges amongst tufts of other liverworts – *Herbertus aduncus* subsp. *hutchinsiae, Pleurozia purpurea, Bazzania pearsonii, B. tricrenata, Scapania ornithopodioides, S. gracilis* and *Plagiochila spinulosa*.[18]

Macgillycuddy's Reeks and Brandon Mountain, Co. Kerry

The Macgillycuddy's Reeks in Kerry reach 1,039 m at their highest point and are made up of a number of other summits above 900 m. Despite their promising aspect, these mountains are botanically a disappointment. The arctic-alpine and alpine species recorded by Praeger above 914 m included alpine scurvy-grass, roseroot, starry saxifrage, mountain sorrel, dwarf willow, stiff sedge, alpine hair-grass, green spleenwort and alpine clubmoss. The hoary whitlow-grass, another arctic-alpine, can be found lower down but the best places to encounter the arctic-alpine and alpine species are the cliffs south of Lough Eagher at the head of Cumloughra Glen, and the series of coombs – steep cliffs with boulder scree – north of Lough Gouragh. The Kerry speciality, the strawberry-tree, is found at an altitude of 160 m, while the delicate Tunbridge filmy-fern and Killarney fern make it to 600 m and 460 m respectively.[22]

Northwest of the Macgillycuddy's Reeks, the Dingle peninsula sticks out into the Atlantic like a long, ridged finger built of sandstones and slates with its more geologically complex northwestern tip fringed with dramatic sea cliffs. The highest point there is Mount Brandon (952 m). Falling away from the eastern side of the summit the cliffs drop into a series of lakes, sometimes called paternoster lakes – they are strung out like rosary beads – each one lower than the previous one. Growing near the highest lake, at 715 m, are alternate water-milfoil and quillwort, at their most elevated stations known in Ireland. Praeger, writing in the *Botanist in Ireland*, reckoned that these cliffs were a repository of interesting species: 'the richest alpine ground in the country'. Expeditions by Curtis between 1988 and 1990 in search of alpine bistort have brought renewed evidence of their richness.[23] The Mount Brandon range, located in one of the remotest areas of Ireland and set in stunning scenery, would certainly repay more intensive investigations by botanists.

The arctic-alpines recorded, apart from the bistort, include alpine lady's-mantle (found only here, at one other site in south Kerry and near Lough Ouler, Co. Wicklow), alpine meadow-grass (also only here and in the Benbulbin mountain range, Co. Sligo), alpine meadow-rue, alpine saw-wort, dwarf willow, yellow saxifrage, purple saxifrage, starry saxifrage, mountain sorrel and the alpine species, holly fern. The holly fern, like two other ferns present – the parsley fern and green spleenwort – is one of the true mountain ferns, and is usually found growing in crevices of base-rich rocks. The victim of unscrupulous plant collectors in the past, it is restricted to western Ireland where it has been recorded from seven sites, the most easterly being in Co. Fermanagh.[16]

Caha Mountains, Counties Cork and Kerry

The Caha Mountains, made up of a great ridge of Old Red Sandstone, lie some 40 km southwest of Macgillycuddy's Reeks. The northern side presides over the majestic Kenmare Bay while to the south they slope down to Bantry Bay. The Cork–Kerry border runs through the high ridge, Hungry Hill being the highest point at 685 m. The interest of Caha rests with a most exciting discovery, made in July 1964, of the small and delicate recurved sandwort found growing in narrow cracks of bare outcrops of Old Red Sandstone slabs east of Knockowen (658 m) and to the north-northeast of Cushnaficulla summit (594 m).[24] About 1,000 plants were found at each of the locations. The Caha Mountains are the only known station in Ireland for this sandwort and it has never been recorded in Britain. The plant is a short and small tufted perennial with prostrate to semi-erect woody stems, forming a compact cushion of leaves. It is distinguished from the somewhat similar spring sandwort, also found on mountains (locally in Clare, Antrim, Derry and on the Aran Islands, Co. Galway) by having mostly down-curved leaves and 5–7 veins on the white sepals. Its white flowers, which seem large in relation to the overall plant size, bloom from June to August.

How is it that recurved sandwort only occurs on the Caha Mountains and nowhere else in Ireland or Britain? The nearest recorded station is in the Serra de Gerez in Portugal from where it extends through the Pyrenees and Alps and further eastwards, in suitable siliceous mountain ranges, to the Romanian Carpathians.[7] Geological evidence – no signs of glacial smoothing on the stone slabs: their present surface corresponds exactly to the bedding plane of the sandstone and knowledge of known movements of the ice sheets in the area – shows that the summits of both Knockowen and Cushnaficulla were spared the rigours of the ice sheets and overlooked the glaciers moving around below. Clearly the peaks were ice fee and could have acted as refugia for the sandwort during the last and earlier glaciations.[25,26] Webb was of the opinion that the recurved sandwort was present in Ireland long before the last glaciation.[7]

While the recurved sandwort does not fall into the category as one of the 16 arctic-alpine species in Ireland, it is the only true 'alpine' species in the country according to the criteria of Webb as laid out earlier in this chapter. The presence of this sandwort on the Caha Mountains strengthens the argument that many species of the Irish flora are not recent immigrants but members of a more ancient flora that was able to survive in glacier-free areas during the Ice Age.

Benbulbin mountain range, Co. Sligo

These mountains are part of a Carboniferous limestone plateau that has survived the gradual down-wearing of the surrounding landscape over millions of years. The whole area, reaching 450–600 m in height, extends over about 500 km² between Lough Gill in Co. Sligo and Lough Melvin in Co. Leitrim. There is no evidence from glacial deposits or markings by moving ice sheets to suggest that the mountains were covered by ice during the main phase of the Midlandian cold stage to the end of the Drumlin phase of the Midlandian cold stage (79,000–13,000 years ago), so they would have been available as refugia for flora and fauna when the ice sheets tore up and scoured the lower ground, destroying all forms of life.

Evidence that some of the existing Benbulbin mountain flora thrived at lower levels many thousands of years ago comes from plant materials identified from interstadial deposits of mud and moss peat uncovered beneath a drumlin at Derryvree, Co. Fermanagh, and from silt, exposed below glacial till by a river slicing through a drumlin at Hollymount, near Lisnaskea, Co. Fermanagh. They date from before 30,000 and 40,000 years ago respectively. Analysis of the plant materials indicate that the vegetation of the time was characteristic of a cold climate in a tundra landscape. The species identified included the following arctic-alpine and alpine plants: dwarf willow, mountain sorrel, fringed sandwort, purple saxifrage and mountain avens.[27] Today the cliffs and

Benbulbin, Co. Sligo. An uplifted carboniferous limestone plateau with dramatic cliffs, the home of many rare arctic-alpine plants.

Benwiskin (514 m), Co. Sligo, as dramatic as the nearby cliffs of Benbulbin (F. Guinness).

screes of Benbulbin and surrounding mountains are one of the most important habitats for these species in Ireland, and include the only known site for
the fringed sandwort. It is highly likely that in the face of approaching ice
sheets these and other species moved up the mountain to take refuge from the
advancing ice glaciers. Whether they survived the long period of polar desert
conditions, with intense cold, is less certain.

The best known part of the Benbulbin mountain range is the spectacular
western spur where the eponymous summit rises to 526 m with its high, sculp-
tured profile. Two large, cliff-walled valleys, each with a lake – Glencar Lough
in the south and Glenade Lough in the east – bisect the two mountain lobes
and provide topographical diversity to an already very dramatic landscape. The
Benbulbin area, extending from Co. Sligo to Co. Leitrim, is so extensive that
it would take a botanist at least seven days, working at a feverish pitch, to do
the place justice. There are, however, two 'hot spots' for the arctic-alpines and
alpines.

The first area is the cliffs of Annacoona in the Gleniff Valley, guarded at the
northwest entrance by Benwiskin (514 m) which rises to a remarkable pinnacle, like the Matterhorn, surveying the landscape. The Annacoona cliffs face
northeast, overlooking the great cirque of Gleniff, gouged out by a glacier. On
a still summer's day the croaking of ravens, rolling around and playing aero-
batics along the steep cliffs, the occasional shrieking of a peregrine and the
bleating of sheep are the only sounds in this otherwise silent valley. On the
cliffs at Annacoona the arctic-alpine flora starts from an altitude of about 244
m upwards. The rarest species is fringed sandwort which has its home here on
the upper sections of the limestone cliffs, between 300 and 550 m. This small
and deceptively dainty, white-flowered and slightly hairy perennial is a member of the Caryophyllaceae or chickweed family and was first discovered by the

eminent Welsh antiquarian and natural historian Edward Lhwyd on one of his visits to Ireland in 1699. He recounted the discovery in a letter to Tancred Robinson, a great friend of the British botanist John Ray: 'In the same neighbourhood on the mountains of Ben Bulben and Ben Buishgen, we met with a number of the rare mountain plants of England and Wales, and three or four not yet discover'd in Britain.'[28] Irish specimens of fringed sandwort were assigned to the special endemic subspecies *Arenaria ciliata* subsp. *hibernica* by Ostenfeld & Dahl in 1917 who also separated off two other subspecies, *A. c. pseudofrigida* found in arctic Europe and Arctic sandwort *A. c. norvegica* found in Shetland, arctic Europe and America.[29] There is one record of *A. c. norvegica* from the Burren in Co. Clare but it has never been rediscovered despite repeated attempts by many botanists. Endemic species, or subspecies, are restricted to a specific geographic region and have evolved the differences that separate them from their close relations due to their isolation, or in response to soil or climatic conditions.

Annacoona is the only known Irish station for alpine saxifrage, first discovered here by the botanist John Wynne in 1837. Its leaves are purple underneath and it has a very hairy inflorescence with white petals and reddish sepals. Within the Benbulbin area alpine meadow-rue is also confined to Annacoona. Amongst the species listed by Praeger found on the cliffs and escarpments, the following occur in profusion:[3] alpine scurvygrass, hoary whitlowgrass, mountain avens, yellow saxifrage, mossy saxifrage, brittle bladder-fern, green spleenwort, limestone bedstraw and common milkwort. More locally abundant are lesser meadow-rue, moss campion, purple saxifrage, upland enchanter's-nightshade, mountain sorrel, tea-leaved willow, blue moor-grass, holly fern, beech fern and Irish eyebright. Raven in *Mountain Flowers* writes that the Benbulbin eyebrights he saw on his visit resembled some, but not all, of the specimens of *Euphrasia lapponica* he had seen in isolated populations in northern Scandinavia[1]. The following species are rare: Welsh poppy, wood vetch, several hawkweeds including *Hieracium hypochoeroides*, cowberry, alpine bistort, dwarf willow, juniper, stiff sedge, maidenhair fern, large thyme and alpine meadow-grass (found only here and on the Brandon Mountain, Co. Kerry). Isolated trees or small clumps of them, firmly rooted in the vertical cliffs, are a curious sight – rock whitebeam, wych elm and yew are all present, only ever to be touched by birds and flying insects.

The other interesting place for arctic-alpines and alpines is a section of the north-facing cliffs some 5 km northeast on the Tievebaun Mountain, Co. Leitrim. The cliffs are northwest of Glenade Lough. The exciting section extends for about 800 m at an altitude of 213–366 m. Many species already growing at Annacoona are found here, together with the chickweed willowherb, a unique speciality of these precincts. First discovered here by R.M. Barrington and R.P. Vowell in 1884, it is a low, small, creeping, almost hairless willowherb with runners above the ground. The flowers are purplish-pink and the seed pods turn red when ripe. Partial to streams and wet places, especially dripping rocks, this willowherb has two sites at Glenade. The first is a wet cliff, where 100 plants grow in an area of about 25 m^2. The second occurs along a small stream where a 30 m stretch accommodates about 70 plants. Also at Glenade, on an inaccessible vertical cliff, is the northern rock-cress, at one of only two locations in Ireland, the other being a site in the Galty Mountains, Co. Tipperary.[16] This rock-cress is a small, slightly hairy plant with lobed lower leaves and small white, sometimes lilac flowers born on flowering stems some 8–25 cm tall. The seeds are carried in a long flattened pod. Golden saxifrage is here, found in wet spots on the cliff between 215 and 366 m. It is low and loosely tufted perennial with spreading and creeping stems that are square. The flowers are small, yellowish and without petals. Wych elm and rock white-beam grow on the cliff face wherever they can get a toehold.

One curious feature of Benbulbin's flat top, as previously mentioned, is its covering by a thick blanket of peat bog, with all the attendant peatland plants. Where the underlying limestone pokes up through the vegetable skin a calci-cole flora develops including several alpine species. During the colonisation process several species of mosses, especially *Breutelia chrysocoma,* settle on the limestone pavement, thrive and proliferate, and they soon produce layers of humus which can then be colonised by the seeds of heather and other erica-ceous species. The new arrivals draw most of their nutrients from the acidic moss humus rather than from the limestone below by ensuring that their roots grow initially upwards or horizontally.[30] Gradually the bog builds up, becom-ing more and more acidic with time, and the plants then exist on whatever nutrients they can draw from their own mounting pile of peat humus plus those that fall out of the sky with the rain.

Slieve League, Co. Donegal

'One of the finest things of its kind' was how Praeger described the mountain of Slieve League which brutally confronts the Atlantic Ocean at the end of the southwestern promontory of Co. Donegal. Made up of very old rocks – ancient schists, gneisses and quartzites laid down some 500 million years ago and then thrust up in the Caledonian upheavals – Slieve League rises to 595 m at its sum-mit. It is essentially a quartzite peak, with some Carboniferous sandstone and even less limestone occurring on the summit. Like the Benbulbin mountain range it was almost certainly ice-free in days of glacier supremacy, a haven for arctic-alpine plants and other refuges. The southern side of the mountain has been truncated by the continual pounding of the Atlantic to form some of the most impressive cliffs in Europe. At sunset, the cliff structures, made mainly of quartzite and gneiss, glint and reflect the light in a way that signals their long and tortured history. On the north side of the mountain more cliffs plummet from about 460 m, equally dramatically, down to the dark and seemingly sinis-ter Lough Agh that sits at an altitude of 245 m. Starting from the village of Teelin to the southeast, one of the best walks in Ireland can be had by ascend-ing the summit including a bracing passage along a knife-edge ridge, appro-priately named 'One Man's Path'. The northern precipice is one of the finest sites in Ireland for arctic-alpine plants and has attracted the attention of many distinguished botanists and naturalists for more than a hundred years. The number of arctic-alpine species is greatest here, and progressively declines southwards down the west coast and even more rapidly as one moves south-wards along the east coast of Ireland.

Not only is the total number of arctic-alpine and alpine species on the north-facing cliffs of Slieve League the largest in the country but there are more species here than in any other similar habitat of comparable size in Ireland. Hart, who lived in Donegal and was at leisure to climb up and down Slieve League, reported many in his *Flora of the County Donegal,*[31] thus supplementing earlier work.[32] The species, listed again later by Praeger in *The Botanist in*

Slieve League cliffs, Co. Donegal.

Ireland include bearberry, green spleenwort, stiff sedge, mountain avens, dwarf juniper, alpine clubmoss, mountain sorrel, alpine bistort, holly fern, dwarf willow, alpine saw-wort, yellow saxifrage, purple saxifrage, starry saxifrage, roseroot, lesser clubmoss and alpine meadow-rue.

H.J.B. and H.H. Birks, together with Ratcliffe, visited Slieve League in September 1967 when they explored the shattered and gully-seamed cliff above Lough Agh.[33] The most interesting site here is a north-facing outcrop of calcareous schistose rocks extending for about 91 m at an altitude of 400–460 m. They added the brittle bladder-fern and mountain everlasting to the list for the area as well as recording 29 bryophytes of interest. Most of these are characteristic of calcareous rocky outcrops and are generally widely distributed in Ireland, apart from the liverwort *Gymnomitrion concinnatum*. Two mosses were of particular interest. One was the rare oceanic *Leptodontium recurvifolium*, providing a link between its previously known Irish localities in Kerry, Galway and Mayo and the western Scottish Highlands. The other, *Orthothecium rufescens*, also provided a connection between the Scottish Highlands and its previously known Irish sites on the Carboniferous limestones of Sligo and Leitrim, and the Burren, Co. Clare.

The basaltic plateau of Counties Derry and Antrim

The upland plateau that forms most of Co. Antrim and three-quarters of eastern Co. Derry is made up of volcanic outpourings that settled out over the landscape in level sheets of lava as recently as 65 million years ago. This is, therefore, the newest part of Ireland. The northern edges of the plateau from Lough Foyle in the north to Belfast Lough in the east are scarped with some impressive cliffs. Where the basalt cooled slowly it split up into a series of vertically jointed polygonal columns which appear in their most dramatic form at the Giant's Causeway.

Basalt rocks are composed of 45–55% silica and are classified as basic rocks. They also contain lime, and disintegrate through weathering to produce a comparatively fertile clayey soil, rich in calcium carbonate, providing an attractive environment for many arctic-alpine and alpine plants. Binevenagh, Co. Derry, in the northwestern part of the plateau, looks out over the flat and sandy coastline of Magilligan. Binevenagh has high and dramatic north-facing cliffs, standing over a jumbled, tortured mass of land slips, fallen rock and other debris. These cliffs are famous as one of the best locations in Northern Ireland for a wide range of arctic-alpine and alpine plants growing at uncharacteristically low levels. In fact, the interesting species reported here include two plants not found anywhere else in the province: purple saxifrage, growing sparingly between 275 and 330 m, and moss campion. The moss campion, noted here for its profuse growth and for having flowers that range in colour from deep purple to white (rare), is especially abundant around the screes above Bellarena and at the eastern end of the cliffs. Other species present are alpine scurvygrass (not seen recently[34]), hoary whitlowgrass, mountain avens on the cliffs at 240–335 m, limestone bedstraw, dwarf willow and juniper.

Some 58 km further southeast on the high Garron plateau, sitting behind Garron Point on the Antrim coastline, there is an extensive tableland of bare and desolate blanket bog at an elevation of 305–366 m. The bog is deep and wet with many pools and small lakes. Growing here is the rare marsh saxifrage which has bright yellow, often red-spotted, flowers. It was formerly recorded from eight sites in Ireland, spread though six counties. Since 1970 it has only been recorded at this location, at three sites close together on the Nephin Beg Range, Co. Mayo, and at a mineral flush in the wet blanket bog near Bellacorick, Co. Mayo. It is also in decline in Britain.[16,35] On the Garron plateau it grows at a mineral flush, fed by a spring arising from the basalt rocks, and surrounded by the moss *Drepanocladus revolvens*. Other associated species are daisy, bogbean, selfheal, sharp-flowered rush, bog-sedge, glaucous sedge and large yellow sedge.

Garron Bog is also the home of two rare alpine sedges that grow at about 300 m in the area southeast from the Falls, in the upper Glenariff River to Trosk, high above the village of Carnlough. The few-flowered sedge occurs fairly commonly over a large area – at about 20 stations – extending over at least two 10 km squares of the national grid. It is a loosely tufted, creeping and mat-forming sedge with a shortish stem, up to 25 cm high and bluntly three-sided. The flowers are on a single bractless spike. First discovered by the Rev. H. W. Lett in 1889, this is one of only two Irish locations, the other being a watery peatland site on the edge of the Red Moss of Kilbroney, a somewhat miniature Garron plateau, at an altitude of 340 m on the Mourne Mountains behind Rostrevor, Co. Down.[34] The other sedge is the tall bog-sedge – first found by Miss Elinor D'Arcy in 1901 when she was only 11 years old – well-established on Garron Bog at several sites near pools, where it grows with *Sphagnum* moss and other sedges. Its leaves are 2–3 mm wide and its stems reach up to 40 cm. Until 1981 the Garron site was thought to be the only place where it grew in Ireland but then another location was discovered in an upland blanket bog in Co. Tyrone where it was growing on the west side of Lough Carn. It was later discovered in 1985 at Mill Lough, near Lough Fea and also at Lough Ouske, Co. Derry.[34]

Sperrin Mountains, Co. Tyrone, manifesting erosion of the shallow peats.

Sperrin Mountains, Counties Tyrone and Derry

The Sperrin Mountains are made up of old rocks, mainly schists and gneisses in the northern parts, with Old Red Sandstone and a little limestone in the southern sections. The area is covered by upland blanket bog with a series of summits each rising to the region of 610 m. This is where the cloudberry was first found in 1826 by Edmund Murphy and Admiral Jones. It was growing in a single patch on a north-facing slope of wet blanket peatland at an altitude of about 533 m, west of the Dart Mountain summit. Today it flourishes almost submerged in the surrounding vegetation.[36] A member of the rose family, it is a small, blackberry-like plant with a white flower – a low, downy, creeping perennial spreading vegetatively by rhizomes. It is described as a 'shy flowerer and fruiter' in Ireland as it seldom, if ever, sets fruit. This is thought to be due to the overwhelming presence of plants of a single sex – the stamens (the male organ consisting of a filament and a pollen sac called the anther) usually set in a ring outside the flower centre, and styles (columns of filaments arising from the female organs terminating in the stigma receptive to pollen), usually located within the ring of anthers in the flower centre, are borne on separate flowers that are located in many separated single sex patches.

The Mourne Mountains, Co. Down

The Mourne Mountains stand up as a group of granite hills in south Co. Down with some flanking Silurian rocks. Carlingford Lough lies to the south. Many summits exceed 600 m, and the highest point is Slieve Donard at 850 m. Amongst the granite outcrops are some impressive cliffs and dramatic pinnacles that have originated by longer periods of weathering of the rock. Blanket bog covers the uplands and where the Silurian slates have been worn down by the weather, producing a richer soil, more interesting plants occur. The arctic-alpine and alpine flora is disappointing – already we are on the eastern coast of Ireland – and consists of the usual run-of-the-mill species. Amongst the plants of the higher ground, recorded by Praeger, are alpine saw-wort, dwarf willow, cowberry and alpine clubmoss. Lower altitudes host starry saxifrage, roseroot and the parsley fern. On the high cliffs of Slieve Bignian and Eagle Mountain Praeger recorded the very rare native form of the rosebay willowherb.[3] It was still at the latter site in 1985 at an altitude of 455 m.[34] Also at the high altitudes are the brittle bladder-fern and the stag's-horn clubmoss with its long and decorative 'antlers'.

The Galty Mountains, Counties Tipperary and Limerick

The Galtys were thrust up during the dramatic Hercynian earth movements some 300 million years ago that were also responsible for creating the mountain ranges of the southwest of Ireland. This large crustal upfold has been worn down over millions of years. First the uppermost limestones were stripped off the summits, to survive only in the surrounding plains; next, the Old Red Sandstone was eroded along the crest to reveal the old Silurian rocks at the core of the upfold. Thus, the upper parts of the Galtys are made up of Silurian slates, shales and conglomerates to form a series of fine conical peaks that climax at 919 m on Galty Mountain. The bulk of the mountains rise above 762 m. The outstanding arctic plant of the Galtys is the northern rock-cress found at 293 m on a rock buff west of Lough Curra. This and the Glenade cliffs, Co. Leitrim are its only sites in Ireland. It rarely flowers on the Galtys. The best area for the mountain species, according to Praeger, are the cliffs over Lough Muskry.[3] Investigating the area before him, the intrepid Hart found the arctic-alpines roseroot, starry saxifrage and mountain sorrel.[37]

Mountain fauna

The fauna of Irish mountains and uplands contains very few surprises and, like the flora, is somewhat impoverished. None of the mountain ranges are high or extensive enough to provide the habitats for the true mountain species of birds such as are found in the Scottish Highlands – the ptarmigan, snow bunting and the dotterel. Even when it comes to invertebrates, especially the better investigated groups of butterflies and moths, the range of species is not one to go wild about. However, some interesting discoveries of relict arctic-alpine aquatic beetles have been made which might suggest that they survived the glacial phases of the Ice Age in some of the ice-free mountain summits. Here we will look more closely at the characteristic mammals, birds and invertebrates of mountain and upland areas.

Mammals

The largest living quadruped in Ireland is the red deer which is essentially a creature of the mountains and uplands. While there are several herds and scattered groups throughout the country, the deer in the Killarney Valley area, Co. Kerry, are probably the only ones with a claim to represent the native deer that roamed Ireland during the postglacial period. Once abundant throughout the country as a truly wild species, several herds managed to survive in the more remote areas of Erris, Co. Mayo, Connemara, Co. Galway, and in the Galty Mountains, Counties Tipperary and Limerick, until their extinction in the

Two red deer hinds (F. Guinness).

mid-nineteenth century (see p.65). Testimony of their once widespread distribution in Ireland is evidenced by the incorporation into numerous place names of the Irish word *fiadh* meaning 'deer'. For example, *Cluain-fhiadh*, 'the meadow of the deer', is a parish in Co. Waterford, and *Ceim-an-fhiaidh*, 'the pass of the deer', marks the route taken by these animals when moving from valley to valley of the Lee and Ouvane areas in Co. Cork.

The red deer living wild in the Wicklow Mountains and woods are the descendants of escapees from Lord Powerscourt's demesne in the 1920s, although some authors date their liberation from the 1860s.[38] By the mid 1930s there were approximately 50 animals living wild in the Glencree and Glenmalur areas.[39] Numbers thereafter increased to about 250–300 animals during the war. Surveys in the early 1970s found only about 75 animals living in the open uplands, centred around the Mullaghcleevaun–Kippure (about 25 animals) and Glendalough–Glenmalur (about 50 animals) areas.[38] A further possible 30 were living in the woodlands near Glendalough to give a total population of approximately 105 for the Wicklow hills. Numbers since then have prospered because counts in June and August 1971 found a minimum of 168 and 187 respectively in the Wicklow upland area.[40]

It is remarkable that there was no published systematic work on the diet of red deer in Ireland until 1993 when Sherlock & Fairley gave an account of the food of a small herd (a stag, five to seven hinds and calves) living in a 24 ha enclosure of open terrain, at Mweelin in the Connemara National Park, Co. Galway.[41] The altitude ranged between 60 m to a maximum of about 120 m. The vegetation of the this area comprised 36% grassland/heath, dominated by heather and purple moor-grass; 35% peatland, dominated by purple moor-grass, common cottongrass, black bog-rush, bog asphodel and bog-myrtle;

16% grassland/bracken, dominated by bracken with the main grass being Yorkshire-fog and 13% grassland, comprised mainly of creeping bent, Yorkshire-fog, mat-grass, sheep's fescue and sedges of the genus *Carex*. The food of the deer was determined by faecal analysis of 50 samples collected over one year. Grasses were the main food, forming at least 75% of the diet – primarily sheep's fescue, creeping bent, sweet vernal-grass and Yorkshire-fog. The last three species were eaten most in summer and least in winter. Purple moor-grass, the dominant grass of the area, was only of importance in early summer when most palatable. Heather, the second most important food, was mainly eaten in winter. The diet of the Connemara red deer was comparable to that of the red deer living in the Scottish Highlands.

The goat is a frequent inhabitant of many Irish mountains. Here they are feral, having descended from domestic stock, either escaped or turned out by farmers mostly in the early part of this century. When in the wild for several generations, and sometimes within ten years, domestic goats revert to the wild or feral form. Those that have lived in the wild longest are shaggiest, wearing less patterned coats than their domesticated cousins. Despite the modern dairy goat weighing approximately twice that of the feral variety, there is no evidence to support a common assertion that feral goats represent a throw back to a wild type or ancestor of the modern goat. The degree of genetic purity of feral goats is considered high if there are no hornless adults and if none of the goats have small dangling tassels of hair on either side of their throats. Both these features are relatively recent characteristics of modern domesticated goats.

Many goats that were released into the wild have bred successfully to form small herds which have maintained and, in some cases, increased their numbers during the past hundred years. Feral goats are thought to live for about 12 years and weigh, on average, about 51–63 kg. They are browsers on vegetation, rather than grazers, and can cause damage to trees by stripping off the bark, especially during cold weather – ash, elm, yew, rowan, holly and hazel are favourite species to nibble. Lever remarks that approximately 20 goats living on the cliffs of Rathlin Island, Co. Antrim, are possibly the descendants of some liberated in about 1760, while those on Achill Island, Co. Mayo, also date

Feral goat.

from about the mid-eighteenth century.[42] In the Mullagh More area of the
Burren, Co. Clare, a lowland herd of approximately 60–70 feral together with
domestic goats wander and feed off the limestone pavement and in hazel
scrubland. They move around in sub-groups with considerable interchange of
individuals between the different herds. They also welcome more domesticated beasts in their midst, thus demonstrating the openness of the feral gene
pool to new blood. Rutting starts about mid-September, intensifies in October,
and is over by the end of December. The first kids are born five months after
mating. A feature of the Burren goats is the unusually high survival rate of kids.
The availability and high nutritional status of the food supplied by the karst
environment – despite appearing rather impoverished to the layman – probably accounts for such healthy results.[43]

The goat in Ireland is celebrated as the central figure in the 'Puck Fair', a
ceremony dating back to at least 1613. A male goat is first crowned as 'Puck
King of the Fair' and then 'His Majesty Puck King of Ireland'. According to
Murray, quoted by Whitehead,[44] the name Puck is a derivative from the
Slavonic word *bog*, which means God.

The Irish hare, once considered to be a separate species until a critical examination demoted it to the rank of a subspecies *Lepus timidus hibernicus* of the
mountain hare, occurs only infrequently and at very low densities on Irish
mountains. When disturbed from its 'form' or day resting place on the hillside,
it takes off madly, sometimes pausing upright on its hind legs to examine the
intruder, to another distant destination on the mountain. In northwest and
west Scotland these mountain hares frequent the arctic and alpine zones of the
high summits, sheltering there amongst the boulders. Further south in northern England, in the Peak District mountains, the species is generally confined
to the heather and cottongrass in vegetation zones that are found between 300
and 550 m above sea level. On the Isle of Man, a sort of halfway house to
Ireland, they are restricted to a generally lower altitude, between 153 and 533
m. In Ireland the hares seem happiest on even lower mixed farmland habitats.
Here they have little or no competition from the brown hare, normally absent
from these parts. On the lowland Irish farmlands the mountain hares reach
densities of up to ten times higher than recorded on lowland moorland bogs
– a response to better feeding conditions and shelter.[45]

Birds

At the Annacoona cliffs in the Gleniff Valley, Co. Sligo, numerous ravens populate the air above the escarpments. One unusual species here, however, nearly 10 km from the sea, is the chough, rarely found breeding so far inland. The
1982 national chough survey showed that three-quarters of all inland breeding
sites were found within 8 km from the sea; the site furthest out was 19 km away
in Macgillycuddy's Reeks, Co. Kerry.[46] The Gleniff choughs are therefore
quite remarkable. Another unusual bird around the cliffs, noted in the summer of 1996, was the mistle thrush, a species unknown in Ireland before 1800
when the first one was shot in Co. Antrim. Soon afterwards it bred for the first
time in Co. Down and since then the thrush has been on the increase and has
colonised almost the whole of Ireland. Not normally associated with bare and
naked landscapes, the Gleniff birds were probably breeding in the wych elm or
rock whitebeam trees that seem to sprout out of the cliff faces. However, mistle thrushes have also been known to nest on rocks.[47]

The ring ouzel, a summer visitor from northwest Africa and the Mediterranean, is the only bird confined to the higher and wilder mountain areas of Ireland. This is a somewhat mysterious thrush, not well known to Irish naturalists. Prior to 1900 it bred in all counties except Meath, Westmeath, Longford and Armagh,[48] but breeding numbers have declined this century to an estimated population of only about 270 pairs, found principally in the Wicklow Mountains, the Mourne Mountains, Co. Down, the mountains of north and west Donegal, and the Kerry mountains – where they may have been increasing in recent years. They are also reputed to be in the mountains of south Connemara although Whilde writes that they have not been reported nesting there for many decades.[49] The male is as black as the male blackbird but it has a white bib; the female, brown like her counterpart, has an off-white bib.

Although several historical records of breeding at sea level exist, the ring ouzel seldom nests below 300 m. Steep-sided valleys and ravines are favoured habitats with most nests placed on rock outcrops or ledges. Abandoned buildings and walls will sometimes be used, as well as dense bracken or heather. Little is known about the ecology of the ring ouzel in Ireland. Some basic studies would be most valuable.

Eight other birds could be said to be characteristic but not dependent upon mountain and upland areas. These are, in descending order from the summit: peregrine falcon, raven, hooded crow, hen harrier, meadow pipit, merlin, red grouse and the golden plover. Both the red grouse and golden plover also occur on lowland blanket bogs and they are discussed in Chapter 4.

The peregrine and raven inhabit all the major inland and coastal mountain systems where there are suitable cliffs for nesting. They are equally at home in coastal cliff habitats. Both are widespread throughout the country. The num-

Comeragh Mountains, Co. Waterford, where ring ouzels breed.

bers of breeding peregrines in the Republic prior to 1950 was estimated rather uncertainly at some 180–200 pairs. A dramatic population decline, similar to that experienced in Britain, followed during the 1950s and 1960s. Possibly as few as 14 pairs were thought to have been successfully breeding in Ireland by 1970.[50] This was due to the presence in the countryside of seeds dressed with organochlorine chemicals to prevent insect attack on crops. These were eaten by the woodpigeon, stock dove and rock dove which in turn were preyed on by peregrines which accumulated in their bodies an ever increasing load of the persistent chemicals. If not directly killed by the poison, sub-lethal levels interfered with the metabolism of calcium, affecting its deposition in egg shells. The resultant thin shells led to a high incidence of egg breakages, and elevated residue levels in the embryos brought about a decline in breeding success. Without enough young birds recruited, the population went into serious decline. It was only when the chemicals were withdrawn that the population began to recover. In 1981 all Northern Ireland and approximately 50% by area of the known breeding range in the Republic were surveyed and at least 278 breeding pairs noted.[51] Today there are probably over 500 breeding pairs throughout the whole island. Numbers are still increasing with most of the old traditional breeding sites once again occupied while new sites are being established. Quarry-nesting peregrines, first noted in the late 1970s, are on the increase. A survey of 48 quarries, active and disused, in nine counties of eastern Ireland in 1991 and 1992 revealed 21 breeding pairs. If this occupancy rate was extended to all the 300 quarries in the Republic then there may be up to approximately 130 breeding pairs of peregrines in this somewhat unusual habitat.[52] In 1977 some 35 pairs bred in Northern Ireland quarries.

In 1986 Noonan carried out a study of peregrines breeding in 2,025 km^2 of Co. Wicklow and found 34 territories, or one pair per 60 km^2.[53] The 12 successful eyries produced 2.4 fledged chicks per nest. This figure compared with 2.17 fledged chicks from a longer-term study in five southeastern counties in Ireland over the period from 1981–6. However, when these results were expressed as the mean number of chicks fledged per pair of peregrine holding a territory the figure was only 0.91 chicks. It was also found that breeding performance at coastal, compared with inland, sites was higher with 0.95 and 0.78 chicks respectively produced per pair of peregrines holding territory.[54]

Ravens are more numerous than peregrines in Ireland with an estimated population of 3,500 breeding pairs in 1988–91.[55] However, this would appear to have been a gross over-estimate, and the true breeding population is more likely to be in the order of 1,000 pairs, divided between mountain, upland and coastal habitats.[56] Their shared interests in sometimes similar habitats with peregrines can lead to spectacular aerial encounters. But how do two large and extremely agile birds get along together when they require similar breeding sites? The mechanism for apportioning out available cliffs is not clear but may well be based on precedent of who got there first. If either occupant moved off, for whatever reason, or died, the site would be up for grabs. Their mutual respect for each other has been witnessed and filmed by the author in aerial encounters during which a peregrine will playfully stoop on a raven that will suddenly flip over on its back and point its massive claws upwards, without actually grappling with the peregrine.

Historically ravens were relentlessly persecuted by man because they were perceived as predators of young lambs and sickly sheep, and by 1900 only a few pairs survived in a small number of remote coastal areas. With the relaxation of this murdering grip at the beginning of this century, a remarkable population increase commenced which has led to the species unfurling into virtually all the hills and mountain areas of the country. In a study of ravens in Co. Wicklow during 1968–72 a population density of one breeding pair per 25.3 km^2 was found, close to the one pair per 23.9 km^2 recorded in north Wales moorland for enclosed sheep farms. In both Wicklow and Wales the raven occupied generally similar habitats.[53] Highest densities are in the western uplands where the greater sheep numbers provide the attendant supplies of carrion – the amounts of which were indicated by a study on the blanket peatlands around Glenamoy, in west Mayo, during the early 1970s. The stocking levels on these bogs at that time was roughly one ewe per ha, and losses between October and April were estimated at about 7–10% of total numbers. On average about 1.0–1.4 carcasses per km^2 per month became available to the predators. It was also found that carcasses weighing 30–35 kg disappeared in less than two weeks, indicating the intensity of scavenging by ravens, hooded crows and foxes.[57]

The hooded crow is more a bird of the uplands but, like the peregrine and raven, it has an interest in other habitats, as evidenced by the large population in Ireland, estimated at about 290,000 pairs. The success of the species is a reflection of their ability to adapt to all available food sources. A constant feature of the mountains and uplands, hooded crows move around singly or in pairs, always on the scrounge for sheep carrion or nests of other breeding birds that are quickly plundered. In the mountains and uplands they generally build their nests in low, often isolated trees but will also resort to cliffs and low bushes. Essentially carrion feeders, they have done well in recent years, seldom short of a dead lamb or ewe whose carcasses have increased proportionately with higher stocking densities. During the winter hooded crows often come together in large roosts: close to 170 individuals were counted in one flock at Youghal, Co. Cork on St Patrick's Day in 1978. As a subspecies of the all black crow, hooded crows will interbreed with the black carrion crow and produce fertile offspring. However, the opportunity for matrimony is not great in Ireland as the carrion crow is scarce, and found principally in the northeast of Ireland – although it has been creeping down southwards towards Dublin in recent years.

The hen harrier is most likely to be seen quartering moorland below 500 m, especially in areas covered by young forestry plantations which, in their early stages of development, offer excellent breeding habitat for the species. A dense growth of tall vegetation such as heather is also suitable nesting habitat. Formerly widespread throughout Ireland, these docile-looking birds were persecuted by gamekeepers to the point of extermination in the second half of the nineteenth century and were thought to have become extinct in 1954. Fortunately a few pairs were lurking in the Slieve Bloom Mountains, Co. Laois, and on the Waterford/Tipperary border. Numbers picked up dramatically as large areas of amenable breeding habitat became available to the species through a reinvigorated State afforestation programme. By 1973–5 there were 250–300 breeding pairs on the Irish uplands.[58] Since then, however, they have declined again, dropping to probably fewer than 100 pairs. Reasons advanced for this reversal relate to maturing forestry plantations together with the clearance and reclamation of marginal uplands, representing a loss of breeding and

Hooded crow. Widespread
throughout Ireland.
(F. Guinness).

hunting habitat for the species.[59] However, this explanation is not entirely satisfactory as afforestation is not a thing of the past and new plantations, providing renewed attractive habitat, are still being created all around the country. Today most of the estimated 60–80 pairs are located in the uplands of
Kerry, Limerick, Cork, Clare, Tipperary and Laois.[60] Some also breed in
Tyrone, Fermanagh and Antrim. Recent sightings in Galway and Mayo may
relate to breeding birds. Hen harriers have also decreased in England and
Wales but appear to have remained stable in Scotland. Recent estimates for the
population breeding in western Europe, excluding Ireland and Britain, gave
4,160–6,610 pairs.[61]

The buzzard, a common breeding bird on inland cliffs and in woodlands in
Donegal, Derry, Antrim and Down during the nineteenth century, was persecuted by shooting and poisoning until it became extinct shortly before the turn
of the century. At the same time buzzards remained widespread in the western
upland areas of Britain. Following several attempts earlier this century to re-
establish themselves in Antrim they finally managed reinstatement there in the
early 1960s. Since then they have spread to all six Northern counties with an
estimated population of 120 pairs in 1991. The population has also spread out
of the North into adjoining counties and southwards into the Republic where
the population rose from one known pair in 1977–9 to 26 pairs reported

1989–91. Most were in Donegal (13 pairs) followed by Monaghan (7 pairs), Wicklow (3 pairs), Louth (2 pairs) and Cavan (1 pair).[62] Their recolonisation has been facilitated by a more enlightened attitude by game keepers and farmers and a reduction in the amount of poison laid to protect lambs from corvids and foxes. Moreover the use of strychnine was banned in the Republic in 1992 in conjunction with an attempt to reintroduce the white-tailed sea eagle to the Dingle Peninsula area.

The kestrel, despite possibly being the commonest bird of prey in Ireland, occurs at lower densities than encountered in most other European countries, the reasons for which are not entirely clear.

The passerines, apart from the ring ouzel, characteristic but not dependent upon the mountains and uplands include the ubiquitous meadow pipit, whose small size and nondescript streaky brown plumage belie its tenacity for survival in a hostile environment. With an Irish breeding population estimated at over a million pairs there are plenty to spread around in all Irish habitats ranging from farmland, rough grasslands, young forestry plantations, peatlands and mountains and uplands where, above the altitudes of 500 m, it is the commonest nesting bird. Managing to find enough invertebrates, particularly flies (including mosquitoes) populating grassy and heathery slopes, the pipit, in turn, is the principal food item for the merlin as well as main host-cum-victim to wandering cuckoos. In recent years a decline in the numbers of meadow pipits breeding in southeastern and eastern Ireland has been noted – probably a consequence of the agricultural improvement of marginal lands. Today its strongholds are in the western and northwestern counties.

Merlins are equally at home in lowland blanket bogs as they are in the mountains and uplands. The estimated size of the Irish breeding population is 200–300 pairs, concentrated mainly in the uplands of Wicklow, Galway, Mayo and Donegal. They also occur in the uplands in Northern Ireland. A special survey carried out in 1985 by Haworth in the great expanse of lowland blanket bog between Errisbeg and Clifden in west Galway revealed the presence of 12 pairs, eleven of which were breeding on wooded islands in small lakes, the other in a coniferous plantation. Eight nests were successful in their breeding outcome and 32 merlins fledged.[63] In the uplands of Wicklow merlins breed in coniferous plantations while in Northern Ireland they often settle in the abandoned nests of hooded crows. A study by Toal in Derry, Tyrone and Antrim found that of 22 recorded nests 19 had previously been taken over from hooded crows in trees and only two were on the ground. All nesting took place above 150 m and most sites were either in sitka spruce plantations, or on the edge of them.[63]

Other birds frequently occurring but not in any particular way tied to these regions are the wheatear which likes open spaces strewn with landmarks such as boulders under which they can nest or in hollows in turf banks, and wren, also able to exploit opportunities in seemingly barren areas. Another bird, not well known and whose ways, like those of the ring ouzel, are somewhat mysterious, is the twite, a small brown finch. It is found in the remote western coastal areas from Donegal to Kerry, but also in some mountain and upland regions where it nests in heather or low bushes. Some 750–1,000 pairs are estimated to breed in Ireland and the population is thought to be declining.[60] Both the twite and the ring ouzel offer plenty of scope for study by naturalists.

Invertebrates

The coldness and harsh climate of the mountains and uplands have restricted the number of invertebrate species in these habitats and most attention has been paid by naturalists to the more spectacular butterflies and beetles. The only butterfly confined to the mountains and uplands is one of the hardiest of them all, the small mountain ringlet, which in Europe is seldom found below an altitude of 460 m. In Britain, when it occurs, it is usually between 200 and 900 m. Adults are a drab, sooty brown with a band of black spots fringing the margins of their outer wings, each surrounded by a lighter tawny zone. Its caterpillars are grass-green and feed on mat-grass. There are only four known specimens from Ireland, all preserved in the scientific collections of the Natural History Museum, Dublin, and the Ulster Museum, Belfast. One was from 'a grassy hollow about half way up the Westport side of Croagh Patrick,' Co. Mayo, June 1854; the second from the hilly slopes on the eastern shores of Lough Gill, Co. Sligo in 1895 and the third from Nephin Mountain, Co. Mayo in 1901. The fourth specimen is just labelled 'Irish 30.6.18.' Almost every year entomologists try in vain to rediscover this elusive prize but despite repeated searching it fails to be turned up, thus leading to the conclusion that it is probably now extinct. One difficulty in recording its presence is that it flies only in sunshine, spending the rest of its time lurking in damp mountain and upland grasses. If it still exists in Ireland it is most likely to be found in the Nephin Beg area, Co. Mayo, which is considered to offer the best habitat opportunities.[64]

The large heath, another upland inhabitant, has been recorded up to 365 m at the Windy Gap, Co. Kerry. Unlike the mountain ringlet it is not confined to mountain and upland areas, with many occurring on the lower blanket and raised bogs. The adults are on the wing for only a short time in the summer – from the middle of June to the end of July. The caterpillar is about 2.5 cm long, grass-green in colour, striped by dark green on its dorsal surface and white along the sides. It is thought that common cottongrass and purple moor-grass are probably important food for the caterpillars, as well as white beak-sedge when it is available. The large heath is a very variable species as regards its colouring and wing markings. There are several subspecies, with two recognised in Ireland – *Coenonympha tullia scotica* and *C. t. polydama*. The former is confined mainly to the south and western Ireland.[65] The latter occurs in many parts of the country but its main stronghold appears to be in the Midlands and in the north of Ireland.[66]

The emperor moth, easily identified by its prominent eyespots on the upper and lower wing surfaces, is on the wing from April to end June especially on upland boglands. Another moth, the beautiful yellow underwing, takes it name from the yellow central area, bordered by black, on the underwings. Both these moths may be encountered on Irish uplands and mountains together with numerous other smaller, paler moths exploding upwards for a brief dashing flight when disturbed by a hill walker or roaming beast before plunging back down into the protective vegetation.

In contrast to the highly mobile butterflies and moths, many other invertebrates are yoked to their local environments. One interesting group is the water beetles belonging to the family Dytiscidae which, although most are well able to fly, tend to remain confined to very specific aquatic habitats, especially within the mountainous environment. These water beetles have evolved adaptive devices to make their aquatic lifestyle easier – their heads are generally sunk into the thorax and the body is smooth and rounded, both facilitating their passage through water. They also possess broad hind legs, flat and fringed with hairs to act as efficient paddles. Although rising to the surface, tail first, to renew the oxygen supply is still necessary, the water beetles can also hibernate, particularly in order to overcome cold conditions. Both the adults and larvae are aggressive carnivores. Some larvae reach up to 6 cm long and will successfully tackle small fish and even take on, working with their fierce looking hard jaws, a tasty-looking finger of a hapless bug hunter. Several members of the Dytiscidae found in Ireland have been identified as glacial relicts that 'chilled out' in their mountain-top pools as the ice sheets were banging around in the valleys below.

A particularly rich site for these relict species is the top of Doughruagh Mountain (526 m), a northern outlier of the Twelve Bens of Connemara, west Galway. Several small, shallow pools pepper the summit. The vegetation is meagre and includes bog pondweed, water lobelia, water-milfoil, *Myriophyllum* sp., bulbous rush and the sub-aquatic moss *Scorpidium scorpioides*. These often mist-shrouded and rain-drenched pools are the unlikely spots, because of their barren mountain summit locations, for spawning frogs. The ensuing tadpoles enter into the diet of the rapacious larvae of two very rare Dytiscidae found here: the alpine and smallest of the great diving beetles *Dytiscus lapponicus* and an arctic-alpine species *Agabus arcticus*. The nymph of another glacial relict, the water boatman *Glaenocorisa propinqua*, has also been recorded here[67] as well as on the Peakeen Mountain, Co. Kerry and in the Blue Stack Mountains, Co. Donegal. It has also been recorded from Lough Nacartan (30–60 m above sea level), Killarney, Co. Kerry, and in Upper Lough Bray (425–457 m above sea level).[68] The only other Irish records of *Dytiscus lapponicus* are from Co. Donegal, the Partry Mountains, west Mayo and Co. Kerry. As for *Agabus arcticus*, it has been found in pools in the Wicklow Mountains and from Glenariff and Lough Evish in Co. Antrim. The adults in the population of the glacial relict stonefly *Capnia atra* living in the Devil's Punch Bowl (over 700 m above sea level) near the summit of Mangerton Mountain, Co. Kerry, are brachypterous – short winged and non-flying – considered to be a selective advantage as because they cannot fly they are prevented from being blown away to an unsuitable area in such a windswept region.[69] Another insect survivor from the Ice Age is a small alpine caddisfly *Tinodes dives*, discovered in 1983 at the summit of Benbulbin, Co. Sligo.[70]

The discovery of three montane insects new to Ireland on the summit of Slieve Donard in the Mourne Mountains, Co. Down, in early July 1992 showed that there is still a great deal to be learnt from Irish mountains. The summit of Slieve Donard is a large expanse of stony ground, gently sloping from 825–850 m. Its vegetation is typical of summit heaths – dominated by dwarf willow, heath bedstraw, crowberry and pill sedge with some alpine clubmoss where sheep grazing is less intense. Under the stones at the summit two carabid beetles, *Miscodera arctica* and *Notiophilus aesthuans*, were found. Also discovered here were some red galls or wart-like structures on the dwarf willow that signalled the presence of the sawfly *Pontania crassipes*.

4

Peatlands

Ireland is justly famous for its extensive cover of peatlands that extend out, like a wet, heavy vegetable blanket, over large tracts of the landscape. According to Taylor there are 1,345,658 ha of peatlands in Ireland (taken as a whole), close to 4,000 more than in Britain, thus making Ireland custodian of the seventh greatest extent of peatlands in the world. Moreover, 17.2% of Ireland's land surface is occupied by peatland, the third highest proportion of any country in the world, surpassed only by Canada and Finland with 18.4% and 33.5% respectively.[1] Huge chunks of Donegal, Mayo, Galway and Kerry are smothered by lowland and mountain blanket bogs while expansive areas in the Central Plain – Kildare, Offaly, Roscommon, Tipperary, Westmeath, Longford, east Mayo, east Galway, and in Northern Ireland, the Bann Valley – are taken up by raised bogs and, to a lesser extent, by fens.

This chapter explores the nature, composition and distribution of peatlands, discusses the history and formation of the three major peatland types in Ireland – raised bogs, blanket bogs and fens – and describes their characteristic floras and faunas.

In view of their extent it is not entirely unexpected that the earliest accounts of Irish vegetation should concern peatlands. In 1652 Boate provided the first classification of bogs, distinguishing them from heaths. He described two major types: red bogs 'the earth in them for the most part is reddish and overgrown with moss of the same colour; in parts of vast extent' – these are the raised bogs found in the Midlands – and wet bogs, which he divided into four categories that hold true today and correspond to blanket bogs, true fens, eroded peat or bare mud around fens, and reed swamp fens with the early stages of alder–willow carr.[2] He believed that the origin of the bogs was due to the 'wretchedness of the Irish who let daily more and more of their good land grow boggy through their carelessness'. He interpreted the remains of trees in the bogs as support for his theory. Thirty-three years later, in 1685, William King published a remarkable paper entitled *Of the Bogs and Loughs of Ireland* which was mainly concerned with bog drainage but contained the first clear account of plant succession over time.[3] Moreover, he had a good understanding of raised bog hydrology, drawing an analogy between the bog and a bladder:

> 'Tis to be observed, that bogs are generally higher than the land about them, and highest in the middle: the chief springs that cause them being commonly about the middle, from whence they dilate themselves by degrees, as one would blow a bladder; but not always equally, because they sometimes meet with greater obstacles on one side than the other: whoever has seen bogs, cannot doubt of this; and besides if you cut a deep trench through a bog; you will find the original spring and vast quantities of water will run away, and the bog subside..'.

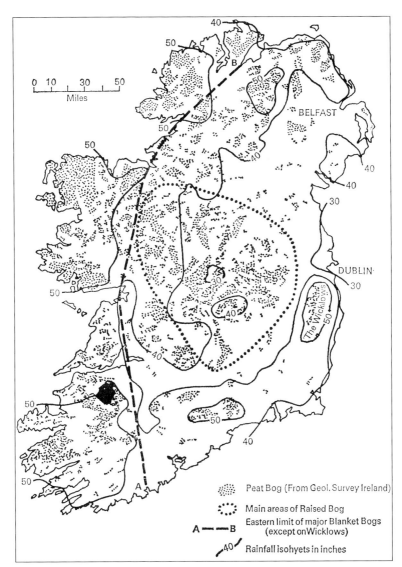

The distribution of bog in Ireland. From J.B. Whittow (1974) *Geology and Scenery of Ireland*. Penguin Books, London.

The word bog has been derived from the Irish *bogach* meaning 'soft ground' and has been in use in the English language since the early sixteenth century. The material taken from the bog and used for burning as a fuel is known as peat in England but called turf in Ireland.

Bogland can arouse a sense of awe in naturalists, while eliciting a less positive response from many thousands of others to whom the bog is associated with economic hardship. The natural world of bogs has not only fascinated genera-tions of naturalists but has fired the imagination of countless painters, sculptors, photographers, writers and poets. Heaney has explored the mysteries and fascination of bogs in *Bogland, Belderg and Bog Queen.* In *Bogland* he writes:

> 'I had been vaguely wishing to write a poem about bogland, chiefly because it is a landscape that has a strange assuaging effect on me, one with associations reaching back into early childhood. We used to hear about bog-butter, butter kept fresh for a great number of years under the peat. Then when I was at school the skeleton of an elk had been taken out of a bog nearby and a few of our neighbours had got their photographs in the paper, peering out across its antlers. So I began to get an idea of bog as the memory of the landscape, or as a landscape that remembered everything that happened in and to it. In fact, if you go around the National Museum in Dublin, you will realise that a great proportion of the most cherished material heritage of Ireland was "found in the bog". Moreover, since memory was that faculty that supplied me with the first quickening of my own poetry, I had a tentative unrealised need to make a congruence between memory and bogland and, for the want of a better word, our national consciousness. And it all released itself after "We have no prairies – but we have bogs".'[4]

Peat is a soil consisting of about 92% water, the balance being made up of largely undecomposed remains of plant material (roots, stems, leaves, flowers, fruits, seeds, pollen) and insects. Due to the overwhelming presence of water, oxygen is excluded and bacteria, fungi and small invertebrates cannot carry out their daily job of breaking down the accumulating layers of organic material. Only a few specialist microorganisms can operate in such anaerobic conditions. Instead of the normal production of nitrates, phosphates, sulphates and

Peat – undecayed spongy vegetation material with a water content of some 92%. Note remains of former Scots pine forest smothered by subsequent growth of peat.

carbon dioxide, the creatures operating in peat generate a series of oxygen-free compounds such as methane or 'marsh' gas, hydrogen sulphide, ammonia and occasionally phosphine. The famous 'will o' the wisp' – curious glowing and dancing low intensity lights over the bogs – is no more than methane fumes sparked off by the highly inflammable diphosphane gas (P_2O_4), also exuded from the bog, which ignites spontaneously on contact with air.

The vegetation mass of the bog persists through time as undecayed spongy material or peat. If vegetation keeps on being added the mound becomes thicker and thicker, like a growing compost heap but without the normal composting processes going on inside. The peats that comprise raised bogs are made up almost entirely of undecomposed bog mosses, *Sphagnum* spp., while the remains of grasses, sedges and rushes form the bulk of blanket bogs.

The chemical composition of peats from seven widely separated raised and blanket bogs was examined by Walsh & Barry in 1956.[5] Water content varied from a mean of 94% by volume for raised, 92% for lowland blanket and 91% for one upland blanket bog with little variation according to depth of peat. The mean pH for 64 samples from all horizons in the seven bogs was 5.04, well below the neutral point of 7.0 but higher than the usually quoted levels of 3.5 and 4.2 for raised and blanket bogs respectively.[6] Ash content averaged 2.4%, with negligible differences between bog types – highest levels were in surface and basal layers. Nitrogen content was low at a mean 1.23%. Overall concentrations of total and readily soluble phosphorus were very low compared to a normal soil. The amount of peat that had decomposed (material passing through a 200 mesh sieve) was an average of 32%. The high acidity and low nutrient status make peats an infertile soil for crop production. The precipitation of atmospheric elements both sea-derived salts and dust were considered by Walsh & Barry to be important sources of nutrients in the peat.

To the unappreciative eye most peatlands appear monotonous, dreary, brown or sometimes reddish deserts, devoid of any natural history interest and only suitable for rough grazing, peat for fuel, or forestry development. Viewed for centuries as wastelands and impediments to the traveller, boglands have challenged engineers, agriculturists and other 'improvers' bent on taming these apparently unproductive expanses. To the naturalist, however, peatlands are fascinating wet, cold ecosystems.

The first detailed survey of the peatlands of Ireland was carried out between 1809 and 1813 by Commissioners, appointed by the British Government, to assess the potential of peatlands for agricultural use. The four resultant and magnificent folio volumes – *Reports of the Commissioners Appointed to Enquire into the Nature and Extent of the Several Bogs in Ireland and the Practicability of Draining and Cultivating Them* – with beautifully engraved, sepia-coloured maps, containing the finest details of the bogs surveyed, were published in London between 1810 and 1814.[7] One of the most active engineers of the survey was Richard Griffith, credited with surveying about 80,000 ha of lowland bog in keen detail (approximately 20% of the Irish sites) and a further *c*.100,000 ha of mountain bog.[8] At the end of their work it was calculated by the Commissioners that the total peatland area in the whole of Ireland was 1,200,000 ha, of which 650,000 ha was raised and low level blanket bog and 550,000 ha mountain blanket bog. Approximately one third of the total was examined in detail, with the remaining 800,000 ha considered unproductive mountain bog, or too remote or inaccessible for immediate attention. The most promising 400,000 ha were closely inspected, of which 300,000 ha were Midland raised bogs.

Little action was taken to implement the Commissioners' recommendations, namely the drainage and reclamation of the most promising peatlands, and it was not until the Second World War that the peatlands of Ireland started to be exploited on a grand scale. Following a need for greater self-sufficiency, the Turf Development Board was established in 1943 to maximise the fuel resources of the bogs. The Board was succeeded by a more effective semi-State body, Bord na Móna, in 1946, which proved so successful and technologically innovative that, in recent years, naturalists have become increasingly concerned about the rapid disappearance of peatlands. With today's sophisticated machinery it takes only about 20 years to completely eradicate a unique 9,000 year-old ecosystem spread over several thousand hectares.

The need for up-to-date information on the distribution and status of peatlands in the Republic of Ireland prompted Hammond of An Foras Talúntais (The Agricultural Research Institute) to carry out a study which was published in 1979.[9] Drawing upon his own field work, the National Soil Survey and all other available sources, including the 1973–4 aerial survey of Ireland, Hammond produced a new peat map (scale 1:575,000) which brought up to date the one produced by the 1920 Geological Survey.[10] The results from Hammond's work were as follows (all figures in hectares):

1. **Raised Bogs**
    cut-over   176,120
    in industrial production   74,110
    intact surface   61,070
    Total   **311,300**

2. **Blanket Bogs**
    (a) Lowland
    modified   85,590
    in industrial production   7,970
    intact   243,610
    Total   **337,170**
    (b) Mountain
    modified   115,630
    intact   321,060
    Total   **436,690**

3. **Fens**
    Total   **92,510**

GRAND TOTAL   1,177,670

The conclusions that can be drawn from his figures are that only 19.6% of the raised bogs and 73% of the blanket bogs of Ireland remained intact when he carried out his survey. Since then, the areas of intact boglands have diminished even further. Although fens have not been cut for peat many have been drained, reclaimed, dried up and lost for ever. In the absence of detailed studies the Irish Peatland Council have identified 48,240 ha of fen (52% of the original total) of potential European conservation importance.[6]

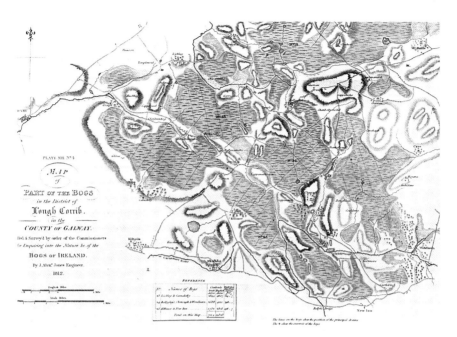

Map of part of the bog in the district of Lough Corrib, Co. Galway. British Government [7]. (D. Burke).

Formation of raised bogs

Raised bogs started their lives as shallow lakes. At about the time of the first evidence of man in Ireland, some 9,000 years ago, there were large areas of open water all over the country. These waterbodies had been left behind by the melting ice in the river valleys and low-lying areas, especially in the Midlands and in regions where glacial drift had been deposited as drumlins which obstructed the runoff and drainage of waters. Most of these waters were alkaline and rich in minerals, conditioned by the underlying and nearby rocks. Vegetation first colonised the margins of the lakes. But mud and clay silts settled progressively on the lake bottoms, often as a white marl, to form an impervious layer, sealing the lake water off from the underlying water table. This seal later played an important role in the hydrological and nutrient control of the future raised bog. The fringing vegetation gradually grew towards the centre of the water while at the same time other submerged or floating plants thrived and multiplied. Organic material, sloughed off from the dead and dying vegetation, drifted to the bottom of the water to form a layer of fibrous fen peat, 2–3 m thick, resting on the mud-clays. Thus the basis for a raised bog was laid down.

The history and evolution of Ballyscullion Bog, Co. Antrim – a fine example of a raised bog – was originally investigated by Jessen in his pioneering studies on late Quaternary deposits and flora history of Ireland,[11] and has more recently been re-examined by Smith who established, by radiocarbon dating, that its fen peat was laid down about 9,000 years ago.[12] The plant species involved in the early stages of raised bog formation were: (a) open and shallow

Former shallow lake, then fen, now developing into a raised bog.

water species (bladderworts, pondweeds, yellow water-lily, white water-lily and ridged hornwort); (b) reedswamp species (common club-rush, common reed and great fen-sedge), and (c) fen species (dominated by sedges and grasses, with flowering species such as meadowsweet, marsh-marigold, cuckooflower, bogbean and common marsh-bedstraw, etc.). The tree species comprising the fen carr were principally willow, birch and alder. As the willows and birch moved towards the centre of the fen which was becoming drier and drier woody fragments broke off these shrubs and fell through the water to form a layer of wood-peat sitting on top of the fen peat at the lake bottom.

Deposition of the wood-peat, which can be as thick as 2–3 m, ceased about 7,000 years ago at Ballyscullion Bog. The lake by then was in its last stages as a lake. The supply of essential inorganic and other minerals required to feed the floating vegetation was cut off from the underlying rocks by the two sealing layers, thus creating opportunities for the gradual colonisation of the fen surface by the very resistant *Sphagnum* mosses. These are specially adapted to survive life in the bogland environment by deriving both their inorganic nutrients and water supply entirely from rainfall. The fen was now in the early stages of becoming a raised bog.

Without the mosses *Sphagnum* spp., of which there are about 30 different kinds in Ireland, there would be no peat bogs. *Sphagnum* leaves are composed of a single layer of cells. Most of these cells are large and dead yet play a vital role in water storage: they are equipped with pores allowing water to be sucked into the cell cavity by capillary action. When full, *Sphagnum* is a bloated, sponge-like soft mass, mostly green and glistening, which can hold over 20 times its dry weight of water. It tends to grow upwards, rather than laterally, which assists the formation and development of hummocks. Where *Sphagnum* is the dominant species it can grow at a rate of 3–4 cm per year. Scattered amongst *Sphagnum*'s dead cells are other cells, thin living ones, containing chlorophyll and manufacturing by the process of photosynthesis the sugars and other raw materials necessary for plant growth.

The remarkable physical properties of *Sphagnum* and its mildly antiseptic qualities led to its use as an important dressing for wounds during the First World War. It was considered superior to the more conventional cotton wool and was four times as absorbent. During those troubled years the Society of United Irishwomen collected *Sphagnum* throughout the country. It was then taken to special depots, turned into dressings and sent all over the world. Feehan & O'Donovan state that nearly one million tonnes of *Sphagnum* were gathered for this purpose.[13]

During its metabolic activities, *Sphagnum* manufactures a group of chemicals known as unesterified polyuronic compounds that are deposited in the cell walls. These compounds have the capacity to give up their hydrogen ions in exchange for minerals such as calcium, sodium and potassium which are absorbed from the falling rain. Thus the minerals move through the cell walls and enter the cell while hydrogen ions leave the cell wall and pass into the surrounding soil and water. The abundance of hydrogen ions released by the *Sphagnum* mosses into the bogland creates the acidic conditions that set the ecological agenda for the peatlands. In other words what started as a lime-rich fen becomes, with the establishment of *Sphagnum*, a fully-fledged acidic bog.

The growth of a raised bog is a result of the interplay between small hummocks, or mounds, and wet hollows. This hummock-hollow cycle of bog growth, known a the 'regeneration or enatiodromic complex' was originally postulated by the Swedish botanist Osvald[14] but recent work by Casparie and others have called his explanation into question.[15] The way the bog grows is likely to be a far more complicated affair than postulated by Osvald and the process is not fully understood yet. Hummocks are formed principally by *Sphagnum fuscum* and *S. imbricatum*, replete with water. As they accrete and pile up, the *Sphagnum* mosses raise the level of the bog and, in the process, drag up with them the water table of the bog. Several *Sphagnum* species may succeed each other in the hummocks until the summits become dry and suitable for colonisation by lichens, other mosses such as *Leucobryum glaucum* and

Fig. 4.5 Transect from lake margin to bog (not to scale). From Mitchell & Ryan[26].

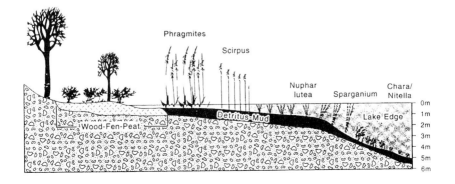

Racomitrium lanuginosum, and flowering species such as heather. Vegetation fragments peeling off the big hummocks then land in wet hollows and other *Sphagnum* mosses start life. These include *S. pulchrum, S. cuspidatum* and *S. papillosum*. They line the ground and produce a slight drying out of the hollow before the hummock-forming *Sphagnum* mosses take over, and a new hummock is gradually built up. What was a wet hollow is now a hummock and the former hummock, because it is surrounded by higher *Sphagnum* growth, becomes a wet hollow. Whatever the mechanism, it is an extremely slow process inducing peat accumulation of about 1 mm per year. Providing waterlogging remains stable and continues to inhibit the availability of oxygen necessary for most decomposition processes, the rates of decay cannot ever match the rates of growth and the bog will keep thickening upwards. Raised bogs have the deepest deposits – up to 13 m – of all Irish peatlands and, as a general rule, they are found in places where the rainfall average is 800–900 mm per annum.

During the long history of raised bog growth – *Sphagnum* peat was being laid down at Ballyscullion Bog some 7,000 years ago – fluctuations of rainfall occurred which led to the drying out of bog surfaces. A dry period about 4,500 years ago allowed Scots pine to colonise many bog surfaces and flourish for about 500 years. Then wet conditions returned, and renewed waterlogging killed off the pines, whose dead stumps were then smothered by the subsequent upward growth of *Sphagnum* mosses. Entombed in an anaerobic and acidic environment the roots exhibit, when exposed by turf cutting, a remarkable freshness. Often called 'bog oak', although it is generally known as 'bog pine', this ancient tortured timber testifies to the extraordinary preservative qualities of the bog, which is said to keep butter unadulterated for more than a hundred years.

The presence of roots, stumps and trunks in the bogs raises a recurring question: did Scots pine become extinct in Ireland or did it survive as an indigenous species? Mitchell & Ryan in *Reading The Irish Landscape* argue that it became extinct in historic times and certainly before its reintroduction by man some 300 years ago. Speight, in an ingenious piece of research, examined three selected insect groups, comprising *c.* 400 species, to see if there was evidence of survival of an indigenous Scots pine fauna in Ireland. His conclusion was that the present-day Irish fauna of Scots pine-associated insects provides little evidence to support the hypothesis.[16]

As the raised bogs grew, their surfaces rose above the surrounding ground, producing a domed profile, not dissimilar to a loaf of brown bread rising up some 5–8 m above the surrounding countryside as it gradually baked. The water within the rising bog, derived mostly from rain, is also lifted higher than that of the surrounding land. It is not fully understood how, or whether water moves around in this suspended 'water bag'. Nor are the relationships between the water bag and the water in the surrounding land well known. The natural discharge of water from the raised bog is a complex process which often involves a series of small lakes connected together by natural drains leading outwards to the edge of the bog.[17] The lakes, or soak areas, are generally richer in nutrients and they allow plants more typical of fens to flourish. A classic soak system once existed at Pollagh Bog, Co. Offaly, where the Rannoch-rush (now extinct in Ireland) was discovered growing by John J. Moore in 1951 – almost certainly encouraged by the outflow of nutrients. This was its only

Raised bogs on either side of the river Suck, north of Ballinasloe, Co. Roscommon
(A. Walsh).

known location in Ireland.[18] Prior to the announced development of the bog
and the ultimate demise of the rush, Moore transplanted some specimens to
the nearby Raheenmore Bog and Lough Roe Bog, Co. Offaly, in 1959. It was
seen on Lough Roe Bog in 1960 but not subsequently at either site. The almost
certain loss of this species from Ireland is one of the clearest examples of plant
extinction during the twentieth century. The Rannoch-rush is one of eight
species of vascular plants that are known to have become extinct in Ireland.[19]
Intact soak systems are now rare in Ireland with probably the finest remnant
being at the Clara Bog National Nature Reserve, Co. Offaly, where it will now,
after a long conservation struggle, be protected from man's interference.

Many raised bogs have a liquid core, including Fairy Water Bog (175 ha),
Garry Bog (121 ha), Co. Antrim, and in Derrandoran Bog, Co. Tyrone.[20]
Some of these liquid reservoirs have been known to burst. Since the beginning
of the eighteenth century, Ireland holds the distinction of having experienced
more bog bursts than any other country in the world, numbering about 25.
The most famous occurred in Co. Kerry at the head of the Ownacree Valley,
11 km north of Headford, near Killarney, three days after Christmas 1896. A
spell of wet weather commencing in September had followed a dry summer
and rain intensified several days before the outburst. A family of eight –
Cornelius Donelly (Lord Kenmare's quarry steward), his wife and six children
– together with their home and livestock, were carried away and engulfed in a
devastating torrent of swirling, brown, mousse-like liquid. The bog that burst
extended over some 1,380 ha and was at an altitude of 200 m on the hill above
their farm. Some of their bodies, their livestock and furniture were carried
down the valley, a portion of one of the beds being picked up in the Lake of
Killarney some 22.5 km away: 'a vast mass of peat and water precipitated itself

down the valley, the flood ceasing only when it entered the Lower Lake of Killarney, fourteen miles distant. When the flow finally died down, about a week after the outburst, a great saucer-shaped depression, at its deepest no less than forty-five feet below the former slightly convex surface, showed the amount of the extruded material.' So wrote Praeger[21] who, with Sollas, was commissioned by the Royal Dublin Society to investigate the tragedy.[22] An estimated 4.58 million m^3 of water and bog had been discharged in this burst.

Flora of raised bogs

The surface of a typical undisturbed raised bog consists of a mosaic of pools, ponds, hummocks, hollows and so-called lawns. The characteristic flora includes heather, which is usually dominant but often stunted, cross-leaved heath, deergrass, bog asphodel, common cottongrass, hare's-tail cottongrass, bog-rosemary, the moss *Racomitrium lanuginosum* and cranberry. The cranberry, of cranberry sauce fame, is a member of the Ericaceae or heath family and has creeping stems and delicate pink down-turned petals. Real cranberry sauce is made from the larger berries of the North American species *Vaccinium macrocarpum*, but Irish bog cranberries can be harvested in the autumn and eaten stewed or made into a jelly. The North American species has been introduced to a few bogs e.g. Woodfield Bog, near Clara, Co. Offaly.[13] Of all the species, *Sphagnum* mosses are the most important constituents of raised bogs with about ten different species widely distributed either in the pools, in hummocks and on the lawns. *Sphagnum* mosses exhibit a wide range of colours from red to yellow and green to brown. Two species turn red in the autumn which, together with the reddish-brown colours of the cottongrasses have given rise to the term 'red bog', an alternative and often-used name for raised bogs. The peat from these bogs is also reddish. Green *Sphagnum* species are generally found in the pools, the commonest being *S. cuspidatum*.

Fairy Water Bog, Co. Tyrone

The Fairy Water Bog lies in the Fairy Water river valley, 12 km southeast of Castlederg and 3 km north of Drumquin, Co. Tyrone. Drumlins litter the river valley where a series of bogs grew out of fens. Fairy Water Bog extends over 175 ha. Its ecology was described in 1959 by Morrison.[20] The bog is remarkable for the extensive growth of *Sphagnum imbricatum*, rising in orange-brown hummocks 50 cm above the surrounding water levels of the pools in the so-called 'Regeneration Complex' area. The Complex consists of a maze of meandering *Sphagnum*-filled pools occurring between irregularly dispersed hummocks of *S. imbricatum*. In this wettest part of the bog, the dense covering of *Sphagnum* supports a low shrubby layer of heather, cross-leaved heath, common cottongrass, deergrass and carnation sedge. In the wet troughs, hollows and pools the aquatic bog moss, *Sphagnum cuspidatum*, grows luxuriantly together with *S. subsecundum* and *S. auriculatum*, along with the bogbean, great sundew and lesser bladderwort.

The pools in the 'Regeneration Complex' are deep and act as 'windows' for the liquid core, at least 2.5 m in depth, beneath the bog's surface. The liquid core separates the dome of *Sphagnum* peats from the denser and lower fen peat. The close proximity of such a large water supply to the surface provides the bog skin with extra wetness that makes the vegetation more ecologically interesting, as exemplified by the thriving growth of *S. imbricatum*, no longer present on other raised bogs. Historically the role of *S. imbricatum* as a bog builder was much greater than today. Its disappearance may be due to drier, more continental conditions but also to burning and drainage.

The largest part of Fairy Water Bog is occupied, rather unusually, by a community of sedges or *Scirpetum*, more frequently found on the wetter blanket bogs subject to occasional burning and intensive grazing. Such impacts clear the other competing vegetation and allow the *Scirpetum* to establish itself. In the *Scirpetum*, the deergrass dominates, alongside lesser amounts of heather, cross-leaved heath, common cottongrass, hare's-tail cottongrass, bog asphodel, carnation sedge and ten different species of *Sphagnum*.

Other raised bogs of interest

Apart from Fairy Water Bog, Co. Tyrone, there are several other classic sites that are worth visiting to observe raised bog in its finest form. Clara Bog (665 ha) lies some 2 km south of the village of Clara, Co. Offaly, and is one of the largest remaining raised bogs in Ireland. It has a well developed hummock and hollow surface and a fine soak system with an associated birch woodland (see p.267). Moud's Bog (550 ha), 4 km northwest of Newbridge, Co. Kildare, is one of the largest and most easterly raised bogs in Ireland. Parts of it are rather dry but in the wetter spots the typical hummock and hollow topography prevails. Heather is dominant with much hare's-tail cottongrass. There is plenty of white beak-sedge in the shallow wet depressions.

On Derrycashel Bog (8 ha), west of Termonbarry, Co. Roscommon, the traveller comes across a colony of one of the strangest plants, which has a single globular flower held high on a stiff stem. The pitcherplant has taken to the Irish raised bog like a duck to water and is now firmly established as a member

The pitcherplant thriving on a raised bog, Co. Roscommon. First introduced to Ireland in 1906, it is now an established member of the Irish flora.

of the introduced Irish flora. It is a lurid plant, made up of fat clusters of root leaves standing upright 10–15 cm high above the bog surface, and coloured purple and green. The flowers are purple, solitary, and at least 2.5 cm across. There is one at the end of a leafless stalk, standing 30–45 cm above the bog surface.[23] The leaves are curled over with fused margins to form a tube with a flap at the top. Pitcherplants are lazy insectivores, doing little to catch their flying protein other than keeping their tubular mouths open. Once the innocents have stumbled and tumbled down the tube, the slippery entrance ring and slimy walls make it impossible for them to crawl out of their trap. They drown in water contained in the tube and their proteins are digested by enzymes in the liquid.

The Derrycashel Bog colony originates from an introduction of some roots and seeds by Benjamin St George Lefroy, brought to Ireland from Canada in 1906 (not 1904 as often stated). By 1927 it had spread to cover 32 ha of the bog surface where today some 6 ha of the pitcherplant colony has been set aside for protection from turf extraction. There was an earlier introduction to Ireland, in 1892, in Lisduff raised bog, Co. Laois, but this colony had died out by 1910.[24] A number of other introductions have been made by misguided naturalists. Two other species of pitcherplant – *Sarracenia drummondii* and *S. fulva* – were also brought to Derrycashel Bog but only the common pitcherplant, *S. purpurea*, survived. Successful transplants from Derrycashel were made to Coolatore Bog, Co. Westmeath – but it was reported as not doing well in 1968 – and from Coolatore to Woodfield Bog, near Horseleap, Co. Offaly. More transplants went, in 1963, to Moneyieran Bog, northwest Mayo and to an unspecified raised bog in the Midlands. Plants were also taken to a bog near Baylough but have not been seen there since 1969. Another transplant was made in 1966 to a small bog on the Abbeyleix Estate, Co. Laois, where it had grown substantially by 1980. It is also well established on the raised bog at Moanveanlagh, east of Listowel, Co. Kerry. A small colony exists on blanket peatland at Bellacorick, Co. Mayo. The pitcherplant has proved able to adapt and to colonise extensive areas of Irish peatlands. As an alien species, it disturbs the natural ecology of this specific habitat and causes concern for the few remaining intact raised bogs.[25]

Mongan Bog (136 ha) lies 2 km east of Clonmacnoise, Co. Offaly. It has a very wet surface and exhibits perhaps the best examples of hummocks, hollows and pools of any raised bog in Ireland. It is an important roosting and feeding site for Greenland white-fronted geese which move between here, the nearby Shannon callows and the Little Brosna river callows.

Addergoole Bog (310 ha) is the most westerly example of a raised bog in Ireland. It is positioned on a flat flood plain on the eastern shore of Lough Corrib, Co. Galway. A well-developed soak system ensures that the bog's surface is very wet. At the northwesterly side a fen has grown which provides an interesting botanical contrast with the adjacent acidic community.

Formation of blanket bogs

Lowland and mountain blanket bogs are mostly confined today to the western seaboard regions and on the Wicklow and other upland areas where rainfall levels exceed 1,250 mm per year over more than 235 days. These levels of precipitation ensure that the soils are waterlogged, deprived of oxygen and acidic. The depth of the peat is usually only 2–6 m, which is shallow in comparison with raised bogs, although it is possible to find some quite deep deposits. The underlying terrain of blanket bogs is often undulating and rocky, with out-crops poking up through the vegetation skin where it thins out. While the peat formed in raised bogs is almost entirely composed of *Sphagnum* mosses, the peat from blanket bogs is much darker and made up mostly of dead grasses and sedges. However, some blanket bog peats also have much *Sphagnum*. Because blanket bog formation takes place under very wet conditions it can develop directly upon mineral soils without having to pass through the fen stage as is the case with raised bogs.

A change of climate to wetter conditions – more rainfall and more rain days – may have been the ultimate factor in triggering the start of blanket bog growth as recounted by Mitchell & Ryan.[26] Evidence comes from growth pat-terns on raised bogs. At Ballyscullion Bog, Co. Antrim, a less humus-rich type of peat, indicative of wetter conditions which inhibited the humification process, was being laid down about 4,200 years ago while on Fallahogy Bog, Co. Derry, another raised bog, it was happening about 4,450 years ago. The speed-ing up of growth on these bogs was almost certainly related to a deterioration of climatic conditions to wetter and possibly colder weather. Concurrently large areas of upland soils that had once been well drained and farmed by the Neolithic settlers (who had been in Ireland for about 1,000 years by this time), were pervaded by nutrients leaching from the surface layers into the lower stratum – i.e. 'podsolized'. They became waterlogged and overgrown by bog-rushes, *Juncus* spp., that paved the way for the growth of upland blanket bog. The timing of blanket peat initiation varies considerably throughout Ireland. A pine stump, rooted in mineral soil, and overlain by blanket peat at an alti-tude of 630 m above sea level at Tonduff North, Co. Wicklow, was dated as

Lowland blanket bogland with well developed surface water pools. Peat from these bog-lands is burnt in the Bellacorick power station, Co. Mayo – large cooling tower in distance – to generate electricity.

being some 4,200 years old, while a sample of peat taken about 2 cm above the soil at 520 m above sea level in the Liffey Head Bog, Co. Wicklow, gave an age of some 8,230 years old. Radiocarbon dates for peat initiation from blanket bog sites in the west and north have yielded figures dating from about 5,000 years ago.[27] The waterlogging of the soil was facilitated by the formation of a thin impermeable layer of leached minerals, forming what is called an 'iron pan', some 30 cm below the land surface. With no downward escape, water was trapped in the upper stratum, by now poor in minerals and acidic in nature because of the leaching. The water-loaded soil provided ideal conditions for blanket bog to spread laterally, either from some small nodes of peaty growth in shallow pools and depressions or from patches that had developed on the sides of hills and uplands. Blanket bog is able to develop and survive on slopes of up to 15°. During the spread of the blanket bog, many areas where Neolithic settlers had been farming and erected stone walls were overwhelmed. The walls marked off good pastures and lands into enclosures as has been discovered when excavations revealed their presence. While a few classic sites have already been unearthed, principally in the Belderg Valley in north Mayo, it is quite likely that very extensive areas of similar field patterns remain under other blanket bog areas, particularly along the western coastline which would have been attractive for landings by the Neolithic settlers.

A blanket bog grows generally the same way as a raised bog does. But the species involved in the process are somewhat different. There is usually less *Sphagnum* moss on blanket bogs so other species have to take on the role of occupying wet hollows, gradually building these up until they become drier and eventually become hummocks. The wet spots on the surface of blanket bogs are often dominated by white beak-sedge and as it grows, raising the level of the bog, the sedge area becomes less wet and more amenable for the growth of purple moor-grass and black bog-rush which then carry on building up the bog to a slightly higher and drier level.

Large expanses of blanket bogland can be a dreary and dull experience in the absence of any landscape relief, especially on a 'soft' drizzly day. However, a closer perusal of many sites will – as, indeed, in the case of raised bogs – show extensive remains of tree stumps and trunks, exposed by peat cutting and marking the presence of a once large and densely stocked forest of Scots pine with occasional remains of oak, downy birch and yew. The forest remains date from two different periods: the first growth, accounting for the deepest stumps, took place about 7,000 years ago, and the secondary forest growth represented by the shallower stumps goes back some 4,000 years. The secondary growth took place on top of a thin layer of humified peat, established during the first phases of blanket bog growth, sometime between 4,500 and 4,200 years ago. Climatic conditions became drier for a relatively short period, favouring the resurgence of trees and inhibiting bog expansion. Following the establishment of the secondary forest the climate became wetter again and the soils experienced renewed waterlogging. The trees died and their roots were swallowed up by the rising layers of blanket bog. In most places the depth of peat sitting on top of these stumps is 1–2 m. There are many locations for viewing the remains of the old pine forests but some of the most spectacular are at the northern end of Lough Mask, Co. Mayo and south of Louisburgh, at the north end of Doo Lough Valley, on the edge of Lough Nahaltora, also in Mayo.

On the summit plateaux of many Irish mountains, there has been severe ero-

Remains of Scots pine forest at Lough Nahaltora, Co. Mayo.

sion of former blanket bog cover. As well as the more general gullying of the peat, some tops have evidently suffered sheet erosion down to the underlying mineral soil and rock debris, leaving characteristic residual peat 'islands' 2–3 m deep and with steep, bare and receding sides. Quite often, there are recolonisation stages around the peat islands, restoring a cover of grassland, heath or even the beginnings of bog again. These features are well developed on Slieve League, Co. Donegal; Galtymore Mountain, Co. Tipperary; Mangerton Mountain, Co. Kerry; Comeragh Mountains, Co. Waterford, and the Wicklow Mountains around Lugnaquillia Mountain.

Flora of blanket bogs

The plants growing on raised and blanket bogs are generally similar with no species excluded from or restricted to either type. However, differences occur in the associations and frequencies of various species. Western blanket bogs are frequently dominated by the black bog-rush and purple moor-grass while Midland raised bogs are vegetated by *Sphagnum* mosses and heather.

The presence of black bog-rush on western blanket bogs is a conundrum, as this rush is normally found in base-rich environments, especially fens – its normal habitat elsewhere in Europe. Several explanations have been offered. One is that the higher rate of mineral deposition arising from sea spray in western Ireland might provide just sufficient minerals for the rush to survive in an otherwise hostile environment. Another factor might be the low levels of aluminium in western blanket bogs as it is known that the accumulation of this metal in the soils of base-poor mires in Britain inhibits the development of bog-rush. It may also be possible that the black bog-rush on western bogs maybe a ecotype with a nutrient physiology unlike the fen form.[28] Another explanation postulates that the high moisture levels, particularly in the western regions, may prevent blanket bogs from reaching the oxidation and aeration levels characteristic of raised bogs and consequently may not develop such high levels of acidity, a condition which might just be tolerable by the black bog-rush. Experimental investigations to address this problem were carried out by Gorham.[29] The results suggested that it was the mildness of the climate that was the factor allowing this rush to flourish on the western blanket bogs, though this does not explain its puzzling adaptation to acid conditions.

It has also been argued by Boatman that low levels of grazing and low incidences of fire on the western blanket bogs had allowed the rush to survive there, in contrast to Scotland where greater grazing pressure from herds of wild deer and domestic animals caused it to disappear during the early part of the nineteenth century.[30] But Doyle robustly refuted this hypothesis, arguing that very severe grazing pressure was a feature of most of the western blanket bog during the early nineteenth century.[31] Doyle also established that the black bog-rush was either absent or featured as a minor element in the vegetation of islands found in bog pools within the blanket bog area. The islands were effectively isolated from grazing and fire impacts.

Doyle, O'Connell & Foss examined the vegetation of 12 peat islands found in pools and small lakes in northwest Mayo blanket bogs.[32] There were marked vegetational differences between the islands and surrounding bogland. On the islands, heather grew vigorously up to 30–50 cm tall, and dominated the other vegetation, mostly juniper and crowberry. The heather scrub provided ideal conditions for the growth of four epiphytes on heather stems – *Frullania tamarisci*, *Usnea* spp., *Hypogymnia physodes* and *Frullania fragilifolia* (one island only). The additional vegetation cover allowed increased abundance of the mosses *Hypnum jutlandicum* and *Sphagnum capillifolium* and especially the lichen *Cladonia portentosa* which occurred less frequently on the open main-

Pipewort, a North American species, frequently found in bog pools and along lake margins in the west of Ireland.

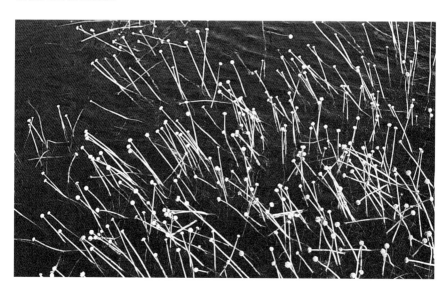

land bog where there was less vegetational cover. The heather on the open bog seldom grew higher than 20 cm and had a sparse, straggly form. Black bog-rush and purple moor-grass dominated the open bog. Differences in hydrology and isolation from fire and grazing by sheep are key factors in explaining the vegetational differences between the islands and surrounding bogland.

Blanket bogs in general exhibit a 'grassy' appearance due to the abundance and dominance of grasses and sedges. The difference between the two can often be difficult to establish. The stems of almost all sedges are triangular in cross section and their leaves are channelled. The stems of grasses, on the other hand, are usually round and their leaves generally soft with an easily removed sheath around the stem. Two ericales, bog-rosemary and cranberry, are distinctive of raised bogs and seldom found on blanket bogs – although bog-rosemary has been introduced in recent years to the Bellacorick bog complex, Co. Mayo.[33] The species which are most characteristic and abundant in lowland blanket bogs are the following:

1. Purple moor-grass, found sometimes quite large tussocks and forming extensive sheets, particularly in the drier parts of the bog. The grass is tall, up to 1 m high, and its leaves are covered with long silky hairs.

2. Deergrass, growing in much smaller tussocks, favouring the drier parts of the bog.

3. The two best-known sedge species of the bog are hare's-tail cottongrass with a single inflorescence later turning into a single cotton ball, and the more frequently occurring common cottongrass, distinguished by having 3–7 loose dropping spikelets that develop into many 'cotton heads'. The cottongrasses are scattered throughout the bog, standing high above most of the other flora, their fruiting heads in summer sporting long, white cottony hairs, bobbing backwards and forwards in the wind, like shadow boxers. In the autumn the

Common cottongrass, one of the best known sedges to be seen on blanket bogs.

leaves of the bog cottons turn to a rich reddish-brown to provide a warming colour to endless tracts that otherwise would be quite drab at that time of year.
4. Black bog-rush, rising up to 60 cm above the ground, found in the wetter parts of the bog.
5. White beak-sedge, which also seeks out the wetter areas. For some unexplained reasons it is now becoming less frequent in peatland habitats. The nutrient-rich rhizomes of both the white beak-sedge and bog cottons are the preferred foods of Greenland white-fronted geese when visiting blanket and raised bogs.

Less widely distributed in the typical lowland bog are heather and cross-leaved heath, neither attaining the same height or shrubby growth on western blanket bogs as on raised ones, probably because of excessive herbivore grazing but perhaps also because of climatic factors – weather changes, increased wetness or Atlantic winds. Bog-myrtle is one of the few woody shrubs of blanket bogs. It is also, curiously, the only species living in a true bog environment that can utilise atmospheric nitrogen with the assistance of nitrogen-fixing bacteria which live symbiotically in the root nodules. The insectivorous plants, the sundews, butterworts, pitcherplant and bladderworts are the only other species, employing different tricks to trap insects, to get their nitrogen fix from non-conventional sources. Bog asphodel, a member of the lily family, brightens up the bog with its orange-yellow flowers in July, and its deep orange fruits in August. It has a creeping rootstock, unlike other members of the family, and spreads laterally to form often extensive patches. Farmers believed that cattle grazing on it developed brittle bones, likely to break. So did William Hudson (1730–93), a London apothecary who managed the Chelsea Physic garden, and who was responsible for giving the bog asphodel its scientific name, *Narthecium ossifragum* – *ossifragum* means 'of broken bones'. For a long time scientists scorned the idea as ridiculous, but Whilde points out that chemicals contained in the plant are thought to inhibit the proper functioning of vitamin D, thus giving rise to rickets.[34]

Three other frequent bog dwellers and well-known exponents of trapping insects are the following sundews: the oblong-leaved (locally frequent in the west, unknown in the east), round-leaved (frequent and locally abundant on bogs) and great (locally frequent in the northwest, west, and parts of central Ireland, rare elsewhere). Around their circumference their small leaves sport thin red needle-like extensions of eyelash-like proportions, each armed with a drop of sticky liquid secreted by special cells in the highly modified leaf. Once an insect is stuck to the droplets it is slowly digested by special enzymes secreted from short glandular hairs on the leaf surface.

A weird liverwort, *Pleurozia purpurea*, very dark purple, and worm-like in shape, and the green and black moss *Campylopus atrovirens* provide bizarre diversity and colour to the bog. Where the flat peatland surface opens up to form small shallow pools, the muscular and leathery-looking bogbean grows profusely, shooting up its green fleshy stems to carry pink and white flowers whose their fringed petals give the inflorescence a hairy look. Also in the ponds is the bog pondweed with its floating, often reddish, leaves. Their energy-rich nutlets are eagerly sought after by mallard and teal in the autumn and winter.

There are many fine examples of both lowland and upland blanket bog in Co. Mayo which are worth visiting. The Owenboy Bog National Nature Reserve extends some 480 ha south of Eskeragh on the Ballina to Belmullet road, about 8 km east of the desolate-looking Bellacorick peat-burning power station. This extensive area of Atlantic blanket bog exhibits, in parts, a vegetation closer to that expected on a raised bog. There are many mineral-rich flushes surrounded by interesting mosses, dry heathy ridges and some poor quality fens. Sections of the bog are dangerous to walk over because of deep pools. Greenland white-fronted geese gather here to feed on bog cottongrass stolons and other high energy foods. In the same region, albeit further west, lies another fine lowland blanket bog of which 732 ha are protected as the Knockmoyle National Nature Reserve. The reserve lies north of the Bord na Móna works at Bellacorick and between two tributaries of the Oweniny River. Access to the Nature Reserve at Knockmoyle is by road, north from Bellacorick, but walking the reserve terrain can be both difficult and dangerous due to many wet bog holes. To the west of the reserve is the ruin of Sheskin Lodge, once used as a retreat by the writer and naturalist T.H. White during the winter of 1939–40. White wrote about the Lodge in his diary: 'This has two or three miles of the Owenmore and about 10,000 bad acres of grouse. We might get between 6 and 60 salmon, and between 20 and 50 brace of grouse, according to the weather and season.'[35] When in residence at Sheskin he started to write *The Godstone and the Blackymore*,[36] an account of his adventures and shooting expeditions in west Mayo, which, together with W.H. Maxwell's *Wild Sports of the West*,[37] are compulsory reading for anyone with an interest in the natural history of western Ireland.

In July 1957 Tom Barry discovered a remarkable mineral (iron) flush in the wilderness of the Bellacorick Bog, some 4 km northeast of Bellacorick. Set in this, the largest and most desolate lowland blanket bog in Ireland, the flush provides the right ecological conditions to sustain a remarkable gathering of rare mosses, ferns and flowering plants. How the flush acquired its botanical prosperity is difficult to discern. The flush species could have been formerly widespread throughout the north Mayo area, and, as the bogs formed, sprawling out across the landscape, the species depending on minerals became more and more restricted until they were finally focused into the flush area. Or the plants could have arrived by other means, such as by animal dispersal – seeds stuck into the mud on feet of migratory waterfowl – after the bog formation when the flush provided the only conditions where they could grow amidst a hostile acidic environment. Whatever the explanation, purple moor-grass, sedges, bog cottongrass, great fen-sedge and common reed are the commonest species surrounding the flush. Visiting the area in October 1957 Scannell discovered marsh saxifrage growing in the company of lesser spearwort, marsh arrowgrass, bogbean and sedges surrounded by wild angelica and common reed.[38] It was a new site for the marsh saxifrage in the county. Until its discovery here it had only previous been known from six locations in Ireland: on lowland peat bogs in the Midlands – in Tipperary, Westmeath, Offaly and Laois – at a site in Co. Antrim (Garron plateau – see p.109) and at another in a bog west of Belderg, Co. Mayo, all records dating back from the middle to the end of last century. By 1970 it had almost certainly disappeared from its Midland sites and was only known from a single station in Co. Mayo (the 1957 record above) and in Co. Antrim. In 1987 Lockhart discovered three other stations in Co. Mayo – at small mineral flushes on the Nephin Beg mountain range, at an altitude of about 150 m above sea level. Two sites were within about 200 m of each other some 2.5 km northeast of Maumykelly; the third was about 5 km further south, some 2 km southeast of Lough Nambrackkeagh.[39]

Marsh saxifrage is a boreal, circumpolar species of wet bogs. The plant is low, loosely tufted or mat-forming with reddish-brown hairs on the stems and leaf stalks. The flowering stem is erect, 15–35 cm high, bearing only a few flowers (June–September) with bright yellow petals which are sometimes spotted with red. At its Nephin Beg sites it grows in moss dominated lawns which at two sites contained the rare boreal relict moss *Homalothecium nitens.*

At the Bellacorick flush two mosses, *Meesia triquetra* – new to Ireland and not found in Britain – and *Homalothecium nitens* – then also new to Ireland – were gathered during the 1957 investigations.[40,41] A fuller vegetation description of the flush flora was later provided, including alpine scurvygrass, another new record for the district.[42] Later Synnott discovered both the marsh fern and bog orchid at the Bellacorick flush, both new records from west Mayo.[43]

Further southwest towards Nephin Beg Mountain (627 m) lies the largest intact river catchment with undisturbed lowland blanket bog in Ireland. The Owenduff Bog extends over some 6,000 ha to the west of the mountain range. Within the bog is a diversity of habitats ranging from streams, rivers, lakes, mountain heaths to, of course, blanket bog. Large and conspicuous hummocks of the woolly fringe-moss can be seen covering large areas. The region is now included in a new National Park which has as its main objective the protection of the valuable peatland ecosystems and landscapes (see p.441). In Co. Donegal, Lough Barra Bog (1,121 ha), one of the few examples of lowland blanket bog in the county, lies south of the Glenveagh National Park. Many small lakes and pools occur on its surface with the additional relief of the River Gweebarra running through it. This is important habitat for golden plovers, merlins and Greenland white-fronted geese. Within Glenveagh National Park the small, dome-shaped Derrybeg Bog (19 ha) sits at the head of Lough Beagh. Although it resembles a Midland raised bog in shape it is occupied by a characteristic lowland blanket bog vegetation.

The Slieve Bloom Mountains, straddling Counties Offaly and Laois, contain fine examples of upland blanket bogland with luxuriant growth of heaths, not damaged by overgrazing, and extensive carpets of *Sphagnum* mosses and lichens.

The Black Bog (194 ha), Co. Tyrone, is one of the largest intact blanket bogs in Northern Ireland. There are many hummock, hollow and pool areas on its surface as well as an infilled bog lake. Butterflies such as the marsh fritillary and the green hairstreak are frequently seen here. Other good examples of blanket bogs in Co. Tyrone are Moneygal Bog (122 ha) near Castlederg which has a well-developed dome with large *Sphagnum* hummocks, Mullyfamore (13 ha), which is a feeding site for the Greenland white-fronted goose and Teal Lough and Slaghtfreeden Bog (240 ha), north of Cookstown.

At Craig-na-Shoke, Co. Derry, there is a small National Nature Reserve covering 90 ha of mountain blanket bog, which at its highest point (560 m) shows classical signs of erosion brought on by weathering with isolated peat hags and erosion channels. A large area of lowland blanket bog displaying a well-developed system of hummocks and hollows on its surface occurs at Lough Naman Bog (41 ha), Co. Fermanagh and is protected as a National Nature Reserve.

Formation of fens

Fens are generally shallow water bodies found in the lowlands – especially the Midlands – and have alkaline and mineral-rich waters supplied from underground or surface sources. Fens covered large areas some 7,500 years ago. Most of them evolved into raised bogs and those that survive today have been modified, in one way or another, by the actions of man. Fens are interesting because of their rich and varied vegetation reflecting mineral-rich and alkaline waters (pH above 7). Within any fen ecosystem there may be many habitats: open waters with floating or emergent vegetation; extensive reed and sedge beds that encircle and often penetrate the whole water body; 'fen carr', a special type of damp or wet woodland, in the driest parts of the fen, and finally a thin skin of sedges and rushes rising from squidgy peat, forming a trembling and dangerous surface to walk upon. In comparison with raised and blanket bogs there are significantly more plant species in fens – up to 200 compared with perhaps less than 150 in the raised or blanket bogs. The bottom of the fen is usually lined with a thin layer of black fen peat, made up of the remains of rushes and the so-called 'brown' fen mosses often coated in calcium, sitting on a layer of white marl.

It was not until the work of Duff & Small in June 1928 that fen, as a vegetation community, was discovered in Ireland at Lough Neagh. Previously no distinction had been made between the acid peatlands and the fenlands in Ireland. This was done by Duff & Small through measurement of the water pH and vegetation comparisons with the fenlands of East Anglia.[44] Soon afterwards White published the second paper on the fens of Lough Neagh[45] from which Tansley concluded that they were probably the most extensive fenlands remaining unspoiled in Britain and Ireland.[46] Since then successive lowerings of the Lough have starved the fen and carr communities of their essential water supply. Stony and sandy shores now form much of the shorelines.

In her paper – which drew upon Duff's survey of the ecology of the Moss Lane region in 1928[44] – White defined the Irish fen as 'characterised by an assemblage of over one hundred woody and herbaceous species, by a peaty soil, by neutral or alkaline ground water, which varies from several inches below the soil surface in summer to as much as several feet above it in winter and early spring.' In White's time, the fen community extended in a strip along the shoreline, one to several hundred metres wide, stretching southwards from Washing Bay shore and fringing the southern and southeastern shore up to Hog Point over a distance of approximately 40 km. White identified three plant associations in the fen: the fen, fen carr and swamp carr, each with its characteristic species. The fen areas were submerged in 30–90 cm water from October to March each year.

Flora of fens

The commonest sedges and grasses in a typical fen are black bog-rush, great fen-sedge, common reed and purple moor-grass. Intermingled between these species – which sometimes occur in quite extensive patches – are other typical fen species such as wild angelica, hemp-agrimony, broadleaved cottongrass, fen rush, long-stalked yellow sedge, slender sedge, lesser pond-sedge and several orchids including some scarce species in Ireland such as early marsh orchid, fragrant and fly orchids. The aquatic species include stoneworts, often heavily encrusted with lime, duckweed, fen pondweed and fan-leaved water-crowfoot.

Scragh Bog (16 ha), Co. Westmeath, is perhaps the finest fen of its kind in Ireland. In the words of Praeger 'it is a long narrow lake on the limestone,

entirely covered by a thick felt of vegetation, so that it can be traversed on foot
from end to end by the venturesome'.[47] It contains a wide range of habitats
from open water to fen carr. The floating mat of sedges covering much of the
fen is made up principally of the following sedges: lesser tussock, bog, flea,
slender, dioecious, fibrous tussock, great fen and the bogbean. Scragh Bog is
the Irish headquarters of the rare round-leaved wintergreen, which is found
growing in mossy tussocks or amongst clumps of grey and eared willows together with cranberry. This wintergreen has been recorded from only 12 sites within Ireland, eight of which are located in Co. Westmeath. It appears to be
increasing in range despite living in vulnerable habitats.[19] In the shallow
waters and drains running into the fen are fen pondweed, frogbit and the rare
stonewort *Nitella tenuissima*.

The other classic fen in Ireland is Pollardstown Fen (225 ha), the largest
remaining calcareous, spring-fed fen in Ireland. Located some 3 km northeast
of Newbridge, Co. Kildare, on the north side of the great glacial gravel dump
of the Curragh, it boasts the biggest expanse of the great fen-sedge in Ireland.
The depth from its surface to the marl base was found to be 5.2 m in 1961. At
present, the place is in transition between a traditional fen and a raised bog, as
testified by the presence in parts of the upper vegetation stratum of characteristic acid-loving plants that can thrive, isolated from the underlying base-
rich soil and water. Heather, *Sphagnum* mosses and cross-leaved heath are the
principal indicators of the advent of acidic conditions. Common in the fen
proper are common reed, the great fen-sedge, black bog-rush, blunt-flowered
rush and glaucous sedge. In the wet areas there are bogbean, intermediate
bladderwort and fen pondweed.

Pollardstown Fen, near Newbridge, Co. Kildare.

Fauna of peatlands

There are very few specialist animals, apart from some insects – such as the widely distributed sawfly *Tenthredo moniliata,* only associated with the bogbean – that are dependent upon peatland ecosystems.[48] To most creatures, raised and blanket bogs are hostile environments, akin to cold deserts with low levels of nutrients, poor shelter and little cover. Fens offer more comfort through their greater vegetational diversity and mineral-rich waters. Consequently they support a wider range of fauna. However, the animals that do inhabit the barren and inhospitable bogs have managed, in one way or another, to exploit this impoverished habitat.

Birds

Of all the birds that live on peatlands the red grouse is the most characteristic. Not only is it dependent upon the shoots, buds and flower heads of heather and to a lesser extent of bilberry and crowberry, for its principal food supplies, but it is an abiding resident, summer and winter, of the peatlands. The Irish red grouse was formerly thought to be an endemic subspecies (*Lagopus lagopus hibernicus*) of the red grouse living in Britain. However, today the Irish bird is considered taxonomically indistinguishable from its British cousin *Lagopus lagopus scoticus,* although its winter plumage tends to be paler[49] – as is that of the red grouse found on the islands of Harris and Lewis in the Outer Hebrides.[50]

Red grouse are thinly scattered throughout Ireland on lowland and upland blanket peatlands as well as on the raised bogs in the Midlands. *The New Atlas of Breeding Birds in Britain and Ireland: 1988–1991*[51] estimated that there were 1,000–5,000 breeding pairs throughout the country but the numbers are considered to be an under-recording due to inadequate observer coverage.[52] However, red grouse have been on the decline in Ireland since the 1920s. The reasons are complex but related to a deterioration in the management of the bogs, as illustrated, for instance, by the lack of rotational burning to stimulate the growth of young heather, which is essential food for the grouse. Diminished predator control, associated with the dismemberment of large estates during the past several years has also been a contributory factor. Long-term climatic shifts towards wetter conditions, less favourable for heather growth, may also have played an important role. The *coup de grâce* was delivered by EU and Irish subsidies encouraging the breeding of black-faced mountain sheep (first introduced into Ireland from Scotland in the mid-nineteenth century) with the result that excessive numbers on western upland areas in the past 25 years have wrought devastating ecological damage to moorland vegetation cover. Heather that once thrived waist-high on many western hills and upland areas has been exterminated, its dead grey stems, prostrate on bare peat, a testimony to happier days.

Research into red grouse population dynamics on the extensive lowland blanket bog around Glenamoy in northwest Mayo was carried out in the 1960s and 1970s by Watson & O'Hare.[53] Population densities were 2 or 3 pairs per km^2 compared with up to 100 pairs per km^2 on good Scottish moors. These differences were remarkable despite similarities between the growth, cover and the mineral content of the heather plants in both Mayo and Scotland. When the Glenamoy study plots on level peatland were fenced, drained and fertilised, the density of grouse increased to a more respectable level of 10–15 pairs per km^2. Fencing out the sheep alone on the hillside plots also resulted in higher grouse densities. At Glenamoy there was a higher percentage of egg losses and greater losses of chicks through predation compared with Scotland. However, these losses alone did not explain the low densities of adults at Glenamoy. It was also found that predation by foxes was a major cause of winter mortality amongst grouse at Glenamoy.[54]

Another characteristic bird of blanket bogland is the golden plover, classified as a threatened species in the *Irish Red Data Book*.[55] These plovers breed in small numbers and at low densities on lowland and upland peatlands, mainly in west Galway, west Mayo, as well as in Donegal and Antrim. The total number breeding in Ireland has been estimated at 300–350 pairs.[53] Numbers, like those of the red grouse, have declined markedly during this century.

The curlew is essentially a peatland bird although it does breed in rough pasture, especially the grass meadows of the callowlands along the River Shannon. Adults return from wintering in coastal areas to the raised bogs by February while upland blanket bogs are not occupied until April. Most of the breeding grounds are vacated by the end of July. Unlike the two previous peatland breeders, the curlew, while possibly experiencing a small reduction in numbers in recent years, has a fairly healthy breeding population estimated at 12,000–15,000 pairs throughout Ireland.

Other species commonly found breeding, but in low densities, on raised and blanket bogs are the common snipe, meadow pipit, skylark, merlin and hen harrier. Both the merlin and hen harrier, like the golden plover, are classified as threatened species in Ireland. The mallard and teal also breed in smaller numbers, while the kestrel is a frequent visitor to the bogs in search of invertebrate prey and will sometimes breed in deep heather. The number of different bird species breeding on peatlands is always small. For example, a survey of 20 ha of wet lowland blanket bog, characterised by purple moor-grass, heather and common cottongrass at Letterfrack, Co. Galway, was carried out by Nicholson in 1934. Only three species represented by 28 adult birds were detected by walking through the area. These were four meadow pipits, 22 skylarks and two golden plover. The overall result of 56 breeding adults per 40 ha fell in the middle

Golden plover nest
(F. Guinness)

of the range of results from similar surveys carried out in 17 peatland areas throughout Britain.[56] Another investigation of an intact raised bog, Mongan Bog (136 ha), Co. Offaly, carried out over the 1985 breeding season, found a similarly impoverished bird population, with only four definite breeding species. The wetter conditions on the raised bog allowed the mallard and common snipe to breed. Both the ubiquitous meadow pipit and skylark were present. The curlew was strongly suspected, but not proven, as a breeder. The small number of species breeding on Mongan Bog was considered to be typical of most Irish raised bogs. When compared with a representative range of western blanket peatlands raised bogs harbour even fewer breeding species.[57]

Watson & O'Hare conducted systematic counts for birds and mammals over an extensive area of unfenced and chemically untreated lowland Atlantic blanket bog at Glenamoy, Co. Mayo.[58] Their results were as expected – few species of birds and mammals occurred and their density was low. Numbers in spring fluctuated considerably between years. The mammals recorded included hares (average density about 1 km^2, range 0–5 km^2) and very few foxes, badgers, otters and small unidentified rodents. Eleven species of birds were recorded (Table 4.1).

Table 4.1 Number of birds recorded on lowland Atlantic peatland at Glenamoy, Co. Mayo. (data from Watson and O'Hare.[58])

Species	Spring (3,575 hectares)	August (2,937 hectares)
Meadow pipit	567	509
Skylark	199	375
Red grouse	188	172
Snipe	176	81
Golden plover	60	3
Mallard	13	0
Raven	0	12
Stonechat	0	9
Wren	6	1
Jack snipe	6	0
Pied wagtail	4	0

If shrub vegetation, such as willow, birch or gorse, occurs on the bog, additional species of birds are attracted. These would typically include linnet, stonechat and whinchat. If the terrain of a blanket bogland is rocky and rough enough, it will appeal to wheatears. Finally, hooded crows are frequent inhabitants of blanket bog areas, surviving as consummate scavengers of carrion, eggs, young of birds and frogs. They breed wherever they find small trees or shrubs.

The Greenland white-fronted goose was traditionally known as the 'bog goose' because of its historical preference for blanket and raised bogs where it found both space and isolation from man. Moreover there was an abundant supply of energy-rich stolons in the white beak-sedge, the principal food plant taken by the geese.[59] However, over the years and with increasing disturbance from the commercial development of bogs, the goose has discovered equally productive feeding habitats in the rich callowlands along the Shannon and Little Brosna river valleys, in turloughs, on improved grasslands, and especially on intensively cultivated farmland such as the Wexford Slobs, Co. Wexford.

Fens support a larger and more complex breeding population of birds than found on blanket or raised bogs because of the more diverse vegetation. Amongst the passerines, reed buntings, *Emberiza schoeniclus*, and sedge warblers, *Acrocephalus schoenobaenus*, nest in reed beds, their specific names reflecting the generic name *Schoenus* of the black bog-rush, a common constituent of fens. The great fen reed beds in the Central Plain and elsewhere in Ireland once echoed the booming bittern, extinct as a breeding species since the 1840s. The last days of the bittern make sad reading – a story of both direct and indirect persecution through drainage and repeated shooting resulting in the bittern being progressively banished from the island of Ireland. Today it is only recorded as a scarce vagrant, mostly during the winter months, but 'booming' echoed through the landscape in Offaly, Clare and Wicklow a few years before 1940, in May 1945 and spring 1962 respectively.[60,61] Would the bittern make a suitable case for re-introduction in the new millennium? The reed warbler is only a recent colonist in Ireland and, although now breeding regularly, occurs mainly in eastern and southern coastal localities.[52]

On the open and marshy ground around fenlands, lapwing and common snipe breed. The birch and willow trees of fen carr attract breeding willow warblers, chiffchaffs, blackbirds, song thrush and the dunnock. Where there is open water the characteristic species are little grebe, moorhen, coot and mute swan. Teal and mallard are also frequently breeders while the water rail is probably more widely distributed than records suggest. The redshank and black-headed gull are other fen or edge nesters.

Mammals

The most likely mammal to be encountered on blanket and raised bogs is the Irish hare. In Europe and Britain the Arctic, or mountain, hare generally keeps to the high ground, but in Ireland it behaves like some of the arctic-alpine plants, which seem just as happy at low levels as at high altitudes. The Irish hare possibly evolved a wider ecological range to fill the unoccupied lowland niches which in Britain are populated by the brown hare. As a further difference, the Irish subspecies does not assume the Arctic hare's complete white winter colouring, generally only managing a whitening of the ears, feet and tail. In summer they are a warm reddish-brown. Although Irish hares are the only Irish mammal to be generally but infrequently seen on blanket or raised bogs, it is not their optimal habitat.

A hare survey carried out from 1967 to the early 1970s in a study area consisting of blanket bog and low hillsides characterised by black bog-rush, purple moor-grass and some dwarf heather around Glenamoy in west Mayo, produced an average of one hare per km^2, a density similar to higher altitude and apparently more suitable arctic-alpine habitat in west Scotland. Where the bog at Glenamoy had been converted into agricultural grassland with increased cover provided by lodgepole pine and shelter belts, densities initially peaked at 125 per km^2 before settling down to a less crowded 40–50 per km^2.

Factors which would appear to be controlling the number of hares on the boglands are the nutritional value and availability of food, cover/shelter and the abundance of predators. With regard to the Irish hare's diet, a study of the stomach contents of 20 animals shot in the highlands of Co. Antrim in winter showed that the food taken was made up of upland grasses (44%), heather (28%), bog cottongrasses (15%), sedges (10%) and other vegetation (2%). In the case of the mountain hares in Scotland heather accounts for approximately 90% of the winter diet.[62]

The other hare present in Ireland is the brown hare. It was introduced many times from Britain during the nineteenth century – possibly as a source of food for the table – but few hares are believed to have been surviving in the areas of introduction by 1900. There were four recorded introductions in Co. Cork (Ballyhooly, Castlemartyr, Castle Hyde and Trabolgan) from about 1845 to about 1882. Extensive examinations of hundreds of hares in the field in Counties Waterford and Cork by Smiddy over a 20 year period have failed to turn up any hares other than Irish hares and it is unlikely that any of the introduced creatures survived in that region.[63] Up-to-date information on the brown hare's present-day distribution elsewhere in Ireland is lacking but populations would appear to have established themselves in Fermanagh, Derry and Donegal. Their preferred habitat is agricultural land, extending up the edge of mountain peatlands.

Amongst the other mammals to be found on peatlands are the wood mouse and pigmy shrew, both in very low densities. In a study of their abundance on the blanket boglands at Glenamoy, Co. Mayo, traps were set in three separate areas of bogland: (i) drained, fertilised and fenced; (ii) fenced only; (iii) a 'control' area –unfenced, undrained, and not fertilised. Ten times the number of wood mice were caught in the treated area (maximum of 7.7 per ha) than in the control zone (0.8 per ha) while the fenced area produced intermediate numbers. Only five shrews were caught, all on the treated plot.[64]

Otters are also recorded on lowland blanket bogs, especially when close to the sea or rivers, and there have been several records of them establishing their breeding holts in bog banks. Their presence is linked to that of frogs, whose numbers on a bog can often be extremely high, thus offering an abundant supply of food. Fairley found frog remains in 93% of otter spraints collected from watercourse localities in south Mayo and Co. Galway during March 1984.[65] These results support other findings from Scotland where the frog can, under certain circumstances form an important dietary item for otters. Badgers generally avoid peatlands, where food resources and cover are inadequate. However, it is not unusual for badgers to make their setts in the dry margins of bogs or under large boulders.[66]

Amphibians and reptiles

The European frog is more common in fens than bogs. It is surprising to come across frogs in upland blanket bogs at heights up to 400 m, but it does happen. They can also be extremely numerous in mountain summit pools. In the same way, one would not expect to see the common lizard, *Lacerta vivipara* – the only lizard in Ireland – in boglands, but it is not unusual to spot one sunning itself on a rock or piece of wood. *Vivipara* means that the female retains the eggs inside her body until they hatch. The smooth newt – the only newt in Ireland – comes as a surprise to many people as it is not well known. It is often confused with the viviparous lizard and it occurs in small numbers in some bogs but is more frequently seen in fens.

Invertebrates

Snails and slugs turn up quite frequently on blanket bogs, but are least frequent on raised bogs. In an environment markedly deficient in lime they face the difficulty of gaining enough calcium to build their protective shells. Hence the only mollusc in upland blanket bogs is the large and glistening black slug *Arion ater* which carries the remnant of a shell inside its body rather than outside it. This slug is the largest invertebrate found on peatlands. Fens with their alkaline and mineral-rich habitat offer more prospects to molluscs.

Because there is little protection from storms, high winds and rainfall, a lack of wintering sites and no continual supply of food, few species of insects live exclusively on the bogs. However, that is not to say that peatlands have few insects. For example, a survey on Mongan Bog, Co. Offaly, recorded over 150 species of moths and butterflies.[67] Amongst the butterflies and moths only the large heath butterfly could be described as a bog dweller. It is seldom found in other habitats. This greyish-brown lepidopteran, fairly widespread throughout Ireland and locally abundant on wet boggy peatlands up to 300 m, is on the wing from July till the end of the summer and has a characteristic zigzag flight as it flits along looking for nectar. The caterpillar reputedly feeds on purple moor-grass, cottongrass and also on white beak-sedge when it is available.

The green hairstreak – which is not so restricted to boglands – has green underwings and brown upper ones, and always sits with its wings folded. Its bright green larva is frequently seen feeding on heather, gorse and broom. Amongst the other butterflies and moths most likely to be encountered on peatland is the emperor moth. The males fly rapidly around the bog during day with the remarkable ability to detect females up to 2 km away. The female flies and lays her eggs at night. They are both sometimes extremely numerous on bogs. The young caterpillar starts life coloured black and orange and later turns green, feeding on heather from late May until the end of the summer. Its large, pear-shaped and silken cocoon is often found empty on the bog. The fox moth is one of the commonest moth species on wet bogland dominated by purple moor-grass. It occurs throughout Ireland. The male flies both during the day and at night while the female only ventures forth at night. Both sexes are brown. Their larvae are velvety black and feed on heath. The northern eggar moth, which has similar larvae, is also seen in bogland.

The rapid exploitation and total loss of many raised bogs in recent years has focused the attention of zoologists on the need to investigate insects that might be considered tyrphobiont species, i.e. those obligatorily associated with peatlands. Bond visited Mongan raised bog, Co. Offaly, 12 times between 1983 and 1987 to study the lepidoptera there. He found 31 local or rare species. The following list, based mainly on the Mongan bog investigations, could be considered to embrace Irish tyrphobiont lepidoptera.[68]

1. *Biselachista serricornis*	Only one Irish specimen known.
2. *Aristotelia ericinella*	All Irish records from raised bogs.
3. Large heath	Records from raised bogs and lower level blanket bogs.
4. Purple-bordered gold	Very local species.
5. *Thumatha senex*	Very few Irish records, but occasionally occurs in other habitats too.
6. *Celaena haworthii*	A few records from mountain areas too.
7. Beautiful yellow underwing	? also on blanket bog.

Two other lepidopteran species that were not recorded at Mongan Bog were considered to be good indicators of raised bog: *Catoptria margaritella* (seen in large numbers on a raised bog near Daingean, Co. Offaly, on 22 July 1976) and *Xenolechia aethiops* (seen at two other raised bog sites in Co. Offaly, but nowhere else in Ireland). Other surveys by Good and Higgins concerning terrestrial insects and spiders respectively failed to discover any species considered tyrphobiont.[69,70]

Bond carried out a preliminary survey of the butterflies and moths of Pollardstown Fen, Co. Kildare, extending over seven days in 1984, 1989 and 1990.[71] The fen contained a distinctive and highly interesting fauna and amongst the 159 species recorded there were several fenland moths scarce in Ireland, including the first recording for the country of a cosmopterigid moth, *Cosmopterix lienigiella*, which is reported to feed on the common reed. The moth *Elachista triatomea* was also found – its first published recording in Ireland. The importance of Pollardstown fen as an insect habitat is also supported by the discovery of a hoverfly *Platycheirus amplus* here in 1988 by Speight & Vockeroth. This was its first recording in Ireland and Europe.[72]

A total of 58 spider species have been recorded in the fen. During recent surveys in 1993 and 1994, van Helsdingen found 52 species including two new to Ireland – *Pirata tenuitarsis* and *Centromerus levitarsis* – and 17 new to Co. Kildare.[73]

Two dragonflies commonly occur on bogs: the four-spotted chaser (a brown-bodied creature with a brown triangle at the base of its hind wings) and the black darter (the female has a brown body with a black triangle on the thorax and yellow bases to the wings, the adult male is jet black). Bogs play host to two damselflies: the emerald damselfly, the female of which has an entirely bronze-green body with reddish-green eyes, and the large red damselfly, *Pyrrhosoma nymphula*, with a bright red body and black legs.

A representative list of dragonflies and damselflies on the Brackagh Moss Nature Reserve (110 ha) in Co. Armagh, were recorded between June and September 1977.[74] The nature reserve is a cut-over blanket bog where peat extraction ceased around the turn of the century. The old peat cuttings are flooded with characteristic plants such as bogbean and bottle sedge. Most of the species were caught flying over the pools. They were the brown hawker, a hawker dragonfly easily distinguished by its amber wing membrane; the four-spotted chaser; the commonest of the *Sympetrums*, the common darter and black darter; the banded demoiselle; the emerald damselfly; the blue-tailed damselfly; the azure damselfly and the variable damselfly.

The most conspicuous terrestrial insect to be encountered on the bog is the large, sun-loving, marsh grasshopper. A dark green creature extending about 3 cm from head to tail, it prefers sheltered areas with extensive coverage of *Sphagnum* mosses and is often associated with bog asphodel and cottongrass. The normal call of the male is a soft ticking sound made by tapping the forewing with the hind tibia. It is most commonly seen during August and September, especially on wet bogs in Kerry, Galway and Mayo and less usually on Midland raised bogs. In flight its large body resembles a locust. The mottled grasshopper is also frequent and was the only grasshopper species found in the lowland blanket bog at Glenamoy, Co. Mayo, during the International Biological Programme investigations, 1960–80. Its population density was estimated at about 0.02 individuals per m^2 with a strongly clustered distribution.[75]

One group of animals that appears to thrive in peatland are roundworms, or nematodes, which are adapted to survive in this marginal habitat. About 49 genera with about 80 species were detected living in the blanket bogland at Glenamoy, Co. Mayo, with a mean density of 500,000 individuals per 2.6 km^2. One of the remarkable features of the Irish lowland blanket bog is that there are two to three times as many species of nematodes, collembolans and enchytraeids as would normally be found in a comparable area of mineral soil.[75]

Moth flies are small, hairy midge-like flies with scale-covered wings. Sixty species have been recorded from Ireland and one of them, *Sycorax silacea*, has close association with fenland. Haliday gave the first description of it in 1839, based on a specimen collected in Hollywood, Co. Down. The adult females are reputed to suck blood, especially from amphibians such as the European frog. Another moth fly and a great rarity is *Telmatoscopus maynei*, known only from three localities, including the Scragh Bog, Co. Westmeath.[76]

Three species of flightless water beetles belonging to the family Dytiscidae and indicative of old wetlands, were also found at Scragh Bog, and in another nearby fen close to Monintown, in August 1986.[77] They were *Hydroporus glabriusculus*, *H. scalesianus* and *Lacornis oblongus*. All are endangered species in much of Europe but in Co. Westmeath they are presently safe from drainage and agriculture intensification.

5

Lakes and Rivers

As Praeger pointed out in his *Natural History of Ireland*, this is essentially a country of lakes – from Lough Neagh, the largest sheet of fresh water in Ireland or Britain, down to hundreds of lowland meres and mountain tarns. The generally high levels of precipitation, the soils' high clay content, and the complex drainage systems in the concavity of Central Ireland have all conspired to create a mosaic of water wonderlands orbiting around the great liquid spine of the River Shannon. Arising in the highlands of Co. Leitrim, this languid river ambles slowly through the Midlands, fanning out into the vast Loughs Allen, Ree and Derg, sometimes spilling out over its banks onto the adjacent low-lying callowlands between Athlone and Portumna, before passing into the shallow, muddy vastness of the Shannon Estuary and disappearing into the sea.

Many parts of Ireland are also peppered with a bewildering number of lakes and rivers, small, medium, and large, many acidic and others calcareous, most fringed by reeds and rushes, many supporting floating or submerged vegetation. Coarse fish cruise in the more still waters while the network of faster flowing rivers provide conduits for the elusive salmon and silvery sea trout. These two species glide and thrash between the worlds of salt and fresh water, driven by a genetic impetus. What Ireland may lack in mountains and broadleaved woodlands is more than adequately compensated by an aquatic heritage of lakes, pools and rivers.

The world of fish is a complex *mélange* of native and extrinsic species manipulated by man since the arrival of the Normans in the twelfth century, and more especially over the past 300 years. In this aquatic milieu several mammals suited for a wet life are also found. Some, too, are interlopers, such as the notorious escapees from commercial fur farms.

Two freshwater invertebrates have teased the imagination of Irish naturalists and provided economic gain for many fishermen. The first is the freshwater crayfish and the second is the freshwater pearl mussel. This is capable of producing fine quality pearls, and has been greatly esteemed since one was presented to Anselm, Archbishop of Canterbury by Gilbert, Bishop of Limerick in 1094.[1] Amongst the birds exclusively dependent upon the freshwater habitat are the kingfisher, Irish dipper and grey wagtail, while a range of non-passerine species from the little grebe and tufted duck to the Canada goose require lakes or sluggish rivers for their breeding activities. Others such as the grey heron and common sandpiper also need the proximity of water to feed. The much reviled piscivorous cormorant also works the waterways, removing fish as it passes by. Finally from the first days of autumn, when migration begins, Ireland's broad range of wetlands plays host to tens of thousands of wildfowl and waders streaming down from the Arctic and other northerly latitudes in search of food and warmer climes.

This chapter describes the physical and biological characteristics of the principal Irish lakes, explores the origin and general ecology of two giants, Loughs

Grey heron, widespread throughout Ireland but generally nesting only in small colonies (J. Barlee).

Neagh and Corrib, and considers rivers, focusing on crayfish and mussels, dippers and kingfishers, as well as Ireland's ubiquitous aquatic mammal, the otter. Finally the history and ecological impact of two alien aquatic mammals, the muskrat, now extinct, and the mink, very much alive, are assessed.

Lakes

Approximately 2% of the total surface area of Ireland is covered by about 4,000 lakes extending over some 168,000 ha. Very few are large – only 23 exceed 1,000 ha while most are less than 100 ha. All Irish lakes except Lough Neagh, and the turloughs set in Carboniferous limestone, originated through glacial action and the scooping out by the advancing ice sheets of gigantic basins.[2] Supporting evidence comes from the configuration of the lake bottoms which shows, in the cases of Loughs Erne, Ree, Derg, Corrib and Mask, straight deep trenches and submerged scarps. These troughs suggest the dislodging and dragging away of large longitudinal slabs along joint or fault points by shifting ice. In contrast, the floor of Lough Neagh is generally even, the result of a downward slump in the basalt rocks some 35 million years ago which created a depression later to be filled with water.

Virtually all Irish lakes are shallow. Lough Ree, Co. Westmeath, for instance, is generally less than 6–9 m deep. A line of deeper soundings, ranging from 16–34 m, with the deepest of 36 m measured to the west of the island of Inchmore, stretches from the north to the south. This is the result of the glacial dislodging phenomenon mentioned above. Lough Derg, Co. Tipperary, has a shallow northern section which is 3–6 m deep with a maximum of 13.5 m, and troughs of 30 m in the south section. The east-west section from Scarriff Bay to Youghal Bay reaches down to a maximum of 36 m. The southern portion of the Lough is scarred by a north-south gully whose depth varies from 27 m to a maximum of 34 m. Lough Mask, Co. Mayo has a shallow eastern half and also a narrow glacial trench, running parallel to the western shore, where the greatest depths measured are 56–58 m.

Nearly all of Ireland's largest lakes repose on limestone rocks and entertain a richer flora and fauna than water bodies set on acidic rocks because of the greater availability of nutrients. Lake water quality is usually assessed on three basic parameters. First, the average value of phosphorus – the growth-encouraging nutrient. Although it occurs naturally, phosphorus also enters water bodies as organic waste such as fertiliser runoff and sewage discharges. Second, the concentration of chlorophyll *a*, the green pigment found in algae, an indicator of algal abundance. Third, the degree of water transparency, reflecting the amount of suspended material such as fine particles of soil, peat silt, as well as density of planktonic algae. Most of the largest lakes on limestone are classified as being naturally mesotrophic. The biological productivity of these mesotrophic lakes, i.e. the total mass of all living organisms, usually expressed by dry weight per unit area, is higher that those with a lower nutrient status, described as oligotrophic.

There are also high levels of dissolved calcium bicarbonate in limestone-based lakes which has conspicuous ecological consequences. For instance, most freshwater invertebrates carrying exoskeletons such as the molluscs and crustaceans depend upon a liberal supply of calcium to build up their shells and as a consequence they find it less easy or impossible to live in calcium-depleted water. Moreover, this alkaline environment induces a more rapid breakdown and recirculation of organic materials from decayed plants and animals, including the release of the important nutrient phosphorus from the muds and silts lying at the bottom. Another ecological benefit is that the particulates suspended in the waters are easily precipitated or flocculated due to chemical reactions. They fall to the lake floor, clearing the water, and allow sunlight to penetrate more deeply, thus inducing a richer growth of plants rooted on the bottom. Apart from the chemical composition of the water which greatly influences the plant and animal communities, the other key ecological factors governing aquatic life are the amount of dissolved oxygen, the speed of water movement and the temperature levels.

The size and growth rates of trout can be taken as a simple indicator of biological productivity. Alkaline waters induce faster development and contain bigger trout than their acidic counterparts.[3] They also carry a much more exuberant flora and fauna than the more nutritionally impoverished lakes found on the non-calcareous rocks and classified as oligotrophic. The latter, however, are biologically redeemed, to a certain extent, in that they are well supplied with dissolved oxygen so essential to support the 'breathing' of invertebrates and fish life. Their oxygen levels are higher than in mesotrophic waters because of the lesser presence of organic life – ranging from submerged or emergent aquatic vegetation to minute phytoplankton – drawing from the resources.

The nutrient status of several of Ireland's largest lakes has been artificially enhanced by the discharge of animal and human wastes together with excessive runoff of nitrates and phosphates from fertilisers spread on adjoining farmland. Lough Derg, Co. Tipperary, and Lough Oughter, Co. Cavan, are presently the most severely affected. They have been classified by the Environmental Protection Agency as 'strongly' and 'very' eutrophic respectively. A little eutrophication can be beneficial to plant and animal growth but after a certain point it will influence the ecology negatively. In contrast most of the smaller lakes occurring along the western fringes of Ireland, in west

Galway, west Mayo, the greatest parts of Donegal, Kerry, Cavan and Down, are poor in nutrients and generally acidic in character because of the siliceous rocks they are sitting on.

If the size of trout is a telltale sign of the trophic status of water, the presence of some plants is another good indicator. One is the fan-leaved water-crowfoot, a member of the buttercup family which occurs in lime-rich lakes and rivers and is only very rarely encountered in acidic waters. Forming dense mats, sometimes covering bank to bank, in slow ponderous rivers, it displays a startling white mass of delicate flowers, held on rigid stems above the surface. The divided, submerged leaves, especially designed to allow water to run through (like crow's feet), are spread underneath. Another lime-loving aquatic plant is the green-flowered fen pondweed whose floating leaves are usually oval while the ones underneath are lanceolate, again to offer the least resistance to water. Both types of leaves are thin and translucent, often with a reddish colour, displaying a network of opaque veins. Fen pondweed is often found growing on bare marl.

The stoneworts are a remarkable and under-appreciated group of plants that flourish best in lime-rich waters. They are algae, belonging to the class Characeae of the green algae, although their large feathery fennel-like form visible just below the surface of shallow lakes is suggestive of a higher more sophisticated stage in evolutionary terms. Last century stoneworts were classified as flowering plants. Some of their cells can be extremely large, up to 15 cm in length. They live entirely submerged, with a system of root-like rhizoids fixed onto the substrate, and are characteristic of highly calcareous – or sometimes brackish – waters. As they are sensitive to pollution their abundance provides a good biological indicator of clean waters. During the process of photosynthesis they extract carbon from the calcium bicarbonate contained in the water and secrete the residue through their cells' walls. Their rough and crunchy feel in the hand is due to this coating of lime, giving rise to their common name. Several stoneworts are found in Irish lakes such as the hedgehog stonewort (fairly widespread throughout Ireland), the coral stonewort (found only in nine locations in highly calcareous waters), the rough stonewort (widely distributed) and the lesser bearded stonewort (common in most places except in the southwest).[4] *Nitella* is another genus of stoneworts found throughout Ireland. These are taller, slender and more delicate than *Chara* spp.

Plants growing mainly in acidic lakes and waters include the six-stamened waterwort, a minute, low-creeping, often submerged plant with almost sessile (stalkless) leaves and very small white or pink flowers. The intermediate water-starwort is another small water weed with submerged linear leaves, and scarcely recognisable small flowers clumped together. The water lobelia is found in shallow water around lake margins – the stems arise from a rosette of narrow leaves to bear delicate blue flowers in a loose, graceful raceme some 15–30 cm above the surface. Another characteristic plant is the bulbous rush with tousled little flower heads. This rush occurs in two forms: on wet ground the plant is tufted with low stems; when growing in water (the variety *fluitans*) it extends up to 1 m with grass-like leaves that are either submerged or floating. Then there are the pondweeds, submerged perennials with flower spikes sporting numerous small greenish, petal-less flowers. Their fruit, or nutlets, stacked together like corn on the cob, are relished by waterfowl during the autumn

Confusing aquatic plants. From left to right: pipewort, quillwort, water lobelia and two forms of shoreweed.

and winter. Some pondweeds have floating leaves but all have submerged ones that vary in shape according to the depth and speed of the water. The bog pondweed carries both submerged leaves (lanceolate and long-stalked) and floating ones (oval or oblong, often reddish). The blunt-leaved pondweed has only submerged leaves that are linear and grass-like. Finally, the stiff-pointed quillwort is not a flowering plant – it reproduces by spores and lurks around the margins of lakes in water up to 1.5 m deep. The root knob gives rise to a dense prickly tassel of slender dark green 'quills', 7–23 cm long. The leaves have four longitudinal air canals with easily seen horizontal partitions inside that are helpful for buoyancy and separating the species from the similar look-ing water lobelia which has hollow leaves with a central longitudinal partition.

The interest that the Irish have in water dates back to prehistoric times. The Celts believed that a vast lake lay under the surface of the earth which offered a safe route to the afterlife but was also a place where knowledge was kept. That they found water in the ground when they dug it up reinforced their belief, and the outpourings from this alleged subterranean reservoir in the form of springs or wells were sacred. In the big imaginary lake were salmon growing fat and wise, snapping up hazel nuts as they fell into the water from overshadowing trees. Then once every seven years either the hazel nuts or salmon escaped and passed into the River Boyne and who ever found them was endowed with wisdom.[5]

Ireland's two largest lakes, Lough Neagh, Co. Antrim, and Lough Corrib, Co. Galway, deserve special attention in view of their ecological interest and they are highlighted here to underscore many events that are characteristic of other freshwater bodies. Lough Neagh, moreover, because of its mythological associations and the dramatic biology of the eels, holds a special grip on the Irish psyche.

Ireland's largest lake – Lough Neagh

Commenting on historical and legendary names, Joyce states 'Among the many traditions handed down by the Irish people, none are more universal than the bursting forth of lakes.'[6] Nearly all Irish lakes owe their origin to an enchanted well or fountain that was in some way insulted, whereupon it got cross and gushed forth, thus bringing ruin to the people around it. Composing his own account of the eruption in the twelfth century of Lough Neagh, Cambrensis braided together elements of early paganism and 'modern' Christianity. What happened to the area was not unlike Old Testament rebukes:

'They say that an accident was responsible for the rise of this remarkable lake. There was from ancient times in the region now covered by the lake a people very much given to vice, and particularly addicted, above any other people in Ireland, to bestiality. There was a saying well known to that people that if a certain fountain of the district which, because of a great fear of it that had been inherited from a barbarous superstition, was always covered and sealed, should be left uncovered, it would immediately overflow to such an extent that it would wipe out and destroy the whole district and people. It happened, however, that a young woman came to the fountain to draw water. She filled her vessel, and, before covering the fountain, ran quickly to her little child, because she had heard him crying where she had placed him a little way off. But "the voice of the people is the voice of God", and when she hurried back she met such an overflow from the fountain that both herself and her boy were swept off immediately. Within an hour the whole people and their flocks were overwhelmed in this local and provincial flood. The whole area was covered with a sea of water which remained there and made a permanent lake.

It looked as if the author of nature had judged that a land which had known such filthy crimes against nature was not worthy not only of its first inhabitants but of any others for the future.'[7]

According to Joyce, the ancient name of the territory was Liathmhuine. A Munster chieftain of the name Eochy Mac Maireda who had invaded the plain and expelled the inhabitants ruled at the time of the flood. All his family was killed except one daughter and two sons. The lake was called Loch-nEchach (Lough Neagh), meaning Eochy's lake.

Cambrensis reports that the lake sometimes fostered fish specimens of mythological proportions:

'There is a lake in Ulster of a remarkable size. It is thirty miles long and fifteen miles wide. From it a very beautiful river called the Bann flows into the northern ocean. Here the fishermen complain not of a scarcity of fish, but of too great catches and the breaking of their nets. In our time a fish was caught there – one that had come down from the lake, and not from the sea – which had the shape more or less of a salmon, and was of such size that it could not be dragged or carried as a whole. Accordingly it was cut up and carried about through the province.'[7]

Eight major rivers drain into Lough Neagh, supplying about 88% of the total water input. It used to be a bigger lake, when in late glacial times Lough Beg (700 ha), fed by the River Bann, and Portmore Lough (183 ha) were part of it. They are now separate entities. Lough Neagh forms an inland freshwater 'sea' with an exceptionally even bottom sloping gradually from the shore to a depth of about 15 m. There is only one deep channel, descending to about 33 m, south of Toomebridge, which would appear to have been gouged out by a tongue of ice working along a fault plane.[2] The relatively shallow waters are alkaline with a pH varying from 7.2–9.0 with a mean of 8.2. About 33% of the 125 km shoreline is made up of sheltered bays, the rest being mostly composed of rock. It was the regular historical flooding of the Lough's shores by its alkaline waters that inhibited the development of acid bogland and encouraged the growth of a fen vegetation around the margins of the Lough.

Glacial Lough Neagh. From Whittow [8].

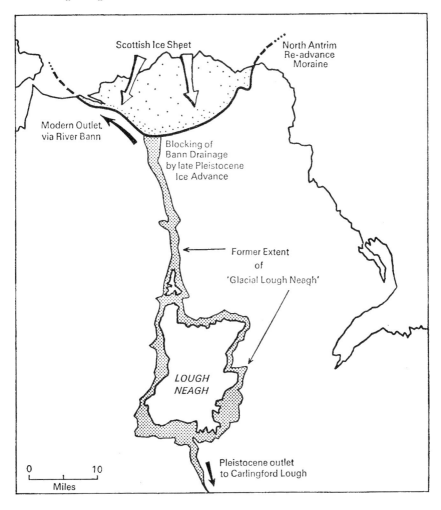

The area now occupied by Lough Neagh started life during the Carboniferous period (280–370 million years ago), when a downward slump occurred in the region. Some 65 million years ago, volcanic outpourings from the earth's bowels, spewed out through deep fissures in the North Channel, spread over the Cretaceous landscape and left behind a mantle of basalt of varying thickness. The slump was coated with basalt. Another collapse due to the weight of this volcanic material occurred some 35 million years ago, with the basin sinking to about 366 m below present-day sea levels. Initially the area must have been free-draining as no sediments were accumulated during the Palaeocene or more recent Eocene periods. The older deposits in the basin date from the Oligocene period when Lough Neagh, the oldest surviving lake in Britain or Ireland, came into being.

During the Oligocene period there was a considerable inflow of freshwater sediments in the form of unconsolidated gravel, sands, silts, muds and other materials out of which grew a sort of plug 350 m thick which filled the initial declivity and brought the Lough's bottom close to what it is today. Extending over an area of some 500 km^2, these deposits are known as the Lough Neagh Clays.

In the Pleistocene period the basin's sediments were relatively unaffected by the two major ice invasions. The first came from Scotland with glaciers moving westwards in the northern areas and southwards in the northeastern parts, thus effectively bypassing the basin. In this first invasion the Lough was positioned centrally between the ice flows, a sort of null point with little ice-sheet movement. The Lough's clay deposits remained unscathed and unplucked. However, in the final glacial phase the Lower Bann drainage near Coleraine was blocked so that the waters, instead of continuing to drain northwards as usual, overflowed southwards, following a fault valley leading through Newry to Carlingford Lough.[8] That the water levels were once higher in Lough Neagh, due to the blockage of the Lower Bann drainage, is testified by the raised beach cliffs that occur in several places on the eastern shore, a remnant of the once wider lake circumference.

Conditions in the Lough were ideal in postglacial times for a prolific growth of diatoms, microscopic aquatic plants that incorporate silica into their cell walls thus creating a sort of exoskeleton around themselves. Up to 46 species of diatoms and close relations, the desmids, or freshwater algae, made up a busy cocktail in the Lough's shallow waters.[9] When these tiny organisms died their siliceous 'exoskeletons' fell in their millions to the bottom to form compact white beds, up to 1 m deep in the Toome area. This occurred after peat deposition had already taken place, and prior to further peat deposition, so that the white material is set between layers of brown peat. The lowering of the water in the Lough makes this visible in places. Known locally as Bann Clay, the white material is wet and soap-like before being cut. When dried it retains its whiteness and becomes very light. It can be used in industry as an inert insulator or filler. Implements and hearths dating from the Neolithic period have been found in it.

The magical petrifying properties of the waters of Lough Neagh were first celebrated in 1652 when Boate's *Irelands Naturall History* was published. Unable to understand the origin of silicified wood that was washed up on the shore Boate reiterated earlier beliefs that the waters of the Lough had strange powers of fossilisation. The wood was literally as hard as stone and pieces of it

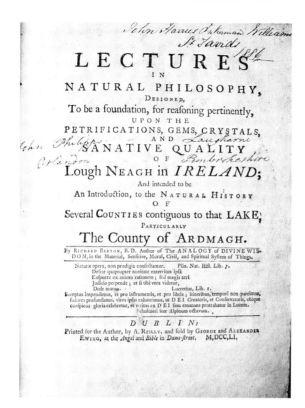

Dr. Barton's *Lectures in Natural Philosophy* (1751).

were sold in Belfast to sharpen knives and other blades. The 'magic', however, was more than likely to have happened during the Oligocene period when the wood had spent a long time marinating in silica-rich water. Drenched and saturated with this mineral it was left resembling stone. But this was not known until much later and the story of the petrifying properties of Lough Neagh continued to be uncritically protracted by many writers, notably Harris & Smith in *Ancient and Present State of the Co. Down* (1744) [10] and by Barton in his beautifully printed and illustrated book published in 1751, the title of which requires to be quoted in full in order to capture the cultural sentiments of the period: *Lectures in natural philosophy, Designed to be a foundation, for reasoning pertinently, upon the petrifications, gems, crystals, and sanitive quality of Lough Neagh in Ireland; And intended to be An Introduction to the Natural History of Several Counties contiguous to that lake, Particularly The County of Ardmagh.* [11]

The evolution of the vegetation of the Lough and its hinterlands has been summarised by Harron. [12] It appears that most of the formerly extensive fenlands fringing the Lough have been lost through a series of drainage schemes which have brought down the water levels by about 1 m since 1847–58, when the first bout of reclamations took place. Today only at Antrim Bay, Blackers Rock and Portmore Lough are there examples of the vegetation that once dominated much of the Lough's shoreline.

Apart from its fen vegetation, Lough Neagh is also celebrated as the location of five wetland plants that are generally restricted to the Lough area within

Ireland. The following records are from the *Flora of Lough Neagh* unless otherwise stated.[12]

1. RIVER WATER-CROWFOOT
Confined to three close spots: the fast-flowing Six Mile Water near to Dunadry Station; at Muckamore, lower down on the river, and for a short distance above Muckamore where the river debouches into the Lough. This is the plant's only known Irish location, first discovered by Samuel Alexander Stewart in 1865. In Britain it occurs mainly in the south and east, is rare elsewhere and absent from the northernmost areas.

2. EIGHT-STAMENED WATERWORT
Since it was first found by William Thompson in 1836[13] it has widened its distribution considerably, spreading along the Lagan canal to Belfast and then southwards. It occurs in the shallow waters around the Lough and is confined to northeast Ireland. As in Britain, where it is also found, its survival is threatened by fluctuation in water levels.

3. IRISH LADY'S TRESSES, *Spiranthes romanzoffiana* subsp. *stricta*
Widespread in North America, but within Europe it is confined to Ireland and Britain. First found by Praeger at Portadown in 1892. The subspecies S*piranthes romanzoffiana* subsp. *stricta* occurs only in the northern part of Ireland and in western Scotland while the subspecies *Spiranthes romanzoffiana* subsp. *gemmipara* has been recorded from 15 localities in south Kerry and west Cork, albeit not recently, as well as in southwest England. It also grows on the shores of Lough Corrib, Co. Galway, where, because of its variability, it might bring on a taxonomic headache if examined too closely.

4. HOLY-GRASS
First found in the reed beds at Selshan in the southeast corner of the Lough by Meikle in 1946. This is its only known location within Ireland where it covers about 17 m^2 in two spots, one on each side of Selshan drain. Rare within Britain but known from 15 localities in Scotland.[14]

5. NARROW SMALL-REED, *Calamagrostis stricta* var. *hookeri*
First found by David Moore in 1836 on a small island in the Lough and along the shore in damp meadows. Within Ireland it is known from three sites along the shore of Loughs Neagh and Beg and is on the verge of extinction as a result of drainage and land reclamation. In Britain it also occurs in a fen at Stow Bedon in Norfolk – its only known station.

One other Lough Neagh aquatic speciality had been the club sedge, first discovered by David Moore on Harbour Island near Toome in July 1835. It became extinct soon after June 1886 when it was last observed by Stewart. Grazing cattle, wandering onto the island, were almost certainly responsible for its demise. It is known in Scotland from four localities in Inverness-shire.

A curious ecological feature about the flora of Lough Neagh is the occurrence of a group of plants that in Ireland are normally almost exclusively maritime in their distribution. The reasons for their presence have teased and flummoxed many botanists. They include the rock sea-spurrey, little mouse-ear, field mouse-ear, sea mouse-ear, hare's foot-clover, sea plantain, horned pondweed, sea club-rush, grey club-rush, *Scirpus lacustris* subsp. *tabernaemontani*; long-bracted sedge (which, like the rock sea-spurrey, usually require a high degree of salinity to flourish) and the wild pansy, *Viola tricolor* subsp. *curtisii*. At Lough Neagh they are found on the generally sandy shoreline.

How these 11 came to congregate here is quite a mystery. An early explanation was that they colonised the area during a period of land submergence when the sea ingressed into the Lough basin. However, 5,000 years ago, when the sea rose for the last time, it did so by a maximum of 4 m, and the Lough is about 15 m above sea level.[15] It is therefore unlikely that any saline water following the channel of the River Bann could have entered the basin. Another, more likely, explanation is provided by the last re-advance of the Scottish ice sheets which blocked the upper part of Belfast Lough and the Lagan, then full of sea water, and created a saline lake which went on to overflow into Lough Neagh. Thus the basis for a marine environment in what is now the Lough Neagh basin area may have been laid.[16] Such an action would also explain the presence today of two other marine related and relict animals; the fish, pollan, and the ghost shrimp. As to the Arctic charr, also looked upon as a kind of 'glacial relict', it was abundant in Lough Neagh up to about 1837 but by 1847 was pronounced extinct, possibly as a result of over fishing.[17] The pollan, despite being anadromous by nature throughout the rest of its European range, ceased to be migratory once in the Lough (although, interestingly, a few were caught in the Bann estuary over 50 years ago). In other Irish lakes such as Loughs Derg and Ree on the Shannon system it is also generally sedentary apart from one incidence of migration, when quite large numbers, emanating from Lough Erne, moved downstream from fresh water to the saline waters of the Erne estuary in 1952, following the construction of the hydroelectric scheme.[18,19] They were still being caught in the estuary up to 1955, but their status there is uncertain today.

The odd phenomenon of the displaced maritime plants is paralleled by the erratic presence of six species of Lepidoptera found inland in the Lough Neagh area despite having an exclusively or an almost exclusively maritime distribution in Ireland.[20] While these are obviously not aquatic species they are discussed here in the context of the maritime plants mentioned above. They include the Noctuid moths archer's dart, white line dart and the rosy minor as well as the garden dart, galium carpet and the anomalous *Stilbia anomala*. The first three exhibit an exclusively maritime distribution elsewhere, living amongst vegetation on sand dunes. The next two are mainly maritime but have also been found inland within short distances of the coast. The final one also occurs on hills around the coastline as well as on the coasts itself. Beirne argues that the most plausible explanation for their presence at Lough Neagh is their migration there at some point in the past when there was a direct connection between Lough Neagh and the sea.[20] According to him, the six species first arrived in Ireland during the postglacial period and settled in coastal habitats where they have remained until today. In Britain and on the Continent, however, they are not restricted to the maritime zone.

Eels

Lough Neagh is famous for the teeming populations of the European eel, the only European freshwater fish that departs the Continent to spawn elsewhere. The story of the eel begins just after Christmas when the baby eels (elvers)

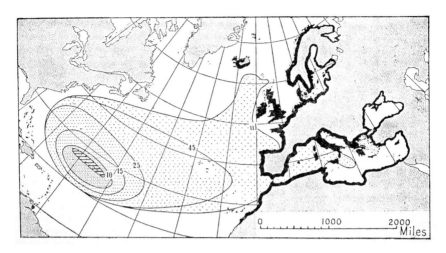

The distribution of the European eel during its various stages of development. From A. Hardy (1959) *The New Naturalist: The Open Sea: Fish and Fisheries.* Collins, London.

arrive along the Irish coastline having travelled through the Atlantic Ocean from the warm waters of the Sargasso Sea, east of the Bahamas and southwest of Bermuda, where they were born. Until recently it was thought that the trip to Europe took between two and three years. Now it is known to take only about a year. In fact calculations made clear that even if the elvers drifted passively in the North Atlantic Current, moving at speeds of 15 km per day, they would reach Europe within approximately a year. The elvers on arrival are small, 5–7 cm long, and because they are transparent they are called 'glass eels'. They lurk in the coastal waters, especially in estuaries, for a month while they pass through a period of physiological adaptation for life in a freshwater rather than a saline environment. When this has been achieved and when water temperatures have risen they wriggle their way up the rivers into the lakes where they remain until they become sexually mature. At some stage during the summer the elvers begin to feed and can be said to enter the 'yellow eel' stage.

The exodus from the estuaries to the rivers starts anytime from early February onwards and can go on until July. May is the peak month for movement. On their upward trek the elvers often travel together in dense packs, especially on dark nights to avoid predators such as other fish, larger eels already present from previous years with a taste for newcomers, or gulls. Their ability to scale apparently insurmountable obstacles such as cliffs and the walls of dams is legendary. Once in the rivers most male elvers remain within about 15 km of the estuary for their first year of life, and in subsequent years make the final journey up into the lakes.

Eels are carnivorous, eating small fish, invertebrates and even fish eggs. Moriarty examined the food remains in the stomachs of 858 eels collected from 12 large Irish lakes to find out what they were eating.[21] Their principal foods were water hog-lice, freshwater snails, non-biting midge larvae, caddis fly larvae, mayfly larvae, freshwater shrimps and fish.

In fresh water the yellow eels feed and grow until they become sexually mature, which happens from the time they are about nine years old. Their colour changes from yellow to silver, and their fat content rises from about 8% to over 30%. They are preparing for their long and sometimes much delayed journey to the Sargasso Sea. The switch from yellow to a more subdued silver may be a device to blend into the maritime environment and thus avoid predators. The bulk of silver eels migrating down the river and on to the Sargasso Sea are between 9 and 19 years of age. Some yellow eels aged 36 years have been found still feeding in Irish fresh waters while in Scotland some have been found to be over 50.[21,22] On the eve of their journey, the fully grown male silver eels are seldom longer than 50 cm and the females rarely shorter. Their migration takes place in the autumn, the greatest movements occurring on stormy dark nights with no moon when the rivers are brimming or in flood. If conditions are right most silver eels will have reached the coast by September–October.

Very few elvers are caught commercially on their incoming run up the rivers. It is on their return journey that they are trapped and harvested in their thousands every year. One of the largest eel fisheries in Europe operates at Toomebridge, just as these aquatic pilgrims leave the precincts of the lake to begin their 48 km journey down the River Bann. Any slipping through the nets might still be caught further down at Coleraine. And if they pass that point there are other fisherman awaiting them at sea, as explained in Heaney's *A Lough Neagh Sequence*, written in praise of both eel and fishermen.[23]

'At Toomebridge where it sluices towards the sea
They've set new gates and tanks against the flow.
From time to time they break the eel's journey
And lift five hundred stones in one go.

But up the shore in Antrim and Tyrone
There is a sense of fair play in the game.
The fishermen confront them one by one
And sail miles out and never learn to swim.'

Other important eel fisheries exist on the River Corrib, Co. Galway, at the entrance to Lough Corrib, and at Killaloe, Co. Clare, on the River Shannon.

Brown trout and their feeding ecology

Several varieties of brown trout have been historically recognised from Lough Neagh but today apparently only two remain – known locally as the 'dollaghan' and 'salmon trout'.[24] The survival side by side of such closely related varieties is based on the sharing out of sometimes limited food resources and the establishment of preferences. The separation of the feeding ecologies provides a mechanism for maintaining genetic isolation. In Lough Neagh significant isolation has already taken place.[24]

The general feeding pattern of the brown trout in Lough Neagh is that most of them feed benthically – on the lake bottom – during the winter months and early spring. Then they leave the depths and ascend to mid- or surface water to feed on nymphs and insects until August. During spring the larvae and pupa of long-legged gnat-like insects with their bodies longer than their wings (Chironomidae) are, along with crustacea, an important source of food for the trout. The marked abundance of chironomid fly larvae (with worm-like bodies up to 30 mm long) and pupae (which may be either free-swimming or rather immobile hard cocoons) on the bottom, and later adults, are of equal importance to the trout as to the pollan, eels and perch cruising in Lough Neagh.[25] As summer arrives both the freshwater shrimps and water hog-lice become more abundant and mobile, moving to the upper layers of the lake, and assume greater importance as food items for the trout. Unlike in many other freshwater lakes in Ireland,[26] zooplanktonic organisms such as Cladocerans – especially the water fleas *Daphnia* or *Polyphemus* – are not important food items for the trout in Lough Neagh, possibly because there is better and more nutritious fare available. The pollan, in contrast, while feeding in the benthic zones in winter and spring, consume large amounts of planktonic Cladocerans, especially *Daphnia* in the summer, thus skilfully avoiding competition for the favourites of the trout, water hog-lice and freshwater shrimps.[27]

There are five species of freshwater shrimps in Ireland, two native and three interlopers. Until recently Lough Neagh had only the native species, *Gammarus duebeni celticus*, which is confined to Ireland and Brittany.[28] It has been joined by three others which have managed to replace it in many areas of the Lough.[29] All these shrimps appear similar but can be separated on close examination by their different types of eyes.

The first interloper, *G. tigrinus*, was brought to Northern Ireland from North America during the First World War, and has become the dominant gammarid in Loughs Neagh and Erne where its superior reproductive capacity gives it an edge over the native species. It has spread through the North. In 1982 it was discovered in the stomachs of perch taken from Lough Conn, Co. Mayo.[30] The second interloper, the European *G. pulex*, was introduced to Northern Ireland from Yorkshire at the end of the 1950s to provide 'stocked' angling waters with extra feeding. It has also spread across Northern Ireland fresh waters and displaced *G. duebeni celticus* from its preferred rocky shore habitat in Lough Neagh.

The third non-native species, the North American *Crangonyx pseudogracilis*, was until recently thought to have been restricted to ornamental ponds. Unlike the gammarid amphipods it does not crawl on its side but walks upright and is coloured blue-grey to olive-greenish. Following its discovery in 1969 in the People's Garden, Phoenix Park, Co. Dublin,[31] it went on to be found in parks and aquaria in Dublin City, at a goldfish pond at Lisnavagh, Co. Carlow, in an 'aquatics centre' in Co. Cork, in a shallow suburban pond in Co. Galway, and later in the Royal Canal. More recently it has appeared in the low-lying limestone reaches of the rivers Boyne and Liffey.[32] It had probably been present in Lough Neagh for some years prior to its discovery there in 1993.[29] The final and fifth amphipod present in Ireland is *Gammarus lacustris*, considered to be a glacial relict, and a native species. It is generally restricted to lowland lakes and ponds in northern and western Ireland.[33] It can reach a length of about 25 mm and is coloured like *G. pulex*, gingery-brown to olive or greyish.

Whether these three introduced species from North America and Britain will harm or seriously damage the native amphipod communities or make a positive contribution to Ireland's fauna remains unknown for the present. However, amphipods do constitute an important part of the brown trout's winter diet.

Waterfowl

Not only is the Lough a major fish habitat but, together with Lough Beg, it is one of the most important wildfowl wetlands in Europe, with a mean annual peak count of 111,518 ducks, geese and swans for the winters 1989–90 to 1993–94.[34] Six species occur in internationally important numbers. Their 'five year peak mean' for the winters 1989–90 to 1993–4 were:

Bewick's swan	267
Whooper swan	1,069
Pochard	32,201
Tufted duck	23,500
Scaup	2,457
Goldeneye	12,479

A further 11 species occur in nationally important numbers for the same period:

Little grebe	394
Great-crested grebe	978
Cormorant	773
Mute swan	1,426
Shelduck	165
Wigeon	3,448
Gadwall	124
Teal	1,889
Mallard	5,272
Shoveler	173
Coot	6,692

Whooper swan. Up to 12,000 winter in Ireland.

Goldeneye in Lough Neagh have increased almost threefold from a mean of 4,520 in the 1960s. Numbers of great-crested grebes have similarly increased and tufted duck have recovered their numbers after declining for some years. Their resurgence is linked to falling numbers in the roach population, an introduced species now suffering from a fungal disease, no longer competing with the tufted duck for food resources.

Aside from wintering wildfowl, Lough Neagh together with Lough Beg holds the largest breeding population of great-crested grebes within Ireland or Britain. Surveys by Perry during 1995–6 found a stable community of 1,205 breeding pairs, a much higher density than any reported before. According to evidence from radio tracking, about 85% of the grebes move to nearby sea loughs in October, principally Belfast Lough, where congregations of up to 1,600 have been recorded in the shallow waters off Macedon Point, Co. Antrim, between December and February. Smaller numbers winter in the Loughs of Carlingford, Strangford and Foyle.[35]

Lough Corrib, Co. Galway – the second largest lake

Lough Corrib sits some 8.5 m above sea level, stretches about 43 km from south to north and covers 17,000 ha. Its shoreline is complex, especially in the southeastern section, with bays, reefs, and shallow waters rarely sinking below 6 m, in which a myriad of rocks and islands, small and large, are anchored. The northern half is quite different, with deeper water – up to 46 m in the north-east – and a more irregular bottom. Lough Corrib is nutritionally complex, offering up a wide spectrum of water habitats. The eastern, southern and southwestern sections rest on the western extremity of the great Carboniferous limestone plain of Central Ireland, with the shores and shallow waters hosting a calcicole vegetation. But in the western parts the waters lap granites or Connemara schists, replaced in the remaining northeastern areas by Lower Carboniferous shales and sandstones. These older, non-calcareous rocks

The small breeding population of shoveler in Lough Corrib is augmented during the autumn by migrants from other European countries.

releasing few nutrients are less propitious to growth than limestone.

Lough Corrib contains important wetland plant communities, especially in its lower parts where extensive reedswamps are locally dominated by common reed, great fen-sedge and common club-rush. The area also exhibits dense growths of aquatic macrophytes, especially stoneworts and pondweeds. It harbours one of the best communities of freshwater fish in Ireland (see below), a distinction paralleled by the number and diversity of breeding and wintering bird species.

The vegetation of the lower Corrib basin was studied by Mooney & O'Connell during the summers of 1985–7.[36] The area embraced by this first major botanical survey covered 652 ha in the zone south of a line from Annagh Point to Muckish Point. Outside the aquatic communities, the bulk of the vegetation fell into the following categories: bog moss *Sphagnum subnitens*, and bog-myrtle (225 ha); common reed and slender sedge (121 ha); a community dominated by black bog-rush – used for thatching (66 ha); a common sedge community (47 ha); a purple moor-grass and false oat-grass community (38 ha); a community dominated by common club-rush (34 ha) and a community dominated by great fen-sedge (22 ha).

On the base-rich and wet soils fringing the eastern margins of the lake, the hard rush, with stems up to 1.2 m, and the blunt-flowered rush are found growing. Sitting down lower is grass-of-parnassus which is not a grass but a close relative of the saxifrages and a most delicate-looking perennial: from the heart-shaped leaves clustered in a rosette rise the stems 15–40 cm long, each bearing a solitary five-petalled white flower. Also found on the wet limy pastures is the marsh thistle and a range of orchids for which this is a favourite habitat. The fragrant orchid, smelling sometimes like cloves, appears alongside the lesser

Mare's tail is frequent in lake margins, especially in Central Ireland.

and greater butterfly-orchids whose greenish-white flowers exude a vanilla scent. Moving closer to the water the vegetation becomes taller, dominated by black bog-rush, very much more at home in a lime-rich habitat than on the acidic blanket bogs of Connemara. The slender sedge and lesser pond-sedge occur here also, often in extensive patches. So does common meadow-rue with bushy yellow flowers, yellow loosestrife and the marsh helleborine. Around the edge of the lake and often extending into shallow water are tall, sometimes extensive, stands of the great fen-sedge and the common reed with its long, silky, dark purple flower heads. In the water the lime-loving fan-leaved water-crowfoot, fen pondweed and the stonewort *Chara aculeolata* are suspended just below the surface.

The wide ecological spectrum offered by Lough Corrib means that both breeding and wintering bird populations have been attracted by it for centuries. However, it was not until the early 1960s that ornithological surveys revealed that the lime-rich waters of the southern end of the Lough, close to the Menlough Quarries, were a major staging area in Ireland for two migratory waterfowl, the pochard and the coot. They are lured by the extensive beds of the stonewort algae, *Chara* spp. and *Nitella* spp., growing in dense forests on the marly lake bed. Internationally important numbers of up to 22,000 pochard were recorded here in the 1960s and early 1970s, declining to 8,660 in the mid 1980s with further declines to 2,500–3,000 during the early 1990s for unknown reasons. Up to 9,300 coot and fewer tufted duck (*c.*1,000) were also observed congregating in these southern parts in the early 1970s. Both pochard and coot, gathering on the Lough in the early autumn, represent the first flush of immigrants from Continental Europe. When most of the stonewort has been consumed, the birds move on, redistributing themselves in other habitats throughout the country. Counts carried out during February 1996 by Delany and colleagues have re-confirmed the importance of Lough Corrib when peaks of 8,375 pochard, 2,676 tufted duck and a remarkable 25,000 coot were noted.[37] The other ornithological 'hot spot' at Lough Corrib is a reed-fringed bay, south of Mountross and south-southwest of Headford. On 7 February 1965 there were 150–200 gadwall, 1,000 tufted duck, 1,000

Coot. Apart from occurring in vast numbers (up to 25,000) on Lough Corrib, Co. Galway, in the autumn and winter, there is a sizeable breeding population in the reed beds of the Lough (J. Barlee).

pochard, 300–400 coot and many other waterfowl there.[38] More recent counts here have revealed much lower numbers but nevertheless the Inlet remains a key wildfowl haunt within the Lough.

Under difficult meteorological conditions such as fog or mist the Lough becomes a navigation guideline to passerine birds, travelling south during the autumn migration. Sometimes thousands of migrating thrushes and chaffinches stream along the western side, clearly following the path offered by the shoreline. One morning in late October 1964 up to 1,842 redwings were recorded per hour moving south, and up to 1,300 fieldfares, with smaller numbers of chaffinches and other species.[39]

The naturalist Tony Whilde, who lived on the shore of the Corrib for many years, carried out a study of the common gull and other seabirds breeding in the Lough. The name 'common gull' is a misnomer, for the species is not common, being found principally in the wilder and more remote spots of western Ireland, northern England and particularly Scotland. With its multifarious islands and complex shoreline, Lough Corrib offers the most attractive breeding habitat.

Table 5.1 The numbers of breeding gulls in Lough Corrib, Co. Galway in 1977 and 1992 (from Whilde et al, 1993[41]).

Species	1977	1992
Great black-backed gull	35	6
Lesser black-backed gull	2,587	389
Herring gull	611	6
Black-headed gull	4,660	5,284
Common gull	972	696
Total	**8,865**	**6,381**

In 1992 the 696 pairs breeding on Lough Corrib represented nearly 20% of the national total, the remaining bulk being widely scattered in many other

Lesser black-backed gull over breeding colony, Lough Corrib, Co. Galway.

smaller colonies in Ireland. Upon returning from their coastal wintering areas such as Inner Galway Bay, Clew Bay, Co. Mayo and the Shannon and Fergus Estuaries, Co. Clare, in February and March, the common gulls lay their first eggs in mid-April. The low breeding success of the colony (0.66 chicks fledged per pair over 7 years) was due to flooding of the nests by the Lough's fluctuating water levels. By the end of July, the breeding colonies are deserted, with most of the young and adults dispersing to the western and southern coastal areas, where they remain until the following February. Only one ringed bird was recorded outside the country, travelling to Lake Geneva, Switzerland.[40]

A major event of the year at Lough Corrib and at the other large limestone lakes in Ireland is the 'hatching' of the mayfly, or greendrake. When news of their emergence breaks, anytime from the beginning of May until August, anglers all over the country go into a fever as the rising of the brown trout from the muddy depths is signalled by the emergence of these delicate insects. The nymphs of the mayfly leave their underwater burrows in the mud or sand to break the surface. Provided they have not been snapped up by a fish, they shake off their nymphal encasements and stretch their wings. The adult thus acquainted with the air is known by fishermen as a 'dun' and by scientists as a 'sub-imago', or greendrake. The dun is weak and light and gets blown by the wind into the vegetation on the banks. It remains hidden and quiescent for a while and then undergoes a second transformation, sometimes within minutes of the first, and sheds another layer of skin. It is now scientifically known as an imago. This second moult, occurring after a fully-winged state, makes mayflies unique among insects. The black drake is the male spinner and the grey drake the female spinner. These new adults are shiny bright and fly immediately. But life for spinners is short and sharp as their outing into the world will not exceed 12 or so hours, during which all their energy is focused on the business of reproduction. As a nymph the mayfly had grazed on the algae coating the stems of plants 'in much the same manner as a sheep grazes on pasture land' – according to Harris[42] – but just before emerging its mouthparts degenerate thus putting a stop to feeding. All the available time as an adult is spent on courtship and copulation. Great clouds of tripping insects are suspended over the lake, each male seeking a female and darting incessantly up and down the swarm to find one. Once fertilisation has taken place, the females release the eggs into the water. They are held together by a gelatinous substance and possess suckers to attach themselves onto rocks or weeds. All the successive development phases – from egg to spinner – are strongly dependent on air and water temperature. The cold will have an adverse effect whereas warmth will speed up all the metamorphic processes. Once the eggs have been entrusted to the lake or river, the adults collapse – the dying female spinner is known as the 'spent gnat' by anglers – and the brown trout, still lurking below, snap up the remains of these poor epicureans.

Mayflies. From Fitter & Manuel [75].

There are approximately another 33 species of mayfly that occur in Ireland, including a family called Caenis, known as broadwings, or the angler's curse. The nymphs are very small, less than 9 mm long, and the adults or duns emerge in

June–September often occurring in large
numbers on Irish lakes. When they emerge,
fish are very difficult to catch with an artificial fly because of the general confusion
over the water, hence their alternative
name.

Other lake insects

Caddisfly. From Fitter & Manuel [75].

Irish lakes contain many fascinating and
remarkable insects, some of which are
unknown in Britain. These include the lesser water boatman which was first
reported from Lough Derg, Co. Galway, by Walton in the 1930s.[43] It belongs to
the family of Corixidae, part of the sub-order of water bugs, the Heteroptera.
They live submerged and swim around propelling themselves forwards by their
hair-fringed hind legs. They are herbivorous – unlike most other corixids.
Lesser water boatmen also inhabits other alkaline loughs of the Shannon area
including Lough Ree, Co. Westmeath.[44] Outside Ireland it has only been
recorded from Canada and northern Scandinavia. With regard to the caddisflies, or Trichoptera, no fewer than three of the Irish lake-dwelling species are
absent from Britain. Like the lesser water boatman, the caddisfly *Tinodes maculicornis* lives in calcareous lakes where the case-less larvae construct their tube-
like homes on the calcite-encrusted stones and boulders. Ireland is the only
place in the world where this species is abundant. Abroad it is only known from
France, Portugal and Switzerland.[45] The third species of particular Irish interest is another caddisfly *Limnephilus fuscinervis*, also rare in Europe. The larvae
were only described in 1985, when they were discovered living in superbly cam-
ouflaged cases among leaf and stem debris of reeds which had accumulated in
erosion holes on the bare peat substratum at the edge of a reed swamp. Another
very interesting caddisfly species is *Apatania auricula*, whose distribution is most
curious. Confined to the southwest of Ireland with the exception of one lake in
Co. Clare, it has also been reported from a confined area of Europe lying
between Finland, Sweden, Latvia and Poland. This caddisfly may be a glacial
relict which survived in ice free refugia in the southwest during the glaciations.
The larvae are abundant in the littoral zones of many of the Kerry lakes where
they serve as food for brown trout. On the Killarney lakes the adults may be
found flying during most months of the year and can occur in incredible numbers along the shoreline. In addition to *Apatania auricula*, the Killarney lakes
contain an amazingly diverse trichopteran fauna of 71 species, almost half the
known Irish caddisflies.[46]

Rare and endangered lake breeding birds

Several species of lake nesting birds in Ireland are of particular interest
because of their small and vulnerable populations. These fragile communities
are precarious because they are at the very edges of their respective European
distribution ranges where ecological conditions may not be the most
favourable with regard to food supplies, breeding habitat and the presence of
certain predators. The species include a diver, a scoter, a goosander and a
grebe.

Until 1900 the black-necked grebe was a rare winter visitor to Ireland. Its first
recorded breeding attempt was at Keel Lough, Achill Island, Co. Mayo, in

1906, followed by the establishment of a small colony – up to 15 pairs – in a turlough near Brierfield, Co. Roscommon, in 1915 until drainage destroyed the habitat in 1957. At nearby Lough Funshinagh, about 4.8 km west of Lough Ree, breeding of the grebes was first discovered by Darling some years before 1918. In 1930 Stoney, Humphreys and two English ornithologists estimated at least 250 breeding pairs. In 1932 some 300 pairs were judged to be breeding, marking one of the most remarkable ornithological events in Ireland.[47] Other species recorded breeding at Lough Funshinagh were gadwall, pintail, shoveler, tufted duck, pochard, red breasted merganser, and possibly the spotted crake, qualifying the Lough as Ireland's premier breeding haunt for aquatic birds. Rats and oologists took their toll of the black-necked grebe colony and it declined to extinction by the late 1960s. There was one subsequent breeding record of one pair in 1982.[48] Ireland is at the northwestern edge of its Eurasian distribution and there are some 500–1,000 pairs breeding in northwest Europe with approximately 33 pairs recorded in Britain during 1988.[49] It is more than likely that the species is now extinct in Ireland.

The small breeding population of the red-throated diver is confined to remote mountain and moorland lakes in west Donegal which marks the southern limit of its breeding range in northwestern Europe. Further north in Scotland, where environmental conditions are more attractive for the diver, an estimated 1,200–1,500 pairs breed.[49] Since the first breeding record in Donegal in 1884 modest numbers (5–15 pairs) have nested most years since then. During 1997 a survey of 175 Donegal loughs produced a maximum of six confirmed breeding pairs.[50] These shy and most sensitive divers are amongst the rarest of all lake breeding birds in Ireland apart from the pintail (1+ pairs) and garganey (< 10 pairs).[51]

The third lake nesting bird of special Irish interest is the common scoter, found now only in three western and one Midland lake. In Ireland it is at the extreme southwestern edge of its Palaearctic distribution. It was first recorded breeding in Lower Lough Erne, Co. Fermanagh, in 1905, after which the population peaked at 152 pairs in 1967. Since then it has been in decline until extinction after the 1992 breeding season.[51] Deteriorating water quality affecting the supply of scoter food, possible predation of incubating females by feral mink and competition for food from introduced roach were all held responsible for the scoter's demise.[52] A survey in 1995 showed small breeding numbers on Loughs Conn (24–26 pairs and probably declining) and Cullen (5 pairs, probably declining), Co. Mayo; Lough Corrib (30–41 pairs, probably increasing), Co. Galway and Lough Ree (37–39 pairs, probably stable), Co. Roscommon.[53] Despite such a small population of some 96–111 pairs, Ireland holds a significant proportion of the population breeding in European Union countries, prior to the membership of Finland and Sweden.

The goosander, like the red-throated diver, is another northern species trying to establish a breeding foothold on the southwestern edge of its Holarctic and boreal breeding range. While not typically a lake nester, preferring clear fast flowing salmonid rivers, goosanders are frequently found in lakes adjacent to streams and fast flowing rivers. The first known breeding record was in Donegal in 1969 with intermittent breeding subsequently at least two separate locations.[54] It is thought that 1–2 pairs may now be breeding in the county with the possibility of at least one further pair in Co. Mayo.

Inland breeding terns

Sandwich, common and Arctic terns are essentially coastal breeders preferring shingle beaches and small offshore islands as nesting sites as well as islands in coastal loughs. But they also breed on many of Ireland's larger inland lakes. Big colonies of common terns formerly existed on many of Connacht's larger lakes – Carrowmore, Carra, Conn, Mask in County Mayo and on the Corrib, Co. Galway. By the early 1940s numbers had declined, possibly due to predation from increasing numbers of breeding gulls. During the all Ireland 1984 tern census, 423 pairs of common terns or 16% of the Irish total were breeding on inland lakes while only 3.2% or 73 pairs of Arctic terns bred inland. Similar results were obtained from the 1995 national survey which showed 17% (919 pairs) and 2% (62 pairs) of common and Arctic terns respectively nesting on inland waters. Most inland common tern sites are outside the range for coastal feeding so the birds prey upon freshwater fish. Both common and Arctic terns breeding in Lough Corrib, Co. Galway, have been observed feeding pike fry to their chicks. Inland nesting sandwich terns are less common. During the 1984 survey a colony of 164 pairs terns bred on an island in Carrowmore Lake, Co. Mayo but by 1995 the colony was extinct. The Carrowmore birds fed in the nearby coastal waters of Broadhaven Bay, up to 10 km from the breeding site. Also in 1984 there was one colony of 78 pairs in Lower Lough Erne, Co. Fermanagh which by 1995 had declined to 61 pairs. The only other inland freshwater site in 1995 was at Sessaigh Lake, Donegal (2 pairs).[55]

Fish communities and endangered fish

There are very few important and undisturbed freshwater fish communities remaining in Ireland as many natural ecosystems have been perturbed by drainage or impoundment schemes. Others have been enriched by excessive runoff of nutrients, principally nitrates and phosphates, from municipal sewage works, industrial discharges, silage effluents or fertilisers. Of the 12 systems (lakes and rivers) listed as undisturbed fish communities for Ireland and Britain by Maitland & Campbell, three are Irish lakes.[22] They contain almost full representations of the original stenohaline fishes although some are mixed with species that have been introduced. They are:

(i) Lower Lough Erne, Co. Fermanagh: Atlantic salmon, trout, rainbow trout, Arctic charr, pollan, pike, bream, minnow, rudd, roach, stone loach, European eel, three-spined stickleback and perch.

(ii) Lough Leane, Co. Kerry: Twaite shad, Atlantic salmon, trout, Arctic charr, gudgeon, tench, perch, European eel and three-spined stickleback.

(iii) Lough Corrib, Co. Galway: sea lamprey, brook lamprey, Atlantic salmon, brown trout, Arctic charr (the population would now appear to have collapsed[56]), pike, bream, minnow, rudd, roach, stone loach, European eel, three-spined stickleback and ten-spined stickleback.

Amongst the rarer and endangered species of native freshwater fish found within the geographical context of the 'British Isles', Maitland considers there are five particularly important species within Ireland.[57]

1. ALLIS SHAD
Now uncommon around the coast with no certain breeding sites.

2. TWAITE SHAD

Becoming scarce and sporadic around the coast but reported as common in
certain areas, particularly in the estuaries of the rivers Barrow, Nore, Suir and
Munster Blackwater (Youghal Bay). A commercial fishery operating in
Wexford Harbour had a mean annual catch of 400 kg for the years 1965–76.[58]
Twaite shad only breeds in a few rivers. A non-migratory population in Lough
Leane, Co. Kerry, apparently isolated for thousands of years, has developed
subspecific characteristics earning recognition as *Alosa fallax killarniensis*.

3. ARCTIC CHARR

Declining number of populations in Europe. There are important populations
in several Irish lakes but it would appear that their populations in both Loughs
Corrib, Co. Galway and Conn, Co. Mayo, have collapsed.[59] Recently discovered in a previously unrecorded site at Lough Anscaul, Co. Kerry.[60]

4. POLLAN

Only five probable remaining populations, all in large Irish lakes.

5. SMELT

Declining numbers in coastal waters and estuaries. It migrates into clean rivers
to spawn just above the estuarine limits before returning to the sea. There are
only a few remaining breeding populations in about eight rivers in Britain and
three in Ireland – rivers Shannon (they spawn in the tail race of the hydroelectric power station at Ardnacrusha which has sheer rock sides – the eggs
attach themselves to moss[59]), Fergus and Foyle. There is some evidence that
they might be spawning in the rivers Suir (Carrick-on-Suir), Barrow (St
Mullins) and the Nore (Inistioge).[61]

Lampreys are a particularly interesting group of fish with several rare and
endangered species. They are jawless, without scales or pectoral fins, possessing a funnel-shaped sucking mouth used to fasten themselves onto another
fish host. They are eel-like and slippery, with a fin cresting along the back and
tail. The adult lamprey attaches itself onto the flesh of its larger host and gnaws
away to extract blood for its nourishment. The river lamprey is about the thickness of a finger, some 30–40 cm long. It is silvery-white with a tinge of blue or
green on the back. The brook lamprey is much thinner and shorter at 12–16
cm. It is often used as bait to catch other fish. The sea lamprey, in comparison,
is a monster, as it reaches 1 m in length and is stouter than the river lamprey.
Its back is marbled with brown, black and olive spots set on a grey or green
background. It is, quite unbelievably, a delicacy, and won historical fame
because Henry I of England is reputed to have died from eating too many of
them. The young sea and river lampreys migrate from lakes and rivers to sea
at the end of summer or the beginning of autumn. They will be back several
years later to spawn and die. Once hatched the young lampreys spend three to
five years ensconced in the mud, slowly developing. The brook lamprey is a
non-migratory species remaining in fresh water all its life. Its relationship with
the river lamprey is uncertain, but it would appear that they have diverged
genetically while in isolated populations.

The sea lamprey is thought to be present in most Irish estuaries and accessible lakes. Although generally migratory, resident populations have been

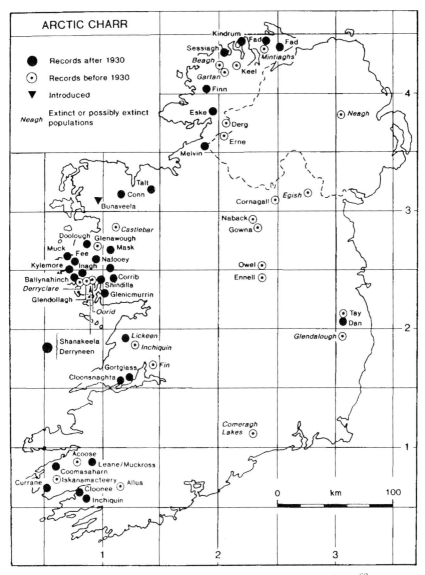

Lakes from which Arctic charr have been recorded up to 1992. From Whilde [63].

recorded in Loughs Conn, Co. Mayo, and Corrib, Co. Galway, and in the River Lee Reservoir, Co. Cork [62], while returning migratory adults were common in the River Fergus, Co. Clare, in the 1960s. In 1984 spawning was recorded in the River Mulkear at Annacotty, Co. Limerick.[63] The river lamprey also inhabits shallow coastal waters and accessible rivers. Very little is known about its distribution in Ireland but it is thought its main breeding area is in the Lough Neagh catchment, as well as in three rivers in Co. Louth, and possibly in the rivers Nore, Co. Kilkenny, and Bandon, Co. Cork. The brook lamprey is found mainly in the Lough Erne catchment, Co. Fermanagh, and in small streams in limestone regions.

In a review of current knowledge on the distribution of the lampreys in Ireland, Kurz & Costello found all three species spawning in the main channels or the lower reaches of the tributaries of the rivers Slaney, Barrow (downstream from Borris), Suir, Blackwater (downstream from Fermoy), Shannon (downstream from Lough Derg) and in the rivers and streams of the Killarney National Park and around Lough Gill, Co. Kerry.[64]

Rivers

There are more than 13,500 km of main river channel in Ireland. Some are large and placid, others are fast-flowing upland streams. The topographical peculiarity of the country is that it does not have a raised central spine and what mountains and hills it does possess are scattered around the margins of the island. This general physiography dictates that rivers and streams, commencing on the seaward side of the uplands, have a short, swift and often turbulent run to the sea. Those arising on the inland side have much longer and rambling courses, sometimes covering three times the distance they needed to have covered had they gone straight to the nearest bit of coast. The Shannon, together with other rivers pushing across central Ireland – the Nore, Barrow and Suir – have cut and eroded their way through the harder sandstone and shale rocks that form a sort of barrier along the southern parts of the limestone plain.

The River Shannon, the longest river in either Ireland or Britain, runs some 344 km from its point of origin in the mountains near Lough Allen, Co. Leitrim, to the tidal waters at Limerick before flowing on for another 88 km through a muddy and generally shallow estuary.

In the northern part of the lowlands the River Erne runs a very idle course, billowing out into large lakes before gathering speed at Belleek as it plunges down over limestone to meet the Atlantic coastline below Ballyshannon. Other rivers travelling through the Central Plain also expand into lakes – the Shannon has its Loughs Ree and Derg; the River Corrib has Loughs Carra, Mask and Corrib. Of the approximate 75 river catchments in Ireland, the River Shannon is the largest, draining an area of some 10,400 km^2. The Liffey is an even more coiling, reluctant river. Arising in the Co. Wicklow upland blanket bog at 549 m, on the inland side of the Leinster mountains, its source is a mere 22.5 km from where it meets the sea in Dublin City. Yet the Liffey takes a 116 km trip around and about the countryside before it gets there.

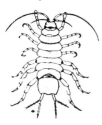

Water hog-louse.
From Fitter &
Manuel[75].

The general ecological characteristics of Irish rivers are very much conditioned, as are the lakes, by their underlying geology. Rivers that run across granite and the generally acidic formations of Donegal, Mayo, Galway, Kerry, Cork, Wicklow, and elsewhere are nutrient-poor while those washing over limestone and other base-rich rocks are nutrient-rich. Rivers in calcareous areas are much more productive and support a greater diversity of invertebrates than those in base-poor regions. They have good populations of crustaceans – freshwater shrimps, water hog-lice and freshwater crayfish – as well as molluscs, flies, beetles, caddisflies, bryozoans and other microinvertebrates.

The speed of the water, oxygen concentration, temperature and presence of silt and other particulates are also important factors. In the upper reaches of rivers, the currents are fast, the water well oxygenated and the temperatures lower than further down. In such swift, shallow tumbling streams, one finds a specialist benthic community of insects characterised by the mayflies, caddis-flies, stoneflies, non-biting midges and blackflies. In general stoneflies are commoner in the upper reaches and mayflies in the lower reaches of rivers – although (to only quote one exception) the mayfly, *Electogena lateralis,* is found in the upper parts of river systems such as the River Flesk, Co. Kerry while stonefly species are also found lower down. The invertebrate populations in turn determine the fish and avian life of these rivers.

Several riverine invertebrates and vertebrates are indicators of the ecological health of waters. Amongst the invertebrates, the freshwater crayfish and fresh-water mussels, including the freshwater pearl mussel, are of particular interest.

Freshwater crayfish

The freshwater or white-clawed crayfish is the largest freshwater invertebrate in Ireland and the only species of crayfish recorded in the country. It is also found in Britain, France, Iberia, Italy and parts of the former Yugoslavia. The European crayfish, a closely related species, has been reported from one lake in Ireland but the information proved false. Exotic cousins such as the signal crayfish have tempted many aqua-farmers as a candidate for cultivation, but have not as yet been introduced.

Within Ireland, crayfish are commonly found in alkaline streams, rivers and small lakes where the levels of calcium carbonate derived from the underlying limestone rocks, are high. The crayfish depends on this chemical to build its tough exoskeleton which it moults and manufactures again several times during its life time. For this reason crayfish will not survive in waters with a pH of 6.0 and lower. Other factors affecting distribution include summer water temperatures which should be higher than 10°C, predation by eels and mink, water pollution and, in some areas, disease. During a survey of freshwater cray-fish in Ireland, Lucey & McGarrigle found that the fresh waters supporting crayfish had a pH range of 7.2–8.4, an alkalinity of 34–356 mg per litre and hardness of 47–402 mg per litre.[65]

The presence of just one species, and the relatively clean waters of Irish rivers and lakes have facilitated their widespread distribution. Their absence from Donegal, Kerry, Louth, Wexford and the larger parts of Cork and Wicklow as well as western Connemara is thought to be correlated with a poor supply of calcium and carbonate ions character-istic of these areas.[65] They are only occasionally reported from northeast-ern Ireland.[66] Moriarty who, together with Reynolds, has investigated cray-fish distribution in Ireland for many years, also notes that they rarely occur in lakes larger than 1,000 hectares.[67]

Many people are quite surprised by their first encounter with these slow-growing miniature green lobsters because of their small size, rarely big-

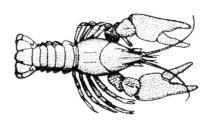

Freshwater crayfish. From Fitter & Manuel[75].

ger than about 15 cm long. Like their marine cousin the common lobster they turn bright red when dropped into hot water. In their river or lake habitats they spend most of the day lurking in holes and shelters, generally emerging at dusk or in full darkness to feed. They are omnivorous and opportunistic feeders and can even leave the water during warm summer months to graze on the bankside vegetation.

A study of a population in Blessington Lake, Co. Wicklow between 1989 and 1993, revealed a sparse and patchy distribution of about 500 individuals – with a carapace length greater than 3 cm – per 100 m^2 of rocky shoreline.[68] This is one of the few large gatherings studied in Irish lakes or ponds and what was discovered is probably generally applicable to other crayfish populations throughout the country. During the investigations 1,356 crayfish were caught. Males outnumbered females in the ratio of 1.44–1.0. Mating activity occurred in early to mid-October. Females were generally sexually mature at 2–3 years old, probably a reflection of harsh environmental conditions (low temperatures and limited availability of food). In areas of good crayfish growth (more sheltered conditions and better areas for feeding) they will mature more quickly. The fertilised eggs, carried by what are known as the 'berried' females, become hatchlings the following June. At Blessington, breeding success was high with about 80% of mature females carrying 55–65 eggs. Most adults, apart from the largest males, moulted twice a year during the summer months (May/June and August/September). After the first moult the carapace increased in length by an average 9% while in the second moult the average increase was 6.5%. Freshwater crayfish are an important food for both the otter and mink. In some areas crayfish remains have been found to form up to 76% of the bulk of otter spraints.[69] They are also predated by several fish, including the trout, eel, rainbow trout and perch, the hard exoskeleton being apparently quite well received by piscine digestive systems.

Ireland was the last European country to be free of the crayfish plague fungus *Aphanomyces astacis* until it was identified on some crayfish collected in 1987 from Lough Lene, Co. Westmeath. Its discovery had been preceded by a sequence of stock losses in other Midland lakes: White Lake (1985) and Loughs Bane, Glore and Owel (1986). It is thought that the plague fungus had been introduced accidentally by fishermen and their gear.[70] The disease has also occurred in the rivers Boyne and Shannon.[71]

Pearl mussel

The freshwater pearl mussel is a large native bivalve mollusc, up to 8 cm long, which lives burrowed in the sediments of Irish rivers. One of the animals with the greatest longevity, it is reputed to live up to about 130 years. Already much sought after by the eleventh century, as testified by references to it in a document dated 1049,[1] freshwater pearl mussels are still hunted today but on a much smaller scale. With the arrival in European markets of the more sophisticated oriental pearls, fishing in Ireland declined as their quality could not compete with their Eastern rivals.

Pearls are created in response to a grain of sand or small piece of grit inserting itself in the body tissue of the mussel. The offending material is isolated and neutralised by secretions of calcium carbonate called 'nacre' – mother of pearl – until a round shiny nugget is formed. Such was their attraction in historical times that the prospect of fishing for pearls in Co. Derry was used as one of the minor inducements offered by Charles I to the City of London adventurers to undertake the plantation of Co. Londonderry.[72]

Sir Robert Redding, writing about pearl fishing in the North of Ireland in the *Transactions of the Royal Society* in 1688, records that about one shell in a hundred has a pearl and that one pearl out of a hundred 'be tolerably clear'. Poor people tried their luck at finding them in between seasonal tasks: 'The manner of their fishing is not extraordinary, the poor people in the warm months before harvest is ripe, whilst the rivers are low and clear, go into the water, some with their toes, some with wooden tongs, and some by putting a sharpened stick into the opening of the shell take them up'. Rich ladies wore them around their neck or down from their ears, such as the one bought for '50 shillings that weighed 36 carats, and was valued at 40 L' or the one which a miller 'sold for 4 L 10 s to a man that sold it for 10 L who sold it to the late Lady Glenanly for 30 L with whom I saw it in a necklace; she refused 80 L for it from the late Duchess of Ormond'.[73] Given that most freshwater pearls are of poor quality, lacking luminescence, the 'poor people' would have had to prise open 10,000 molluscs each before coming across a gem.

These mussels were once widespread throughout Ireland and found in river systems in Donegal, Tyrone, Derry, Cork, Wexford, Waterford, Kerry, Down and Galway, and probably other counties too. However, habitat destruction, pollution, increased peat siltation arising from overgrazing of upland peatlands by sheep, and over-exploitation of the mussels for their pearls have wrought great havoc in the remaining colonies, which in some cases have been totally wiped out. However, Ireland and Scotland are probably the last two places in Europe today where the species is still very well represented. In recognition of the danger they face Irish pearl mussels are now legally protected.[74,75]

While the ordinary freshwater pearl mussel *Margaritifera margaritifera* prefers slightly acidic waters, its even rarer and close relation *M. m. durrovensis* is found in harder, more lime-rich waters. Both look somewhat similar but the umbos (the humps of the shell on both sides of the hinge) in *M. m. durrovensis* do not become eroded in contrast to the sometime very eroded character of the *M. margaritifera* umbos. *M. m. durrovensis* is extremely rare in Ireland and it is thought that there are no more than about 2,000 individuals, all concentrated within a 10 km stretch of the main channel in the River Nore, Co. Waterford. Why and how this endemic bivalve population has survived in only one very specific location is a mystery. About 280 km of the tributaries of the rivers Nore, Barrow and Suir in southeast Ireland were carefully examined from June to August 1991 in the hope of finding other colonies. Of the 79 tributary rivers explored only four had freshwater pearl mussels, all eroded forms of *M. margaritifera*, showing a habitat preference for sandy gravel near the banks and often occurring under overhanging trees, usually alder.[76]

Neither *M. m. durrovensis* nor any specimens of the other two large freshwater bivalve molluscs, the swan mussel and duck mussel (both pearl-less), were encountered in the above surveys. The swan mussel averages about 14 cm in length but can reach the huge size of 20 cm or more and is usually found in lakes and canals, while the duck mussel is normally smaller than 10 cm. Both live, as a general rule, in waters with higher than average alkalinity and hardness levels.[77] At present it is suspected that they might belong to only one species.

An early reference to these two mussels in Ireland was provided by Piers who, when describing peatlands in *A Chorographical description of the County of West-*

Meath (1682), wrote: 'In them [the bogs] is found, especially in slimy pits covered with water, a certain shell fish, which we may call the bog-mussel, in shape and size like the sea mussel, but flatter and broader, the shell in colour much brighter and greyish, by many degrees thinner, very brittle and broken.'[78]

While such a location might seem odd for a species that prefers alkaline waters, the underlying geology of the peatland area mentioned by Piers is Carboniferous limestone, and bog pools can be lined with deposits of calcareous marl, so that upward flushing of alkaline waters may have created suitable conditions for those molluscs.

In his survey of the swan mussel in the south of Ireland Lucey notes that the main concentrations are associated with the River Shannon and the numerous lakes sitting on Carboniferous limestone within its catchment. Given its partiality to sluggish waters, the swan mussel also occurs in large populations in the Grand Canal. Undoubtedly the construction of the canal network during the nineteenth century provided a 'mussel way', which facilitated its dissemination through Ireland. The swan mussel is absent from the southwestern parts of Ireland, reflecting the generally acid nature of waters there, while this is where the freshwater pearl mussel is most abundant.[79] The swan mussel provides exciting scope for scientific investigation. There is, at present, no published information on its reproductive cycle in Ireland.[79]

The reproductive biology of the freshwater pearl mussel had not been studied in Ireland until Ross spent four years looking at a large colony in the River Owenea in Co. Donegal.[80] Here the mussels grow over 7 cm long, and the adults can either be male, female or hermaphrodite. The females use their arrangement of curtain-like gills to form a type of primitive brooding chamber, or marsupium, in which the fertilised eggs are protected and incubated. Spawning takes place over an approximately two week period in July, coinciding with the highest air and water temperatures. The spermatozoa are taken into the body cavity of the female through the inhalant siphon and wafted over the eggs in the marsupium. There they develop into very small shelled larvae, glochidia. These remain in the marsupium for about another four weeks and all are expelled by the second week in October. They drift off and fall to the river bottom. If one of their special fish hosts – salmon – passes close enough, a sticky thread of about 2 mm protruding from the glochidia attaches the larva onto its host. In Ireland the salmon is the only host so far known. The glochidia, clamped onto its host's skin or gills leads a parasitic way of life, drawing nourishment from the tissues, blood and mucus of the fish. They remain encysted for several weeks until the now tiny mussel drops off to continue life on its own. This extraordinarily bizarre life cycle was not unravelled until 1862 when Houghton discovered the true parasitic nature of the glochidium of the closely related swan mussel.[81]

Ross found a total absence of young mussels (smaller than 5 cm) in the river despite production of mature glochidia each year. Thus whole cohorts of young immature mussels appear to be missing while at the same time the overall population is apparently surviving and doing well. One explanation may rest with the decline of salmon and brown trout (another potential glochidia host) in the river, for without an adequate provision of fish the glochidia cannot complete their life cycle. If, however, the glochidia were only successful in their hunt for salmonids once every four years then this sporadic input might be sufficient to balance out previous or subsequent mortality.

Salmon

The Atlantic salmon occupies a special place in the history, mythology economy and angling world of Ireland. But most importantly they are a crucial element of wild nature which up until now has survived continued and often brutal assaults by man including intensive drift netting at sea, pollution of rivers and lakes, physical damage to their gravel spawning areas from drainage schemes, the smothering of the gravel beds by peat arising from bog exploitation and soil coming from erosion of overgrazed uplands, unscrupulous poaching with use of poisons, explosives, electrocution and illegal netting. Moreover salmon are subject to a series of often fatal bacterial and viral diseases. Their survival as a widespread and self-sustaining population in Ireland is a triumph of nature over man's greed and his worst environmental excesses.

Their annual migrations from the Atlantic feeding grounds off southern Greenland, where stock from North America, Scandinavia and other locations in Ireland and Britain intermingle in areas where surface water temperatures range from 4–8°C, bring them through our estuaries and on up into the cool rivers and lakes. Their migrations sustained the first known human settlers in Ireland, Mesolithic peoples living on the River Bann, Co. Derry, some 9,000 years ago. Their regular travels together with those of eels through Irish rivers provided one of the few guaranteed food sources before the arrival, several thousand years later, of Neolithic farmers who came with their own food supplies – crops and domestic animals. Salmon provided exceptionally rich food that could be cooked and eaten immediately or smoked and stored for later consumption. More importantly the salmon were available at the time of year when other gatherable foods were scarce. From these earliest days the pursuit of the salmon developed into a sophisticated art with a distinctive culture of fish spears, specially constructed wooden or stone traps and other cunning devises to entrap this valuable source of food.[82]

Fish returning to fresh water having spent only one winter feeding on pelagic crustaceans and small fish in the sea are the silver coloured grilse, averaging around 3.5 kg, which may appear in rivers from midsummer (June) onwards. Those that remain in the sea for two or more winters before returning to the rivers are normally much larger and are known as 'spring fish'. Such salmon may reach up to 14 kg. Most of the older 'spring fish' enter the rivers between Christmas and May (the main runs are in late winter and early spring) whereupon they lurk in the rivers until the onset of the breeding season. They are keenly fished by anglers. However, most adult salmon returning to fresh waters are grilse rather than these older fish. Once in fresh water salmon do not feed, yet they are sufficiently curious to be attracted to artificial lures and natural baits cast literally over their snouts with deadly precision by the best anglers.

The grilse and older fish that survive their journey from the Atlantic, avoiding being caught in salmon drift nets strung along the coastline or at special weirs, make their way into the rivers and lakes of Ireland to seek out silt-free gravel beds on river bottoms. Most fish return to their natal rivers where they hatched some three or more years previously. The females hollow out a nest or redd in the gravel bottom in which the eggs – most hen fish produce about 1,100 eggs per kg of body weight[22] – are laid normally between late October and early January. The attendant cock fish fertilises the eggs and both return to the sea as spent fish or kelts, some to return to breed again but most dying at sea. The eggs hatch in March or April, first into alevins then into fry of which only about 10% survive over the next 2–3 years while they remain in the river before becoming smolts, usually 12–16 cm long, usually in April at the beginning of their third year. The smolts then move down the rivers into the sea and onwards to the rich Greenland feeding grounds.

All major Irish rivers have varying runs of salmon. Amongst the most famous are the Moy, Co. Mayo (grilse from June–September and spring fish February–May), the Corrib, Co. Galway, (grilse in June, spring fish in April), the Suir, Co. Waterford, (June and July for grilse, February–May for spring fish), the Shannon, Co. Limerick, (spring fish in March–May, grilse in June–July), the Erriff, Co. Mayo, (grilse from June to September and spring fish April–June) and the Liffey, Co. Dublin (spring fish February–May and grilse September–October). Large catches of salmon are commercially taken by legal nets and traps at some of the largest salmon runs. For example, at the famous Lough Foyle fishery, upwards of 80,000 per annum were taken several years ago but numbers caught today are considerably less, reflecting a decline in the North Atlantic population. Dramatic declines in salmon catches also occurred during the summer of 1998 in the drift net fishery of northwest Mayo and in Sligo, areas normally noted for good runs of salmon. A total of 120 boats were licensed for drift netting in the area but catches were so poor that fewer than 25 boats were operating for much of the catching season. Alarmed by the salmon decline, the North Western Fisheries Board requested the Central Fisheries Board to suspend the commercial trapping of salmon at the weirs on the river Moy at Ballina to allow all available salmon upstream to spawn. Many of the fish weighed only 0.5–1.0 kg, smaller than usual, and were carrying a larger burden than normal of the naturally occurring sea lice *Lepeoptheirus salmonis.*

Outside Ireland and Britain the salmon is an endangered, locally threatened or extinct species. Although under considerable commercial and other pressures the wild salmon of Ireland are not yet considered to be an 'officially' threatened species.[51] Ironically, the artificial farming of caged salmon with the production of relatively cheap fish may save the wild salmon in Ireland by making drift netting at sea and illegal poaching less attractive economic propositions. As long as wild salmon survive they will continue to run up the major Irish rivers as well as a large number of often small and seemingly insignificant rivers, a special feature marking Ireland out from other northwest European countries.

Dipper and kingfisher

There is little quantitative information on the breeding birds of Irish waterways. In one study carried out over a two year period in 1983–4 and covering a 4.5 km stretch of the River Flesk, Co. Kerry, five species (dipper, mallard, grey wagtail, pied wagtail and red-breasted merganser) were found to be breeding while another six (cormorant, grey heron, mute swan, tufted duck, moorhen and kingfisher) were recorded without evidence of any breeding.[83] The Flesk is a fast-flowing, turbulent river with a stone and gravel bed and steeply cut and eroded banks. A narrow strip of trees, principally alder, ash and holly, bordered most of the surveyed section. The geology of the area is Old Red Sandstone producing nutrient-poor waters. Breeding densities of the dipper, mallard and grey wagtail were generally similar to those found on comparable rivers in Northern Ireland and Britain.

The Irish dipper, *Cinclus cinclus hibernicus*, one of the three Irish subspecies of birds – the other two being the jay, *Garrulus glandarius hibernicus*, and the coal tit, *Parus ater hibernicus* – is distinguished from the nominate race, *C. c. cinclus*, that inhabits Britain and the Continent, by its browner belly. This subspecies has also been found to occur in northwest Scotland. No differences in body size or general ecology have been detected between the Irish and British races so far, despite intensive studies in recent years in Ireland by Perry and others.[84] The distribution of the dipper population along rivers is very closely related to the availability and suitability of feeding resources, as evidenced by data from a study carried out in the catchment of the River Wye in mid-Wales.[85] They are found where the frequency and abundance of mayflies, caddisflies and stoneflies are greatest and also where breeding sites are at hand, namely bridges – i.e. in the shallow, unpolluted, bolder-strewn, fast-flowing streams and rivers. In Europe this habitat generally occurs above 300 m. In Ireland, however, given the generally flat topography, dippers are found lower down. In their study in northwest Ireland, Perry & Agnew found 72% of the 54 nest sites below the altitude of 100 m and none over 200 m.[86]

The Irish breeding population of dippers has been estimated at between 6,500 and 8,000 pairs.[87] They are most abundant in the province of Ulster and generally south of a line from Wicklow to Galway. Large areas in the low-lying Midlands where the rivers are slow and placid are without them.

Dippers appear to be doing well if the results of a series of surveys of six river systems in northwest Ireland are extrapolated to the whole country. Totals of 25, 41 and 54 breeding pairs were found in 1972, 1982 and 1992 respectively, a twofold increase of the population in 20 years. As most dippers in the survey (94% in 1992) bred on bridges, their nest sites were not difficult to locate, removing a large potential source of error. It would appear that on the rivers examined there was plenty of scope for population expansion unless the availability and supply of invertebrate food were to be adversely affected by such factors as organic pollution or the acidification caused by coniferisation of upland areas. However, this does not seem to be the case at present.[86]

The diet of nestling dippers studied in northwest Ireland during April 1985 was found to be composed mainly of caddis larvae (73%) with the balance mainly composed of mayfly nymphs. The diet of the adults was different and made up by only 24% of caddis larvae, with most of the remainder consisting of mayfly nymphs. These results were generally confirmed by a subsequent study in April 1992.[88] It would appear that the selection by the adult dipper of the rather big caddis larvae to feed the young is related to their calorific

Dipper.

value and ease of capture compared to other riverine invertebrates. Catching such large food units and ferrying them to nestlings ensures optimal transfer of energy while cutting down the number of feeding trips (from 400 to 100) needed per day. The dietary preferences of Irish dippers were very similar to those found in both Lancashire and mid-Wales.[89]

In contrast to the dipper, kingfishers are more numerous in the generally slow-moving waterways of the Midlands with greatest abundance in the eastern counties and in northeast Ireland. This colourful bird favours large sluggish rivers with sandy or soft earth banks suitable for nesting, but ponds and especially the Royal and Grand Canals will also draw them. An accessible and abundant supply of food, mostly minnows, sticklebacks and some aquatic invertebrates, is a prerequisite for their attendance at waterways. There are some 1,300–2,100 pairs in Ireland, a small but stable population not subjected to harsh wintry weather, unlike their continental cousins which can suffer great losses as was the case in the winter of 1962–3.[90] Kingfishers have, however, a remarkable capacity to recover from adverse situations and, if necessary, each can produce two or three families, of up to six nestlings, in one summer.

Otter

The otter is present in greater numbers in Ireland's lakes and rivers and along the coastline than in any other comparable European region, as shown by a national survey conducted in 1980–81 which found evidence of otters in 92% of 2,373 randomly chosen sampling sites throughout the country.[91] The evidence came from the presence of spraints, or droppings, left at strategic locations to mark off territories, rather than sightings of the animals or their tracks.

Irish otters can probably be recognised as a distinct subspecies *Lutra lutra roensis*, on the basis of their darker colour and lesser extent of white on their throat.[92] Ogilby had originally proposed their elevation as a new species in 1834. He did this somewhat rashly, and based on only one almost black otter from Roe Mills, Co. Derry, hence their name *roensis*.[93] But, however shaky his single specimen proposal was, he was on the right track. The occurrence of dark, sometimes almost black, specimens, continued to be noticed over the next hundred years, leading eventually to a successful claim for subspecific rank. Proof came from Dadd who, in 1970, examined the skins of Irish and British otters in the British Museum with the aid of a reflectance spectrophotometer which determined scientifically the colour intensity of the pelts. He found a complete separation between Irish and British otters. Irish animals were much darker and the pale colour beneath the throat was much less extensive and prominent than in English otters, and was almost absent in some specimens.[94]

Otters are shy creatures and very sensitive to human disturbance. While some people may be fortunate enough to observe otters going about their daily business, most will rarely encounter them. If levels of human activity or disturbance are high, otters will spend most of the day holed up in secure spots in reed beds, burrows and other locations, only to emerge at dusk or night to fish. They do not hibernate and are most active during the autumn and spring. Along the west coast they are equally at home in the sea, often swimming out to nearby islands as well as fishing and playing around close to the shore. Elsewhere they are in most lakes and river systems throughout the country

Otter. From Corbet & Southern[92].

where their spraints, characteristic foot prints on soft mud or sand, and long piercing whistling calls make their presence known. Studies in optimal habitats in Sweden have shown the home range of the male may be up to 15 km in diameter while the female – left alone to look after the two or three cubs that can be born at any time throughout the year – has a range approximately half that.[95] After mating the male lives as a bachelor, maintaining and feeding within his territory which is marked by spraints. The young are born in a holt some 60–70 days following mating and are initiated to the water at about two and a half months old. The young remain with their mother for another nine and a half months during which they are taught social skills and how to hunt and catch food.

Most studies of otter food in freshwater habitats in Irish and other European locations have shown that fish were the most important prey. In a study covering some 178 km² in the middle reaches of the River Blackwater, Co. Cork, during May to September 1984 a total of 303 spraints were collected and analysed to express each food category as its percentage frequency and percentage bulk.[96] Fish constituted 81% of the bulk and 68.7% of the frequency of all prey items (Table 5.2).

Table 5.2 Percentage frequency of prey taken by otters on the River Blackwater and its tributaries, Co. Cork, in summer (from O'Sullivan, 1994[96]).

Prey items	% Frequency
Eel	26.9
Salmon and trout	25.0
Stone loach	7.7
Other fish	9.1
Amphibians (European frog)	0.3
Mammals	2.0
Birds (mostly moorhens and coots)	9.8
Invertebrates (mostly beetles)	16.5
Freshwater mussel	0.1
Plant matter	2.6
Total	**100.0**

Muskrat and American mink

Of all the animals that have been introduced or have escaped from captivity in Ireland, the muskrat holds the prize as the most dramatic. Few animals can carry the distinction of being responsible for an Act of Parliament to expedite their annihilation, and none have endangered the banks of the Shannon with a potential flooding catastrophe as did the muskrat. The story of this pest in Ireland has been unravelled by Fairley.[97] Two females and one male were imported from North America to a farm near Nenagh, Co. Tipperary, in 1929, probably during June. Before proper accommodation could be arranged the muskrats gnawed their way out of their cages and vanished into the country-side. By 1933 they were well established, thriving and multiplying around the mouth of the Nenagh River where it enters Lough Derg at Dromineer Bay. Their elusive and nocturnal habits assisted their initially unnoticed population spread and it was not until April 1933 that three muskrats were shot at Dromineer. Soon the rodents were posing a serious threat to the banks of the Shannon and other rivers by undermining the soil with extensive under-ground tunnelling systems. Moreover if they spread to the new hydroelectric station at Ardnacrusha, on the River Shannon south of Killaloe, they would have raised an even more serious threat by tunnelling through the banks there. The Government acted quickly and a special *Musk Rats Act, 1933* was rushed through the Dáil. It provided the framework for an eradication pro-gramme which proved highly effective.

The muskrat extermination campaign headquarters was set up in the old military barracks at Nenagh. Two experienced trappers were brought in from England and they were assisted by up to ten local trappers. Stalking began in September 1933. Gin or steel traps were used, often set at the underwater entrances of burrows. The aim was for the muskrat to drown, ensnared in the trap, without being able to gnaw its caught limb free as it did on dry land. At the beginning of the campaign about 30 muskrats were caught each week. The bag grew to a total of 300 by 10 January, 1934. By the end of May 1934 the last of the 487 muskrats had been suppressed, leaving river banks safe. This story demonstrates the speed at which colonisation by introduced species can pro-ceed and what dangers can arise out of the importation of animals.

Another immigrant species is the American mink which has been steadily escaping from fur farms throughout the country for nearly 40 years. It first broke out in 1961 from a farm near Omagh, Co. Tyrone and immediately began its career as a feral animal on the nearby River Strule.[98] Over the years more escapees have come out of farms and mink are now widely established throughout the country. To most people they would seem, on first instinctive consideration, to be unwelcome and predatory settlers threatening fish and game bird populations. But is this the case?

The first study on feral mink, based on a collection of 108 individuals either killed or trapped in the wild between 1975 and 1978, was conducted by Fairley.[99] Most (94%) had retained their original wild pelage, 'an extremely dark brown', while the remainder were of the colour varieties from the mink farms. The male mean body weight was 1.26 kg and the female 737 g, which was close to the weights of animals living in the wild in North America. Mink normally dwell near water and will eat whatever prey is at hand. The food remains in the guts of 12 mink caught outside the Clogher Valley, Co. Tyrone,

American mink.
From Corbet &
Southern[92].

showed a range of prey ranging from lagomorphs – probably rabbits – to brown rats, mice, birds (ducks, pheasants, moorhens and coots), frogs, fish (salmon and trout), insects and crayfish.

In a subsequent investigation 2,510 mink scats (faeces) were analysed from two rivers (Inny and Glore) and two loughs (Ennell and Lene) in Co. Westmeath. Freshwater crayfish were the major food taken in two of the study areas, especially in the summer. In one lake where there were few crayfish, mink focused on the large breeding population of waterbirds. The consumption of fish was highest in winter. Perch and eel were the most frequently taken species. Lagomorphs (rabbits and hares) and brown rats were the main mammalian prey, while frogs were seasonally important. The total percentage occurrence of each food category for all the scats is shown in Table 5.3.

Table 5.3 Percentage occurrence of each prey category for 2,510 mink scats collected from Rivers Inny and Glore and Loughs Ennell and Lene, Co. Westmeath.

Prey category	% Occurrence
Mammals (mostly rabbits and hares)	4.8
Birds (mostly moorhens, coots and mallard)	17.2
Fish (mostly perch)	17.0
Frogs	7.4
Crayfish	44.6
Other	9.0
Total	**100.0**

The results demonstrate the ability of the mink to hunt both aquatic and terrestrial prey. There was no evidence that game birds were taken although they were present in the study areas. Trout only made up 2.4% of the occurrence of the food taken and amongst the waterfowl ducks only contributed 5% towards the occurrence of the food. Seasonal variation confirmed that the mink was an opportunistic predator, adapting its diet to the availability of prey.[100]

However, concerning the interactions of the mink with other related species, a comparative study of the diets of the mink and otter living in the same area in the Irish Midlands showed a significant dietary separation between the two Mustelids. Mink took more birds, a substantial number of mammals and considerably fewer fish. There were also differences between the relative amounts of some fish species eaten.[101]

The studies carried out on the newcomer indicate that the mink is not the deadly vandal feared by many countryside lovers. However, it is true that dense

Lough Eske, Co. Donegal, with the Blue Stack Mountains in the distance. The Lough is a fine example of an oligotrophic waterbody.

breeding colonies of ground-nesting sea birds such as terns and gulls, or water-fowl, can be particularly vulnerable to mink. Lake islands, for instance, which might offer some form of security from mammals such as foxes, rats and badgers, hold no defence against this very skilled swimmer. Mink will – on some rare and exceptional occasions – wreck havoc among ground-nesting colonial birds, but on the whole it cannot be accused of causing more damage than the otter, stoat, fox or possibly brown rat, all long-established members of the Irish fauna.

6

The Burren and Turloughs

The Burren is the strangest place in Ireland. Composed mostly of naked Carboniferous limestone and extending over some 450 km^2 in the northwest corner of Co. Clare and on some adjoining territory in Co. Galway, it is a dry rocky skeleton of a landscape. When Lieutenant General Ludlow, appointed by Oliver Cromwell as one of the Commissioners for the civil government of Ireland and second-in-command to the Lord Deputy, Henry Ireton, reconnoitred the area in November 1651 he reported:

> 'After two days' marching, without anything remarkable but bad
> quarters, we entered into the Barony of Burren, of which it is said,
> that it is a country where there is not water enough to drown a man,
> wood enough to hang one, nor earth enough to bury him; which last
> is so scarce, that the inhabitants steal it from one another, and yet
> their cattle are very fat; for the grass growing in turfs of earth, of two
> or three foot square, that lie between the rocks, which are of lime-
> stone, is very sweet and nourishing.'[1]

As you look southwards over Galway Bay, the rounded hills of the Burren appear like a school of grey whales, cruising slowly through. At this distance the region takes on a desert-like character that has been compared to parts of

The naked rocks of Mullagh More preside over this southeastern corner of the Burren, where most of the territory is protected within the 1,673 ha Burren National Park.

Arabia Petraea, between the Red and Dead Seas in Jordan. On closer approach, however, the Burren's physiography draws one deeper and deeper into an intimate world of smooth and shattered limestone pavements, clints, grykes, glacial erratics, then on into cliff-walled valleys, terraced or rounded hills, with patches of glacial drift splattered on their sides, some upland blanket peatland, a few forestry plantations, hazel scrubland, grassy pastures, turloughs and, in early summer, a quite stunning profusion of flowers, flourishing in all available nooks and crannies of the limestone and on banks of glacial drift. The Burren is, without a doubt, Ireland's premier natural history jewel.

This chapter will examine the evolution of the Burren landscape and describe its distinctive flora and different types of plant communities. Why is there such a bewildering profusion and diversity of plant species, many of which are more abundant in the Burren than anywhere else in Ireland or Britain? Here arctic-alpine plants rub petals with 'southern belles' from the Mediterranean area. With such a curious flora, what about the fauna? What about the turlough, such a special feature of the Burren karst landscape and one shared with parts of former Yugoslavia, especially Slovenia, Croatia and Montenegro? These turloughs are hollows, or depressions, on the land surface which fill with water welling upwards through a 'swallow hole' from subterranean depths in winter, and drain out during the summer. Not only do these temporary lakes nurture a flora and fauna adapted to alternating water levels but they form part of an important winter habitat to many thousands of wildfowl that visit Ireland from two major European areas – arctic Russia/northern Europe and Greenland/Iceland. But first a few words about the history and origin of the landscape.

What do the rocks say?

Ireland has the largest continuous area of Carboniferous limestone in Europe. It begins in Dublin Bay and extends across the country to the Aran Islands, Galway Bay. Most of it is smothered under more recent geological deposits, including great swathes of drift dropped or moulded by the glaciers or, particularly in the Midlands, by the extensive vegetable blankets of raised bogs or peatlands. As a consequence, the beneficial impact of the limestone on the flora in such parts is very reduced if not totally cancelled. In only a few places has the limestone been thrust up by the deep Hercynian convulsions, cleaned of its more recent burdens by erosion, and exposed to the light of day. Where this has happened the flora bears testimony to the change. The better-known Carboniferous limestone areas in Ireland are around Lough Erne in Co. Fermanagh; the Benbulbin mountain range in Sligo and Leitrim; the wide flat region stretching eastwards of the great Loughs of Conn, Carra, Mask and Corrib in Galway and Mayo; the Aran Islands; the limestone outcrops around Lough Ree in Co. Westmeath and Lough Derg in Tipperary, Clare and Galway; the limestone of central Clare extending southwards across the Shannon to emerge as a Burren outlier around Askeaton and Mullough in Co. Limerick; and the promontories and islands of much of Lough Leane and Muckross Lake in the Killarney National Park, Co. Kerry. All these areas display unusual and often striking vegetation. But there is no place to rival the Burren, Co. Clare – either in Ireland or in Britain – where the legacy of largely naked Carboniferous limestone occurs in its purest and most extensive form.

Around 340 million years ago Ireland, along with the rest of northwest

Limestone terraces near Glencolumbkille. These originated during periods of ocean retreat between the deposition of the carboniferous limestone.

Europe, was inundated by a warm, almost tropical, sea that came and went, drowning and evacuating the land in turn for approximately 40 million years. This warm milieu hosted a high concentration of plants and animals. The animals, in particular, took full advantage of the bountiful supply of calcium, oxygen and carbon that impregnated the waters to manufacture their stiff shells and body parts. When these plants and animals expired, their remains fell, like continuous snow, to the oozy, muddy bottom, where they accumulated and resulted in the deep limestone beds, sometimes 1,000 m thick and more, surfacing in the Burren today. During this protracted deposition of sediments there were long periods when the sea retreated, exposing tracts of the ocean floor before flooding it again. The major terraces carved in the Burren hills, especially on the eastern side of Glencolumbkille, date from this period of ocean retreat. Frederick Foot, a government geologist who mapped the Burren in 1862, wrote:

'The limestone rises into hills, upwards of 1,000 feet in height above the sea, intersected by valleys and deep ravines, their sides being in a step-like succession of bold bluffs and steep perpendicular cliffs with broad terraces of bare rock at their feet, which present to the geologist all the appearance of sea beaches, elevated from time to time.'[2]

Later, when the ocean was in full possession of the land again, sands, dark muds and clays were washed into the sea by rivers flowing from other raised lands away from Ireland, over millions of years, turning the sea from a clear to a muddy, murky environment. These new additions settled out on top of the limestone and became hardened and compressed to form the Upper Carboniferous sandstones and shales. The sea then dropped again, allowing growth of tropical forests on reefs and spits, the debris from which, accumulating in backwaters and lagoons, became transformed into coal. However, most of the coal that was formed in what was to become Ireland was stripped off later by erosion and by the Ice Age glaciers. The only two small exploitable deposits were at Castlecomer, Co. Kilkenny, and Arigna, Co. Leitrim. They have been mined past the point of economic gain. Bigger intact deposits are located under the Irish Sea in the Kish Bank, off the Dublin coastline; there are also two small deposits at Bridgetown, Co. Wexford.

The Carboniferous period came to an end about 300 million years ago when movements in the bowels of the earth under Europe and Asia, known as the Hercynian, pushed the deeper Carboniferous and other rock deposits up above the rest of the land. The youngest and uppermost coal layers were stripped away by frost, wind and water erosion. The underlying sandstones and grits were then laid bare and worn off in turn, revealing below the older and lower Carboniferous limestones that now command the Burren landscape. However, due to divergent upthrustings and different eroding forces, some of the capping layers endured. For example, impressive sandstone deposits have survived at the Cliffs of Moher, to the southwest of the Burren, where they preside dramatically, revealing their horizontal bedding, some 204 m above the rumbling Atlantic Ocean. Some other small patches of the upper Carboniferous shales have escaped erosion in the Burren proper – on Slieve Elva, at Poulacapple (northwest of Corkscrew Hill) and in a few other small localities. Around Lisdoonvarna, just outside the southern limits of the Burren, a few coal measure shales have persisted. These have been weathered away in places to expose deep Carboniferous limestone ravines. One can walk, in dry conditions, along these chasms, tripping along on a 300 million year old tropical sea bed while stepping on fossil remains of crinoids, the ancient relatives of starfishes and sea urchins, and other exotic fossilised plants and animals. Further on inside the ravines one can ramble on the fossil corals of *Lithostrotion, Zaphrentis* and *Carinia* and look up to the perpendicular walls of the more recently formed coal-bearing shales to observe the coiled 'Catherine wheel'-like fossil forms of *Goniatites*, the predecessors of the octopuses and squids.

Limestone pavements

The legacy of all the accumulation and stripping off processes produced the dry rocky mass of the Burren, dominated in many areas by hectare upon hectare of pale grey limestone pavements. Despite being mostly of a very dense and pure kind, i.e. made up of almost uncontaminated calcium carbonate, the rock is sometimes tainted by chert – an impure version of limestone composed of a mixture of minerals which, when weathered, yields a type of clayey residue that is washed away without forming noticeable deposits. The pavements first occurred as flat layers when the shells were building up at the bottom of the sea. Today, however, there is a bewildering array of surfaces ranging from the almost smooth to a tortuous jagged, rocky and jumbled mass of stones. These morphological differences have arisen over enormous spans of time and are the result of slight variations in the nature and structure of the rock making it more or less vulnerable to scoring, scratching, fracturing or splitting as well as deviations in the erosion processes.

Grykes traversing the limestone pavement. The microclimate in the grykes approximates that of a woodland, providing shelter and good growing conditions for a wide range of plants.

Limestone is a soft rock susceptible to water erosion whereupon it disintegrates into its component parts of calcium and magnesium carbonates that either dissolve or remain suspended in the water. The process is more rapid when the rain is slightly acidic. On virgin pavement, falling water initially makes its way by capillary action into the minute cracks and joints in the stone and these eventually open out as the limestone dissolves away to yield the characteristic gullies or grykes gaping like open cuts across much of the Burren pavement, particularly in the western areas. The wider, deeper, more pronounced grykes run along a north-south axis with smaller grykes striking off at right angles to the main seams. The clints are the big limestone blocks bounded by the grykes. Some grykes are so deep that a person could stand upright in them, mummy-like. However, most are normally no more than a metre in depth and 10–40 cm wide.

In some areas of limestone pavement the surface has escaped erosion and remains remarkably smooth. On more fractured and frost-tormented pavements there are runnels, hollows, grooves, rills, channels and pits, all adding to the extraordinary diversity of the terrain where many of the plants find their toeholds. The nature of these 'karrens', or weathered surface patterns, are determined by the chemical composition and physical texture of the limestone which make it more or less susceptible to erosion.

Many glacial erratics – some composed of granite and schists caught up in the glaciers moving south from Connemara – strew the pavements. They sit like lonesome Beckettian visitors, often on a small rock pedestal which is there because it has been protected from erosion.

About 25% of the Burren's surface is naked limestone, the remainder being covered by a mosaic of thin soil, derived from glacial drift, supporting in most cases a rich calcareous grassland. Hazel wood or scrubland is an important Burren feature which occurs on sheltered pockets of soil but also, remarkably, on stark limestone pavement. Ash, a customer of lime-rich environments, needs more than just rock on which to root and will only form woods where the blanket of soil is substantial. The only permanent river in the Burren is the Caher which arises to the northeast of Slieve Elva and flows northwest then west to debouch on Fanore beach. It survives as a river because the drift soils on the valley floor have clogged its escape holes down into the subterranean world. All other Burren rivers are half-hearted and temporary affairs. The Rathborney runs for several kilometres northeast of Caher Valley, before petering out underground. In dry periods it can disappear completely but despite this erratic behaviour it is the home of a rare caddisfly *Tinodes unicolor* which is the dominant form of insect life in the river. The case-less larvae live in tubes they construct on rocks in the river. Elsewhere in Ireland the species is only known from a site in each of Donegal and Wicklow.[3] The Castletown River too has a short life line that ends not very far from to the largest Burren turlough at Carran. Many other turloughs pepper the Burren which, together with a few permanent lakes, counterbalance the aridity of the all prevailing rocks.

Erosion

The Burren is being slowly nibbled away. Two estimates of erosion rates were made in the 1950s and 1960s, and these allow a better understanding of the history and geomorphology of the Burren. The first was carried out by a French scientist, Corbel, who based his calculations on the annual runoff of water from the study area, the average dissolved calcium carbonate content of the water and the specific gravity of the limestone.[4] Ten years later the Irish geomorphologist Williams modified these measurements by taking a higher specific gravity for the pure Burren Carboniferous limestone and making other adjustments.[5] The Williams erosion rate was 0.05 mm per annum while Corbel's estimate was about double that. However, Farrington, an experienced geomorphologist, expressed reservations as to the accuracy of these calculations because no distinction had been made between dissolved materials arising from limestone pavement, overlying banks of drift or underground sources and, more importantly, the results had been based on too few samples.[6]

The rain falling on the Burren is quickly channelled into the grykes and other orifices connecting the rock carapace to an Orphean network of caves. The acidic waters flowing off the impermeable shales capping Slieve Elva travel downwards, on the eastern side of the hill, into a complex and ramified underground water system which has resulted in the development of the largest assemblage of caves so far discovered in the Burren, the Poulnagollum–Pollelva complex, which has over 11 km of galleries. Indeed the Burren is a speleologist's dream with much remaining to be discovered about the honeycombed subterranean underworld.[7] The most famous of these underground sites is Aillwee Cave, discovered in 1944 by a local farmer Jack McGann who, following his dog which was chasing a rabbit, entered a hole in Aillwee Mountain that led him to the vaulted space. Located some 2.5 km southeast of Ballyvaghan, the cave was opened to the public in 1976 and displays a range of spectacular stalactites, underground caverns and rivers. There

Surface erosion of the pavement is hastened by the growth of certain filamentous cyanobac-teria (formerly regarded as algae) e.g. *Nostoc* spp., that flourish in small surface pools.

is even a cave that was used as a hibernation pit for a brown bear with claw mark to prove it. Some of the caves extend underwater into the Atlantic. Set along the base of a submerged cliff, at a depth of around 10 m below the low tide limit at Doolin Point, southwest of Lisdoonvarna, are the submarine entrances to the Green Holes of the Hell complex. In the sheltered confines of Anemone Arcade, part of the Hell complex, large dahlia anemones festoon the walls and common prawns grow to giant proportions, sustained by a plentiful food supply washed down by the surge of the sea.[8]

Apart from the weathering and solution of the limestone rocks into massive cave systems, the two other major impacts that have shaped and eroded the Burren have been the Ice Age and activities of man. At the start of the Ice Age, about two million years ago, glaciers swept over the Burren, scooping off most of the remaining coal measures, sandstones and shale coverings. But the details of what happened during the earliest ice movements have been obliterated by the last two glacial advances. During the first of these (the Midlandian (Main) cold stage, some 79,000–65,000 years ago) ice sheets from the Connemara mountains travelled southwards across a dry Galway Bay. Boulders were plucked up, transported and dropped as erratics, especially on the hill summits in the northern parts of the Burren. The second and last ice incursion is known as Drumlin phase of the Midlandian cold stage (35,000–13,000 years ago). It was less dramatic, coming in from the northeast and travelling towards the southwest, as evidenced by the direction of the glacial striae (scratch marks on the rocks) and by the direction of the long axes of the drumlins found south-east of Mullagh More. The striae only survived subsequent erosion on the soft limestone when they were protected afterwards by a covering of soil now removed. The glaciers also brought pure limestone glacial drift, or till, scraped

Glacial erratics, often from distant origins, have been 'dumped' on the pavement, and are sometimes found sitting on rock pedestals that have been protected from erosion.

and amassed along the way to be deposited in the Burren in varying thickness. Since the end of the glacial period there has been considerable erosion of the drift, exposing the underlying limestone rocks and adding to the already bare skeleton. During both the first and second of the final glacial advances the summits of Slieve Elva (344 m) and nearby Knockaunsmountain (299 m) – about 25 km to the southwest – stood above the surrounding sea of ice and were ice-free refuges, where some flora and fauna had a chance of surviving. The erratics conveyed by the last ice sheets were limestone, in contrast with the granite and schist boulders from Connemara of the first glacial movements. They were dropped as high as 300 m on the northern slopes of Slieve Elva and 240 m on the southern ones.[9] The deposition of sands, gravels and, most important of all, boulder clay or till, were other Ice Age legacies that make the Burren a vast theme park of glacial geomorphology.

Vegetation history

The first to try to unravel the vegetation history of the Burren since the end of the Ice Age was Watts, who investigated the pollen and macrofossil remains preserved in the muds and silt in two small loughs at Gortlecka and Rinnamona southwest of Mullagh More.[10] He found that in the late glacial period, about 11,500 years ago, when the glaciers were finally melting, a sparse and low vegetation started to grow. This was shown by pollen remains of mugwort, thrift, stonecrop, meadow-rue and members of the Caryophyllaceae, the pink family, forming a vegetation somewhat similar to that found in tundra and cold steppe environments today. Later, in the early postglacial period, the commonest macrofossils were those of mountain avens and dwarf willow. Other species included juniper, fairy flax, creeping willow, burnet rose and fringed sandwort – all present in the Burren today except the fringed sandwort which is confined to one part of the Benbulbin mountain range, Co. Sligo. Following in the footsteps of the tundra vegetation, and still in the early post-glacial period, trees rapidly established themselves – first juniper, then copses of birch and willow, then pine and hazel, then oak and elm. Aspen also grew in places while the guelder-rose occurred in the birch woods.

The absence of pollen of the spring gentian and other southern species from these muds and silt samples does not necessarily prove that they were absent in the early postglacial period, as argued by some commentators. Many south-ern species are poor pollen producers with few and small seeds. If the plants were sparsely distributed it would be difficult to encounter their pollen remains. More sampling of other mud sediments in the region would be required to dismiss the presence of spring gentian as an ancient dweller, and conclude its immigrant status. For any flowering plant to survive the Ice Age in or close to the Burren would have meant overcoming the triple blow of physi-cal destruction by glaciers, permafrost conditions and the subsequent expan-sion of woodland – which meant that such small shrubs and herbs as the moun-tain avens and spring gentians, unfit for a wooded environment, had to migrate again.

Large areas of the Burren were covered by open pine forest for a consider-able part of the postglacial period while the mosaic of hazel scrub, bare pave-ment and grasslands that characterise the region today were secondary. The conifers persisted a long time, only disappearing from the Burren about 1,500 years ago, and the reasons for their demise are not clear. The fact that they sur-vived to such a late date, despite the Burren being apparently one of the areas most densely populated by humans during the Neolithic period, seems to indi-cate that man was not an active agent in their destruction. The yew was also an important species in the vegetation history of the Burren, probably occurring in extensive woodlands in the middle part of the postglacial period from about 5,100 years ago as shown by pollen deposits in lough silts. Thereafter there was a rapid rise in its pollen deposits to constitute one fifth of all the pollen remains. This was followed by quasi-extinction: from about 2,000 years ago yew became an insignificant species in the Burren. Today some remnants still cling grimly onto the cliffs and steep slopes where it can evade the bite of the goat which is immune to the toxicity of the foliage.

Thus the Burren was heavily wooded prior to the arrival of the first Neolithic farmers some 6,000 years ago. Where there was sufficient soil in the uplands, pine and hazel dominated, while ash, elm, alder and oak formed extensive low-land woods. The rising levels of pollen from herbs and grasses dating from about 4,600 years ago suggest increasing agricultural activity and a certain amount of deforestation. Corroborative evidence of the former extent of the woodland cover in the Burren comes from the work of Ussher who, just after the turn of the century, sent over 70,000 bone remains excavated from the Edenvale, Newhall and Barntick caves, south of the Burren and near Ennis, Co. Clare, to Scharff, Keeper of the Natural History Museum, Dublin, for iden-tification. Amongst the specimens were remains of woodland birds such as the jay, sparrowhawk, great spotted woodpecker and a massive lower mandible of a finch – possibly the eastern Siberian form of the hawfinch.[11] The last two species are now extinct in Ireland. The jay, obviously more widespread in the extensive boreal period woodlands, contracted its range as the woods disap-

There are numerous megalithic remains in the Burren, testimony of a large Neolithic population, but fewer remains of later settlers. Here in the lake is a circular crannóg – a lake dwelling – constructed by Late Bronze Age people.

peared and survived, as a sort of relict species, cowering in the remaining broadleaved woodlands of Co. Wicklow. Since the turn of the century, however, it has broken out from Wicklow and eastern Ireland to spread gradually to most woodland areas throughout the country, although it still remains scarce in some regions.

The Neolithic and later settlers were possibly responsible for exposing some of the limestone pavement seen in the Burren today although the persistence of the pine forests to about 1,500 years ago is a sign that woodland removal was not widespread nor wholesale. Hazel scrublands and other woods would have been cleared first, freeing up the thin soil skin underneath to be developed as grassland for grazing cattle and sheep. If grazing pressure had been intense then some of the slim layers of soil would have been candidates for erosion, with material washing down into grykes, gullies and cracks. However, there is no hard evidence to show that the drift cover was more extensive in the post-glacial period than it is today. In fact, evidence is lacking as to whether the limestone pavement is being increasingly exposed or increasingly colonised by vegetation. It is very evident, nonetheless, that when grazing animals are removed from the Burren pastures hazel scrub is very quick to reinvade not only the fields but limestone pavement too.

Early and later botanists

The flora of the Burren has attracted naturalists for hundreds of years. The first known published records date from the observations of the clergyman Richard Heaton, from England, who visited the Burren in the late 1640s. He saw mountain avens, spring gentians and juniper which he reported to the

British botanist Richard Howe who then published the records in *Phytologia Britannica* in 1650. The next published record was a close relation of the tall and white-flowered meadowsweet but smaller with clearly different pinnated leaves (lobed leaves with the leaflets arranged in two ranks on opposite sides of the axis). This was the dropwort, still confined to the Burren area today, and appearing in K'Eogh's herbal *Botanalogia Universalis Hibernica* in 1735 – 'it grows ... wild in the barony of Burrin'. After the turn of the century Walter Wade, first Professor of Botany at the Dublin (later 'Royal' Dublin) Society, visited the Burren, noted several species and published the first record of the attractive, yellow-flowered, shrubby cinquefoil in 1804.[12] By the middle of the century the reputation of the Burren as a centre for wild flowers was gathering momentum. Botanical rambles were becoming vogue, one of the earliest in 1852 being led by a Dublin clergyman, the Rev. Thaddeus O'Mahony, whose purpose it was to get people acquainted with the magnificent works of the Creator.[13] Following him was Foot who, upon being extremely taken by the local flora, wrote the first extensive paper on the botany of this region, published in 1864. It included notes on the ecology of 114 listed species and the first botanical map of the Burren. When describing mountain avens which, he noted, completely carpeted large areas, he reported that: 'The old woody stems are much used as a fuel' – a reflection of the antiquity of the avens, old enough to have woody stems. Curiously Foot makes no reference to hazel either as a species or as part of scrub-woodland. Ash is mentioned as 'very abundant in the dwarf form' while holly, yew, juniper, creeping willow and other woody species are recorded in locations where they still occur today. Foot advised that maps of botanical districts, including the stations of the different species, be prepared so that 'In years to come, by means of such documents, botanists could form an idea as to whether certain species were dying out or increasing.'[2] Fifteen years after him, Thomas Corry, a young and brilliant botanist from Northern Ireland took a ramble in the selfsame spot and published his results.[14]

Despite Foot's advice the first major ecological study was not executed until a hundred years later when the investigations by Ivimey-Cook & Proctor appeared in 1966.[15] Sixteen years earlier Lousley had provided an account of the Burren's flora in *Wildflowers of Chalk and Limestone*.[16] In 1957 Webb initiated the Burren Survey Project, sponsored by the British Ecological Society. His *Catalogue Raisonné, a systematic list of the plants with brief notes on their distribution* appeared in 1962.[17] Webb provided a delimitation for the Burren that embraced the true karst region, extending over some 450 km^2, and reflecting a certain ecological coherence. Since then there has been a host of scientific publications and books,[18,19,20,21] but Webb & Scannell's *Flora of Connemara and the Burren* embodies the most comprehensive and detailed account of the Burren flora published to date.[22]

Why so many flowers?

Although the Burren occupies only 0.5% of the area of Ireland it holds a remarkable 81% of the 900 native plant species found in the whole of the country. This special position is enhanced further by the fact that there are in the Burren – and the Aran Islands – 21 plants which, although occurring sparingly in other parts of the country, are more numerous here than elsewhere. Nine of them, listed below, are even more numerous than anywhere in

The Burren National Park presently embraces the Mullagh More area and contains some of the Burren's most interesting features. Nevertheless the whole Burren is of special scientific interest.

Scotland, England (the Upper Teesdale region of Yorkshire has a good representative range of the Burren flora) or Wales: maidenhair fern, mountain avens, Irish eyebright, spring gentian, dense-flowered orchid, thyme broomrape, shrubby cinquefoil and fen violet.

So why is there such a profusion and diversity of species crammed into this relatively minute area of Ireland – a veritable Ali Baba's cave for the botanist?

Limestone soils, replete with calcium carbonate, support more plants than any other soil type in the islands of Ireland or Britain. They are termed base-rich because of the presence of calcium and magnesium which, in chemical terms, are bases as opposed to acids. Soils deficient in bases are described as poor or acid. Lime-loving plants such as many of the orchids are called calcicoles. Large quantities of calcium are not vital for the calcicoles *per se* – although some is needed for the construction of cell walls – but calcium plays an essential indirect role in stimulating the activity of soil bacteria, especially those which absorb atmospheric nitrogen by a complicated chemical process of nitrogen fixation. This fixation leads to the formation of nitrates which, upon seeping out of the bacteria, become dissolved in water and make themselves available for absorption by the roots of plants – thus supplying them with one of the essential growth nutrients. This is the reason why lime, which is strictly calcium oxide obtained by burning limestone rock (calcium carbonate), has to be added to acidic soils, to trigger the bacteria into appropriate nitrogen fixing action. The two other essential plant growth nutrients are phosphates (derived from phosphorus) and potassium.

Nowhere else in Ireland is there such a collection and concentration of orchids as found in the Burren. Of the 27 species known in the country, 22 occur in the Burren. Their profusion here is due to the lime-rich soil which encourages the growth and activity of microscopic fungi known as mycorrhiza. The latter play a fundamental role in the nourishment of the orchid seedlings as they lie in a sort of torpor between germination and sending up the leaves that then provide the means for the orchid's existence.

The limestone soils in the Burren are classified as rendzinas: shallow, crumbly, well-drained and organic soils allowing easy penetration by roots, and ingress of air. Such conditions make for optimal efficiency of microorganisms, including the nitrogen-fixing bacteria. The well-drained limestone soils are also free from many toxins that inhibit growth and which are associated with waterlogged, acidic soils.

Not only do plants benefit from the presence of calcium carbonate but the naked limestone rock acts as a giant storage heater, boosting and stimulating growth. On warm sunny days the temperature of the rock surface can be 8°C higher than the adjacent air, whose mean annual temperature is about 10°C, with the lowest readings occurring in January at a mean of about 6°C, and the highest in July at about 15°C. Frosts and snowfall do occur, but infrequently and are of short duration. Precipitation levels are the lowest along the west coast with just over 100 cm per annum – about the national average. However, around and on the more elevated locations in the western Burren, rainfall is higher – Corrofin 124 cm, Ballyvaghan 152 cm and Kilfenora 133 cm. The average relative humidity is high and benefits the plants in sheltered locations, whereas on exposed ground, this gain is lost to strong winds which induce considerable evapotranspiration – summer average 42.5 cm, winter average 12.5 cm – leading to desiccation of the plants and inhibition of growth when conditions become severe.

The presence of calcium in the soil facilitates the delivery of phosphates and potassium to the plants. However, as both are generally in short supply in the calcium-rich Burren soils, the fast-growing, nutrient-greedy, herbs and taller grasses cannot get enough of them to shoot up quickly into their usual tall and straggly forms in the spring. As a result, many of the ground-hugging plants, including most of the rarities and Burren specialities, have a chance to get on with their own lives without becoming swamped and deprived of essential light by lanky competition. Other ecological factors are also working in favour of the petite ground dwellers. One is the strong and often persistent westerly winds, making it difficult for anything too high to survive; the other factor, and a very major one, is the risk of being grazed by cattle, sheep, goats, horses, hares and rabbits, which inhabit the Burren in larger numbers than a casual observer would first suspect. D'Arcy & Hayward state that the density of sheep, cattle and dairy cattle in 1989 for the District Electoral Divisions of Ballyvaghan and Corrofin – covering 62,500 ha of the Burren – was about one livestock unit per 0.81 ha.[20]

Cattle, sheep, goats and pigs have been present in the Burren as farm animals from at least Christian times, as evidenced by bone remains excavated at the Cathercommaun ring fort, 5 km northeast of Corrofin, dating from about 800 AD or earlier. During the excavations in 1932 just over 4,000 kg of animal bones were recovered. Of these about 96% were of cattle, with 1% each for sheep, goats and pigs while the remaining 1% was split between red deer and horses.[23] In the earlier Neolithic period the farmers were almost certainly utilising the large tracts of upland pastures for grazing cattle.

Botanical highlights from Black Head to Poulsallagh

One of the best places to visit to enjoy the Burren flora is the 10 km coastal strip meandering from Black Head to Poulsallagh. The landscape has the appearance, especially when the flowers are at their best at the end of May and early June, of a gigantic rock garden, strewn with a bewildering mix of species. The area could be considered as a fractal of the Burren, i.e. a miniature replica of the whole region. There are extensive limestone pavements, smooth and fractured, grykes stuffed with vegetation and glacial erratics strewn around haphazardly. Limestone pastures stretch out from either side of the road, bristling with many different species of grasses, herbs, orchids and other colourful plants. Further out the escarpments and hillsides slope gently and orderly upwards in horizontal strata. Pockets of hazel scrubland hug the hills in places. Thriving inside these thickets, in moist and mild conditions, are liverworts, mosses, ferns and lichens which compete with each other to smother the boulder-strewn floor or the stems and branches of the runt trees.

In the Burren the rules that preclude many plants from sharing the same perimeter have been rudely transgressed. So has the condition of altitude. Flourishing at sea level is the spring gentian which in its European alpine habitats rarely descends below 900 m, and the mountain avens, one of the few genuine arctic-alpine species which on its home territory lives happily with snow on top and/or a frozen soil (permafrost) underneath for most of the year. The leaves of the mountain avens are waxy and hairy underneath – a feature suited to combat evapotranspiration caused by high winds. Its hospitality towards the much-needed pollinating insects extends to providing a solarium within the flower cup, where temperatures are several degrees higher than the surrounding air – no effort is spared to attract winged visitors when there is little time to reproduce. It grows here vigorously, forming dense swards of giant strawberry-like cream flowers – not very far from the maidenhair fern and the wild madder, both dwellers of the southerly Mediterranean–Atlantic regions.

The profusion of mountain avens is quite remarkable and led Praeger to exclaim: 'He who has viewed the thousands of acres of this arctic-alpine plant in full on the limestones of the Burren region of Clare, from hill-top down to sea level, has seen one of the loveliest sights that Ireland has to offer to the botanist.'[24] Interspersed with the mountain avens along the Black Head–Poulsallagh coastal strip are blue moor-grass which dominates all grass-

Blue moor-grass is very much a grass of pastures and rocky areas on limestone. It is more abundant in the Burren than anywhere else in Ireland.

land communities in the Burren – and is easily recognised by its steely blue flowerheads in late April/early May; bearberry, a prostrate, mat-forming ever-green undershrub with pink flowers and red edible berries, no doubt eaten by bears in the Arctic – it is locally abundant, especially on hill tops where it replaces mountain avens, but is apparently decreasing for unknown reasons; the dense-flowered orchid, small (12–25 cm high) with greenish-white flowers packed in a short tight spike, sparsely distributed in the Burren despite the congenial nature of the soil. Its distribution outside Ireland is almost entirely Mediterranean (it is found on the Isle of Man, but is otherwise absent from Britain). Finally clumps of startling bright blue spring gentians are 'the chief glory of the Burren flora'; according to Webb & Scannell. They grow best on thin soil overlaying limestone pavement. The flowers are bright blue, solitary, and their petal tube or corolla is 15–25 mm long. Groups of plants often occur together in large mats. Its peak flowering time is 10–15 May. Strictly speaking gentians are not arctic-alpine or alpine plants (see p.94) – despite being com-mon in European alpine pastures.

Amongst the other plants are bloody crane's-bill with big, bright purple-crim-son flowers (up to 2.5–3 cm in diameter), adding another contrast to the grey limestone pavement. It is one of the most spectacular Burren plants with one of the longest flowering seasons – from May to August – common both on lime-stone pavement and in rocky grassland. The Irish saxifrage is a very variable species, sporting different degrees of hairiness, compactness as well as differ-ent leaf lobes. It sometimes cross-breeds with the closely related mossy sax-ifrage. Growing in large conspicuous clumps, often in association with thrift and pellitory-of-the-wall, it can be seen emblazoning the ground on the sea-ward side of the Black Head–Poulsallagh road. A stiff, reddish-pink stem, up to 10 cm long, arising from a rosette of green and reddish-coloured lobed leaves leads to a white flower. The Irish saxifrage looks very similar to its close rela-tive the mossy saxifrage which, however, occurs more frequently in the central areas of the Burren than in the western or eastern parts. According to Webb all forms of the Irish saxifrage may be distinguished from mossy saxifrage by the absence of creeping, leafy stolons and by the erect flower buds, and by the fact that the leaf-segments, though they may be mucronate (sharp-pointed), do not have the long arista (fine hair-like tip) found in mossy saxifrage.[25] Other plants in the area are limestone bedstraw, spring sandwort, stone bram-ble and wild madder.

A most attractive and intriguing alpine species in the Poulsallagh area is Irish eyebright, which differs slightly from other Continental forms. Its diagnostic features are its bushy, shrubby growth, sometimes revealing a copper colour, its narrow and acute toothed leaves and the absence of hairs on the margin of the fruit capsules. Its white petals are fused, forming the corolla. In the centre of the flower is a yellow eye spot and there are two well-marked lips to the flower – the upper one with two and the lower with three notched lobes. The Burren carries such a profusion of it that Foot wrote in 1864: 'If any one should ask "Why do you mention such a very common plant as the humble eye-bright?" my answer is "Go to Burren, and tell me if you ever saw it growing so luxuri-antly at such elevations, and of such a size as it does there."'[2] Irish eyebright occurs in suitable habitats along the western seaboard from Limerick to Donegal. Outside Ireland you would have to travel to the Vosges Mountains in Europe or to Gotland in southeast Sweden to catch another glimpse of it.

Irish eyebright has its Irish
headquarters in the Burren.

Despite its pretty name and attractive colouring, Irish eyebright lives as a par-
asite on the abundant and prostrate wild thyme, plugging its roots into its
host's stems and sucking out nutrients. The thyme, which does not manifest
any signs of duress, is obviously an attractive host as two other species are also
tapping its resources: dodder, a slender and twining annual with a thin and
rootless red stem, lacking hairs and chlorophyll, with pale pink flowers scattered and prostrate along the stem; and the thyme broomrape, a bizarre reddish-brown plant with flowers arranged in a spike. The broomrape at least is
justified in that it is without any chlorophyll and therefore unable to manufacture its own food. Dodder will also parasitize common bird's-foot-trefoil,
lady's bedstraw and a few others.

There are five specialities from the Poulsallagh area. The first is the pyramidal bugle, a low, squat and somewhat hairy plant, although sometimes attaining 15 cm, with purple-blue flowers, half hidden in large bracts arranged in
spikes, and could be described as a shy flowerer. It grows as a rare species in
the grassland sward and is notoriously difficult to find. Not known from anywhere else in Ireland apart from a few specimens on Doon Hill, southwest of
Ballyconneely, Connemara, it presents a boreal-montane distribution on the
European mainland. The hoary rock-rose, a yellow-flowered lime-demanding
creeping undershrub, occurs no where else either and forms big sunny patches on the drift-covered pavements between Black Head and Poulsallagh. It is a
rare but widely distributed species in Britain and widespread on the Continent.
The lesser meadow-rue is a tall member of the buttercup family – up to 1 m
high – with greenish flowers, found in crevices along the same coastal strip as
the hoary rock-rose. The Scottish scurvygrass, a small hairless perennial with
fleshy heart-shaped leaves, has a thickish stem and white flowers. It is fairly
common on exposed coastal rocks near Poulsallagh. A controversial species,
often treated as a subspecies or ecotype of the common scurvygrass, it is,
according to Webb & Scannell, distinctive in its extreme form because of its
very small size, dark green leaves and white flowers which, when they first
open, do not project above the leaves.[22]

The fifth speciality in the Poulsallagh area is the maidenhair fern, found growing in the sheltered and moist security of deep grykes. Its distribution within Europe is Atlantic–Mediterranean rather than a perceived more restricted focus in the Mediterranean area. Its scarcity and attractive appearance led it into many Victorian Fern Cabinets during the Victorian collecting fern craze. There is now a large cultivated stock of the native maidenhair fern in garden centres, as well as several exotic species including *Adiantum cunneatum*. The maidenhair fern is dainty with very black, shiny and naked stalks bearing leaves up to 30 cm long. The pinnules of the leaf are fan-shaped with straight sides and a curved almost wavy outer margin. The leaves die down from November to February. Lhwyd, who discovered it on the Aran Islands around the end of the seventeenth century, signalled his discovery in a note published in 1712. Within Ireland it is confined to the west, from Clare to Donegal, but nowhere does it attain such abundance as in the Burren, although it is locally frequent on the

Maidenhair fern is an Atlantic-Mediterranean species, only able to survive in the protection of the moist and sheltered grykes in the Burren. Nowhere else in Ireland does it grow in such profusion as in the Burren.

Aran islands. O'Mahony, quoting earlier texts, mentions that an immense quantity of this fern used to be brought from the Burren for making 'capillaire', a hair improver. In the days of old herbalists maidenhair fern was made into a syrup which was not only efficacious for many diseases but, again, especially potent when applied to the hair for promoting the length of tresses.[13,26] The scientific name for maidenhair fern is *Adiantum capillus-veneris*, and *capillus-veneris* means 'hair of Venus' which must reflect the ancient use of the fern as an improver of human hair.

Limestone pavement

Naked limestone pavement occupies large areas of the Burren and comes in many different shapes, from smooth to highly fractured and rough – almost rubbly. Many of the grykes hewn in the rock have soil-covered floors, providing an attractive environment for plants that enjoy moisture and protection.

The microclimate on the gryke floor is broadly similar to that of a Burren hazel woodland as regards temperature, light intensity and relative humidity. Measurements in both habitats showed little variation between these parameters. As a result there are considerable similarities in their floras. Some microclimatic differences, however, do exist and these are thought sufficient to explain floristic elements unique to the two habitats. In a study located on the south side of the Caher river valley, some 4 km south of Black Head, and extending over 1 ha of pavement grykes and hazel woodland, seven species of higher plants were found to be restricted to the grykes and were absent from the woodland. In shallow grykes (< 55 cm) the species present, in descending order of occurrence, were herb-robert, wood sage, wild thyme, purple moor-grass, bloody crane's-bill, bracken and the fern hart's-tongue.[27] The species found in both the grykes and the woodland were blue moor-grass, sheep's fescue, violet species, ivy, burnet rose, maidenhair spleenwort, bramble, false brome grass and hazel.

Apart from the smooth limestone pavement, the other major type of limestone pavement has a shattered surface, also manifesting grykes, and is found especially in the eastern parts of the Burren. Walking across it can be hazardous as the rocks are unstable and sharp. This jagged environment is probably due to frost splitting and splintering. There is less protection here for plants, so fewer species occur than in the grykes. Wood sage – normally found on acidic soil but plentiful in the Burren – blackthorn, burnet rose and the purple-flowered herb-robert are the commonest species on the broken pavement.

Grassland communities

Surveying plant communities is a far less exciting business than chasing the beautiful and the rare, but it is an essential activity to botanical understanding. Twenty vegetation communities have been identified within the Burren using the quantitative and mathematical techniques of Braun-Blanquet.[15] These communities range from salt marshes, fens and limestone grassland to woodlands. While nobody has published details about the percentage cover of the Burren by the various communities, it is clear that grassland predominates, covering up to approximately 20% of the area.

Amongst the limestone grasslands the commonest and most characteristic community is known technically as a *Dryas octopetala–Hypericum pulchrum* association because both mountain avens, *D. octopetala*, and slender St John's wort, *H. pulchrum*, are its two main indicator species together with up to 50 other plants, grasses, bryophytes, lichens and algae. This community, found on the thin, dark and organic rendzina soils overlaying the bare limestone ranges from the north and west coasts to the flat, low-lying country between Kinvarra and Gort, and stretches to Corrofin in the east and to Lisdoonvarna in the south. The surprise species in this community is heather, which is normally a calcifuge, not usually found in a calcareous environment. But if calcium is leached or lost out of the soil by too much rain, a peaty layer can develop, thus allowing heather to form mats. Chalk-limestone heaths are well known in Britain where the heather is mixed with calcicole plants. Heathers occurring in such habitats are probably calcium tolerant ecotypes.

Heather frequently dominates the community together with a group of large calcareous mosses, including *Breutelia chrysocoma*, *Hylocomium brevirostre* and *Neckera crispa*. Other characteristic plants of limestone grassland are squinancywort, fairy flax and wild thyme. Several of the Burren specialities – Irish eyebright and the spring gentian – are also members of this community. The pioneering plants on organic material or soil on the bare limestone rocks are mountain avens, blue moor-grass, wild thyme and the cushion-like moss, *Tortella tortuosa*.

As the grassland becomes more dominated by mountain avens it is transformed into a heath in which mountain avens occupies up to 75% of the vegetational cover. This species-rich community is confined to the northwestern area of the Burren. On soils containing a high percentage of drift material, the mountain avens heath evolves into a grassland, with a different floral character, dominated by mountain everlasting and mouse-ear hawkweed. The limestone grassland changes its character on exposed slopes and crests of hills where, in its most extreme form, mountain avens, crowberry and blue moor-grass form another open community. Here dark-red helleborine finds its favourite niche. The presence of both heather and slender St John's wort increases with progressive leaching of the soil.

Mountain avens is most abundant in the Black Head area of the Burren.

Eventually the limestone grasslands grade into the more intensively grazed and managed agricultural grasslands supported by heavier and more clayey soils. These are often described as anthropogenic grasslands. They hold far fewer species than limestone grasslands and belong to the Centaureo–Cynosuretum plant association dominated by the common knapweed, Centaurea nigra – displaying bushy pink flowers – and crested dog's-tail grass, Cynosurus cristatus, whose tightly packed green flowers are arranged in a one-sided spike on a long wiry stem, 50–60 cm tall. Some farmers believe that that the wiry spikes left over winter often damage the eyes of grazing sheep. It has also been observed that the advance of grassland, under heavy grazing, has led to a serious loss of both mountain avens and bearberry, especially in the Black Head area of the Burren, during the period 1960–80.[28]

Hazel scrub and woodlands

Another extensive vegetation community in the Burren is hazel scrub, classified in the Braun-Blanquet system as a Corylus avellana–Oxalis acetosella association because hazel, C. avellana, is the dominant tree and wood-sorrel, O. acetosella, the dominant ground herb within the wood. Hazel thrives best in calcicole habitats and its scrub woodland is widespread throughout the Burren. Judging by its distribution, especially in areas on the west coast that would appear hostile because they are too windswept for its development, it could easily colonise much of the landscape if permitted. After the different types of grassland it is the next most extensive plant community. Apart from their intrinsic botanical interest, especially the rich bryophyte flora, these woodlands provide the only effective shelter for the bird and mammal populations within the Burren.

Hazel scrub has colonised much of the agricultural landscape.

Hazel is the dominant species while whitethorn, blackthorn or sloe and spindle-tree also occur. The natural climax of the Burren area would be an ash–hazel woodland, but this only exists in small fragments where farmers and timber merchants have not cut it down, or cleared it away with bulldozers in the last 20 years.

Where there is good shelter such as in the Glen of Clab, Poulavallan and around Slievecarran, other woody species such as rowan, downy birch, ash, goat willow and eared willow will get a chance to grow and achieve dominion over and above the hazel scrub.[15] These areas hold the best developed and probably most natural woodlands of the Burren.

On entering a dense hazel scrub, one is struck by the overwhelming presence of mosses and lichens. Indeed, the moss enthusiast is in for a field day. The commonest species in the hazel scrub are *Eurhynchium striatum*, *Thuidium tamariscinum*, *Hylocomium brevirostre*, *H. splendens*, *Rhytidiadelphus triquetrus*, *Ctenidium molluscum*, *Hypnum cupressiforme* and *Thamnobryum alopecurum*. Amongst the impressive epiphytic flora swaddling the branches and stems *Ulota crispa*, *U. bruchii*, *U. phyllantha* and *U. calvescens* are the commonest.[29] Regarding lichens, Mitchell states that young hazel twigs are first colonised by *Naetrocymbe punctiformis* and *Tomasellia gelatinosa*, which are succeeded by *Arthonia cinnabarina* and *Pyrenula macrospora*. In the final stages of colonisation *Nephroma laevigatum*, *Pannaria rubiginosa* and *Degelia plumbea* become dominant. The widespread and often luxuriant development of these species is a clear indication of a pollution-free environment.[30]

The flowering plants may be restricted by the dense closed canopy of hazel and by the presence of too many large rocks in the ground, but a representative range would include all the following typical woodland species: primrose, wood sanicle, wild strawberry, barren strawberry, bitter-vetch, wood avens, slender St John's wort, germander speedwell, enchanter's nightshade and wood-sorrel.

Butterflies, moths, snails and woodlice

The deluge of colour pouring forth from the limestone grasslands is witness to a riotous insect population, many of which poke the bright flowers with their long and slender proboscises, while the leaves, shoots and other juicy parts provide meals for heaving caterpillars. Of the myriad of invertebrates, butterflies and, to a lesser extent, moths, are the most noticeable and attractive. They are moreover generally the least confusing because there are so few of them and they are relatively easy to identify.

An impressive 90% of the resident butterflies in Ireland (28 species) occur in the Burren. The reason for such a concentration is due to the fact that most butterflies feed on calcicole plants, which occur in prolific density in the Burren. For example, common bird's-foot-trefoil and kidney vetch host the caterpillars of the common blue and small blue respectively, while the caterpillars of the stunning yellow-coloured brimstone and the brown hairstreak – particularly important in the Burren – forage on the leaves of the calcicole shrubs sea-buckthorn and blackthorn respectively.

A particular group of butterflies well represented in the Burren are the fritillaries. The rarest is the pearl-bordered fritillary whose caterpillars feed on violets. The marsh fritillary is also scarce nationally and is local in the Burren. Its caterpillars favour devil's bit scabious and plantains. The silver-washed fritillary is also considered a woodland butterfly like the pearl-bordered fritillary. The dark green fritillary is identified by its all silver white spots on its hind underwing. Its preferred habitat is open, flowery fields and it is the only fritillary considered to be widespread throughout the Burren.

Until 1949, the Burren received little attention from zoologists apart from lepidopterists. One rare butterfly and one rare moth amongst other interesting species attracted them. The first was the pearl-bordered fritillary. Within

Red admiral, one of the many butterflies abundant in the Burren.

Ireland it is restricted to the Burren where it is scarce and local, while in Britain it is fairly widespread, especially in the south. It has been thought that its presence in the Burren may be because it is a woodland relict and the region was wooded until quite recently. However, vegetation history does not confirm this theory and the presence of this rare species remains unexplained. The rare moth is the transparent burnet moth – confined to the Burren in Ireland and a rarity in Britain. In the Burren it is local but very abundant where it occurs. There are also records from other parts of Clare and from Galway and Limerick. Most Irish specimens belong to the subspecies *Zygaena purpuralis hibernica*.[31] Like the other brightly coloured burnet moths it is red and black but instead of having five or six spots on the forewing it has long streaks of red. The conspicuous costume of the burnets, akin to a danger signal, make birds wary of them, so much so that they can fly safely throughout the day.

Many of the night-flying moths in the Burren play an important role in fertilising pale-coloured orchids. The flowers, easier to spot at night by the insects than the darker varieties, exude highly scented chemicals. As the moths come forward and stick their twitching proboscises into the sweet-smelling cavities for a suck of nectar, they unwittingly pollinate and fertilise the flowers. Both the pink-flowered fragrant orchid and the white-flowered lesser butterfly-orchid are on the moth's night flight path.

Entomologists were galvanised into action in 1949 by the discovery of a remarkable noctuid moth never previously recorded in Ireland or in Britain.[32] It was the Burren green, *Calamia tridens occidentalis*, a subspecies not encountered elsewhere in the world. How such a stoutly built and large grass-coloured moth – with a wing span of 37–42 mm – could have escaped the sharp-eyed entomologists is quite a mystery. It frequents flat areas of limestone where the grass and other vegetation grow taller. Within the Burren it is locally abundant and best known from the coast of Galway Bay, from Black Head to Ballyvaghan, but also occurs at Fanore strand and up to 30 km inland.[33] Its larvae are greenish-brown, about 32 mm long with black spots. The natural food plant for the larvae is possibly blue moor-grass but they can be reared on annual meadow-grass or cock's-foot grass. A good place to search for the Burren green, as well as for other moths and butterflies, is around the Poulsallagh area in the southwestern part of the Burren during August and September. However, as with most moths, it shelters during the day and is difficult to discern when sitting on a green background. Around Ballyvaghan is another good spot for it. Other forms of the species are widely distributed in Europe and also occur in Asia. Following on this discovery was another surprise, but not quite so momentous as the species involved was a very small and insignificant-looking 'plume' moth, *Alucita icterodactyla*, previously unknown to Ireland and Britain. After being located in 1952 in the Burren, it was discovered in Cornwall.[34] Elsewhere it is confined to southern France, Corsica and Spain. Another plume moth *Platyptilia tesseradactylea*, first recorded in 1898, is confined to the Burren apart from occasional records in Galway and Tyrone. It is also widely distributed in Continental Europe.

Land snails thrive particularly well in the Burren because of the rich available sources of lime so essential for the construction of their shells. Thus within the Burren there are probably more species of terrestrial snails than anywhere else in Ireland – up to 70. They become most apparent after rain, when they emerge from the rock crevices, nooks and crannies to chomp their way through calcium-rich herbage, algae and other palatable vegetable food. The commonest kind is the large and rounded brown-lipped snail which comes in a multitude of colours and different banding patterns that are controlled genetically. Considerable selective pressure is exerted by the song thrush which preys more vigorously on those snails that blend in least well with their background environments. Amongst the 70-odd species there are tall, conical spire-shaped types – *Balea perversa* – and extremely small snails, only a few millimetres long, such as the translucent *Vallonia excentrica*.

One primitive-looking crustacean that provides a link with the geological past of the region is the sea slater. This giant dark grey woodlouse – up to 3 cm long – is common around the Irish coastline, within the splash zone, a few metres from the upper shoreline. To stay moist and damp it shelters in cracks, crevices and under stones. It is one of seven different species of woodlice that were found in the Burren during a survey in May 1967.[35] The only interesting one from a biogeographic point of view was *Metoponorthus cingendus*, found at Poulsallagh and close to Burren village. It has a Lusitanian distribution, and occurs elsewhere in southern Irish coastal counties, southwest England, Wales, and along the Atlantic coast of northern France, Spain and Portugal. A curious absentee from the Burren was *Armadillidium vulgare*, found mainly in sand dune areas and very common along the south and east coasts. It occurred further south outside the Burren in the dunes at Lehinch, Co. Clare. At Fanore dunes *Philoscia muscorum* occupies its ecological niche, for reasons unknown.

Other invertebrates

Very few invertebrate surveys of the Burren have been carried out. When there have been investigations they invariably turn up new species, not previously recorded in Ireland, whose distribution elsewhere is generally arctic, northern or Lusitanian. The relatively high frequency of new discoveries is a reflection of lack of previous field work. One such survey concerned the invertebrates found in the grykes of limestone pavement near Fermoyle in August 1959. As part of this work *Rhopalopyx monticola*, a hemipteran, was found west of Corrofin, its only station outside the Pyrenees. Another bug, *Berytinus montanus*, new to Ireland, was discovered on an ancient 'green road' near Corker Pass in 1985 where it feeds on black medick.[36] A fly, *Sarcophaga soror*, turned up on the limestone pavement at the top of Corkscrew Hill. The fly is now known as *Pierretia soror*. Since its original discovery by Richards in 1960[37] it has been found at Corrofin and Fermoyle in the Burren, and in Co. Tipperary. Outside the Burren, it is widespread in Europe from Germany to Spain, but is unknown in Britain.[38]

Few people realise that mosquitoes occur in Ireland and that malaria was once endemic in Cork. Altogether 18 species have been recorded and one of these, *Anopheles algeriensis*, has been found only in the Burren, at Lough Bunny. It is also rare in Britain. It appears to be a relict associated with calcareous conditions.[39]

Weevils are small beetles, 3–10 mm long. They are amongst the most endearing of all insects because of their odd profile, slow-moving habits and often bright, attractive colouring. About 2,500 species are known from France, 530 from Britain and a paltry 220 from Ireland. In June 1965 a total of 63 species was recorded from 11 sites within the Burren. Most of the weevils encountered during the survey were common and widespread in Ireland and Britain but several interesting finds were made including *Otiorhynchus arcticus*, one of the largest weevils, with the shortest snout. It was found on the limestone pavement at Poulsallagh, mostly at the roots of sea plantain. This is a true arctic species, which is also encountered in most Irish coastal counties, in Scotland (especially in the north) and in Scandinavia. It exists also as a sub-fossil from the glacial or late glacial periods on the Isle of Man.[40]

Some birds and mammals

The Burren holds no great ornithological surprises but amongst the more interesting breeding birds are the peregrine falcon, occupying steep escarpment cliffs, a few pairs of nightjar and the short-eared owl in the hazel and ash woodlands. The hen harrier nests in young coniferous plantations, and breeding redshank can be encountered at several turloughs. Four passerines are conspicuous amongst the grasslands and generally scattered across the rocky landscape. These are the skylark, meadow pipit, the wheatear and stonechat. The last two species appear more numerous in the Burren than in most other areas on account of the suitable breeding habitats and abundance of a rich invertebrate food reservoir. One consequence of the high density of meadow pipits is the relatively large numbers of cuckoos in pursuit of their favourite foster hosts.

Of all the major habitat types in the Burren – grassland, blanket bogland, limestone pavement, scrub woodland and turloughs – it is the woodlands that provide the greatest opportunities for diversity and abundance of breeding birds. A series of breeding birds surveys covering nine separate woodland areas throughout the Burren was conducted between 15 and 20 April 1962. Most of the woodland was hazel, often mixed with blackthorn with an understorey of holly and brambles. The total area was approximately 120 ha. Twenty species were found holding territories. The commonest ten were chaffinch (18.3% of all 290 territories), robin (13.8%), blackbird (11.4%), willow warbler (11.0%), wren (9.3%), great tit (6.2%), woodpigeon (5.9%), dunnock, (5.5%), yellowhammer (3.4%) and chiffchaff (3.1%).[41] The findings generally correspond with those tabulated below, with the exception of the blue tit and bullfinch which were absent from the list of top ten species encountered in 1962.

Within the scrub woodlands there are quite significant differences in the composition of the breeding bird populations – a reflection of the height and structure of the scrub as revealed by some surveys carried out in the summers of 1977 and 1978. The two woodland areas surveyed were located in the National Park in the southeast corner of the Burren.[42] The low scrub area covered some 20 ha and was dominated by hazel, blackthorn, hawthorn, holly and the spindle-tree. The ground flora was almost entirely mosses but where the light broke through, ivy, common dog-violet and wood-sorrel were able to thrive. The other, taller scrub, covering close to 9 ha, was structured differently: ash, dominated with downy birch, wych elm and willow. A mixed understorey comprised seven different tree species and the ground flora was richer than in the low scrub. The breeding birds found in these two different scrubwoodlands are summarised in Table 6.1.

Table 6.1 Breeding birds recorded in tall and short scrub-woodland in the Burren, 1977 and 1978 (after Moles[42]).

Species	Tall scrub (> 4 m high and 8.4 ha)		Short scrub (< 4 m high and 20 ha)	
	Territories recorded	Territories per hectare	Territories recorded	Territories per hectare
Chaffinch	16	1.90	2	0.10
Willow warbler	15	1.78	9	0.45
Robin	12	1.43	6	0.30
Wren	8	0.95	5	0.25
Blue tit	7	0.83	1	0.05
Woodpigeon	4	0.48	-	-
Tree creeper	4	0.48	-	-
Chiffchaff	4	0.48	-	-
Long-tailed tit	4	0.48	-	-
Great tit	3	0.36	5	0.25
Dunnock	3	0.36	2	0.10
Bullfinch	3	0.36	1	0.05
Blackbird	2	0.24	2	0.10
Goldcrest	2	0.24	-	-
Spotted flycatcher	2	0.24	-	-
Starling	2	0.24	-	-
Mallard	2	0.24	-	-
Magpie	1	0.12	-	-
Hooded crow	1	0.12	-	-
Sparrowhawk	1	0.12	-	-
Moorhen	1	0.12	-	-
Long-eared owl	1	0.12	-	-
Mistle thrush	1	0.12	-	-
Song thrush	1	0.12	-	-
Cuckoo	1	0.12	-	-
Yellowhammer	-	-	1	0.05
Reed bunting	-	-	1	0.05
Common snipe	-	-	1	0.05
Total Territories	**101**	**12.77**	**36**	**1.8**
Total Species	**25**		**12**	

Almost double the number of breeding species occupied the taller scrub and the density of breeding territories was nearly seven times higher. The absence of tall trees required by arboreal species, the lack of plant diversity, and the probable paucity of invertebrates, reduced the attractiveness of the low scrub. Results from the tall scrub compared favourably with those from sessile oak woods at Derrycunihy, Co. Kerry, which shared with the Burren four of the five commonest species recorded: chaffinch; robin, wren and blue tit.

The hazel scrub also provides optimal conditions of shelter and food – in the form of calorie-rich hazel nuts – for a thriving population of small rodents. The highest densities of wood mice recorded in Ireland have been discovered in the Burren scrub. A trapping programme carried out near the Field Station of University College, Galway, at Carran, in 1976 and 1977 found peak densi-

Wood mouse. From G.B.
Corbet & H.N. Southern
(1977) *The Handbook of British
Mammals*. Blackwells, Oxford.

ties of 46 wood mice per hectare compared with densities of seven in a mixed
stand of Norway spruce, sessile oak and sycamore at Adare, Co. Limerick; 22
in Limekiln Wood, Athenry, Co. Galway, and 31 in a deciduous woodland of
mixed sessile oak, ash and beech at Seaforde, Co. Down.[43] As expected, the
mean body weight of the hazel scrub mice was significantly higher than those
living in the less bountiful environment of the adjoining limestone pavement
and grassland.

Pigmy shrews, weighing only 3–6 g, also occur in the scrub but at much lower
densities. This 'screw mouse', as it is sometimes called, is the smallest Irish
mammal and a gargantuan eater as it consumes at least one and a half times
its body weight of food per day. The ceaseless calorie quest is driven by the
need to balance their high heat loss. Small mammals like shrews have relatively large surface areas in relation to their body volume and lose heat faster than
those with a small surface area to body volume.

Pigmy shrews are ubiquitous in Ireland, turning up on remote offshore
islands and on mountain summits. Grid line trapping has revealed densities of
20–40 per ha, the highest in grassland. Territory size varied between 200 and
800 m². Numbers remain constant between December and April, but by the
second half of April, the shrew population, composed exclusively of young
born the previous summer, become sexually mature and increase their weight
by 60% over the previous winter levels. They normally breed once with a litter
size of 2–7. The young quickly take up their territories until breeding next
spring. Woodlice, beetles, small flies and other insects comprise most of their
diet.[44]

Numbers of the most elusive Irish mammal, the pine marten, formerly scarce
in Ireland, have significantly increased in the Burren area, which is now their
main focus of distribution within Ireland. The pine marten is one of Ireland's
most attractive mammals, but only rarely encountered in the wild. Their small,
sharp-pointed faces reveal their Mustelid
origins. On the chest is a creamy-yellow
patch behind which flows a dark brown
hairy coat followed by a long and bushy
tail. The total length of the marten is
nearly 1 m. Its front limbs are extremely
muscular, providing the power and dex-
terity for climbing trees, scrambling
through boulder country or travelling
fast over flat ground. Their dens are usually located in tree holes or in rock

Pigmy shrew. From G.B. Corbet & H.N.
Southern (1977) *The Handbook of British
Mammals*. Blackwells, Oxford.

Pine marten.
From G.B. Corbet
& H.N. Southern
(1977) *The
Handbook of British
Mammals.*
Blackwells,
Oxford.

crevices where approximately three young are born in the spring. The dense
hazel scrub offers an ideal habitat for this crepuscular mammal. A survey
organised between 1978 and 1980 showed the marten to be mainly confined
to the woodland and scrub areas in the mid-western region of Ireland, west of
the River Shannon from north Limerick to Sligo. Other populations are found
in the Slieve Bloom mountain range, in the Boyne river valley (restricted to a
narrow 6 km strip of riverside woodland at Slane, Co. Meath), in the woods of
a private estate at Curraghmore, near Portlaw, Co. Waterford, and in the
mountain regions of the southwest of Ireland (Gouganebarra and Killarney
woodlands). The most frequently recorded habitat type was deciduous woodland underplanted with coniferous species (46% of records), followed by
deciduous woodland (16.5% of records) and then thicket stage coniferous
plantation (16.4% of records).[45] In a detailed study on the behaviour of Irish
martens in the Dromore Forest, Co. Clare, it was found that they worked a regular system of pathways at night and that their home range extended to
approximately 13 ha. Although sometimes considered arboreal, martens spent
most of their time on the ground.[46] Droppings analysis revealed a catholic and
opportunistic diet. They will prey indifferently on birds, especially passerines,
or eggs. Wood mice constituted 10% of their diet, alongside ground beetles,
earthworms, snails and woodlice. In the autumn, they turn to fruits and nuts –
hazel nuts, beech nuts, rowan fruits and many others.[46,47,48]

Reptiles

Easily overlooked but quite numerous in the Burren is the common lizard,
Ireland's only native reptile. Its relative abundance here does not come as a
surprise given the rocky nature of the area and the biology of lizards. On warm

Common lizard.

days they can be seen sprawled on rocky surfaces, absorbing the heat coming to them from all directions. Another reason for their abundance may be related to the copious availability of invertebrate food such as ants.

Ants are also favourite food of larger lizards, one of which was the subject of an attempted introduction into the Burren. It would appear that in 1958 there was an introduction of eight male and seven female green lizards to the area. One of the survivors was encountered by the author on the rocks near Lough Aleenaun, some 7 km northeast of Kilfenora, in 1962. Despite repeated searching over time further individuals have eluded observers so it may be assumed that they failed to establish themselves.[49] A more successful introduction of a non-native reptile has been the slowworm. A live specimen was captured and others were seen in 1977 in the Cappaghmore district, southwest of Kinvarra, which corroborated previous reports by local people.[50]

Turloughs

Close to the woodland at the foot of Mullagh More are a series of small turloughs, a feature unique in Ireland to limestone areas in the west, principally in Mayo, Roscommon, Galway and Clare. Turloughs are temporary water bodies that fill and empty themselves through a swallow hole, or *slugaire*, connected with the underground water table. In the Annals of the Four Masters, which chronicle the history of Ireland from Anno Mundi 2242 (2958 BC) to AD1616, the word 'turlough' is given in Irish as *turlach*, the root of which is *tur* signifying 'dry', while *lach* is a mere suffix and not *loch*, or 'lake', as might be thought and as is nearly always erroneously quoted as such. The Four Masters wrote its genitive as *turlaigh* rather than *turlocha*. Thus a *turlach* is a dried up spot (which has formerly been wet).

Over 300 years ago, in 1684, William King, who later became the Protestant Archbishop of Dublin, read a remarkable paper entitled 'Of the Bogs and Loughs of Ireland' to a meeting of the Philosophical Society of Dublin in which he presented the first known account of turloughs and how they worked. He wrote:

> 'As to those places we call Turloughs, quasi Terreni lacus, or land-lakes; they answer the name very well, being lakes one part of the year of considerable depth; and very smooth fields the rest: if my memory does not fail me, Doctor Brown describes exactly the like in Hungary or else in the way between Vienna & Venice: there are in these, holes out of which the water riseth in winter, and goeth away towards Summer, many hundred acres being drowned by them; and those the most pleasant, and profitable land in the country: the soil is commonly a marl, which, by its stiffness, hinders the water from turning into a Bog; and immediately when the water is gone, it hardens, so that you ride thro' an even grassy field; these if they could be drained would be fit for any use; would make meddow; or bear any grain, but especially rape, which is very profitable. They are chiefly in Connaught; and their cause is obvious enough, it is a stony hilly Countrey; the hils have carvitys in them, through which the water passes: it is common to have a rivulet sink on one side of a hill, and rise a mile, or half a mile, from the place: the brooks are generally dry in Summer; the water that should be in them, sinking between the Rocks, and running under

Rahasane Turlough, Co. Galway, from the west.

ground; in so much as that in some places where they are overflowed in winter, they are forced in Summer to send their Cattle many miles for water.' [51]

Within the Burren there are many depressions or hollows in the landscape that do not appear to be connected with streams or rivers and are 'closed off', i.e. they are without inlets or outlets for water to come in or go out. These depressions were formed during the Tertiary period which started 65 million years ago, some 235 million years on from the end of the Carboniferous era. During the Tertiary period river systems flowed on top of the Upper Carboniferous deposits of sandstones and shales. These rivers gradually worked themselves down and sank through the sandstones and shales and got to work by eroding and washing away the soft limestone beneath. As a result of the erosion, which in some areas proceeded faster than in others, turloughs or solution hollows were formed in the limestone to be later exposed on the surface of the landscape once the overlaying sandstones and shales had been removed by weathering and then glacial scouring. True turloughs are surrounded by a rim of rock. Their only connection to water supplies, below the ground in the form of a subterranean water table, or reservoir, is by means of one or a series of a 'swallow holes'. The entrance of swallow holes varies from 0.5–3 m in diameter. When rainfall is high, water will rise upwards through the swallow hole, rather like a bath filling by water entering through the draining hole, into the turlough, as the underground water table starts rising. Then the turlough will drain out through the swallow hole when the underground water table drops again.

Turloughs come in all shapes and sizes. When a turlough occurs singly it is a 'doline' but when several neighbouring turloughs are coalesced together in response to very high water table levels, this larger area is known as a uvula. Within the Burren, turloughs are generally restricted to the valleys south of Ballyvaghan and east of Moneen Mountain, the Carran depression, and the area southwest, south, east and northeast of Mullagh More. The largest is at Carran. When full, it extends over some 150 ha and can vary in depth from a few centimetres to several metres. Some of the smallest and most steep-sided are around Mullagh More. These can fill up at a remarkable speed as some campers will testify who, having selected a nice, grassy, wind-protected and level camp site on the turlough bottom, went to sleep, only to find themselves floating around in their sleeping bags a couple of hours later.[52]

Outside the Burren and elsewhere in Co. Clare turloughs are most numerous in Galway, Mayo and Roscommon while there are fewer of them in Tipperary and Kilkenny. Longford and Sligo can only boast a few while there is one in Co. Limerick. Coxon, who prepared a detailed inventory of Irish turloughs in the mid 1980s recorded 90 which met the criteria of (a) being seasonally flooded (with open water at least 0.5 m deep for part of the year and a dry floor for part of the year); (b) emptying to ground water (evidenced by a lack of natural surface outlet) and (c) with a flood area of at least 10 ha. Of the 90 documented by Coxon 60 still flood seasonally while the other 30 had been influenced by drainage and no longer represent 'natural' systems.[53]

As a general rule turloughs are flooded during the winter months and they are empty in summer. However, an exceptionally wet summer will see them full while they can be without much water in a very dry winter. The grass that grows in spring after the water has receded is very lush, and turloughs make high quality pastures. There was a time in England – during the nineteenth and early twentieth centuries – when special grasslands, close to rivers, were deliberately flooded for a period of two or three days in winter from December to the end of March. The objective, as related by Mellanby, was to warm the soil and prevent it from freezing. In addition, a thin sprinkling of nutrient-rich silt was deposited onto the pasture. The result was not only a flush of spring grass growth, valuable to fresh young lambs, but better quality grass for summer gazing or hay-making.[54] Many thousands of hectares of low-lying land, mainly in southern England, were once taken care of like this, in a carefully managed regime of water meadows using a network of sluices and artificial channels. There was no need for such water meadows in Ireland – they were already present in the turloughs.

Next to the enrichment by nutrient silts, Irish turloughs enjoy the extra benefit of nitrates and phosphates derived from the droppings excreted by the often large flocks of wintering wildfowl which visit the turloughs. Concerning the additional deposits of lime, Praeger said 'the very light deposit of limy sediment that the water leaves behind, produces a sward particularly beloved by herbivorous animals, large and small. The additional liming contributes further to the vigour and juiciness of the grass and the flowers. The vegetation of the turloughs is usually nibbled to the last leaf – often much more closely shorn than could be done by a lawn-mower.'[55]

The fluctuating water levels dictate the biological rhythm of the plants and animals inhabiting this singular habitat. Those that can endure the longest periods of immersion will occupy the lower parts of the turloughs – it is surprising that so many plants can survive such long periods of dunking but they do. The plants sensitive to wetness stay higher up. Praeger was the first to publish an account of the flora of turloughs based on three sites close to the Burren and west of Gort in southeast Galway. These were: (i) a turlough close to Tirneevin Chapel – steep-sided and small, with a stream atypically flowing through it; (ii) a turlough south of Garryland Wood – an extensive flat area subject to flooding; (iii) Caherglassaun Lough, six kilometres southeast of Kinvarra, and about 32 ha in size. Caherglassaun is famous for the influence that tides at the nearby coast have on it: low water levels in the turlough rise and fall by about 30 cm according to the tidal state. But no sea water enters the turlough directly, the tidal impact being conducted through the underground water network.

The upper level to which water in a turlough rises is marked by two botanical features: the very conspicuous black moss, *Cinclidotus fontinaloides*, growing in great profusion on boulders or stone walls submerged by the turlough and extending from the bottom to a height of about 1–2 m above the upper water limit, and the line of shrubs and trees forming a peripheral ring. Two shrubs in particular – the hawthorn and blackthorn – come closest to the water. The line of the lowest hawthorns, constant around the turlough rim, marks the upper water limit. Another indicator is the dark green moss, *Fontinalis antipyretica*, found on the sides of boulders, which does not, however, extend so far up the sides of the turlough as does *Cinclidotus*.

The largest extant turlough in Ireland, Rahasane Turlough, Co. Galway, sits just outside the Burren to the northeast, spreading over 275 ha of flat grassland through which the Dunkellin River meanders. The winter water levels can be deep and persistent, turning the whole area into a massive lake which draws over 40,000 wildfowl. But from April to October sheep, cattle and horses graze the rich grassland. The vegetation productivity and nutrient status of the dominant wet zone of Rahasane Turlough, characterised by the grass creeping bent and silverweed has been explored by Sheehy-Skeffington.[56] Twenty-one species were identified from the dominant zone of which grasses, notably creeping bent, contributed at least 50% of the total biomass except during the period of intensive grazing. The number of plant species declined during the winter due to natural die-back, but also to flooding and grazing by waterfowl. In March silverweed and white clover were absent from the study area but by the summer they had re-emerged. Creeping bent and creeping buttercup continued to grow during the winter, surviving water inundation and thousands of pecking waterfowl. Coverage of the ground by mosses, mostly *Mnium hornum* and *Eurhynchium* spp. was greatest in March when other vegetation cover was lowest.

From spring onwards, when turlough water levels are lowest, and fine warm weather sets in, remarkable growths of certain algae can be witnessed, transforming the turlough into an apparent snowfield. The series of turloughs at Turlough, in the valley running south to Carran from Bealaclugga were discovered sporting vast white sheets of algae, extending over several hectares, in the summers of 1968–1971. Scannell reported that 'The sheeted alga was so thick in some areas as to resemble parchment in texture and colour, in other parts it was gossamer fineness. Bushes were covered with hammocks of webbed alga, stone walls bore white shawls tasselled where the weight of wet material had pulled from the dried portion, boulders were draped with bleached shapes as though tablecloths had been laid out to dry and whiten.'[57] The

Rahasane Turlough. Summer low water levels. The black moss *Cinclidiotus fontinaloides* is present on most rocks.

ghostly white material was made up of plants of the genus *Oedogonium*, a group of green filamentous alga. Similar deposits, dried out and bleached, have been described from other locations on the Continent as 'algal paper' or 'natural paper', but this phenomenon had never been reported from Ireland until 1972. In the seventeenth century the presence of these bleached algal sheets in Germany was explained as 'having fallen from heaven and being of mete-oric nature'.

In her study of Rahasane Turlough, Sheehy-Skeffington established that the alkaline soils were rich in calcium with moderate potassium levels and fairly high magnesium. Both total and exchangeable soil nitrogen were high for grassland, as reflected in the high nitrogen content of the vegetation. During March and April grazing by sheep and horses removed about 1.2 kg per ha^{-1}, approximately half the biomass for that time of the year. Sheehy-Skeffington concluded that the ecology of the turlough was reminiscent of a tidally-inun-dated salt marsh which is replenished twice daily with a dose of nutrients. However, in the case of turloughs the inundations are much fewer, maybe only one continuous inundation during the winter. When the waters subsided in the spring the turlough plants were left with a coating of fine silts. The flood-deposited silt is probably essential in maintaining the fertile turlough vegeta-tion in an exploitable condition for the herbivores.

One important speciality of the Burren flora is the shrubby cinquefoil, a member of the rose family with conspicuous yellow flowers. It can sometimes reach nearly 1 m in height and as it likes to get its feet wet at least once a year, it normally grows in the girdle zone around turloughs or lakes, but it can also be found in amazingly dense and extensive stands. The remarkable photo-graph in Praeger's *The Botanist in Ireland* that shows a man standing up to the

Shrubby cinquefoil frequently marks the upper water limits in turloughs.

knee height in nearly one hectare of shrubby cinquefoil, was taken at the beginning of May in a depression some 2.5 km southwest of Ballyvaghan. The colonies of shrubby cinquefoil in the Burren are probably the largest in Europe. Outside Ireland its distribution is fragmented with occurrences in the Lake District, Upper Teesdale, the Pyrenees, the Maritime Alps and in southeast Sweden.[22]

A special feature of the turloughs in the Burren is the presence of four species of violets, distributed in and around the turlough according to their tolerance to water immersion. The fen violet is generally found on or near the floor of the turlough and is one of the Burren highlights as well as being listed in the Irish Red Data Book of vascular species. It is confined to turloughs and grasslands subject to flooding in the western part of Ireland ranging from Clare to Fermanagh. In Britain it is rare and declining, due to habitat loss, and is now restricted to Cambridgeshire. It can occur in great exuberance in the Burren turloughs, especially at Caherglassaun southeast of Kinvarra. Webb & Scannell state that 'When in flower it can provide one of the most spectacular sights in the Irish flora, many square yards of turf being converted into a pale china-blue sheet by the presence of literally tens of thousands of flowers, mostly very close to ground level.'[22] Outside its flowering period, from late May to mid-June, it is not easily noticed as it is so much smaller than other violets. It is distinguished from the closely associated heath dog-violet by underground runners, and lanceolate rather than triangular or heart-shaped leaves. The flowers can often be whitish with purple veins.

The next violet, occupying a higher precinct in the turlough about 1 m above the fen violet zone, is the heath dog-violet. The spur at the bottom of the flower is whitish or yellowish. Like the fen violet it has to wait for the water levels to drop before it can flower from about mid-May onwards. Hybrids between the two species are common, especially where their distribution zones overlap.

Growing well above the heath dog-violet zone is the common dog-violet, close to, but secure from, the turlough waters. It has heart-shaped leaves and unscented blue-violet flowers whose spurs are stout and often cream-coloured. As it does not have to contend with water problems facing the fen and heath dog-violet, it is able to flower earlier, from March onwards. Further away from the turlough and preferring a woodland or scrub floor to grow on is the early dog-violet. When in bloom it is easily distinguished from the common dog-violet by its narrower petals and its slender and deep violet flower spur. The common dog-violet is frequently found growing with the early dog-violet.

Praeger measured the lower limit to which ten species descended in one or more of the three turloughs he examined (Tirneevin Turlough, near Gort; Garryland Wood Turlough and Caherglassaun Lough), taking the shrub line of the turlough as the baseline. The results show that that both creeping cinquefoil and silverweed can tolerate longer periods of water immersion than other normally terrestrial species.[55]

Table 6.2 Height below lower limit of shrubs in three turloughs (after Praeger[55]).

Species	Height (m)
Buckthorn	1.83
Stone bramble	1.83
Tormentil	1.83
Common dog-violet	2.43
Dewberry	2.48
Creeping willow	2.59
Common bird's-foot-trefoil	2.74
Ribwort plantain	3.81
Creeping cinquefoil	11.43
Silverweed	11.73

As part of their survey of the Burren plant communities, Ivimey-Cook & Proctor examined the vegetation that covered the floors of 15 of the deeper turloughs which, although totally inundated by water in the winter, dried out completely in the summer.[15] The plant community consisted of a *Carex nigra–Potentilla anserina* association, i.e. one dominated by the common sedge and silverweed. In this association the constant species are creeping bent, common sedge, common marsh-bedstraw, autumn hawkbit, silverweed and creeping buttercup. The turlough vegetation communities were separated into two groups according to the presence (in six turloughs) or absence (in nine turloughs) of marsh pennywort which was taken as a diagnostic indicator. The main floristic variations between all the 15 turloughs were related to grazing intensity. The swards more heavily grazed by cattle were richer in terms of more species, indicating the beneficial impacts of grazing, as well as manifesting a more ruderal or waste ground aspect as evidenced by the presence of silverweed.

The northern yellow-cress, a straggling, prostrate and hairless perennial with small yellow flowers, is another damp-floor turlough dweller which seems to be spreading geographically in Ireland as indicated by an increasing number of turlough sites where it is being found. It also occurs in Northern Ireland, principally on disturbed soil – there are no turloughs in this part of the country – where it is likewise extending its range.[58] It was first spotted in Ireland at Renvyle, Co. Galway, in 1831 and then subsequently at a few other west coast sites.[59] It has a disjunct distribution along the eastern Atlantic coastline ranging from Greenland, Iceland, west Norway and western Scotland to Ireland; it also occurs in montane France, Switzerland and Italy as well as in Russio–Serbia. In Ireland turloughs now appear to be its favoured habitat following its first recording, in 1971, at Turlough in the Burren.[60] More turlough sites were noted by McGowran while Goodwillie extended its turlough habitat range further, including a record from Co. Kilkenny.[61]

There have been very few investigations into the insects of turloughs. One study concerning aquatic water beetles, carried out in August 1988, found that turloughs have a water beetle community that is very special to this habitat.[62] All these beetles, apart from *Helophorus* spp., belong to the family Dytiscidae whose members are large and shiny. Their hind legs are broad, flattened and equipped with hairs which assist them to act like paddles; the body is streamlined to offer least resistance through the water. Their head is sunk into the thorax. They have to come to the surface tail first, to get oxygen which they trap as a bubble between their hardened forewings – sitting on top of their flying wings –and their abdomen. Most can fly, an essential trick should the water dry up and they have to move on. The first three segments of the male's forelegs are modified into suckers which are used to clasp onto the female during copulation. Both larvae (armed with proportionately gigantic mandibles or pincers) and adults are ferocious carnivores terrorising other small creatures in the water such as tadpoles or even small fish. The water beetle community – active in the margins of the undisturbed turloughs – is characterised by some or all of the following:

Hygrotus quinquelineatus – a flightless species found in fen areas.

Coelambus impressopunctatus – found in shallow grassy pools of a temporary nature.

Graptodytes bilineatus – a new species for Ireland found in Cordara Turlough, Co. Limerick, and a turlough near Mullagh More, Co. Clare, along the mossy edges in association with *Agabus labiatus*.

Agabus labiatus – very common in all undisturbed turloughs.

A. nebulosus – in several turloughs.

Helophorus spp. other than *H. brevipalpis* (these belong to another family of water beetles, the Hydropilidae) – in many turloughs.

Berosus signaticollis – a new species for Ireland from Cordara Turlough, Co. Limerick and a turlough near Mullagh More, Co. Clare.

Dryops similaris – a new species for Ireland found in Cordara Turlough, Co. Limerick, and a turlough near Ballycullinan Lough, Co. Clare. A rare species most often found in ancient fens.

The turlough beetle community is very sensitive to excessive trampling by cattle or agricultural 'improvement'. The most fragile species are those that live in the mosses around the turlough's edge – *Graptodytes bilineatus*, *Agabus labiatus* and *Dryops similaris*.

Fairy shrimps, other copepods and freshwater snails

Invertebrates trying to survive in such a wildly fluctuating environment face
problems of either desiccation or drowning. Regrettably, there is insufficient
published work on the range of species present in turloughs, their populations
and general ecology, to appreciate how and which invertebrates have adapted
to such a contrasting life. It is the spectacular rather than the inconspicuous
that inevitably receives the attention. Such a case was the startling discovery of
a 'fairy' shrimp – so-called because of its fairy-like translucence – found in
Rahasane Turlough, Co. Galway, in August 1974 by Young, during a survey by
the Brathay Exploration Group. The shrimp was *Tanymastix stagnalis*. Both
male and female reach up to 20 cm long, and like other Anostraca (fairy
shrimps) they swim gracefully around upside down, on their back. When they
were first discovered here there were tens of thousands of them swimming
around the small basin to the southwest of the main turlough.[63]

Although never previously recorded in Ireland or Britain this species is widely distributed in Continental Europe and North Africa. It is strange that such
a large crustacean should have evaded the attention of naturalists for so long,
unless – and this could well be true – it had only recently arrived in Ireland.
Many of the female shrimps captured at Rahasane were carrying eggs which
were the special fast-hatching summer eggs that allow a rapid build up of vast
populations of the shrimps, but only if the water conditions are right. When
drought prevails the eggs can become encysted as the females die and turn
into dry chitinous husks. The eggs are remarkably resistant and can lie dormant for long dry periods while the turlough is empty of water. As soon as
water returns the eggs quickly hatch into a specialist larva called a nauplius
which starts life with only three pairs of limbs. More and more limbs and body
segments are added with every stage of the many moults before mature adulthood is reached as quickly as within two weeks of hatching. Fairy shrimps have
no carapace over their backs like other crustaceans, such as lobsters and crabs,
and are therefore delicate creatures. They have 11 pairs of thoracic limbs, lib-
erally equipped with bristles. When the limbs are flapped backwards and forwards the shrimp is gracefully propelled along. The bristles also gather up and
whisk along into the mouth a stream of food which consists mainly of minute

Fairy shrimps. Upside-down swimmers. The first two abdominal segments of the female
(top) form a tubular egg sac. The male of *Tanymastix stagnalis* (below) has much enlarged
and greatly modified second antennae that are used to grasp the female during copulation.
From R. Fitter & R. Manuel (1986) *Collins Field Guide to Freshwater Life of Britain and North-
West Europe.* Collins, London.

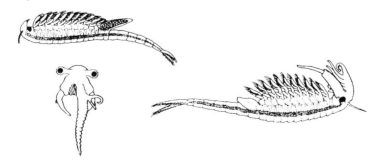

algae. The second pair of antennae in the male has developed into a bizarre copulatory organ used to clasp and hold the female during mating. The first two abdominal segments of the female have been modified to form a short and conical egg sac.

With the facility of dormant eggs it is quite probable that encysted fairy shrimp eggs, caught up in mud stuck onto the feet of migratory birds, may have been transported to Rahasane Turlough from other European wetlands. Transfer could also be subsequently effected from one turlough to another on the boots of hunters or on hoofs of cattle or sheep. In view of the thousands of migratory wildfowl and waders visiting Rahasane it does not appear such an impossible suggestion that they could be an effective transfer agents of the fairy shrimp from country to country.

One way of verifying this was to check other turloughs and lakes with wintering wildfowl to see if the migrant crustacean occurred there as well. Although the first investigation carried out in the many other turloughs and small ponds between Athenry and Gort, Co. Galway, failed to produce suitable evidence, the fairy shrimp was subsequently discovered in at least six other turloughs by Grainger during 1976 in a much wider search zone in Clare, Galway and Roscommon. The apparent absence of *Tanymastix* from water bodies near to Rahasane and their discovery at other more distant turloughs has no easy explanation. At three of the small, shallow-watered turloughs, large numbers of another copepod, *Diaptomus castor*, a well-known inhabitant of temporary pools, was found.[64] Further research revealed the presence of many more copepods including *Diaptomus cyaneus*, and a water flea *Eurycercus glacialis*, both new to Ireland and Britain.[65] Other copepods detected in turloughs were *Pleuroxus trigonellus*, *P. laevis*, *Diaptomus wierzejskii*, *D. gracilis*, *Cypris puber*, and the freshwater shrimp, *Gammarus duebeni*.[66] These copepods survive their inevitable periods of desiccation either as eggs or in their early stages of their lives.

The biology of the fairy shrimp *Tanymastix stagnalis* and its survival in large and small turloughs has been studied by Grainger who found that the best hatching and survival of eggs, encysted in the dried up bottom of the turlough, occurred when the eggs were in the soil and at temperatures between about 10 and 15°C. Some eggs survived one drying period while others at least four drying and wetting periods. Using a computer model to predict the chances of rainfall of at least 200 mm occurring in a two month period – deemed the minimum water necessary to ensure the survival of *Tanymastix* in a turlough – it was found that on a 100 year projection there was little likelihood of *Tanymastix* becoming extinct in small or large turloughs through lack of essential water.[67]

The Mollusca is another group of animals that sustain the water fluctuations with varying success: a richer and more stable community of aquatic snails will be found in those turloughs with the least discrepancy between water levels, while in turloughs that regularly dry out completely in the summer and fill up again in the winter the range will be impoverished. Three Burren turloughs, displaying a range of differing water regimes, were investigated for their molluscan fauna in 1975 and 1976.[68] The first was Lough Aleenaun, a big turlough of 12.5 ha that empties out every summer, thus presenting a great challenge for the survival of molluscs. Here only one species was found; the marsh snail *Lymnaea palustris*. The next turlough, Turlagh na gCoilean, located just east of the village of Turlough, is also large but rarely dries out completely. No snails were found in the upper parts of the turlough, but in the wet centre where the vegetation – dominated by buttercups and pondweeds – formed a damp mass there were large numbers of molluscs. Six species were found: the operculate snail *Valvata cristata* (scarce), the dwarf pond snail (one of the commonest species), the wandering snail (rare, only one shell found), the planorbid snail *Anisus leucostoma* (in vast numbers) and the pea mussels, *Pisidium casertanum* and *P. personatum,* (both very abundant). The final turlough examined was Caherglassaun Lough. Although subject to tidal influence (as described above), the water showed no sign of salinity. The most diverse mollusc fauna was found at Caherglassaun – a consequence of the more or less permanent presence of water in the turlough bottom. Eleven species occurred here. Amongst the least frequent snails found were *Valvata cristata* (a few shells), the planorbid snail *Gyraulus albus* (only a few), an orb mussel or freshwater cockle *Sphaerium corneum* (one) and the great pond snail (several shells but not found alive). Other species were *Valvata piscinalis* (abundant), Jenkin's spire shell (fairly frequent), another operculate snail *Bithynia tentaculata* (very abundant), *Lymnaea peregra* (fairly frequent) and the pea shell mussels *Pisidium nitidum* and *P. pulchellum.*

Other aquatic invertebrates have mastered the vagaries of turloughs.[20] These include the water boatmen, or backswimmers, so called because of their habit of swimming on their back with a large air bubble attached to their abdomen acting as a buoy; the water measurer, a long thin insect walking with measured steps along the water surface, often in pursuit of small prey which it spears with its long beak; the water cricket, skating over the water and snatching its prey with its forelegs, a habit shared with the even more swift pond skaters, and the water scorpion, which sports a long, sinister-looking, hollow tail used as a straw to suck down air from the water surface. Finally there are many water beetles and other invertebrates that together with the water snails and fairy shrimps provide rich pickings for visiting wildfowl and waders.

The aquatic fauna of a doline (a steep-sided depression in limestone caused by solution and collapse) occupying the central fifth of a 31 ha water body at Lough Gealain in the southeastern corner of the Burren was investigated by Byrne & Reynolds in November 1979 and April 1980.[69] The doline reached a depth of 16 m and was explored by divers. The flora clinging to the sides separated out into zones, each characterised by a dominant species. Forming a first ring and extending to a depth of one metre was common club-rush, next came shining pondweed and yellow water-lily descending to a depth of 6 m, mixed with an unidentified stonewort. Lower down was a dense growth of fragile stonewort descending to a depth of 13 m. The invertebrates present were disappointing as they neither represented a unique community of invertebrates nor showed a distributional zonation by depth. Amongst the gastropods, the common wandering snail and the marsh snail – the commonest snail present – could be found in the shallow parts of the Lough but were absent from the doline. Larvae of non-biting midges were dominant in the bottom muds while the caddis larvae *Mystacides longicornis* were the most abundant insects amongst the stoneworts. *Mystacides* is a cased caddis and the larva has a beautifully marked head – pale with dark spots. The species is widespread in Ireland.[70] In addition to turloughs it occurs in large slow-flowing rivers, ponds, lakes and canals and even in a large man-made concrete lake in an Irish university. Absent from the doline were mayfly nymphs, freshwater shrimps and beetles. The most abundant invertebrates observed were ostracods, minute freshwater crustaceans enclosed in a bivalve covering or carapace, the outer layer of which is impregnated with calcium carbonate, and water mites.

Wildfowl and waders

As a former internationally important wildfowl wetland, holding up to 41,600 birds until the mid 1980s, there was nothing to equal Rahasane Turlough in Ireland. The turlough encompasses 275 ha of flat commonage land, west of Craughwell, Co. Galway. Peak numbers of wildfowl occur in January, particularly if the water is shallow, revealing an attractive mosaic of wet swampy grasslands, glinting pools and soggy pastureland. Under these conditions wildfowl come to the turlough to tap the rich food resources whether it be small molluscs and insects for flocks of golden plover and lapwings, worms and other wriggly invertebrates for herds of curlews and dunlin, juicy stolons and leafy grass shoots for Greenland white-fronted geese, wigeon, mallard, teal and other ducks, or submerged vegetation for wild swans. Should they register disturbance they take to the air by the thousand, literally darkening parts of the sky above Rahasane, before landing again in noisy winged sequences.

A series of wildfowl counts was carried out at Rahasane Turlough in the early 1960s in order to establish the ornithological importance of the area.[71] These, together with later information from the mid 1980s,[72] confirmed the value of the site as one of Ireland's premier wildfowl wetlands (Table 6.3). As Rahasane then regularly held more than 1% of the total population of the west European flyway population of wigeon, shoveler, whooper swan and golden plover it was considered internationally important in relation to these species. It also qualified as such by regularly hosting more than a total of 20,000 waterfowl.[73] Moreover another 12 species occurred here in nationally important numbers (more than 1% of the national total). It should be noted that when Rahasane is fully charged with water and, as a result, unattractive to wildfowl, it can be a supreme ornithological disappointment. Also, if the turlough has not been flooded for a while, it fails to attract large numbers of waterfowl underscoring the delicate balance between attractive and unattractive conditions for the visiting wildfowl.

Rahasane Turlough under ideal conditions for wintering wildfowl. Whooper swans in the foreground and wigeon, teal, pintail and mallard in the distance.

Table 6.3 Counts of wildfowl and waders at Rahasane Turlough during the winters 1964–66 (Cabot[71]); the mid 1980s (Buckley & McCarthy[74], quoted by Sheppard[72]) and winter 1995–96 (Delany[75]).

Species	1964–66	mid 1980s	1995–96
Mallard	200–300	777*	72
Teal	800–1,000	3,005*	447
Gadwall	nd	4	0
Wigeon	5,000–8,500	7,760**	5,770*
Pintail	800–1,000	102*	40*
Shoveler	500–600	489**	92*
Tufted duck	50–100	381*	56
Pochard	100–200	356*	0
Greenland white-fronted goose	240–271	59	203*
Mute swan	60–80	125*	45
Whooper swan	100–150	179**	248**
Bewick's swan	200–300	132*	24
Lapwing	600–700	3,995*	1,176
Grey plover	10–20	0	0
Golden plover	3,000–3,500	17,680**	16,500**
Common snipe	25–50	91	14
Curlew	200–300	1,205*	169
Black-tailed godwit	35–40	170*	310*
Redshank	75–100	155	72
Greenshank	5–10	0	0
Dunlin	200–300	3,569*	1,350
Grey heron	nd	22	4
Coot	nd	1,289*	12
Totals	**12,200–17,521**	**41,545**	**26,604**

*= nationally important numbers; **= internationally important numbers. nd=no data.

By the mid 1990s the importance of Rahasane had sadly declined, reaffirming the supreme importance of the other major flooded grassland habitat, the callowlands of the Shannon between Athlone and Portumna and the Little Brosna where 28,922 and 36,767 wildfowl (total 65,689) were respectively recorded during the winter 1995–6 (see p.284). At Rahasane the most recent published counts for the winter 1995–6 show significant declines compared with a decade earlier. The sum of the maximum counts for each species only reached 26,603, down nearly 15,000 or 36% on the mid 1980s total. Only two species, the golden plover and whooper swan (up nearly 70 at 248 birds) remain in internationally important numbers. Likewise the former 12 nationally important species had dwindled to only five. On the positive side, increases were noted in Greenland white-fronted geese (203 in 1994–5) and black-tailed godwit (310). There are no easy explanations for the considerable overall decline in wildfowl numbers visiting Rahasane. Certainly the winters of 1994–5 and 1995–6 were atypically dry, not leaving enough water in the turlough to make it sufficiently attractive for the waterfowl.

7

Broadleaved Woodlands

One of the ancient bardic names of Ireland was *Inis na bhFiodhbhadh*, meaning 'woody island'. Today, however, the country is one of the least wooded territories in Europe with only 6% of its surface clothed by forest. Only Iceland has less forest cover. More surprising still is that most of these woodlands are recent coniferous plantations dominated by two species originating from the Pacific coasts of British Columbia and southern Alaska – sitka spruce and lodgepole pine – sprawling like advancing armies across the landscape, principally on mountains and lowland bogs. Practically all these woods are in State ownership although generous grants from the European Union have made afforestation increasingly attractive to private developers in recent years.

Despised by most naturalists as 'ecological deserts', these cellulose factories have ravaged vast tracts of moorland and other habitats of great natural importance, especially in the western Counties of Donegal, Mayo, Galway and Kerry, and have upset not only the visual aesthetics but the 'feel' of many landscapes. Worse still has been the 'coniferisation' of many of the last surviving examples of our ancient broadleaved woods. Rackham wrote that the Irish Forest Service displayed even greater vigour and enthusiasm than its British counterpart in seeking out and coniferising the already minuscule one per cent of the ancient Irish woods that survived into the twentieth century.[1] Indeed, the remnants of the ancient forests were seen as an excellent starting point to introduce the new alien species as they provided shelter for the young trees. Fortunately this practice generally ceased in the post-1970 period of environmental enlightenment when foresters started uprooting young conifers from their deciduous nurseries in atonement for their previous sins. Of all the woodland in the Republic of Ireland today, approximately 75% is conifer plantations, mostly of recent origin; 10% is deciduous broadleaved forest, and the remaining 15% is deciduous scrub land.[2]

The rise and fall of woodlands in Ireland since the end of the last glaciation 13,000 years ago has been described in Chapter 2. The present chapter picks up the story of the more recent events since the advent of the first Neolithic settlers in Ireland some 6,000 years ago and presents a description of the more important present day broadleaved woodlands. It is a complicated story of a man-induced devastation of a once vast and thriving ecosystem, reduced today to a mere vestige of what it used to be. However, despite its meagre extent, this residue comprises one of Ireland's most interesting ecological facets with some of the finest examples of moist Atlantic oak woods to be found in Europe.

Loss of the deciduous woodlands

Divergent opinions exist as to culpability of man in the disintegration of the Irish forests. Many texts argue that the greater number of trees was destroyed during the sixteenth and seventeenth centuries by felling and burning associated with smelting, tanning, coopering, the exportation of pipe staves and

Forests and woodlands
- Broadleaf
- Mixed
- Conifer

Forest and woodlands in Ireland. From F.H.A. Aalen, K. Whelan & M. Stout (eds) (1997) *Atlas of the Irish Rural Landscape*. Cork University Press.

other wood for construction, etc. – under the aegis of the English settlers. However, Forbes has argued that the occupation of the country by the Normans and Tudors had no material effect upon the woodlands although considerable quantities of timber were cut during that period.[3] In his opinion grazing pressure under the tribal system, starting as early as the Neolithic times, was responsible for the real decline of indigenous woods through forest clearance. Additional evidence has been put forward to support a relatively treeless landscape as early as the Bronze Age.[4]

Advancing forestry plantation
in Glenummera Valley, west
Mayo.

McCracken states that in 1600 about one million hectares or 12.5% of
Ireland was forested. By 1800 the proportion had been reduced to a mere 2%
of Ireland's surface as a result of commercial exploitation following the establishment of English control over the whole country.[5] However, Rackham, working with published survey data for 15 of the 32 counties from the *Civil Survey
of Ireland 1654–6*, supplemented with woodland totals for another seven counties published by McCracken, calculated a much lower woodland area for the
early part of the seventeenth century of only 170,000 ha, or 2.1% of the land
surface – roughly one third of that found in England at the same time.[1] In
other words the English planters, while guilty of some woodland destruction,
had inherited a fairly tree bare landscape. Rackham also examined the
Ordnance Survey Maps 1834–44 and showed that within the intervening two centuries less than one tenth or 17,000 ha of the ancient woodland had survived,
putting the tree cover down to 0.2%.[1] This downward trend was to be partially and privately corrected by improving landlords who set out to embellish
their estates during the course of the eighteenth and nineteenth centuries.
Their effort would not have gained recognition had they only planted single
trees, rows and avenues but they also landscaped fields and laid down
broadleaved woodlands for timber production. The Royal Dublin Society
encouraged the planting of trees from 1740 onwards by presenting prizes for
the best plantations and recommending both broadleaved and coniferous
species for growth. With this support an estimated 53,500 ha of private woodlands, including arboretums, were laid down, but only about 25% were
broadleaved.[6]

Today only about 84,000 ha of native broadleaved woodlands remain,[7] of
which perhaps less than 20,000 ha could be described as ancient, i.e. woodlands that originated before 1600, but which have been invariably manipulated by man to a significant extent.[8] Interestingly this estimate, made in 1986, is
similar to an earlier one of 20,235 ha of 'semi-natural' woodland computed in
1944 by McEvoy, who was reviewing the condition of native woodlands.[9]
McEvoy excluded the extensive areas of hazel shrub communities that occur in
the Burren, Co. Clare.

In summary, ancient broadleaved woodlands have shrunk from covering
nearly 100% to 0.2% of the land surface since the Neolithic farmers felled
their first tree some 6,000 years ago. Over the centuries Ireland has become a

Belvedere House, overlooking Lough Ennell, Co. Westmeath, surrounded by demesne plantations of broad leaved trees. A classic example of the embellishment of the landscape by improving landlords.

huge open space with vast stretches of empty land extending to the horizon. Some offshore islands can be absolutely treeless and the lack of shelter from the wind combined with livestock pressure will not allow regeneration.

The remaining woodlands

The most widespread and characteristic remnants of the former broadleaved forests are dominated by sessile oak occurring in relatively isolated small stands and found mostly on the poorer and generally acidic soils, principally in Kerry, Cork, Galway, Mayo and Sligo as well in Antrim, Down, Wicklow and Derry. There was a time when oak woods where found everywhere, as evidenced by the numerous place names that incorporate *derry* or *derri* – the anglicised version of the Irish word *doire* or *daire* for 'oak wood'. Over 1,300 place names begin with the word in one form or another and many more contain it as a suffix.[10] So upwards of 2,000 of about 62,000 place names which, if in Irish, can be broadly dated to between the fifth and twelfth centuries AD, demonstrate the large and meaningful presence of oak and oak woods at that time.[11]

The two native oaks in Ireland can be separated on close examination by the length of the acorn stalks. The acorns of the sessile oak are without stalks or with short stalks (less than 2 cm) while those of pedunculate oak have stalks 2.5–5 cm long. Moreover, the leaves of sessile oak have a longer and more yellow stalk than the pedunculate oak which has nearly stalkless leaves.

Driving through the landscape one can easily arrive at the erroneous impression that the country is far more wooded than it actually is because of the extent and luxuriance of the hedges. The traveller passing through these green tunnels, many of which are unkempt and wild in character, is tricked into thinking that the countryside is awash with trees, groves, coppices and woodlands. This is not the case. When added together the hedgerows, which are essentially thin strips of woodland, may hold only up to 5% of the total broadleaved tree stock of Ireland. Moreover, they play an important role in providing a limited habitat for a range of woodland flora and fauna.

Although the enclosure of land in Ireland has been in progress, especially in eastern Ireland, in a piecemeal fashion since the medieval period, it was not until the late seventeenth century that the pace accelerated. There was a rapid spread of hedge construction during the eighteenth century, when earth banks were planted with first the quicken-tree, 'quick' or hawthorn and then other trees.[12] In order to prevent the movement of cattle and other animals in and out of fields, and to provide shelter, tough and prickly specimens such as blackthorn were added to the earth banks. Other species followed including gorse, sycamore, ash, hazel, willows, holly, spindle and more exotic trees such as Irish whitebeam, the Devon whitebeam (only in Carlow, Waterford and Kilkenny) and crab apple. Throughout Ireland, hedgerows containing upwards of 60 different types of trees, shrubs and other woody species have been recorded, including both oaks, the pedunculate and sessile.

There has been very little detailed investigation into the ecology or floristics of Irish hedgerows apart from one study in the parish of Knock, Co. Mayo,[13] one at Duleek, Co. Louth,[14] and one on the hedges of Northern Ireland.[15] In the parish of Knock, random 30 m stretches of 31 hedgerows, dating from pre- and post-1837, were selected and the number of woody species present noted. The percentage frequency of occurrence of the ten species recorded was: hawthorn (97%), bramble (84%), blackthorn (48%), gorse (48%), ash (32%), elder (10%), ivy (10%), sycamore (10%), beech (3%) and rose (3%). The pre-1837 hedges contained significantly more gorse and blackthorn and much less ash. As in the Duleek study, a higher number of woody species was found in pre-1837 hedges than post-1837 hedges, but at Knock the difference was not significant, reflecting little enclosure in western Ireland before the eighteenth century. The Knock study concluded that the tree and shrub flora was not as rich as found in other hedges studied in Britain – reflecting either the gener-ally younger ages of Irish hedges or a smaller pool of species contributing to the hedgerow flora.

One interesting aspect of Ireland's lost woodland heritage is the persistence of many woodland flowering plants which, over most of their range, are con-fined to woodlands but spill out into open ground in 'hyper-oceanic' condi-tions in unlikely places. These species, as Webb has pointed out, are abundant and grow freely in the open countryside.[16] Their survival is made possible by the high moisture content of the air, approximating the damp conditions of their former woodland habitat. Occluded sun, due to the large number of overcast days, may also be a contributory factor in their survival. Species that survive outside the lost woodland habitat include pignut, dog-violet, primrose, wild strawberry, bluebell, yellow pimpernel, wood-rush, goldilocks buttercup, lesser celandine and wood anemone. For many of these their only shelter is often a north-facing slope. An extreme case is the wood-sorrel, often found in the open countryside under the protective covering of bracken fronds which provide substitute woodland cover.

Despite the ability of some woodland species to survive outside the shelter of trees, Ireland still has a poor woodland flora when compared with an equivalent area of Britain or the Continent. Praeger pointed out some of the glaring gaps in our woodland flora: stinking hellebore, green hellebore, twinflower, chickweed wintergreen, mezereon, spurge laurel, coral-root orchid, creeping lady's tresses, may lily, butcher's broom, lily of the valley and herb paris.[17] While most absentees might be ascribed to the loss of former extensive woodlands it is possible that some may never have arrived on Irish shores during the postglacial colonisation of Ireland.

Apart from the woodland flowering plants that are simply missing, others – while being around – are very rare. They were described by Praeger as 'old forest' inhabitants and it is quite possible that their distribution may have been more extensive at one stage and that their present day scarcity is a direct consequence of the diminishing forests.[17] These flowering plants and grasses are the narrow-leaved helleborine, toothwort, wood millet, yellow bird's-nest, common wintergreen, bird's-nest orchid and wood fescue. The situation concerning dog's mercury and moschatel is even more puzzling from a biogeographical viewpoint. While the former is common in British woods, often dominating the ground flora, it is comparatively rare in Ireland. Botanists have suggested that the species was originally introduced to Ireland where it found a niche in demesne plantations,[18] but it also occurs in the Burren, Co. Clare, where there is little doubt about its native status.[19] As for moschatel, also common in British woodlands on base-rich soils, it is recorded at one site in the Cave Hill Deer Park, Co. Antrim, where its presence as an introduced species is debatable, and in Co. Dublin where it is presumed to be an introduction.[20]

Under the present climatic conditions and in the absence of any grazing animals or adverse impacts by man the natural climax vegetation of Ireland in areas now occupied by grasslands would be woodland. The first steps in the evolution from grassland pasture to forest would be the growth of a scrub of spiny or thorny plants, blackthorn or sloe, hawthorn, bramble, and gorse, or furze, the latter especially on siliceous soils. The climax would then evolve according to the nature of the soil. On the siliceous rocks and soils these woodlands would be dominated by sessile oak growing in a phytosociological association known as *Blechno–Quercetum petraeae* after the characteristic presence of the hard fern, *Blechnum spicant*, on the woodland floor and the dominant tree the sessile oak, *Quercus petraea*.[21] On limestones the dominant tree would be ash, *Fraxinus excelsior*, together with hazel, *Corylus avellana*, flourishing in the phytosociological association known as a *Corylo–Fraxinetum*. There are other types of woodlands in Ireland, such as the wetland woodlands – to be discussed later – but the two major categories just mentioned encompass most of the broadleaved forests in Ireland.

Sessile oak woodlands

Killarney Valley, Co. Kerry

BOTANY

The Killarney Valley, Co. Kerry, contains the largest and most important sessile oak woodlands in Ireland, which together with the native woodlands elsewhere in the Killarney area extend in total to about 1,200 ha.[22] They grow on acidic soils derived from the underlying Lower Devonian Old Red Sandstone of which the mountains of the area are made. Although some distance from the coast, the woods are 'Atlantic' in character because of the oceanic type climate,

Sessile oak woodland, Lehid Harbour, Co. Kerry, which has been subjected to grazing. Some small holly bushes remain.

as evidenced by the climatological data collected at Muckross House (altitude 58 m) for the period 1983–5.[23] The mean daily temperature (10°C), mild winters (January mean 5.6°C), cool summers (July mean 16.4°C), high precipitation (158.5 cm) spread over 225 wet days, and a high percentage of humidity (84%) provide ideal conditions not only for a luxuriant tree growth but also for a profusion of liverworts, mosses, ferns and lichens smothering all available rocks on the woodland floor, or flourishing as epiphytes on tree trunks and branches. This growth is so profuse that the trees and their sinuous limbs appear hairy. Walking through these woodlands in the summer is the closest one could come to travelling through a tropical rainforest in the Northern Temperate Zone.

The woods are typically found on base-poor soils with a pH of approximately 4.4 and correspondingly very low calcium levels. Diagnostic species occurring with the sessile oak are downy birch, holly, aspen, rowan, honeysuckle, common cow-wheat, bracken, goldenrod and wood sage.

Despite their apparent naturalness and a romantic desire that these oak woods be linearly descended from early Christian times, the reality is quite different. Watts, working with available historical documents, has assembled a continuous narrative from 1580 for the Killarney area. He showed that prior to 1580 the Killarney Valley with its woodlands was a wilderness area *sensu stricto* – nature without impact from man.[24] It then came under heavy exploitation and until 1700 yielded mainly charcoal for ironworks and bark for the tanning industry. Then followed a hundred years of stable management which in turn was followed by another bout of ruthless felling between 1800 and 1815 when the woodland at Tomies Wood, Glena, Ross Island and elsewhere in the Valley were taken down one by one. Since then the woodlands have regenerated and now display an ecology characteristic of ancient woodland. Thus much of the 'native' forest in the Valley is, in fact, less than 200 years old. However, despite the pressure from man and his repeated assaults, the woods kept on regenerating their natural ecological characteristics and as such are thought to be the closest existing fit to the ancient oak forests.

The most extensive oak woods in Killarney are Derrycunihy and Galway's Woods, spreading over some 136 ha on the south side of the Upper Lake. The soils are acidic as they are composed of Lower Devonian gritty sandstones and

Torc Waterfall, Killarney
National Park, set amongst sessile oak woodland. A good site
for filmy-ferns, mosses and
other bryophytes.

soft slaty shales. Sessile oak is the dominant tree, reaching up to 21 m with the
upper branches forming an interlocking canopy. Many of the larger trees are
150–200 years old and in summer their crowns will only allow 20% of the sunlight to reach the forest floor. Beneath is an understorey of shrubs dominated
by holly which extends to a height of 6–9 m. Other shrub trees, although scarce,
include mountain ash or rowan, downy birch, hazel, ash and the yew. Ivy and
honeysuckle are sometimes found entwined with the oak and holly trees.

   The strawberry-tree, *Arbutus unedo*, for which the Killarney area is famous,
belongs to the heath family Ericaceae. It is an evergreen, shrubby tree, whose
specific name *unedo* ('I eat one' – meaning 'one is enough'!) reflects the
unpleasant taste of its deceptive, attractive looking, orange-scarlet to dark
crimson fruit. Normally reaching between 3 and 5 m in height, some specimens extend to 10 m at Killarney. Strawberry-tree wood is pink, fine grained,
extremely hard and much coveted by furniture makers. In the Killarney Valley
it occurs typically along the edges of the oak woods where trees are thinly scattered. In Europe, its centre of distribution is the western Mediterranean. It
extends across the Pyrenees, along the SW coast of France, and then on the
coast of Brittany at the cliffs of Trieux near Paimpol, before appearing in
Ireland. Because of its sensitivity to frost, its distribution within Europe today
is restricted to areas where the mean January air temperatures are greater
than 5°C. Within Ireland it only occurs in Kerry and Cork with an outlying station, some 257 km away, in the Belvoir and Stoney Woods, Lough Gill, Co.

The evergreen strawberry-tree, Killarney, Co. Kerry. Although its centre of distribution is in the western Mediterranean region, it is also a native of Kerry and Sligo.

Sligo, where until recently there was some doubt as to whether it was native or introduced, possibly by monks during their travels from the Continent in the early Christian period. The earliest mention of *Arbutus* in Irish records dates from the eighth century Brehon Laws where it is listed as a species not to be interfered with on pain of penalty (confiscation of a one or two year-old heifer). *Arbutus* was registered in the third priority grouping of trees (*Fodla fedo* – 'lower divisions of the wood') that were protected.[25] Recently Fraser Mitchell settled the argument by showing that *Arbutus* is indeed indigenous to Ireland and has been present for over 3,000 years as evidenced by pollen remains from Lough Inchiquin, Co. Kerry, and from Co. Sligo dating back almost 2,000 years.[26]

The Irish for *Arbutus* is *caithne* and *cuinche* (west of Ireland) and these are incorporated in several place names indicating a formerly more widespread distribution of the species and supporting its native status. For example, one of the many small islands in Clew Bay, Co. Mayo, is called Quinsheen, a diminutive form signifying 'little arbutus island'. However, there is disagreement amongst scholars as to these interpretations.[27] As to its ancestry in Ireland dating back before 2,000 years ago, Mitchell & Ryan state that *Arbutus* could not have survived that last cold snap – the Nahanagan stadial (10,600–10,000 years ago) – in or near Ireland.[28] Webb is also of the opinion that *per*-glacial survival of *Arbutus* must be 'deemed impossible.'[29] Another laurel-leaved plant found in the Killarney woods is the rhododendron, first introduced to the area as an ornamental species in the early nineteenth century after being brought to Britain from the Black Sea region. In fact, this could be considered as a reintroduction, as rhododendron was an important member of the flora some 425,000–300,000 years ago as revealed by the discovery of pollen, seeds and capsules in the interglacial deposits at Gort, Co. Galway, at Killbeg and Newtown, Co. Waterford, and Kildromin, Co. Limerick.[28,30,31] After these interglacial episodes rhododendron apparently died out. Little did those who brought this laurel to Killarney know about its future devastating impact on the woodlands. Indeed, since its arrival, rhododendron has thrived and expanded so single-mindedly, spreading by seed or by suckering, as to engulf the habitat that was hosting it. Rhododendron bushes forming a dense, impenetrable understorey – often in place of the more benign holly – will pre-

Rhododendron – an invasive
and ecologically damaging
species in Irish oak woodlands, Killarney Valley.

vent oak regeneration by stifling any growth about to sprout from the soil. The whole of the ground flora is subjected to the same treatment. Together, all the laurel-leaved species – rhododendron, strawberry-tree, holly and ivy – endow the woods with a special character as their thick shiny refracting leaves bounce the light around stroboscopically.

If the progression of that alien species through the woods had not been checked by control measures – very slow and laborious cutting down of the tangled stems and shoots, and treatment of the exposed stumps with herbicide at great cost to the National Park Authority – the rhododendron would have provided a classic example of a successful takeover of a 'natural' and undisturbed ecosystem by an exotic alien.

The woodland floor is disrupted by boulders and rocks, some of them very big. In between the boulders, the ground or herb layer is poor, a response to low light and scanty nutrients. Here, great wood-rush, bilberry, heather, common bent and wood-sorrel are found. The Irish spurge may sometimes be seen on the woodland perimeter. Webb classified it as an Atlantic species and it has been found often abundantly in west Cork and south Kerry while elsewhere in Ireland it is very rare and local. The commonest ferns on the ground are hard fern, bracken and hay-scented buckler-fern.

Paul Richards[32] described the bryophyte communities of the rocky floor of Derrycunihy Woods as a developmental sequence. Beginning with the colonisation of bare rock surfaces by small liverworts such as *Diplophyllum albicans* and *Lejeunea* spp., more robust species and especially mosses invade to form dense cushions over the blocks, with the liverworts *Scapania gracilis* and *Bazzania trilobata*, and mosses *Thuidium tamariscinum*, *Rhytidiadelphus loreus*, *Polytrichum formosum* and *Hylocomium* species, often mixed with the Tunbridge filmy-fern. On the inclined sides of blocks and outcrops, these luxuriant bryophyte carpets eventually slough off under gravity, and the process of colonisation begins all over again. Vascular plants may invade the more stable bryophyte communities, but the succession is often held indefinitely at an early stage of development. The most dramatic aspect of the Killarney woods is provided by epiphytic bryophytes sitting tightly on branches and tree trunks like a furry swaddling. These bryophytes derive all their nutrients and moisture from the rain dripping and running down the surface of the tree. The moss *T. tamariscinum* spreads onto tree bases from nearby rocks while other mosses such as *Isothecium*

Epiphytic mosses and the fern polypody strewn along oak branches.

myosuroides establish themselves directly on the bark. On the upper trunks and main horizontal branches there are dense mats of *I. myosuroides*, the liverworts *Plagiochila spinulosa, Frullania germana* and *F. tamarisci* together with Wilson's filmy-fern, the moss *Ulota crispa* and the most conspicuous of all the ferns being the polypody fern and intermediate polypody. Kelly also found the following species on horizontal branches: St Patrick's cabbage, navelwort and, actively growing, small saplings of holly and rowan.[22] The lichen flora is equally extremely interesting with 75 different species recorded,[33] and the large species of *Lobaria* and *Sticta* are present. The bryophyte communities include rare and local oceanic liverworts such as *Adelanthus decipiens, Plagiochila puncta-ta* and *Lejeunea flava* and mosses *Sematophyllum demissum* and *S. micans*. Fallen and decaying logs are an important habitat for another group of bryophytes.

The Killarney fern is the species that, more than any other, made Killarney a famous Mecca for fern collectors who descended in droves during the Victorian fern craze. They came to pluck these and other tender ferns which, in the words of the great gardener Shirley Hibberd, were 'vegetable jewellery' and 'plummy emerald green pets glistening with health and beadings of warm dew.' The Killarney fern belongs to the filmy-fern family and has thin, translucent, pale green leaves. The fronds are 20–35 cm long, arising from a creeping and blackish rootstock. By 1916 the collecting had been so vigorous and unrelenting that Scully thought that it had been exterminated from all its obvious stations and only survived in the mountainous parts of the Killarney district.[34] The Killarney fern had been captured and imprisoned in the preservative charms of the Wardian glazed chambers.

The best known ecological niches of the Killarney fern are the edges of streams, in splash zones, and underneath hanging rocks in stream gorges, especially in the presence of waterfalls. But in 1986 a new habitat for the Killarney fern was found by Doyle – in a dense oak wood.[23] The fern was growing on the vertical face of an Old Red Sandstone boulder, nowhere near running water or spray from a waterfall. The woodland canopy was formed by 20 m high sessile oak with a well-developed understorey of downy birch and holly. The fern was protruding from a carpet of moss made up mostly of *Thamnobryum alopecurum* while *Thuidium tamariscinum* was also prominent which together represented the general climax micro-community of the forest floor. It has also been found, though rarely, on the trunks of trees in very humid places.

INSECTS

The ecology of the oak wood is driven by the physical development of the oak leaf. The foliage emerges late and the leaves are not fully open until early summer but when the canopy thoroughly unfolds, it shuts out most of the light from the wood's interior. The plants and herbs on the wood floor have therefore to complete their flowering and fruiting as quickly as they can. For them all things are set when the canopy closes in. Conditions then become ideal for the shade and moisture-loving liverworts and mosses that seem to dominate these woods and turn the environment into a soft green sea stretching up to the canopy. As Mills so graphically describes, the forest canopy is a vast power station feeding its energy into a complex network of consumers ranging from caterpillars to birds to fungi and ultimately bacteria.[35]

Over 200 different insects are associated with the oak – no other Irish tree can boast an equivalent number. This high density is a consequence of the widespread distribution and longevity of the oak in the Irish landscape. Over the centuries, more and more have come to rely on this durable host and to adapt their skills to its resources. A huge army of caterpillars quarry the storehouse of carbohydrates, manufactured by photosynthesis, and locked up in each leaf. More than a hundred different species of insects are dependent on and specially equipped (with suction feet, leaf-cutting and sucking mouthparts, etc.) to exploit this immense larder. The insects most intent on the oak leaves are the caterpillars of moths. They are programmed to hatch in early summer when the leaves are tender and young, tannin-free and in abundant supply. The pale brown mottled umber moth, peppered moth, oak beauty and august thorn moth belong to that gourmet group. The commonest of all is the tiny green oak tortix moth, hatching out in its millions during May and June and likely to devour the whole canopy of a tree within a matter of weeks.

One of the many intriguing features of oak woods is the bewildering array of abnormal and weird-looking growths that can be seen sprouting from leaves and stems. The best known are the ball-like marble galls – first green, changing to brown and woody when mature. On the underside of the leaves are much smaller, circular and almost flattened galls, with names such as 'smooth spangle'; 'silk button' and 'common spangle'. Galls are a form of cancerous growth of the leaf or other vegetative parts, stimulated by the hatching of tiny eggs laid by one of the many different female gall wasps, *Cynipidae* – minute, ant-like insects with relatively large translucent wings bearing a distinctive pattern of veins. When the eggs hatch into larvae the plant tissue rapidly proliferates to envelop the grub, to neutralise it from the rest of the tissue. The oak's reaction is perfect for the grub which is provided with nutritious, juicy food.

The next stage of development is pupation, when the internal tissues of the larva are reorganised to yield a pupa, which breaks out of its skin. Thereafter the pupa remains dormant within the gall, most pupae overwintering within their protective capsule. Winged adults, one or more, emerge in spring. But the story can be more complicated. Often what emerges is not a gall wasp but a parasitic interloper, an ichneumon fly, a cuckoo of the insect world. The ichneumon adult lays its eggs in the formed gall, penetrating it with a long, thin and deadly needle-like ovipositor through which the egg passes to rest either into or close to the unsuspecting gall wasp larva. The invasive ichneumon larva then develops, devouring the gall wasp larva to later emerge itself from the gall.

Two common gall wasps in the Killarney woods are the marble gall and the cola gall, both invader species which have arrived from Britain. Apart from a somewhat bizarre start to life, gall wasps also have complicated life cycles with alternating sexual and asexual generations. Both the mentioned species require the introduced Turkey oak (found in parts of central and eastern Ireland) for their sexual generations. The most frequently found galls on the Kerry oaks are spangles, silk-buttons, currants, artichokes and oysters. While most gall wasps are benign, only one has an adverse effect on oaks. It is *Andricus quercuscalicis*, another recent invader to Ireland, which attacks and destroys acorns. Fortunately for the Kerry woodlands the preferred host is the pedunculate oak – not important at Killarney. The sessile oak is only rarely affected. However, at Kilkenny Castle, where the pedunculate oak does occur, the proportion of acorns 'galled' exceeded 90%. Thirty species of galling wasps on Irish oaks are known.[36]

The yew wood at Reenadinna on the Muckross Peninsula in the National Park is also home for the gall midge *Taxomyia taxi*, living within the distinctive artichoke galls. These gall midges, or Cecidomyiidae, are a very successful group with many widely distributed species in Ireland. A recent note about the occurrence of *Taxomyia taxi* in Reenadinna mentions that it had not been recorded from anywhere else in Ireland outside the native yew woodlands at Killarney.[37]

Twenty-eight species of butterfly are resident in Ireland while another eight, including the red admiral, painted lady and clouded yellow, visit as migrants. Within the Killarney National Park there are 23 resident species and on a good summer's day up to 15 different sorts can be seen flitting about the woodlands.[38] Of the 28 Irish resident butterflies, six, or 26%, could be considered as woodland species on account of their caterpillars' need for leaves of trees or the associated woodland herbaceous plants. This is a low proportion in comparison with Britain where 42 of the 58 butterflies breeding there, 72%, are regularly occurring in woodland.[39]

The following six butterflies are characteristic woodland species in the Killarney Valley. The green-veined white favours the more open and sunny locations within the woodland complex while the purple hairstreak, *Quercusia quercus*, as its scientific name suggests, lives at one with the oak but is rarely seen because the caterpillar usually browses high up in the canopy where the adults also fly – the dark purple streak across the forewings distinguishes it from other hairstreaks. It is rare in the Killarney Valley with records from Ross Island, Tomies Wood and Derrycunihy. The wood white is sometimes encountered, especially around the Muckross Peninsula where the caterpillars feed on vetches. The silver-washed fritillary is a relatively large butterfly with dark

Speckled wood butterfly, one
of the common species in the
Killarney Valley oak woods.

orange wings that has black spots, whose caterpillars feed on violets while the
speckled wood, mostly found flitting among trees, will also explore hedgerows.
This is the only Irish butterfly to overwinter in both the larval and pupal stages.
Although the ringlet is more common outside the woodlands than in, it is nevertheless regarded as a woodland species with the caterpillars feeding on grasses.

THE KERRY SLUG

One of the most bizarre and curious invertebrates to be found in the Killarney
woods is the Kerry slug. It is an exceedingly beautiful animal that occurs in two
principal colour forms. The general body colour of the first variety ranges
from blue-grey to black with white spots. The second variety is ginger-bronze-
olive to dark brown with yellow-gold spots. The Kerry slug is probably an
ancient forest animal that has been able to move out from the woodlands and
live in rough moorland ground but only in sandstone areas where the moisture
and humidity levels are high enough to allow its survival. In this habitat it is
quite usual to encounter the slugs crawling over lichen-covered Old Red
Sandstone boulders. One of its extraordinary attributes is its ability to elongate
itself into a long thin sliver of tissue, an adaptation to facilitate squeezing into
and through narrow crevices. Moderately sized slugs of 2.5 cm at rest can
stretch out to 8 cm and over while the bigger slugs of 4–5 cm can extend to 12
cm! Anybody who has tried to keep these slugs in containers or boxes will
vouch their capacity to disappear, Houdini-like, from what was thought to be a
secure holding place.

   Although often described as crepuscular in habit, the Kerry slug can frequently be encountered in the woodlands during the day where it occurs principally on the lichen and moss-covered tree trunks, feeding by grazing on the
vegetation. It does not appear to have a specific food plant but will eat lichens,
mosses, liverworts, fungi and algae.[40] When not active it retreats to sheltered
spots under stones, bark and fallen branches, often conjuring up its remarkable powers of body elongation. It is relatively frequent in parts of the
broadleaved woodlands at Uragh Wood, on the south side of Kenmare Bay, in
the Killarney Valley woodlands, Co. Kerry, and in the Glengarriff woods, Co.
Cork.

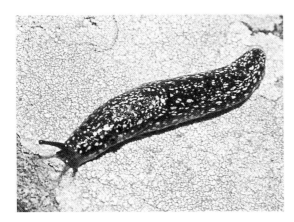

Kerry slug.

The Kerry slug was first described from specimens collected at Lough Caragh, Co. Kerry, in 1842, given the name *Geomalacus maculosus* and placed in a new genus of terrestrial molluscs. The slug was later discovered in north Spain in 1868 and then in north Portugal in 1873. The taxonomic relation-ships between the Kerry slug inhabiting western parts of Kerry and Cork, and the one from the Iberian peninsula was then thrown into some confusion with the discovery, from 1845 onwards, of several apparently different species of *Geomalacus*. In an effort to resolve this puzzle Platts & Speight investigated the intricate reproductive systems of the slugs as well as comparing by electro-pherograms digestive gland extracts prepared from one Spanish and two Irish specimens.[40] The conclusion from both these investigations was that Irish specimens of the slug were conspecific with the G. *maculosus* living in northern Spain and northern Portugal. In other words they belonged to the same species. The only other distinct *Geomalacus* species was G. *anguiformis* from southern Portugal.

MAMMALS

The populations of wood mice and bank voles in the oak and the yew woods at Reenadinna have been studied by Smal & Fairley.[41] The yew wood, with its heavy vegetation cover, was found to contain unusually high densities of those small rodents – higher than any previously recorded. The average was 58.3 mice per hectare with a maximum of 91.9. Under normal circumstances in British woodlands, peak densities are about 40–50 per hectare while in Ireland the previous maximum recorded of 46.3 was for hazel scrub on limestone pave-ment in the Burren (see p.215). In the Reenadinna yew wood the relationship between density and range from home was – as expected – inverse, with excep-tionally low home ranges in the yew wood which, however, expanded in the summer when food was in low supply. The results from this study suggested that the mice and vole populations are self-regulating through interspecific competition for food.

A much larger inhabitant of the Killarney Valley is the red deer which, despite often being thought of as an open moorland and mountain animal, spends a significant amount of time in the woodlands east and north of Lough Leane,[42] especially in the winter. These are probably the only surviving descen-dants of the red deer that once roamed the Irish countryside (see p.65). Their

distribution range contracted as a result of forest clearances and ongoing predation by wolf and man. Eventually the only place where they survived into the
middle of the nineteenth century as a free native species was the Killarney
Valley, where the Herbert family, owners of the Muckross Estate, and the
Viscounts Kenmare, realised the dangers facing this residual population and
proceeded to set up the first deer parks. Despite their efforts, however, numbers went on to decline from about 1,500 animals at the turn of the century to
about 60 forty years ago. A survey carried out in 1970 revealed that there were
110 deer on Torc and Mangerton Mountains. Since then numbers have
increased to about 800 in the National Park area and the animals have started
grazing and sheltering in the woodlands again.[43]

Alien sika deer from the Far East and Japan, introduced to Ireland by Lord
Powerscourt in 1860, thrived so well that one stag and two hinds were sent to
the Kenmare Estate in 1865. There are now over 700 in the Killarney National
Park. They have a stronger preference for life in the woods than their red deer
cousins, where they damage the trees by eating bark, and destroy seedlings by
grazing on them. An even greater issue is the danger of hybridisation with the
native red deer which is putting at risk the 'native' gene pool. Extensive
hybridisation has already occurred in the Wicklow mountains.

BIRDS
Bird life in the oak woods is inextricably linked with the life cycle of the oak
leaf and the production of caterpillars and other insects. Woodland patrons
such as the great tit, blue tit and the special Irish subspecies of the coal tit,
Parus ater hibernicus, have fashioned their life cycles to ensure maximum syn-
chronisation between the hatching of their young and the greatest availability
of caterpillars. Once mid-summer comes and all the bird breeding is done, the
caterpillars that have not fallen prey to tits turn into fully-fledged moths. By
then, the levels of tannins, a complex grouping of chemicals, are making the
oak leaves no longer palatable to insects and larvae. Thus freed from its attack-
ers, the oak tree enjoys a second burst of life and uses this reprieve to manufacture more sugars and carbohydrates before the autumn senescence.

The vegetation structure of the Killarney sessile oak woods has a direct influence on the size and composition of the breeding bird populations.
Noticeably, greatest diversity and densities occur when there is a well-developed understorey of shrubs and vegetation. A study carried out in 1973
revealed the highest number of breeding species (22) in Tomies Wood Lower
while 20 were recorded in Derrycunihy.[44,45] Four species were particularly
abundant within the two woods. The commonest was the chaffinch with a
mean number of 30 territories per 10 hectares, followed by the robin (23),
goldcrest (18) and blue tit (17). A second tier of less numerous species included the coal tit (8), wren (7), tree creeper (5), woodpigeon (3) and spotted flycatcher (3).

Simms explored 19 more diverse sessile oak woodlands throughout Ireland
and found, not surprisingly, a different mix of breeding birds.[46] The most
abundant species, as in Killarney, was the chaffinch. Simms expressed his
results in an index of 'relative abundance' of the bird species in the woods –
not to be confused with the figures in the preceding paragraph – with the
chaffinch scoring 15 followed by the blackbird (11), robin (11), woodpigeon
(10), willow warbler (7), wren (7), blue tit (5) and chiffchaff (4). From the

Killarney data it appears that goldcrests have taken over the ecological niche left empty by the willow warblers due possibly to presence of a holly undergrowth and absence of attractive scrub, especially birch, in the woodlands. With regard to the overall breeding densities, the average in Killarney (130 pairs/10 ha) was lower than in eight southern England oakwoods (142 pairs/10 ha) but significantly higher than in seven Scottish oakwoods (107 pairs/10 ha).[44]

When St Patrick banished snakes from Ireland he may also have swung the crozier over the woodpeckers. Indeed, if Ireland has only three-fifths of the British breeding birds, the discrepancy concerning the woodland species is even more conspicuous.[47] Those missing are wryneck, tawny owl, green woodpecker, great spotted woodpecker, lesser spotted woodpecker, nightingale, marsh tit, willow tit, crested tit, nuthatch, hawfinch, firecrest, tree pipit and capercaillie. Only the rare and occasional breeding records of the redstart, wood warbler and pied flycatcher prevent their inclusion in this list. Why should it be so difficult for these woodland birds to settle in Ireland? After all, Ireland is only 80 km across the Irish Sea from Britain. Moreover, five of the absentees are either summer migrants, flying regularly over the Irish landscape, or have visited the country up to and, in some cases, on more than 100 occasions. Why are they not tempted to settle down?

The dearth of species may be primarily related to woodland size and also to the availability and abundance of food. Research in Britain has shown that most woodland birds are much more likely to occur in forested areas of 100 ha or more than in smaller woods[48] – in Ireland only three sessile oak woodlands exceed 100 ha.[49] However, one could argue that the aggregate total of about 1,400 ha woodland in the Killarney Valley would provide a sufficient amount of forest to meet the habitat requirements of a number of woodland birds. The same applies to the second most important site for sessile oak which is Co. Wicklow, where the aggregate of 1,000 ha, stretching from the Vale of Clara to the neighbouring valleys of the Avoca River, Rathdrum and Glendalough, fail to attract a matching woodland breeding bird population.

One special bird of Irish woodlands is the brown and cryptically coloured woodcock, an extremely elusive bird, seldom seen unless disturbed. However, from mid-February to July the species performs an extraordinary territorial display flight, or 'roding', at dusk, when the male flies a regular circuit above the trees or open ground, uttering two calls, a thin 'tsiwick' and a low, frog-like croak. On first encounter these displaying birds appear like giant fruit bats flapping around in circles. About 4,500 pairs breed throughout Ireland, mostly in broadleaved woodland or scrub habitats. Their eyes are so far set back on the skull that when sitting on the ground, incubating their eggs, they can see any predators approaching from behind without moving their head, allowing them to remain absolutely still. In November there is a massive immigration of woodcock into Ireland from a wide area of Europe as far east as the Urals. During the winter these visitors, together with many Irish birds that have not moved south out of the country, spend the daytime concealed in woodland or scrub undergrowth, emerging at dusk to feed in nearby fields. Their abundance in Ireland attracts specialist hunters, especially from France, as their fast, twisting and almost explosive flight presents a great challenge. Wilson has shown by catching, ringing and subsequently recapturing woodcock at different sites throughout the country, that wintering birds are faithful to their areas of daytime shelter for short periods – up to 20 days – and that the same individuals returned to the same daytime shelter areas in successive winters. Also, once they had arrived in their wintering area they remained in that area for the whole wintering period.[50]

Other Co. Kerry oakwoods

Most of the Killarney Valley oakwoods are below the 200 m contour line although one, Doogary Wood (20 ha) which must be the highest wood in the country, extends up to 280 m. Here, stunted oaks mix with downy birch in an open woodland which is probably the closest fit to original woodland in the whole area. Another significant oak grove in Co. Kerry lines the western slopes of Inchiquin Lough, south of Kenmare Bay. Uragh Wood (87 ha) grows on shallow siliceous soil (pH 4.6 and very low levels of nitrogen and calcium), strewn with massive boulders which greatly impede the traveller's progress. Decaying trees, soggy damp spots, depressions and hidden holes, breast-high ferns in clearings and rocky streams in ravines are further hazards to be reckoned with. The sessile oaks are small, many are stunted and gnarled. The oak canopy, in some places, reaches up to about 9 m. Rowan, downy birch, holly, aspen, hawthorn, juniper and a very occasional yew – from which the name 'Uragh' is derived – occur in their midst. The strawberry-tree is no longer in the wood, having retreated to one of the islands in Inchiquin Lough. One immediately notices active regeneration of all trees, which is unusual for an Irish wood as most of them are open to sheep and other shoot-suppressing herbivores. Uragh is replete with collapsed and rotting timber, rich epiphytic bryophyte communities and an impressive ground flora including bilberry, heather, wood-rush, gorse and broom in drier and more open spots. St Patrick's cabbage as well as the two species of filmy-ferns are also found there. The Kerry slug occurs on boulders and on trees, albeit at a low density of 0.6 individuals per square metre based on 20 quadrat (0.5 m ˜ 0.5 m) samples – the lowest in a survey of 11 acid oak woodlands from Kerry and Cork carried out in September 1973. Uragh Wood also harboured the lowest number of individual snails (3.6) per square metre.[51] A primeval atmosphere pervades this low-lying, damp, dark, near impenetrable, secluded place. Elsewhere in Kerry, intriguing patches of oak cling onto steep slopes at the southern end of Lough Caragh.

Co. Cork

At the head of Bantry Bay, Co. Cork, the Glengarriff Woods (100 ha) are quite extensive and better ordered than Uragh Wood, with tall straight trees and a high canopy similar to that of Killarney. The surrounding mountains, providing shelter from the prevailing winds, have allowed the trees to develop along more regular, less tortured lines. Sessile oak is the dominant tree, reaching up to 30 m high and providing about 70% canopy cover. Above an altitude of about 135 m the sessile oaks gives way to birch which until this altitude had been inconspicuous. Holly is not such an important species as in other oak woods such as the Glen of the Downs, Co. Wicklow. Rowan, yew and strawberry-tree are scattered throughout the wood. Grey willow and eared willow are plentiful. Below the willows are bilberry, bramble, honeysuckle, gorse and an infrequent amount of heather. The ground flora contains an abundance of great wood-rush, hairy wood-rush, bracken, common cow-wheat, St Patrick's cabbage, green-ribbed sedge, glaucous sedge, narrow-leaved helleborine (very rare in Ireland and confined to a few damp woods) and Irish spurge. Filmy-ferns and a rich bryophyte flora are also present. The dominant bird species recorded during a survey of the woods during 14–21 June 1962 were blue tit, great tit, chaffinch, robin and wren. Less numerous were chiffchaff, goldcrests, blackbird, song thrush, bullfinch and woodpigeon. The absence of willow war-blers, whitethroats, blackcaps and spotted flycatchers was noted.[52]

The Glengarriff woods also have a rich insect and other invertebrate fauna. For example the woodland is one of two known Irish sites for the false click beetle, the other being the oak woods at Glencar, Co. Kerry. These beetles are bullet-shaped and matt black in colour. Only two specimens of this elusive fam-ily have ever been caught in Ireland. The larvae live in the dead branches of beech, oak, birch, ash and others but it may also occur in standing trees.[53] Another unusual inhabitant is the large pseudoscorpion *Neobisium carpenteri*, originally described from Glengarriff, its only known locality in Ireland, at the turn of the century. It still occurs at the original site, under the flaking outer bark of a strawberry-tree. Outside the country it is only known from Essex in England and from south Wales. It resembles a species in Spain and Portugal and thus may be another member of the Lusitanian element of the fauna of southwest Ireland.[54]

Co. Galway

One of the largest and ecologically most important sites of lowland blanket bog in Ireland extends some 7,000 ha over flat landscape north of Roundstone and southeast of Clifden in Connemara, Co. Galway. This often thick vegetable skin is dotted with numerous lakes, most of which contain small islands. Undisturbed by man or grazing animals, these tiny self-contained habitats sup-port a very different type of vegetation from that on the adjoining mainland where periodic burning and livestock pressure have reduced the trees to a ghostly presence. The island vegetation creates 'a fascinating and unfamiliar atmosphere of primitive jungle which is quite unmatched even in the most "natural" community on the mainland' according to Webb & Glanville.[55] These island jungles are typically fringed by a heath zone on the windward side dominated either by western gorse or by heather and purple moor-grass. The heath community gives way to woodland which is dense and covers most of the islands while remaining low – 11 m is the maximum recorded height. The tree canopy, severely battered by the wind, slants upwards, from the west. Sessile oak, holly, rowan, yew, downy birch and grey willow are all equally common without any one showing signs of dominance. There is no shrub layer as the canopy is too dense.

Sessile oak is also found on the islands of Lough Corrib, especially on the four large sandstone ones (total area 4.8 ha) in the northern reaches of the Lough.[56] These woods have again probably been little touched by man or his herds and cover the top of each island, creating a dome-like structure. The principal species are sessile oak, rowan and aspen. The trees rise to about 7 m above the ground to form a dense canopy. Hazel and holly feature in a rather sparse shrub layer while wood-rush and bilberry are the main herbs. On the western fringes a dense border of heather, gorse, broom, bracken and cock's-foot grass cover the ground.

The features of Derryclare Wood (8 ha) are close to that of the so-called

'Atlantic' Killarney woods. The canopy layer is formed almost completely of sessile oak with some rowan, downy birch and grey willow. Ash with hazel occurs on the re-crystallised limestone occupying the northeast and southwest central parts of the wood. Hazel also generally dominates in the shrub layer while holly and hawthorn are sparingly scattered throughout the wood. The age of the largest holly specimen was determined by boring a hole into the centre of the tree, extracting the core and then counting the number of annual growth rings throughout the length of the core. It was a young sapling in 1864, which had probably germinated around 1840. The lack of holly in the woods is ascribed to the grazing pressure especially by feral goats – not excluded from the wood until the 1970s.[57] Detailed examinations of the lichens by Folan & Mitchell revealed a close similarity to the oceanic character of the Killarney lichen flora.[58] Ninety-eight species and seven minor taxa, belonging to 40 genera were recorded along with seven species of parasitic lichens including one new to Ireland and Britain and one new to the Northern Hemisphere.

Other sessile oak woods of interest in the county are Glendollagh Wood (3 ha) which is similar to Derryclare Wood and somewhat scraggy in appearance; Hill of Doon (14 ha) at the north end of Lough Corrib – a mixed woodland comprising some fine areas of tall oak with holly occurring underneath; Shannawoneen Wood (38 ha) in the Owenboliska valley – a well-developed wood with an understorey of hazel, birch and holly, and finally Dernasliggaun (19 ha) on the south side of the Killary Harbour – a scrappy, stunted wood full of rich lichen and moss flora including the Tunbridge filmy-fern and St Patrick's cabbage.

Co. Mayo

In Co. Mayo the Atlantic type oak woodlands near Pontoon, at the south end of Lough Conn, were mutilated by clearances but fine remnants (33 ha) still endure, especially on the granite at Pontoon itself. Here sessile oak forms an open canopy of rather bent trees. Associated species are downy birch, ash, rowan, holly and hazel. There is no shrub layer and the ground vegetation is poor.

Perhaps the most exciting place for sessile oak in Co. Mayo is near Louisburgh, where a rare example of a relict Atlantic wood (17 ha) hugs a low hill about 150 m high, situated on the southern coastline of Clew Bay. Here annual rainfall averages 138 cm and the average annual temperature is 10°C. The soils and vegetation of Old Head Wood were examined by Gorham in July 1951.[59] The trees bear the impact of the prevailing westerly winds which inhibit growth through desiccation of the buds on the exposed side, while the sheltered side bushes out naturally, thus creating a bent posture. Sessile oak forms a dense cover of low and variously contorted trees. In the sheltered areas the trees reach 12–18 m high but degenerate to dwarfed and tortured specimens towards the summit, giving way to scrub merging into heath. Downy birch and grey willow are locally abundant on the wood margins, especially in the north-western parts. Other species present are hazel, rowan, holly and ash. Some beech has been planted in the past and is mixed with oak except at the top where it forms an almost pure stand. Where willow branches have fallen down on the wet woodland floor they re-root, and exhibit vigorous vegetative growth with numerous shoots thrusting upwards. Although the western and southern margins have been planted with some coniferous and other exotic species, the

Old Head oak woodland, near Louisburgh, Co. Mayo, with characteristic prolific growth of mosses and epiphytes on boulders, tree trunks and branches.

core of the wood towards the northwest end remains pure and inviting. The lichen flora is rich, as expected for a oceanic western woodland, with spectacular specimens of the tree lungwort, growing as a sprawling epiphyte in mats as big as 5 x 7 cm. This is one of the best places to see it in Ireland. Other lichens include *Cladonia polydactyla, Graphis elegans* and *G. scripta*. Amongst the prolific epiphytes are the fern polypody, mosses and liverworts. In Gorham's study the levels of surface organic material affected the soil properties, and plant distribution was correlated to depth of the humus layer. Wood-sorrel and mosses occurred throughout the wood on the shallow or deep humus layer. At the summit of the wood, under the tortured oaks lie bilberry and common cow-wheat. The redstart, nightjar and long-eared owl – all rare woodland birds – have been recorded breeding here. It is also an outpost for the jay which was first recorded west of the Connacht lakes in 1958 and is still extending its range in Co. Mayo.

Also in Mayo, near the southern border of the county, is a much overgrazed sessile oak and silver birch wood struggling to survive. The Erriff river valley wood at Erriff Bridge is almost certainly the last remnant of a once much more extensive forest, lining the mountain side. Despite those scanty remains, the drama of the wood is heightened by the nakedness of the surrounding landscape to the south, most of which is covered by blanket bog. A rehabilitation programme is under way: sheep have been fenced out and thousands of young sessile oaks have been planted by the owner of the wood, Coillte, with the encouragement and support of An Taisce (the National Trust for Ireland). The ground flora is poor at present as the sheep have grazed it for years. Bird life is diverse and includes the usual woodland species plus tree creepers and spotted flycatchers.

Tree lungwort, one of the most curious-looking of all woodland lichens (F. Guinness).

Co. Sligo

Travelling north to Sligo, one comes across a series of sessile oak woods clustered principally around Lough Gill, at Collooney, Ballysadare and Glencar. The most interesting tree is the strawberry-tree, curiously displaced from its centre of distribution in Kerry and Cork. Praeger claimed it to be 'undoubtedly indigenous' in Sligo on the basis that 'many very old [strawberry] trees occupy chinks on limestone rocks and elsewhere in wild situations among a native tree flora' including yew and rock whitebeam.[17,60] Suspicions were aroused about its antiquity when there was no mention in written records of the strawberry-tree in the area before 1866. However, Mitchell, as mentioned earlier, has shown the strawberry-tree to be indigenous in Ireland with fossil pollen evidence, at least 3,000 years old, from Co. Kerry.[26] The earliest pollen records from Co. Sligo (Slish lake) date from nearly 2,000 years ago thus proving the accuracy of Praeger's early ecological detective work.[61]

Union Wood (28 ha) is a typical western Ireland woodland comprised of sessile oak, holly and rowan. The bedrock is gneiss which produces a calcifuge ground flora rich in ferns and bryophytes. The epiphytic lichen flora is impressive. However, regeneration of the woodland is being inhibited by grazing fallow deer. The wood at the Bonet River is small (9 ha), with a mixture of mostly pedunculate oak, ash and hazel stands on limestone and alluvial soil which changes markedly in the western parts with the appearance of acid rocks. It is claimed to have one of the richest woodland floras in the county with an abundance of wood anemone, wood-sorrel, pignut, primrose and bluebell. In addition to this traditional ground flora, the botanist will encounter goldilocks buttercup, early purple orchid and bird's-nest orchid at its most northerly station. Slish Wood (6 ha), on the south shore of Lough Gill, contains the tail end of a once fine primeval sessile oak wood before it was underplanted with conifers. Aspen and the rock whitebeam, occurring in only scattered patches in the west and north of the country, are found here. The ground is a rich carpet of great wood-rush, bilberry and common cow-wheat.

Co. Donegal

The finest sessile oak wood in Co. Donegal is in the Glenveagh National Park and extends over 94 ha. Before becoming part of the National Park it was severely overgrazed by a herd of red deer – introduced to the Glenveagh Estate in the nineteenth century – and encroached upon by a plague of rhododendron. Some parts of the wood are quite accessible and tame but other sections on boulder-strewn ground can be difficult to negotiate. The wood is dominated by sessile oak with an understorey of holly, while bird cherry, juniper, rowan, whitebeam, downy birch and yew occur sparingly. Glenveagh has a typical western oak wood bryophyte flora with some extensive carpets of the two filmy-ferns, Tunbridge and Wilson's. Several interesting birds have bred here including redstart, woodcock and the wood warbler. Other important Donegal sessile oakwoods are at Ardnamona (29 ha), which is a fine and well-developed wood on the edge of Lough Eske, Carndonagh Wood (13 ha) and Fahan Wood (30 ha). The old scrub woodland at Carradoan (200 ha) provides a fine example of vegetation sequence from open moorland to birch scrub to a low straggly sessile oak community.

Northern Ireland

Sessile oak woods are scarce in Northern Ireland with slightly less than 200 ha of ecologically important sites. The best remaining example of a natural woodland is Banagher Glen, Co. Derry (30 ha), spread along the valleys of the Altnaheglish River and Glenedra Water in the Sperrin mountains, Co. Derry. It is likely that the woodland is a remnant of the primeval forest that once covered the region. Sessile oak is the main canopy species, often mixed with downy birch and rowan growing on acid to neutral schists in the upper parts of the valley. Ash and alder are numerous on the lower slopes with some wych elm reflecting more base-rich soils. Hazel is also common. The woodland is actively regenerating and there is a good bryophyte community and a rich ground flora. Breen Wood (21 ha) in the Glens of Antrim is a mature oak wood composed mainly of sessile oak – some trees reaching 15 m in height – mixed with some pedunculate oak. Rowan, holly, hazel and hawthorn also occur. In the wet valley bottoms, willow and alder dominate.

In Co. Tyrone there are only two oak woods of note. The first is at Boorin (13 ha) where sessile oak grows alongside pedunculate oak over an extensive mantle of wood-rush. Little or no woodland regeneration is to be observed. The second wood is at Drumlea (28 ha). It is mostly composed of sessile oak – some trees reaching up to 23 m in height – mixed with some pedunculate oak. Here again the lack of regeneration is threatening the wood with extinction unless herbivores are excluded. In Co. Down the sessile oak wood (16 ha) near Rostrevor stands on Silurian soils. Some ash is mixed through the oak while the shrub layer is dominated by holly and hazel, all of which are regenerating. Wild cherry flourishes as does the scarce hard shield-fern. Much of the ground is bare with scattered patches of brambles, ferns and wood-sorrel. Wood avens, scarce in many other northern woods, is found here.

Royal fern. Common in damp woodlands, ditches, bog margins and river
margins. Frequent in the west but
much rarer in the east.
(F. Guinness).

Also in Co. Down is Ballyhassan Wood (10 ha), near Quoile, standing on dry
acid soil. Sessile oak prevails, while downy birch, sycamore and other trees are
also present. The traveller will come across bracken and brambles growing
high, but also wood-sorrel, wood sage and honeysuckle.

Co. Wicklow

Co. Wicklow, after Co. Kerry, has the finest stands of semi-natural sessile oak in
Ireland, i.e. least disturbed by man. Most of the woods are found in valleys,
often on steep sides and on acid soils derived from siliceous rocks. All the
woods are well developed without the scraggy appearance and structure of
many of the western oak woods. There are several outstanding sites filling
some deep U-shaped valleys that have been carved out of granite by the glaciers. Near Glendalough, famous for its early Christian settlement founded by St
Kevin in AD 617, an almost pure sessile oak wood (100 ha) with some hazel and
holly has a typical if somewhat impoverished ground flora and hosts a good
variety of woodland birds. The Glen of the Downs, a V-shaped valley and the
largest glacial overflow channel in Ireland, is completely lined with forest (59
ha). The least disturbed and purest parts of the woodland are found on the
western side where holly forms an understorey to the sessile oak.

The development of coniferous plantations in the Avonmore river valley has
eroded much of the formerly extensive oak woodlands but enough of them
remain around Clara and Rathdrum (c.250 ha) to make the area one of the
most important sites in Wicklow. The trees grow tall as a result of their shel-

Sessile oak woodlands at Laragh, Co. Wicklow. Tree growth is much taller and less contorted than in western oak woodlands due to increased shelter. (R.Cabot)

tered position. Further coniferous incursions in the nearby Avoca river valley have mutilated some of the woods but again the remnants are interesting, especially around Glenart Castle and Woodenbridge, where great wood-rush almost smothers the ground. A wilder location is the Devil's Glen, cut by the Vartry River, where the woods (250 ha) flourish in the steep gorge. Sessile oak dominates the community with holly as an understorey. The presence of bird cherry and the Irish whitebeam – both rare in Ireland – provide additional interest. The ground flora is rich and the Welsh poppy, another rarity, lurks nearby.

Towards the heart of the Wicklow Hills, Ballinacor Wood (150 ha) boasts some very old sessile oak mixed with downy birch. The ground flora is a classic one with hard fern, wood-sorrel and bluebell. Unfortunately, the alien invader rhododendron is present in the wood. Finally, in the Glencree river valley the woodland (*c*.100 ha) is small and fragmented on the valley floor and is dominated by sessile oak, downy birch and hazel.

Ash–pedunculate oak–hazel woods

The second major woodland type occurs typically on base-rich soils, particularly in the Midlands, and on limestone pavement or steep rocky slopes, especially in western parts, notably the Burren, Co. Clare. Such woodlands belong to the community of *Corylo–Fraxinetum*, dominated by hazel, *Corylus avellana*, or ash, *Fraxinus excelsior*, and very rarely by the yew. In the Midlands these three species are replaced by the pedunculate oak, and/or ash. This category of ash–pedunculate oak–hazel woodland is noted for its rich herbaceous layer and the trees are happiest growing in lime-rich, free-draining soils especially on limestone drift, on alluvial deposits and eskers. Eskers are fluvio-glacial deposits laid down by sub-glacial streams. They are typically thin long ridges, up to 20 m in height, spanning 200 m in width and extending over several kilometres.

The soil preferences of pedunculate and sessile oak are generally sufficient to segregate these two species. Sessile oak woods are very much restricted to areas of siliceous rocks found mostly in the mountainous and upland parts of the country. Pedunculate oak woods are generally confined to base-rich soils, derived mainly from limestone and are therefore mostly found in the Carboniferous limestone areas of Central Ireland. Pedunculate oak sometimes penetrates into siliceous rock areas, especially where there are mineral flushes. If sessile oak is present, hybridisation will inevitably ensue. This is the case in the Clare Glens, north Tipperary; Barry's Glen, north Kerry; and in the Glen of the Downs, Co. Wicklow.[62] Conversely, where sessile oak penetrates pedunculate country as at Lough Carra, Co. Mayo and at Lough Leane, Co. Kerry, the same phenomenon occurs. The hybrids usually have the peduncles (stalk of the flower/acorn) and auricles (the basal lobes of the leaf) of pedunculate oak and the hairy leaves and long petiole (leaf stalk) of sessile oak.

The status of pedunculate oak in Ireland is controversial. During the eighteenth and nineteenth centuries many improving landlords furnished their estates and demesnes with it, and there is no doubt that several of the surviving pedunculate oak woods in the Midlands originate from such wide-scale plantings. However, some trees at Charleville, Co. Offaly, were shown to be 350–450 years old, i.e. older than any introduction scheme, which, together with other supporting evidence, argues for a continuous presence on base-rich soils of pedunculate oak from the primeval forest to the present day.[63]

The best examples of old stands of pedunculate wood, often mixed with ash, growing on limestone drift are found in Charleville, Co. Offaly, and Abbeyleix, Co. Laois. At Charleville the woodland (170 ha) has large oaks (up to 26 m high) mixed with ash, wych elm and downy birch with an understorey of hazel and hawthorn. The Abbeyleix woods extend over some 120 ha on either side of the River Nore on deep, often wet soil. The large oaks are 24–25 m high. A walk through the woods between the well-spaced trees when the bluebells flood the ground is a magical experience. In general both the Abbeyleix and Charleville woods are the best examples of their kind in Ireland, and have been extensively managed with selective removal of timber. The wych elm was formerly a widespread and characteristic tree of these mixed broadleaved woodlands on basic soils, but Dutch elm disease has caused its general demise across Ireland – as it has across Britain – and only the pathetic dead skeletons now indicate its earlier abundance. It remains to be seen whether significant recovery will take place.

Grey squirrels can be seen romping around in both Abbeyleix and Charleville woods. They prefer deciduous or mixed woods to coniferous plantations as they are partial to the seeds of hardwoods, particularly acorns. The grey squirrel is not a native of Ireland but was introduced to the country at Castle Forbes, Co. Longford in 1911. Warner relates that a wicker hamper containing eight or 12 squirrels, a wedding present from the Duke of Buckingham to one of the daughters of the house, was opened on the lawn after the wedding breakfast, whereupon the bushy-tailed creatures quickly leapt out and scampered off into the woods where they went forth and multiplied.[64] Since then the grey squirrel has spread to most Counties, principally east of the River

Plate 1

Remains of a sixth century monastery, including a later twelfth century round tower, Devenish Island, Lower Lough Erne, Co. Fermanagh

Crucifixion slab, early Christian hermitage, Duvillaun More, Co. Mayo

Mweelrea Mountain with Killary Harbour and Maumturk Mountains in the distance

Red deer stag and hind (F. Guinness)

Plate 2

Part of the northeast facing cliffs, Benbulbin Mountain range, Co. Sligo

Lowland blanket bog with characteristic surface pools. Glenamoy, Co. Mayo

Bank of hand cut blanket bog, Co. Galway

Irish heath in April. Bellacragher Bay, Co. Mayo

Plate 3

Colony of naturalised pitcher plants on Derrycashel raised bog, Co. Westmeath

The River Suck below Ballinasloe before joining the River Shannon

Lough Neagh, the largest lake in Ireland. A view to the southwest, overlooking Toome and the eel traps

The otter is more widespread and abundant in Ireland than in any other European country

Plate 4

A Connemara river in flood, acidic in nature, rich in oxygen, and conduit for sea trout from the nearby sea to freshwater lakes

Mullagh More with slumped beds of carboniferous limestone. The tree in the foreground would hardly support a hanging man

Spring gentians, one of the glories of the Burren, Co. Clare

Rahasane Turlough, Co. Galway, one of Ireland's most celebrated wintering wildfowl wetlands

Plate 5

Glen Inchiquin, Co. Kerry, with Lough Inchiquin and Uragh Wood in the distance

Willow and alder carr woodland, near Newport, Co. Mayo

Uragh Wood, Co. Kerry - an ancient sessile oak woodland

Silver birch woodland, Killadangan, near Westport, Co. Mayo

Plate 6

Abandoned farmland in west Mayo. The 'fossilised' lazy beds or old potato ridges testify to the former importance of these lands

Greenland white-fronted geese, formerly confined to raised and blanket boglands, but now found principally on improved grasslands as here on the North Slob, Co. Wexford, their most important habitat in Ireland

A mosaic of farmland with intact hedgerow systems, Co. Fermanagh

Ballydavid Head, Co. Kerry, with Smerwick Harbour in the distance. One of the wildest stretches of coastline where the Atlantic waves have eaten back the rocks to create dramatic cliff scenery. A favoured habitat of the chough

Plate 7

Inner Galway Bay where long sea inlets penetrate the land providing excellent conditions for the cultivation of oysters

Cliffs of Moher, Co. Clare, where the horizontally bedded sandstone cliffs provide breeding sites for an abundance of seabirds

Banna Strand, Co. Kerry, with the Dingle peninsula in the distance. One of the many fine beaches and associated sand dune systems found along the Irish coastline

Great Blasket island, Co. Kerry. Occupied until 1952, the island is now an important haul-out area for Atlantic grey seals

Plate 8

Increasing numbers of barnacle geese are wintering in northwestern and western coastal areas

Tory Island, Co. Donegal, one of the remotest and bleakest of inhabited islands of Ireland. It is an important observation point for migratory seabirds. (A. Walsh)

The gannet is the largest seabird in Ireland, and numbered some 24,700 breeding pairs in five colonies during 1984-8

The power of the Atlantic is slowly sculpting and forming new coastal landscapes along the western seaboard

Grey (left) and red squirrel. From G.B. Corbet & H.N. Southern (1977) *The Handbook of British Mammals*. Blackwells, Oxford.

Shannon. Its range in Northern Ireland has advanced rapidly over the past two decades for unknown reasons. To the west of Lough Neagh it has reached Dungiven – possibly even as far north as Downhill, Co. Derry – and to the east, some 20 km south of Belfast.[65]

The native species is the red squirrel, which is more at home in coniferous woodlands. Formerly widespread throughout the country, red squirrels became extinct sometime after the middle of the seventeenth century for reasons not entirely clear but probably related to capture and killing of the animals for their fur which was a valuable commodity at the time.[66,67] The last known date recorded for taxes levied on the export of skins was in an Irish statute of 1662.[68] It is generally considered that the red squirrel died out soon after 1662.

After its demise the red squirrel was reintroduced to Ireland in the early nineteenth century and has since spread to all counties but seldom in close proximity with the grey squirrel – due probably to interspecific competition for food and breeding territory. From inquiries carried out by the Victorian naturalist Richard Manliffe Barrington who investigated the reintroduction date, it would appear that the great-grandfather of Francis Synge – a relation of the playwright John Millington Synge – of Glanmore Castle, Ashford, Co. Wicklow, was responsible for the reintroduction at Ashford sometime between 1815 and 1825. There were many subsequent reintroductions of red squirrels brought from England, throughout Ireland during the mid and late nineteenth century.[69] They are now firmly re-established members of the Irish fauna.

Little is known about the red squirrel's feeding ecology in Ireland as only one study has been carried out so far. In Banagher Glen, Co. Derry, they were found to eat seeds of several different conifers such as Scots pine, European larch, Douglas fir and especially sitka spruce – a party of six managed to strip off all the cones from five trees (about 300 cones per tree). Others took beech and hazel nuts, as well as sycamore fruit.[70]

Interesting native woodland belonging to the *Corylo–Fraxinetum* phytosociological association occurs in patches on the dry calcareous soils of the esker ridges in the Midlands. A special survey of eskers and their woodland cover was carried out by Cross in the late 1980s. He discovered that of the approximately 570 km of eskers ridges in Ireland only about 42 km, or 7%, were covered with woodland or scrub, a rather low percentage bearing in mind the limited agricultural uses of the esker.[71] In an attempt to establish links with the past, Cross argued on the basis of analysis of Ordnance Survey maps that 'it seems plausible that those areas of woodland which were present in the 1830s, and which have survived since, occupy sites which have been continuously wooded, (i.e. never completely cleared of woody vegetation) since early post-glacial times'.

The typical esker woodland is dominated by ash, averaging about 9 m in height while the shrub layer is formed principally by hazel, rising no higher than 8 m. Amongst the trees are pedunculate oak and wych elm together with the occasional downy birch, crab apple, Irish whitebeam and introduced beech. In the shrub layer hawthorn has a constant presence while blackthorn or sloe, holly and the spindle-tree are regular. The goat willow is often present while the buckthorn and dogwood are both rare and found only in some of the woods. The ground flora is dominated by wild strawberry, wood avens, primrose, common dog-violet and false brome. The two finest and least disturbed esker woodlands are at Long Hill, Co. Westmeath – 48 ha dominated by ash, with some hazel and some planted beech at the southeast end – and Rahugh Ridge, or Kiltober Esker, also in Co. Westmeath – the most extensive esker wood in the country (51 ha), containing pedunculate oak, hazel, ash and a species-rich flora. Both Long Hill and Kiltober have an interesting assemblage of relatively uncommon species including the columbine, dogwood, wood fescue, buckthorn, stone bramble and Irish whitebeam.[71]

Beech woodland. Improving landlords began many plantations of this non-native species during the nineteenth century and later periods. It was one of the favourites for demenses.

In 1983, Breen, Curtis & Scannell found the narrow-leaved bitter-cress grow-ing on the floor of an esker woodland at Toorlisnamore, about 4.3 km north-east of Kilbeggan, Co. Westmeath. The plant is small and hairless with up to 18 3-lobed leaflets and inconspicuous white flowers. The general ecology, soil con-ditions and associated species of the wood generally matched the native habi-tat of the species in Britain and on the Continent. Based on this evidence the narrow-leaved bitter-cress was considered a native at Toorlisnamore. At its other known Irish stations, i.e. in Clare (Ballyvaghan – where it still persists as a ruderal), Dublin and Antrim (not seen since 1930), it is known as a 'casual' – almost certainly having been introduced at each site.[72]

Areas of limestone pavement and rocky valleys such as in the Burren, Co. Clare, host many stands of hazel scrub that are especially well developed in sheltered corners and gullies. The impact of the westerly winds has been a major factor in preventing the evolution of this 'scrub' to woodland as evi-denced by the frequent sight of trees with their crowns growing horizontally towards the east. Edaphic factors such as the shallowness of the soils also play their role in holding back development of proper woodland. However, when conditions are right the hazel scrub will very quickly spread, colonising valu-able land, much to the annoyance of farmers.

Scrub is normally defined as a closed cover of shrubs usually less than 5 m high. Some hazel canopies reaching 10 m in the shelter of hollows or cliffs are still classified as scrub on the basis of the dominant life form. The Burren hazel scrub is as exciting to the naturalist as the Atlantic sessile oak woodlands in Kerry. A full description of the Burren hazel woodlands is contained in Chapter 6.

Where the calcareous soils are deeper and the site sheltered from westerly winds hazel scrub will give way to a more pure ash woodland as can be seen in small areas of the Burren and surroundings. However, hazel scrub is not con-sidered a development stage leading to fully-fledged ash woodland.[73] For fine-ly developed ash woodland one has to travel to Co. Fermanagh where there are two excellent examples. At Hanging Rock Nature Reserve (15 ha), ash forms a canopy up to 22 m high on free draining soil over limestone. Occurring underneath are some hazel, hawthorn and rowan while ivy, honeysuckle and holly are entwined with the rest. On the ground there are abundant quanti-ties of male fern, enchanter's night-shade, primrose, wild strawberry and wood speedwell. Marble Arch Wood (24 ha), also in Fermanagh, is domi-nated by ash with some wych elm and several exotic trees. The woods also harbour the broad-leaved helleborine orchid.

Enchanter's nightshade, common in woodland.

Yew is the only native Irish conifer to survive from the time when it was wide-spread in the postglacial period. Today it grows in isolated and rocky places on both limestone-rich soils as well as on siliceous rocks. In fact it will only flour-ish and form a respectable stand when

rooted in limestone, as is the case at Reenadinna, on the Muckross Peninsula
in the Killarney National Park. Yew can also be found on the limestone outcrops around Lough Derg, Co. Tipperary, in groves mixed with juniper. On
the shore north of Bounla Island they form, according to Praeger,[17] an open
wood (c.12 ha) with the spread of the whole bush of giant junipers measuring
up to 14 m in diameter and 6 m in height. Irish whitebeam also occurs in the
woods, but much more sparingly. Further south in the Killarney National Park,
Co. Kerry, the yew wood at Reenadinna, extending over some 28 ha, seems to
have been unscathed by the clear felling inflicted elsewhere in the Killarney
Valley at the turn of the nineteenth century – a reflection of the tree's low commercial value at the time. Scattered throughout the wood is ash, principally in
marshy hollows. Around the woodland margins and lake shore, strawberry-
tree, aspen and a special whitebeam, *Sorbus anglica* – not found anywhere else
in Ireland – occur sparingly. Hazel and holly are locally dominant. The wood
has a dense canopy in places which makes it an eerie, dark and almost frightening place. As a consequence of this darkness, the ground flora is lean with
the commonest ferns being hart's-tongue and soft shield-fern. Bracken is present but scanty. Wood-sorrel and an abundance of bryophytes dominated by
the moss, *Thamnobryum alopecurum*, which form a thick carpet over the stones
and ground, also occur.

The breeding bird community is obviously of some interest since the wood is
one of the very few of its kind in Europe. The results from an 11 year annual
bird census 1982–92 showed that the robin, goldcrest, coal tit, blackbird and
blue tit were the commonest species, accounting for an average of 70% of the
total number of territories.[74] As to be expected, the average density of breeding birds was only 73 pairs per 10 hectares, a much lower figure than in the
nearby oak woods that are more diverse in character and offer a wider range
of breeding habitats and feeding opportunities.

Yew also features significantly in the so-called 'crag-land' woodland growing
on shallow calcareous drift over limestone at Garryland, near Gort, Co. Galway.
This woodland is part of a complex array of ecological 'hot spots' – turloughs,
rivers, limestone pavement and hazel scrub orbiting around Coole Lough.
Despite the fact that Garryland Wood was tampered with by the introduction
of many trees it still retains much of its 'primeval' character and magical atmosphere. The least disturbed parts are dominated by pedunculate oak mixed
with some ash. The oaks stretch up to 12 m in height. Where there is less oak
other trees emerge and become locally dominant, whitethorn, blackthorn and
hazel being the commonest. Yews, some fine and mighty specimens, are scattered throughout the wood at varying densities and become dominant on the
dry soil-less knolls where other species find it difficult to establish a toehold.
Their straggly shaggy forms, broad and flaking trunks, and different colour
ranges contrast with the cleaner and almost stainless oaks. The ground flora is
rich and includes several rare species such as the bird's-nest orchid and the
dark-red helleborine.

Coole Park, to the northeast of Coole Lough, was the former seat of Sir
William and Lady Gregory, whose ancestors first settled there in the 1770s.
Lady Gregory had two main loves – books and trees – and had in her
Arboretum (still there today) a row of Irish yew, *Taxus baccata* 'Fastigiata', once
thought to be a completely new species, *T. hibernica*, but now considered a
chance mutation of the common yew, *T. baccata*.[75] All specimens of the Irish

Florence Court, Co. Fermanagh, location of the Irish yew, the source of all specimens in Ireland and elsewhere.

yew growing in Ireland and elsewhere are descended from two seedlings found amongst juniper bushes on limestone rocks at *Carraig-na-madadh*, on the Cuilcagh Mountains, Co. Fermanagh, by a Mr George Willis in 1740. Willis collected them as they were unlike any normal yew – because of their upright form and slender shape – and planted one at his home. He gave the other specimen to his landlord, Viscount Mount Florence who put it into his garden at Florence Court, thus giving this variety its second name 'Florence Court yew'. All Irish yew tree trees in existence today throughout Ireland and elsewhere in the world are thought to have originated from cuttings taken from the Florence Court female tree.

Wetland woodlands – alder–willow–birch

This third major woodland type in Ireland is low woodland (less than 10 m high) or scrub, typically growing on wet or permanently waterlogged soils ranging from alluvial to clay soils and fen peats. The woods are dominated by alder and grey willow. Where there is acid peaty soil, downy birch will develop, and if the water table is higher, then ash will be present. These alluvial woodlands set in a mosaic of shallow pools, often with contorted trunks and branches, offer up a strange water-woodland environment where the diversity of submerged and half submerged roots, branches, floating and emergent vegetation provide ideal conditions for a rich invertebrate fauna.

These wetland woods in Ireland are a special category of forest which until recently had received little attention. As mentioned above they occur on waterlogged soils, or where drainage is impeded, such as wet acid peatlands, river valleys subject to flooding, areas that are irrigated by springs and the margins of lakes which are immersed in water during the winter. The winter flooding is

Alder woodland.

of critical importance in determining the species composition of these woods. Most wetland woodlands are but small scraps, not much larger than 3–5 ha, scattered throughout the country. The largest expanse of this wood type is over 170 ha found on the waterlogged, highly organic and mineral soils along the eastern and southern shores of Lough Leane, Co. Kerry. Alder and ash are the principal species. Most Irish wetlands were cleared by man of their woodlands a long time ago and what endures today at most sites are secondary woodlands that have grown up spontaneously over the past 150 years.

Classically, a wet type of woodland dominated by alder on peat soils was known as a 'carr', but today the word 'carr' has come to embrace all kinds of fen woodlands and scrub. Duff, in 1930, was the first in Ireland to describe carr-like communities on the edge of Lough Neagh (see p.143). But the first systematic description and classification of wetland woods in Ireland was carried out by Kelly & Iremonger who determined the following seven different kinds of communities existing in seven different habitats:[76]

1. River edges especially in lower river courses made up of the most eutrophic of all wetland wood soil. Willows are the usual dominants with rusty willow, *Salix cinerea* subsp. *oleifolia*, the commonest, occasionally together with alder.

2. Stagnant waters near lake shores, usually flooded in winter. Rusty willow is a constant species and usually dominant; alder is very frequent, often co-dominant.

3. Peaty mires irrigated by calcareous waters. Rusty willow; downy birch, alder and ash are the principal trees. Before Kelly & Iremonger's survey this plant

community had not been previously described from Ireland. It most closely resembles the swamp carr of East Anglia.

4. Springs or flushed sites subject to waterlogging but not flooding. Alder is mostly dominant, with ash. This community is the most species-rich of any wet or dry woodland communities examined in Ireland.

5. Wet sticky mineral soils drying out in summer. The soils are free-draining and base-rich. Ash is constant, often dominant; pedunculate oak is local but sometimes dominant; hazel forms an understorey.

6. Relatively dry oligotrophic acid peats. Downy birch is generally dominant with other trees, holly, rowan and pedunculate oak.

7. Waterlogged oligotrophic acid peats. Downy birch is usually dominant but often replaced by rusty willow.

Osiers or willows were planted on wet soils from the early nineteenth century onwards, and probably earlier, in 'sally gardens' which were then coppiced every three or four years to produce stiff rods for basket-making. The wetlands in the River Suir valley and around Lough Neagh were the great centres for this osierculture. The tradition has almost died out and most of these willow beds have reverted to a wild state, creating valuable habitat for other plants and animals. The species planted in the sally gardens were the osier (certainly introduced to Ireland), the almond willow (probably introduced but possibly native in southeastern counties) and various hybrids of willow.

Probable former osier or willow beds at Tibberaghny marsh, River Suir, south of Piltown, Co. Kilkenny.

Very few of these wetland woodlands would appear to qualify as ancient woodland, undisturbed by man. One of the most important in the past was the extensive mosaic of alluvial forest spread throughout the area known as the Gearagh, in the River Lee valley, Co. Cork.

The River Lee arises above the small lake of Gouganebarra, Co. Cork, and flows east to discharge into the tidal waters of Cork. Near Macroom it used to 'spread out in the flat-bottomed valley into a network of clear anastomosing streams and wooded islets untouched by grazing animals – a place of singular charm.'[17] A unique alluvial forest, known as the Gearagh woodland, occupied this area until the valley was flooded in 1954 by the Electricity Supply Board for the Lee Hydroelectric scheme. Much of the woodland was felled and cleared prior to the inundation but at the west end of the Reservoir there remains a small fragment of the much larger wet forest that was formerly strung out along the valley. Before the 1954 flooding, a vegetation survey was carried out by O'Reilly.[77] There were substantial areas of pedunculate oak forming a close canopy with hazel and holly underneath.

Several hectares of the original woodland remain intact to present a unique feature in Ireland. The closest examples in Europe are the alluvial woodlands along the River Rhine, especially near Strasbourg, which are structurally simi-lar to the Gearagh but floristically more diverse. However, the Gearagh is rich in plants and flowers as 108 vascular plant taxa have been identified from the area. In 1985 White published an account of the ecology of this remarkable habitat.[78] Upstream from Toon Bridge the wood is still well structured with ses-sile and pedunculate oak – up to 15–18 m in height – and ash dominating alongside downy birch and grey willow. The understorey is made up of hazel,

Site of the former alluvial forest at the Gearagh, Co. Cork. Stumps of the old forest can be seen in the mud.

hawthorn, spindle and various willows amongst others. The herb layer is diverse with plenty of ramsons and in the wetter spots marsh-marigold, golden saxifrage, common marsh-bedstraw, water mint, marsh ragwort, marsh violet, a small rough horsetail *Equisetum hymale* and hard shield-fern are found.

This type of alluvial woodland habitat is highly attractive to a myriad of invertebrates, both winged and aquatic. Dragonflies, whose lifestyle requires relatively still and muddy-bottomed water for the nymph stages, and branches and twigs for the adults to rest on, are a special feature of the Gearagh. A survey was carried out prior to the flooding to determine the Odonata species present: over 2,700 specimens of 13 species were collected.[79] Of these, seven species represented over 98% of all the records. The two commonest species were the banded demoiselle, found on the wing from mid May to the start of September, and the blue-tailed damselfly which has a slightly shorter season. The other species were the azure damselfly, beautiful demoiselle, variable damselfly, common darter, black darter, emerald damselfly, four-spotted chaser, brown hawker and keeled skimmer.

Alder wood and alder carr are not common in Ireland. Co. Leitrim has some of the best examples around the margins of Lough Allen where there is a 'swamp forest' standing on heavy clay soils and extending over several hectares in a narrow scrappy fringe. Bohan recently discovered a small but important fragment of an ancient alder wood on a drumlin at Cahiracon, Co. Clare, where there were multi-stemmed and massive coppice stools 4–6 m in girth at ground level.[76]

Other wetland woodlands of interest include Glen Bog in Co. Limerick, (12 ha) which has been 'cut over', i.e. the upper layers of the bog have been cut and removed as turf for burning and the bog is now covered with a dense alder–willow scrub, or carr, with some open patches of water. The Corstown Loughs in Co. Meath are extremely calcareous, thus providing ideal conditions for the spread of a thick damp woodland dominated by alder, downy birch and willow. The small area of woodland on the north side of Lough Neagh, Co. Antrim, has some fine patches of alder, with willow in the wetter spots grading into reeds and aquatic plants on the water's edge. In Co. Offaly in the Camcor valley above Kinnitty, Camcor Wood (10 ha) is a well-developed alder wood. Kelly & Iremonger also described a remarkable stand of secondary birch wood growing on cut-over peat next to St John's Wood, Co. Roscommon, which has an understorey of alder buckthorn, a species scarce in Ireland but a characteristic carr constituent in England.[76]

In the small pools, the larvae of the caddisfly *Phacopteryx brevipennis* use the fallen alder leaves both as food and as building material for their distinctive triangular cases made out of discs cut out from the leaves. The characteristic small and circular holes in the floating leaves of the alder is a telltale sign of such caddisfly activity. This species was first discovered in Ireland during 1982 in an alder marsh near Virginia, Co. Cavan, and has subsequently been found in Co. Westmeath.[80]

Birch, an important constituent of wetland woods, also stakes a claim in other habitats. Birch woodlands are typically found on acidic soils in hilly and upland areas but also occur on and around the margins of bogland. It is unusual to find extensive pure birch woods in Ireland and when it happens, especially in woodland clearings, they are only a stage in the natural progression towards oak or ash woodland. Sessile oak is a frequent companion, especially on the upland siliceous soils. Birch occurs in pure stands on and around raised bogs where it can form dense communities of trees up to 12 m high. As one of the hardiest trees in Ireland it is found growing up to altitudes of 570 m.

The two principal species of birch in Ireland manifest different habitat preferences. The silver birch occurs locally in woods, on the margins of raised bogs and on stony lake shores while the downy birch prefers upland siliceous soils and under the right circumstances will form pure stands, frequently as scrub, in its own right. Considerable variations in the shape and features of the downy birch have led to the suspicion that there might two subspecies in Ireland but more research remains to be carried out before they can be named. Hybridisation with silver birch also occurs, further confusing the systematics of these elegant trees.[81]

As a pioneer species, downy birch quickly colonises bare ground by means of its light, airborne seeds. However, the seedling is so small that its tap root cannot normally penetrate herb layers and is therefore rejected from grass fields or other vegetation-saturated soil. Its best chance for a successful 'rooting' is in open woodland clearings where it can pierce the uncluttered ground.

One of the most remarkable birch woods in Ireland is growing on a raised bog, All Saints' Bog, Co. Offaly. The development of woodland here is quite startling as blanket bogs are normally treeless apart from occasional specimens of rowan. The wood here has almost certainly been encouraged by nutrients disgorged from a series of flushes and soaks. It covers some 20 ha in the centre of this 230 ha bogland and has recently been described in some detail by Cross.[82] Downy birch with some silver birch growing up to 10 m in height form the bulk of the wood. Regenerating birch, grey willow, eared willow and the

Downy birch woodland with elongated foxgloves seeking light from the low woodland canopy.

occasional Scots pine make up the shrub layer. Heather, crowberry and cranberry grow further below while on the ground bryophytes and lichens provide almost 100% cover. The All Saints' Bog birch woodland is the only wood of its kind to be found in a survey of over 200 raised bogs in the Midlands, except for a somewhat similar but much smaller patch (less than 5 ha), also fed by flushes, on Clara Bog, Co. Offaly. The history of these two woods is uncertain but the discovery of the insect *Dictenidia bimaculata* – an indicator species of ancient European forests – in rotting timber at both sites would suggest that the woodland has been present for a very long period.[83]

A much smaller patch (50 m x 3 m) of downy birch grows on a stretch of desolate lowland blanket bog north of Bellacorick in north Mayo. The trees are multi-stemmed and no higher than about 1 m. Here again the water table is close to the bog surface and the woodland is fed by a mineral-rich flush. The vegetation surrounding the birch is dominated by purple moor-grass and heather.

8

Farmland

Four-fifths of all Irish land is under some form of agricultural use, of which 75.5% is grassland – grass for grazing, hay, silage, or rough grazing. The percentage of land under tillage, or cultivation, in 1990 was 5.9% – an area similar to that occupied by woods and plantations. In comparison with the other 11 member states of the European Union in 1990, Ireland had the largest percentage of permanent pasture, and the smallest areas of both cropland and forest-woodland cover.[1] With three-quarters of the population living in urban areas, Ireland's landscape can be described as rural with pastoral agriculture as the principal land use.

Earlier chapters, and the three following, deal with distinct habitats, characterised by their own special flora and fauna. While accepting that no part of the landscape has escaped some interference by man, these ecosystems are the closest to what nature had in mind at the beginning. Farmland is, by definition, the most intensively managed part of the landscape and therefore might, on first consideration, appear to offer little natural history interest. But this is not the case. Why? Because, generally speaking, agriculture in Ireland is, and has been for centuries, less intensive than in most other European countries, with the result that many forms of wildlife, which find the going tough in highly manicured farmland environments, have had a respite in Ireland. For example, most of the extensive network of hedgerows and associated wildlife has remained intact since its development towards the end of the eighteenth century. In most other European countries bocage (hedgerow landscape) has become a special feature restricted to small areas.

The amount of land under tillage is small, as noted above. Extensive tillage reduces habitat diversity not only through the removal of hedgerows to create larger and more economic land units but also in the spawning of vast expanses of single species crops – detrimental to wildlife diversity. However, tillage in small doses can have positive aspects, particularly for seed-eating birds, by providing important reservoirs of food. Grassland can also offer much for wildlife ranging from small mammals to invertebrates – especially rough grazing. Finally, in comparison with most other European countries, the application of nitrogenous and phosphorous fertilisers as well as pesticides per unit area of farmland is still very modest in Ireland, with little adverse effects on flora and fauna, either directly or more subtly through enhanced pollution levels of soils and waters.

There is no doubt that the increased availability of food, whether grass, grain, root and other crops, directly benefits many animals and birds living within the broad scope of the agricultural landscape. The Slobs of Wexford are a classic example. Thousands of geese, wild swans, duck and waders are drawn towards the high quality grassland pastures, cereal and root crops grown on the 2,000 ha of fertile land reclaimed from Wexford Harbour some 150 years ago. Today Greenland white-fronted geese, pale-bellied brent geese, whooper

Intact hedgerows provide ecological diversity and shelter for all animals and plants.

swan, Bewick's swan and wigeon graze with impunity the swards of improved grassland and some species sometimes turn to other farmland crops such as sugar beet, potatoes and cereals. Another group of seed-eating birds, the pheasant, quail and partridge also very much depend upon farmland for their food and breeding habitat. The barn owl also occurs more frequently on farmland than in other habitats as its principal prey, brown rats and wood mice are most numerous here. The other two important farmland birds, the rook and woodpigeon, are integral features of farmland. Finally frogs and smooth newts are perhaps more abundant on farmland than elsewhere in Ireland.

Mammals that are particularly associated with agricultural land are the badger, fox, Irish stoat, Irish hare and rabbit. The hedgehog, a curiously disregarded creature worthy of study by Irish zoologists, is more frequent although also common in the urban environment, in farming landscapes than elsewhere. Finally, amongst the smaller mammals, there are seven species of bats living secret and crepuscular lives, flapping around buildings, trees, hedgerows, woodland edges and sometimes over water in search of their insect food, eagerly snapped up from dusk to dawn, when most people are safely tucked up in their beds. Most of the species comprising this somewhat ragbag collection of the larger farmland fauna together with some of the birds mentioned above will be discussed in this chapter.

The flora of farmland holds less interest. However, there is a special grouping of weeds associated with cereal crops which is interesting in view of its historic association with low intensity agriculture formerly practised in the more remote corners of Ireland. They were introduced to Ireland and are the camp followers of early agriculture practices. They are corncockle (now thought to be extinct), shepherd's-needle (also thought to be extinct), corn chamomile, cornflower and darnel. Darnel, belonging to the same genus as perennial rye-

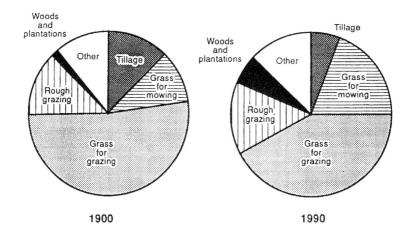

Land use in Ireland, 1900 and 1990. From Fenton & Gillmor[2].

grass can be poisonous to cattle. Once common, these weeds have become rare. They are increasingly endangered as traditional farming practices wither away, restricting their chances for survival. The use of herbicides, seed cleaning and the contraction of the amount of tilled land are all working against them.

Within the broad context of the agricultural landscape there are two areas which are of considerable ecological interest – the ancient pastureland of the Curragh, Co. Kildare, and the low-lying callowlands along the banks of the rivers Shannon and Little Brosna in the Central Plain of Ireland. Their ecological characteristics, together with features of their fauna and flora, will be outlined once a few basic principles concerning the agricultural landscape have been established.

Structure of the agricultural landscape

The structure of the agricultural landscape is defined through the overall land use pattern based on agricultural statistics, coming from the Republic and from Northern Ireland (Table 8.1).

Table 8.1 Land use in Ireland, 1990 (from Gillmor[2]).

Land uses	Republic of Ireland		Northern Ireland		Ireland	
	ha ('000)	%	ha ('000)	%	ha ('000)	%
1. Crops and pasture	4,682.5	68.0	864.0	63.7	5,546.5	67.3
- tillage	415.9	6.0	66.7	4.9	482.6	5.9
- grass for mowing	1,287.7	18.7	286.2	21.1	1,573.9	19.1
- grass for grazing	2,978.9	43.2	511.1	37.7	3,490.0	42.3
2. Rough grazing	966.1	14.0	198.8	14.7	1,164.9	14.1
3. Woods & plantations	407.0	5.9	73.0	5.4	480.0	5.8
4. Other land	833.6	12.1	220.6	16.3	1,054.2	12.8
Totals	6,889.2		1,356.4		8,245.6	

Hedgerow and treeline length

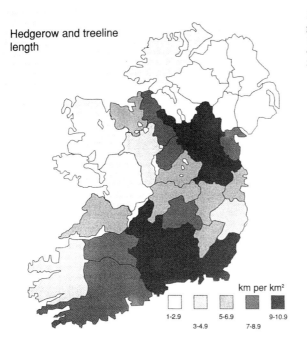

km per km²

1-2.9	3-4.9	5-6.9	7-8.9	9-10.9

Maps showing geographical variation in the habitat composition of Irish counties. From Smal[40].

Arable land

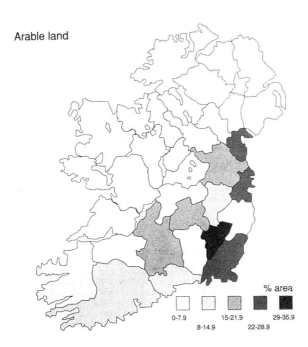

% area

0-7.9	8-14.9	15-21.9	22-28.9	29-35.9

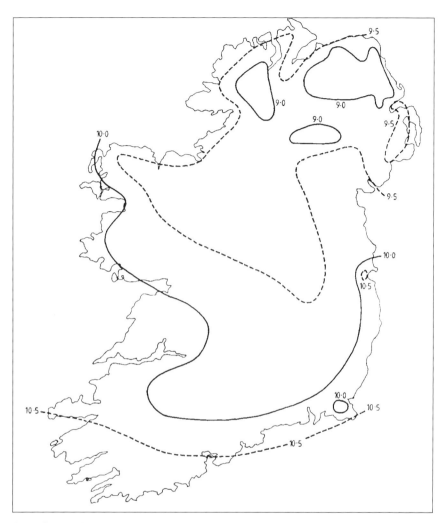

Annual mean daily air temperatures (°C) 1951–80, reduced to mean sea level. From P.K. Rohan (1986). *The Climate of Ireland*. Stationery Office, Dublin.

The area of improved agricultural land reached its peak in 1875 when it covered about 77.4% of the total land area of Ireland. An agricultural recession in Europe was behind a pronounced shift from arable to pastoral farming that took place between 1851 and 1890, when the area of land under tillage in Ireland declined from 43.7% to 16.4%. In the early 1890s, there were more cattle in Ireland than people. The decline of tillage continued into the twentieth century. By 1990 the amount of land under tillage had shrunk to a mere 5.9% and has further declined to 5.6% today.

The decline of tillage and the rise of pastoral farming has been generally beneficial to the ecological diversity of the countryside and its wildlife. The other main agricultural land use shifts this century have been towards a dramatic increase in woodland plantations and a doubling of the area of grassland cropped as silage. Within Ireland there are considerable differences, mostly reflecting soil conditions, in the distribution of tillage as a percentage of agricultural land.

Grasslands

The most striking feature consistently noted about Ireland by visitors is the greenness due to the extensive carpeting of permanent grassland pastures which, in the absence of low winter temperatures, keep on growing, thus staying green for a longer period than in any other European country. Growth can continue to December and restart in March. Grass to the Irish is like snow to the Eskimos. It is all pervasive, and has played a pivotal role in the social, cultural and economic development of the country for nearly 6,000 years since the arrival of the first Neolithic farmers.

Of the 6.22 million hectares of grasslands, 85% are permanent swards of which about 3% are re-seeded each year with perennial rye-grass as the principal species. An indigenous grass requiring deep fertile soil, it is palatable to animals, has a long growing season and responds well to cutting or grazing. Grass for silage crops is made up of the non-indigenous Italian rye-grass either sown as a monoculture or mixed with about 10% perennial rye-grass. These two grasses are used because they produce a significantly higher dry matter yield compared with old permanent grassland which is generally composed of rough meadow-grass (33%), bent grass species (31%), perennial rye-grass (15%), meadow foxtail (11%) and others, including weeds (10%). The agricultural superiority of swards composed of Italian and perennial rye-grasses for fattening cattle has been demonstrated. In special experimental trails, beef cattle were put onto three grass swards made up of Italian rye-grass, perennial rye-grass and old permanent grassland at the An Foras Talúntais centre at Dunsany, Co. Meath. The highest weight gains, expressed as 'carcass output' (kilograms per hectare) over a two-year study period came from the Italian rye-grass (780 kg/ha), followed by perennial rye-grass (749 kg/ha) and then old permanent pasture (590 kg/ha).[3] The best grass produced 32.2% more beef (kg/ha) than the old permanent pasture. Good news for the farmer who upgrades his sward, but not so good for the old permanent grassland, a type of plant community of much greater interest to the ecologist.

Miniature pasturelands developed on unique man-made plaggen soils (sand, seaweed, manure) enclosed within a honeycomb of finely built limestone walls, Inishmore, Aran Islands, Co. Galway.

Overgrazed mountain and
upland peat and grasslands,
Maumturk Mountains, Co.
Galway (A. Walsh).

Only a small percentage, some 18.7% of the grasslands, is classified as 'rough grazing', probably representing communities least manipulated by man though often grazed close to death by sheep. The vegetation composition of old grass swards is very much determined by the soil and generally speaking these grasslands are poor in species. An average old grassland on well-drained soil which is neither calcareous nor acidic would host the following grasses: sweet vernal-grass, common bent, creeping bent, Yorkshire-fog, false oat-grass, crested dog's-tail, cock's-foot, smooth meadow-grass, rough meadow-grass, tall fescue, sheep's-fescue and perennial rye-grass. In addition to these grasses there would be approximately a further 35 species, mostly of flowering plants, that would complete the list of regular constituents of grassland.

The Curragh grasslands

The Curragh of Kildare is a vast flat grassland ranging over some 2,000 ha, set on deep gravel deposits, up to 70 m in places, left here as outwashings by the melting glaciers. In and underneath the gravels are large reservoirs of water percolating out to supply local rivers, streams and marshes. The nearby Pollardstown Fen, a site of outstanding ecological importance (see p.144) is fed by these outpourings. The Curragh itself is a historic landscape, maintained in its present condition for over 2,000 years by controlled grazing. As such it is perhaps the oldest and most extensive area of man-maintained semi-natural grassland in Ireland.[4] Driving through the area is a bewildering experience as the eye is hopelessly searching for a landscape 'fix'. The famous Curragh Racecourse grandstand, the Army camp, sheep, the ever encroaching gorse and approaching traffic provide the only relief.

Historically the area was 'commonage' land on which local farmers were entitled to specific grazing rights. In 1865 a Commission was established to determine the Curragh's rightful owners. It decided in favour of the Crown, as it was then, and the grazing was permitted to continue. But the grazing rights were still unclear and remained in dispute. A second Commission in 1869 settled the squabbles and led to the *Curragh Act, 1870*. The Curragh's reputation as 'a rich and commodious as well as a healthful pasturage' was well known historically and extolled by Monk in 1682. Monk also praised the Curragh sheep 'that bear a fine staple and the sweetest of flesh of any in the kingdom.'[5] Today there are rights for approximately 8,000 sheep to graze the Curragh but under the inducements of EU headage and subsidy payments from the government ewe numbers have crept up to higher levels.

The botanical interest of the Curragh grassland is, at first sight, unpromising. Centuries of grazing, sometimes intensive, have left a species-poor, dry, acidic sward characterised by the crested dog's-tail grass and common knapweed. Other common species include common bent, sheep's-fescue, mat-grass, purple moor-grass and sweet vernal-grass. Swards dominated by mat-grass occur in several areas. The acidic nature of the soil is emphasised by the presence of two calcifuge mosses, *Rhytidiadelphus squarrosus* and *Pseudoscleropodium purum*. Praeger only accorded the area a brief mention in *The Botanist in Ireland* as a 'great gravel mass yielding light-soil plants' such as yellow-wort and common calamint. Amongst the birds 7,000 golden plover were counted here in October 1995, the eighth highest total for golden plovers recorded that winter in Ireland.[6]

In the 1980s Nitare developed a scheme whereby unfertilised grazed meadowlands of conservation value could be identified by the presence of certain brightly coloured toadstools or waxcap fungi, belonging to the genus *Hygrocybe*. These saprophytic fungi living free in the soil are very sensitive indicators of habitat quality.[7] Ancient grassland may have up to 20 species while pastures improved by the addition of chemical fertilisers may have only one or two or none at all. Feehan & McHugh searched parts of the Curragh for these agaric fungi during 1988–90 and found 19 *Hygrocybe* spp. which placed the grassland in the upper range of Nitare's classification – 10–25 species – as a nationally important pastureland. The southeastern part of the Curragh was found to be particularly well-represented by the fungi.[4]

Support for the Curragh's special ancient grassland status comes from a completely different angle, a survey of rove beetles belonging to the family Staphylinidae. These beetles, which include the devil's coach-horse – also called the cock-tail as when disturbed it raises its tail and opens its jaws in a frightening posture – are generally elongate, 1–28 mm long and coloured a metallic or shiny black, or black and orange. Up to one hundred different species of these beetles regularly occur in Irish grasslands and assemblages of them can be used to evaluate the conservation value of grasslands. Good & Butler sampled the southeastern part of the Curragh grassland in 1991–2 and found a total of 51 staphylinid species. Two – *Amischa bifoveolata* and *Tachyporus tersus* – were of particular interest and occurred as dominant members of the Staphylinid community. Their presence suggested that the pastureland of the Curragh was of a different type to other grasslands and was considered to indicate a mature, undisturbed (no fertilisers or ploughing) ecosystem. Two other species of interest were *Cryptobium fracticorne* and *Stenus brevipennis*, both found in mat-grass. They normally occur in marshes or bogs rather than in grasslands.[8]

Shannon callows

Lying alongside the meandering River Shannon, between Athlone and Shannonbridge, are extensive tracts of seemingly monotonous, wet and soggy, flat grass fields. Hedgerows are absent, their job of enclosure being performed by 'wet fences' or field drains. Occasional trees of willow and alder, together with clumps of tall reeds, punctuate the landscape. No houses, no network of

Shannon callowlands in flood during January.

tarred roads contaminate these flatlands. Lever, viewing this landscape in 1842, wrote 'a prospect more bleak, more desolate and more barren it would be impossible to conceive – a wide river with low reedy banks moving sluggishly on its yellow current between broad tracts of bog or callow meadowland, no trace of cultivation, not even a tree was seen'.[9]

These lands, mostly divided up into numerous small units that are owned in common ownership amongst hundreds of farmers, are grazed in the summer by cattle while hay is cut from the drier fields. No tillage is possible. During the winter and spring the fields are inundated by varying depths of flood waters, bringing to the already calcium-rich soils a bouquet of enriching alluvial materials derived from eroded limestone and other calcareous deposits within the River Shannon catchment area. Even peat silt, arising from the excavation of the great Midland raised bogs, has been transported and deposited on these flat fields, providing additional enrichment.

The callows – from the Irish *cala* or *caladh*, meaning 'a low marshy meadow along a river or lake which is often flooded in winter, but always grassy in summer' – are ecologically the most interesting grasslands in Ireland. They extend over 3,500 ha, bordering both sides of the Shannon, but if those of the River Suck are included the figure rises to 5,000 ha. The callows, occurring as a narrow strip on either side of the river banks, cover a swath about 750 m wide, including the river channel in the middle. In some areas they broaden out to 1.5 km.[10] These low-lying meadows are subject to seasonal flooding because there is only a 35 cm drop in water level along the 50 km stretch of river between Athlone and Shannonbridge, an insufficient difference to discharge, at a fast enough rate, all the waters flowing into the Shannon, especially during the winter and spring. The result is a backlog of water that builds up and then spills out of the river into the fields. The only other extensive area of cal-lowland in Ireland is found alongside the River Blackwater, Co. Cork, where 250 ha comprise the Lismore callows. The grasslands of most turloughs (see p. 218) also fall into the category of callowlands but are usually small with their water supplies coming from underground sources, and are more intensively grazed by herbivores – cattle, sheep and horses.

Within the wider context of Ireland and Britain the Shannon callows are the largest single expanse of seasonally flooded grassland community, rivalled only by the Ouse Washes, Cambridgeshire, England, extending over 2,350 ha, and the Ken–Dee Marshes, Scotland, extending over 1,500 ha. Only at the Ouse Washes does the main vegetation, dominated by floating sweet-grass, approxi-mate that of the Shannon or Little Brosna callows.[11,12]

The Shannon callows have survived as an important ecosystem today for two major reasons. Firstly, it has proved impossible to control the flooding of the area despite innumerable political promises to drain the Shannon. The engi-neering effort required to excavate and drop the river level to effect a speedi-er runoff of water and containment with the banks would require a prodigious amount of money in relation to the economic benefits that would follow. Secondly, despite the grasslands being wet and damp, they are still an impor-tant agricultural resource to local farmers. In 1987, 23% of the callowlands were used as hay meadows.[13] The remaining area is put to use as summer pas-ture, mostly for cattle. In fact, many of the agricultural constraints and eco-nomic hardships sustained by the callow farmers are being addressed by the gradual reform of the European Union's Common Agricultural Policy, which now encourages environmentally sensitive methods in place of the former incentives towards productivity. Thus those who hold lands (like the callow-lands) which are part of Special Areas of Conservation – designated by gov-ernment – are entitled to receive additional payments over and above the basic rates for environmentally sensitive farming where plans have been prepared for the farmers under the Rural Environment Protection Scheme (REPS). These extra payments provide economic compensation to the farmers to man-age their land primarily for ecological objectives while continuing to derive some income from traditional low intensity farming.

So, what is so important about these soggy, damp and flooded lands? There are four principal ecological interests. First, the types of semi-natural vegeta-tion communities found here are increasingly rare within a European context – most other similar areas have been destroyed by drainage and reclamation schemes. The plant communities are made up of native species which have been there for many centuries, growing in soil never disturbed by ploughing or re-seeding. The Shannon callows, together with other similar areas in Ireland, would possibly add up to some 10% of all grasslands while in Britain only 4% of the same habitat has escaped drainage and ploughing to remain in a semi-natural condition.[14] Secondly, the vegetation communities and their associated invertebrate populations provide crucial breeding grounds for a great variety and high densities of wading birds in Ireland. Thirdly, the callows are now the last major breeding area in Ireland for the once numerous corn-crake. And fourthly, the grassland communities provide a remarkably rich food repository that attracts, during the winter month, vast numbers of wildfowl occurring in internationally and nationally important numbers.

Botany of the callows

Heery, a plant ecologist who has studied the Shannon callows more closely than anyone else, writes that 'the flora is a tantalising mixture of the commonplace, the unusual and the decidedly rare. The expert botanist can examine an extremely wide spectrum of plant species with relatively little effort, and still find something to make the eyebrows rise, especially in the abundant watery corners and drainage ditches.'[15] The callows of today are lands formerly occupied by extensive marshes and fens with swamp woodland made up principally of alder, willow and birch. During the eighteenth century, engineering and drainage works, undertaken to improve the outflow of the Shannon, eliminated much of what was left. Now the callow grasslands dominate, but if all agricultural activity was suddenly withdrawn, the callows would, within several years, be colonised once again by willow, alder and other woody species. The breeding waders would go, so would the wintering wildfowl, while the rasping call of the corncrake would no longer reverberate throughout the valley. Thus the ecology of the callows today is both dependent on current farming practices and the annual flooding from the Shannon, particularly in the spring. As a result of the flooding, one feature of the callows, and indeed turloughs, is the capacity of many plants to survive and continue to grow during months of submergence in flood waters. In his study of turlough grasslands McGowran found the bent grass, common sedge, lesser spearwort, creeping buttercup and common marsh-bedstraw all actively growing under water.[16]

Heery recorded 216 plants from the callowlands and in a detailed phytosociological analysis of the communities forming the grasslands he identified 16 different types of plant associations.[10] A stroll through a typical callow grass field during the summer would reveal the following 11 plants all common and widespread in this habitat.

1. Cuckooflower. The most frequent plant of the callowlands. A member of the cabbage family (Cruciferae) with long thin seed pods (up to 40 mm), it is 30–60 cm tall and has white or lilac flowers with yellow anthers.

2. Marsh-marigold. These short stout plants have large pale yellow flowers 10–50 mm across, and big kidney-shaped and toothed dark green leaves.

3. Water mint. Its stems can reach up to 75 cm, but are normally shorter. The flowers are purple or lilac while its leaves are pointed oval and when crushed exude a strong mint aroma.

4. Common marsh-bedstraw. A straggling plant with square stems. The flowers are white.

5. Meadowsweet. An erect plant with stems 60–90 cm. The leaves are large and white on the underside. The flowers occurring in dense clusters, are creamy white and scented.

6. Water forget-me-not. Low and creeping. The flowers are small and sky-blue.

7. Common sedge. Has a three-angled stem and rather harsh grass-like leaves, 15–30 cm high.

8. White clover. Low and creeping with white but sometimes pale pink globular scented flowers.

9. Smooth meadow-grass. Has creeping rootstock but erect stems 30–60 cm high.

10. Creeping buttercup. Spreads by rooting runners along the ground. The stems are about 30 cm high with yellow flowers.

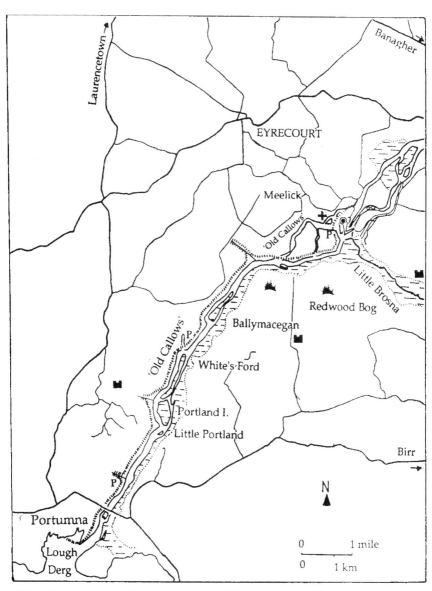

Callowlands between Portumna and the Little Brosna River. From Heery [15].

11. Creeping bent. The stems are 30–120 cm with numerous leafy stolons at their base.

It is surprising that so few rare plants have turned up in the callowlands in view of the antiquity and specific nature of the habitat. Marginal wetlands (flooded areas alongside rivers, lakes, turloughs, flooded limestone pavement, ditches and damp places) are amongst the most endangered of all ecosystems and harbour the largest proportion of rare and threatened plants listed in the *Irish Red Data Book* of vascular plants – 22 species are recorded as rare and threatened of which six are threatened and one is extinct.[17] The paucity of rare species so far noted in the callows probably reflects the vastness of the area and a recent history of botanical investigation. Nevertheless it is known that several plants which occur here have a restricted distribution within Ireland, which makes them rare or unusual. These include the summer snowflake, the blue-eyed grass, the flowering-rush, the opposite-leaved pondweed, the marsh pea and the marsh stitchwort. The summer snowflake is a member of the daffodil family (Amaryllidaceae). It occurs in several locations, mainly in the Little Brosna River callows where it grows as a native under alder woodland, and flowers in May. Forming unmistakable daffodil-like clumps with the leaves 30–45 cm high, its white drooping flowers have green-tipped petals. There are only about 20–30 other scattered known stations in Ireland, making it a rare species. The blue-eyed grass is found in damp pastures and stony places in the west, occasionally in Co. Kerry, and in the centre of Ireland, but is rare and very local elsewhere, only being found in North America, and in ice-free areas in south Greenland, a sort of halfway house on its way to Ireland.[18] Within the callowlands it has been found near Portumna. Its leaves are grass-like, 15–30 cm tall, and the flowers are small, blue, with a yellow centre, opening only in sunshine in June and July. The flowering-rush has long, narrow, three-angled leaves. Its stem, extending some 60–120 cm high, sports a large terminal bunch of rose-pink flowers, 1–2.5 cm across, from June to August. It is rare elsewhere in Ireland. The opposite-leaved pondweed has all its leaves submerged and is only found in clear clean water. In the callows it has been located in the canal alongside the embankment near Meelick. A formerly protected species under the Flora (Protection) Order 1980. The marsh pea is another formerly protected species now removed from the updated 1987 Order in the Republic (but still protected in Northern Ireland). A medium-tall clambering plant, its

Summer snowflake, Little
Brosna River callows
(J. O'Connell).

leaves end in a branched tendril used to clasp and grip other vegetation as it climbs upwards. Its flower of bluish-purple can be seen in June and July. Being a member of the pea family (Leguminosae) its seeds are in a black pod. Many of the ungrazed callow fields along the Shannon host this species while at Clonmacnoise it occurs in profusion. It is also found in marshy meadows in other Midland sites, particularly along the Shannon system. Elsewhere it is very rare. The marsh stitchwort is present throughout the callows but particularly abundant in the hay meadows at Banagher. It is a short, straggly and glabrous plant sporting small white flowers 12–18 mm across visible from May to July. Each of the flower's five petals are split to the base. Though fairly frequent in marshy areas in Central Ireland, it is rare elsewhere.

Breeding waders and other birds of the callows

To the uninitiated eye the callowlands would not appear to be one of the most important breeding habitats for waders in Ireland. However, in 1987, Nairn, Herbert & Heery carried out a detailed census of all breeding waders along the 35 km stretch of callows from the Little Brosna River to Athlone town and found a remarkably high density of lapwing (341 pairs), redshank (400 pairs), common snipe (762 pairs) and curlew (48 pairs).[13] Such densities had only previously been encountered at three other locations in Ireland and Britain: the Erne Basin, Co. Fermanagh, the Ouse Washes, Cambridgeshire, and the North Kent Marshes. Since then, regular monitoring has been carried out at one site at Shannon Harbour to see how the birds are faring (Table 8.2).

Table 8.2 Number of pairs of breeding waders on 220 ha callowlands at Shannon Harbour 1987–97 (data for 1987–96 from Heery[19] and for 1997 from Heery[20]).

Year	Lapwing (pairs)	Redshank (pairs)	Common snipe (displaying)	Curlew (pairs)	Totals
1987	29	26	35	5	95
1988	39	31	45	6	121
1989	33	35	71	4	143
1990	32	43	40	5	120
1991	32	30	70	9	141
1992	21	32	51	6	110
1993	4	15	37	5	61
1994	10	10	35	5	60
1995	7	14	24	5	50
1996	0	7	31	4	42
1997	1	7	20	3	31

The results reveal a serious decline in the numbers of all breeding waders over the last ten years. The most severely affected are the lapwing and redshank. The explanations for the reductions are not at all clear.

Twenty-two pairs of common sandpipers were found breeding in the callows, close to the river banks between Bishops' Island and Athlone, in 1987. It was also found that quail bred in the Clonburren meadows. Today, quail are strongly suspected to be breeding in small, but regular numbers every year in the callowlands where they do not start nesting until early June with the first young on the wing by about mid-July. In 1995 twelve separate birds were heard

Nesting curlew (J. Barlee). Studies by Grant in Northern Ireland of key breeding sites indicate an overall decline of some 25% of the population. Low productivity due to predation of nests has probably been responsible for the population decline.

calling on the callows between May and August.[21] Elsewhere in Ireland quail are rare and erratic breeders (see p.301).

The water rail, one of Ireland's most elusive breeding birds, gives its presence away by squealing like a pig. During 1992 and 1993 five and four pairs respectively nested among 196 ha of callowland at Shannon Harbour. Seven (both males and females) were heard calling during 1994. The shoveler has been nesting in the callows since 1984 with an estimated twelve pairs in the rough grassland close to the water in 1987. There were six pairs in the Little Brosna River valley in 1993. One of the most exciting discoveries during 1987 was two pairs of nesting black-tailed godwit, an extremely rare breeder in Ireland. It is suspected that they have been breeding on the callows in some of the subsequent years but firm proof is lacking. Hutchinson notes that black-tailed godwits have only been recorded breeding in Ireland since 1975.[22]

In recent years the corncrake has become a flagship species of the national bird conservation organisation, BirdWatch Ireland, in their efforts to stave off the extinction of several endangered species breeding in the country. The corncrake is a particularly acute case as it is under attack on two fronts – possibly on its migration to and from the African wintering grounds but most certainly on its breeding grounds in Ireland. The corncrakes' preferred habitat are the hay fields. They lay their eggs from mid-May to early July and the young

SPECIES	MARCH	APRIL	MAY	JUNE	JULY	AUGUST
Corncrake						
Quail						
Water Rail						
Snipe						
Redshank						
Curlew						
Lapwing						
Shoveller						
Grasshopper Warbler						
Meadow Pipit						
Skylark						
Reed Bunting						

– – – – eggs　　▓ haycutting season
───── young

Nesting birds in the callow hay fields. From Heery[15].

hatch from early June onwards. Hay is cut on the callows from about mid-June to the end of August, depending on the weather, but the trend is for earlier and earlier cutting with a switch to using grass for silage. Hay-making destroys their nests and kills the chicks, so the birds stand little chance of breeding successfully. About 200 farmers with land in the callows have voluntarily joined a corncrake conservation scheme under which they are paid £90 per hectare (1998) not to cut their meadows until 1 August by which time the corncrakes have been given a fair chance of bringing off a successful brood.

Corncrakes lay between 10 and 12 eggs and always attempt to lay a second clutch. The survival of the second broods is also critical to the population, in order to ensure production of enough chicks from which several will eventually enter the breeding population. Both the provision of early and late vegetation cover are essential for the breeding success of the corncrake. A cursory glance around Ireland would suggest that there is plenty of suitable breeding habitat, not being intensively farmed, where corncrakes once bred. Why are corncrakes not here? Is it a case of an inadequate number available to go around or are there deeper issues? One way to encourage this bird, which has been little discussed, is the possibility of breeding corncrakes in captivity and subsequently releasing them to the callowlands or elsewhere when they are old enough to feed independently. Reintroduction programmes have worked successfully for the closely related, but non-migratory, pheasants, grey and red-legged or French partridges, so why not for the endangered corncrake?

Not so long ago almost every townland in Ireland had its breeding corncrake. Today (1998) there are only four 'core areas' in the Republic where small populations survive: (i) the Shannon callows; (ii) the Moy river valley and the Mullet peninsula, Co. Mayo; (iii) North Donegal mainland and (iv) Tory and Inishbofin islands, Co. Donegal. National surveys of singing male corncrakes have been carried out by BirdWatch Ireland in recent years. The results for 1998 over 1997 show a relatively stable population nationally with an encouraging 22% increase in the Shannon callows where habitat conservation measures have been the most intensive. But in northern Donegal numbers of singing males declined by a worrying 38%. It is clear that without the concerted management efforts on the breeding grounds co-ordinated by BirdWatch Ireland and funded by the Royal Society for the Protection of Birds (RSPB) and Dúchas – The Heritage Service, the future for the corncrake would be even bleaker.

Table 8.3 The number of singing male corncrakes recorded in the listed 'core areas' in the Republic 1994-98 (data supplied by Catherine Casey, BirdWatch Ireland).

Area	1994	1995	1996	1997	1998
Shannon callows	65	63	54	54	68–70
County Mayo: Moy Valley and the Mullet	19	23	23	18	17–18
Donegal mainland	25	49	69	45	28
Tory and Inishbofin Islands, Co. Donegal	20	39	38	32-34	34
Totals	129	174	184	149–151	147–150

Wintering wildfowl in the callows

The Shannon and Brosna callowlands are the most important flooded grassland wildfowl habitat in Ireland and up to 24,000 ducks, geese and wild swans, joined by up to 40,800 wading birds, can rise from the shallow waters to darken the skies in wheeling flocks. Such sights are becoming an increasingly precious and rare experience. All these waterfowl are found within the 3,500 ha of callows between Shannon and Portumna with the greatest aggregation in the 800 ha of flooded lands alongside the Little Brosna River. Only at Rahasane Turlough, Co. Galway, can similar densities of wintering waterfowl per unit area of similar grassland be encountered (see p.229).

The importance of the Shannon callows as a haunt for huge numbers of waterfowl has long been known to wildfowlers, including punt gunners, but it was not until the first aerial survey of the area was carried out in January 1967 that the full significance of the region became apparent.[23] During this survey, conducted on 4 January, at the time of peak wildfowl numbers, and during ideal habitat conditions, the following birds were counted between Portumna and Athlone: 1.379 swans (mostly whooper and Bewick's but including some mute), 321 Greenland white-fronted geese, 1 greylag goose, 6,200 wigeon and 170 mallard.

Regular aerial inspections of the area have been underway since the mid 1970s and continue today. They are carried out by Oscar Merne, with recent assistance from Alyn Walsh, of Dúchas, and flown by the Irish Air Corps. The latest available data relate to surveys carried out during the winter 1995–6 which confirm the continued supremacy of the callows as one of Ireland's premier wildfowl wetlands. It comes as a surprise to many that such large numbers of wigeon and some other species – especially dunlin and black-tailed godwit – are found here, so far inland from their more traditional coastal habitats.

Table 8.4 Peak numbers of waterfowl observed in the Shannon and Little Brosna callows, winter 1995–6 (data from Delany[6]).

Species	Shannon callows	Little Brosna callows	TOTALS
Mute swan	575*	63	638*
Bewick's swan	21*		21*
Whooper swan	393**	137*	530**
Greenland w-f goose		594**	594**
Wigeon	3,135*	14,000**	17,135**
Teal		4,000**	4,000**
Mallard		700*	700*
Pintail		250*	250*
Shoveler		200*	200*
Golden plover	7,740*	8,100*	15,840*
Lapwing	14,805*	5,070*	19,875*
Dunlin	1,250*	1,000	2,250
Common snipe		122	122
Black-tailed godwit	730**	2,000**	2,730
Curlew			
Totals	**28,649**	**36,236**	**64,885**

** = numbers of international importance   * = numbers of national importance

The outstanding feature of these winter congregations in the Shannon callowlands is that over the years they have shown no signs of decrease, unlike at Rahasane Turlough and many other locations in Ireland. In fact the total numbers of wildfowl have increased marginally from 60,300 individuals to the present 64,800 over the past ten years.[24] The case for the conservation of these

Little Brosna River callowlands in flood.

North Slob, Co. Wexford, showing part of the Wexford Wildfowl Refuge. A vitally important wintering area for the Greenland white-fronted goose and other waterfowl (A. Walsh).

remarkable flood plains as one of the major wildfowl wetlands not only in Ireland but within the context of western Europe is indeed strong. An integrated management plan is required to maintain the ecology of the habitat for both the wintering wildfowl and summer breeding waders and the corncrakes. Such a plan would need to incorporate compensation payments to farmers whose farming activities are restricted in favour of ornithological interests.

Within the callows the Greenland white-fronted goose is a special feature because outside the some 8,000–10,000 birds that winter on the Wexford Slobs, Co. Wexford (1995/6–1996/7),[25] their next largest concentration in Ireland is on these damp grasslands where the geese eat perennial rye-grass and floating sweet-grass during late autumn to the end of November. From early December they root up the stolons of creeping bent. Since 1982 the world population of this subspecies has doubled to about 32,000 birds, but now shows little sign of further growth.

Frogs and smooth newts

Two small and innocent-looking creatures, the European frog and the smooth newt, can both be found wallowing in small pools in the Shannon callows during the spring breeding season when water conditions are right for them. On first sight these amphibians arouse reactions of curiosity and sometimes fear amongst people unfamiliar with them. But neither are guilty of any serious crimes or misdemeanours other than to have confounded historians and confused zoological biogeographers for centuries (see p.70).

The European frog, sole representative of the Ranidæ, or true frogs, in Ireland, is widespread throughout the country, flourishing as an opportunist species and found in an extensive range of habitats in the agricultural landscape, ponds, pools and ditches providing essential spawning habitat every

The European frog – a controversial species. Is it a native or was it introduced to some ponds in Trinity College, Dublin, in the seventeenth century ?

spring. They are also found in and around freshwater and sometimes brackish water marshes, lake and river margins and even mountain summits. In Europe they have been recorded at altitudes of 3,000 m. They are also frequent on blanket and raised boglands. The European frog has a life span of about 12 years in captivity, but in the wild they live for considerably less, perhaps up to seven years. Their colour is variable, changing to harmonise, as far as possible, with their background environment, an adaptation to conceal themselves from predators, especially grey herons. They exhibit three basic colour forms – dark brown, dark olive-green and light gold. However, despite this ploy, they are not generally encountered during the day and tend to be active at night. Other predators are the otter and mink.

Most female frogs in Ireland breed when they are three years old, but the males start one year earlier. A study by Gibbons & McCarthy found that the average number of eggs laid by a female is 1,000, and that Irish frogs are explosive breeders with a greater annual reproductive output than on the European mainland.[26] Although poikilothermic, frogs are remarkably resistant to cold conditions, hibernating in the mud of ponds and ditches to avoid the lowest temperatures. Some time in February or March when the external air temperature rises to about 4°C frogs will emerge from their hibernation from ditches, mud in the bottom of a pond and other moist and sheltered places. The females release their eggs anytime from mid-February onwards when large masses of frog spawn form turgid jelly-like masses in small ponds and other wet zones, often temporary, and especially on agricultural land. The jelly of frog spawn serves to protect the eggs within. A high percentage of eggs hatch into tadpoles but less than 1% survive to young froglets. Thus from an average production of 1,300 eggs from one female each year only about 24 froglets will survive. Frogs do not eat during the breeding season and wait until they have done their business to get out of the water onto dry land whereupon they commence catching insects, especially flies and slugs. During the breeding season frogs living on low level blanket bogland in western Ireland are sedentary and unselective in their feeding habits. The feeding zone of an adult is generally restricted to a few square metres around the individual. During a study of the food eaten by 70 of these peatland dwellers, Blackith & Speight found that beetles were numerically the most important prey (20% of all food items taken) followed by flies (19% of all food items), but slugs provided the greatest proportion of the bulk by weight of the food. The absence of food in their gut during March showed that they did not feed during the spawning period, a well established feature of other frog populations.[27]

The smooth newt, a close relative of the European frog, is encountered even less frequently, but is also widely distributed throughout Europe, penetrating as far north as 64° in Finland. Newts have a smooth skin, without scales, and spend much of their lives in small ponds. They are coloured olive or yellowish-brown with many dark spots on the body. Their bellies and throats are yellow or orange while the breeding males have a dorsal crest running the length of the body. They retain their prominent tail throughout their adult life.

It is unlikely that many people in Ireland will have ever encountered a smooth newt in nature – they are amongst the least known Irish vertebrates. But if they do the newt will probably be in a small still pond or pool of water where the species migrate every spring to gather for breeding. Their distribution throughout Ireland is patchy and they occur in a wide range of habitats, possibly more frequently in farmland, and are dependent upon freshwater ponds for breeding. After hatching from their egg they develop external gills during their aquatic larval stage – like the European frog. But these are soon reabsorbed during metamorphosis, before the creature crawls out of its pond to commence a terrestrial life style, breathing with lungs.

Like the European frog they move towards small ponds for the commencement of the breeding season in February. Both males and females converge to these waters from their dens. The most attractive breeding habitats are small quiet ponds with plenty of weed growth and surrounded by good terrestrial cover. The pH of the favoured ponds is about neutral (5.6) and relatively high concentrations of calcium and potassium in the water may be preferred.[28]

The main period of egg laying occurs from the second half of April to the end of May. The newt tadpoles emerge from their eggs after about three to four weeks and are carnivorous. Metamorphosis occurs about three months later, but can be delayed if weather conditions are inclement. The adult tadpole emerges from the water to start its terrestrial life phase until the following spring when it moves back to a shallow pond for another breeding season. Most breeding adults will have departed their watery habitats by the end of July

Smooth newts – one of
Ireland's three amphibians.

when they retire to the shelter of stones and other protective coverings prior to hibernating.

Adult smooth newts feed on worms, snails, slugs and invertebrates which they often catch by protruding their tongue and pulling the morsel back into their mouth. Their tongues are less mobile and active than those of the frogs.[29]

Both newts and frogs flourish well in Ireland, possibly better than in most other European countries on account of the large numbers of undrained and suitable breeding sites and undisturbed wetland habitat. There would also appear to be ample supplies of food, especially flies.

Bats

Another competitor for flies, but operating at a different height, are the seven different species of bats, several of which can often be seen hawking for their prey over the Shannon callows and other farmland areas in Ireland.

Bats are probably the least loved and least known of all Irish mammals. While the seven species in Ireland occur in a wide range of habitats they are treated here more out of convenience but also because many of them will be encountered in the broader farmland and countryside environment. Seldom seen during the day and glimpsed only briefly at dusk, one bat looks very much like another. Bats are the only true flying mammals, sharing similar characteristics with the birds such as a high metabolic rate and economy of weight. Their wing-like structure, or patagium, is a flexible membrane made up of two layers of soft skin between which is sandwiched a layer of tissue containing blood vessels and nerves. The membrane is stretched out between very elongated fingers, which are as long as the body. The feet are free of the membrane and each hind toe is armed with a claw. The thumb is free on the forewing and is also armed with a powerful claw. The pelvic bone is specially adapted to allow the legs to rotate when the bat hangs upside down at roost.

Little is known about the evolution of bats. Like the insectivores, they eat insects, but locate their prey by echolocation. Bursts of high frequency ultrasound are emitted by the bat which bounce off solid objects such as flying insects or buildings and are picked up by the bat which is immediately able to determine the nature and distance of the object and adjust its flight. The bat's disproportionately large ears are used to pick up the echoing sound waves. They are sometimes assisted by leaf-like flaps of skin around the nostrils, the purpose of which is also to register sounds. Only one bat in Ireland, the lesser horseshoe bat has these unpleasant-looking flaps, endowing its owner with a most ugly face.

When roosting and hanging upside down with their patagia wrapped around their bodies they look like miniature legs of beef strung up in a butcher's cold store. It is the roosting locations of some bats – in buildings, under eaves, in attics – that brings them into conflict with humans. Their presence arouses fear as they are thought – wrongly – to get entangled in hair and to suck blood. For their hibernation bats select roosts where temperatures remain relatively constant but, like the hedgehog, they can occasionally emerge from their torpor to fly around on warm days. Most species in Ireland are thought to be non-migratory, remaining in the neighbourhood of where they were born. Copulation takes place in the autumn but the female stores the sperm until the following April or May when she ovulates, whereupon fertilisation take place. Pregnancy lasts about 50 days and a single baby is born blind while its mother

hangs head upwards, reversing the normal roosting position. The baby begins
to suckle soon after birth.

Their general unpopularity and the lack of 'bat champions' has impeded
knowledge about their distribution and abundance in Ireland. However, a survey
of the distribution of the seven species of Irish bats in the whole of Ireland was
conducted by O'Sullivan in 1985–8.[30] The results of the survey were as follows.

1. COMMON PIPISTRELLE

This is the smallest bat in Ireland (its forearms are less than 35 mm) and the
most widely distributed throughout the country. Over 580 roosts were located
in confined spaces in buildings, mostly under roofs, some of them large with
up to 600 individuals. Most commonly observed hawking for insects along
woodland margins, hedgerows and over water. They have been recorded from
several lighthouses, possibly on local movements, during bird migration investigations conducted by Barrington at the turn of the century. They have been
known to travel up to distances of up to 70 km in Britain.[31]

2. BROWN LONG-EARED BAT

After the pipistrelle, the most frequently recorded bat, including records from
offshore islands with one record from Inishtearaght, Co. Kerry. Favourite
roosting sites are open attics with most roosts containing fewer than 50 individuals. Feeds by picking off insects from shrubs and tree leaves.

3. LEISLER'S BAT

Ireland has the largest population and the biggest known roost of this species
in the world – some 800–1,000 in west Cork. Leisler's bats, both numerous and

The distribution of the common pipistrelle (left) and brown long-eared bat Solid symbols
are records from the survey by O'Sullivan[30]; hatched symbols are records from the
Northern Ireland Bat Group. All distribution maps from O'Sullivan[30].

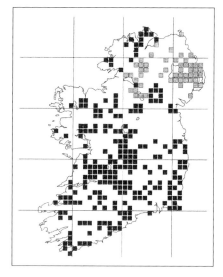
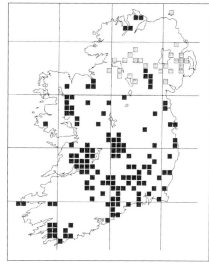

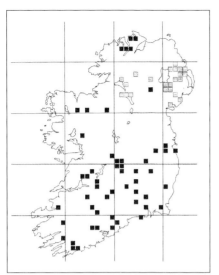 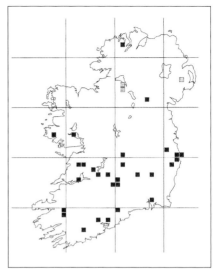

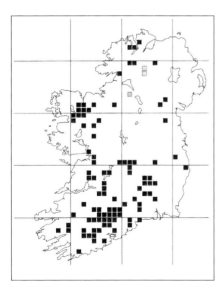 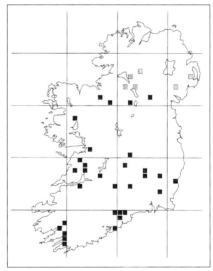

The distribution of Leisler's bat (above left), the whiskered bat (above right), Daubenton's bat (below left) and natterer's bat (below right).

widespread, are the largest bats in the country. Roosting generally in attics, they can be seen hunting insects in the general farmland environment over scrub and woodland areas after dusk. Ireland is also the northernmost station for the species in Europe.

4. WHISKERED BAT
The rarest species in Ireland and the least frequently recorded. It occurs in small roosts (1–10 individuals) in houses and is regularly found roosting with

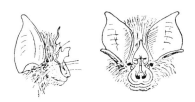

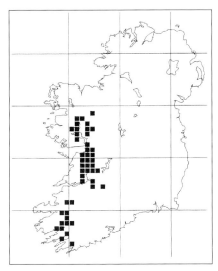

The distribution of the lesser horseshoe bat
(above).

other species. When feeding it picks insects and spiders off woodland leaves.
Most records are from south of a line from Dublin to Galway.

5. DAUBENTON'S BAT
The only bat in Ireland regularly roosting in crevices under stone bridges
although also found in caves and in houses. The restrictive size of the crevices
ensure that roost sizes are small (1–10 bats). They feed more or less exclusively on insects flying over ponds, rivers and lakes.

6. NATTERER'S BAT
Widespread throughout the country but in small numbers. Roosts in very
small groups in cracks and crevices in houses, as well as in caves and tunnels.

7. LESSER HORSESHOE BAT
Restricted to western and southwestern Ireland. Significant population
declines have been recorded in several European countries but the Irish population, estimated at some 12,000 individuals, is now the largest population in
any European country. It is known as the bat of the Irish country house
because it prefers large open roosting spaces in attics. During the winter it
hibernates in caves, and other underground structures even the cellars and
tunnels of large country houses. Listed on Annex IV of the EU Habitats
Directive as requiring special areas of conservation. The bat is threatened by
extinction throughout northern Europe.

Hedgehog
The hedgehog and the pigmy shrew are the only Irish insectivores. Ireland is
without the mole, the common shrew and water shrew, all of which are widespread in Britain.
  Large adult hedgehogs reach up to 240 mm long and weigh approximately
1.1 kg at full adult age. But they experience large swings of up to 30% in body
weight due to the accumulation of fat for hibernation and its subsequent loss.

Hedgehogs are widespread throughout the country where there are hedgerows or woodland edges in the farmland environment to provide cover for nesting and hibernation. They also require access to grassland where they procure most of their food. They are remarkably frequent in the urban environment, finding their way in many gardens. They are generally nocturnal, feeding mostly on insects although earthworms and slugs are popular prey.

The hairs on the hedgehog's back have become modified to form spines, up to 22 mm long, useful as self-defence against nosy dogs, badgers and interfering humans. The spines are not shed regularly like hair and can be retained for up to 18 months. When threatened by danger the hedgehog rolls up into a small ball, protecting its soft parts underneath, while at the same time erecting its spines to act as defensive *chevaux-de-frise*. Their natural enemies are often stated to be the dog, badger and fox. However, studies by Fairley on the diet of the fox in northeastern Ireland showed that there was no evidence of hedgehog remains in the stomach of 340 adult and 163 cub foxes.[32]

Hedgehogs have small eyes and their eyesight is poor which is compensated by an acute sense of hearing. Their snout is elongated and sensitised by the presence of vibrissae, or whiskers, which, on contact with an object, activate nerve endings in the hedgehog's skin. The hedgehog and bats are the only Irish mammals to hibernate during the winter but, as is well known, spells of warm weather will tempt many out of their slumber and they will be encountered wandering around gardens or scuffling amongst the vegetation along farmland hedgerows. Their hibernation period generally starts in October and extends to the end of March.

Hedgehogs spend most of their time in a solitary state, coming together only briefly for the purposes of breeding. Most hedgehogs spend the day in a sheltered den and emerge at night to forage amongst the vegetation for food, chiefly earthworms, slugs, snails and many different small insects which they crunch up, often quite audibly. It is thought that they eat up to 70 g of food each night.[33] Hedgehogs are shrouded in mythology, probably engendered by their curious shape, gait, quilled fur and habit of rolling up into a defensive ball when threatened. Irish folklore relates that they suckle milk at night from

Hedgehog.

the teats of resting cows, and carrying away apples spiked on their quills.

The home range or territory of the hedgehog extends for about 400–500 m from its den and like many other mammals the positioning of their droppings may play a role in marking the territorial limits.[34] Courtship of the female is perfunctory with the male circling the female while snorting. Matthews relates that the female will not accept the male for copulation until she is coming into oestrus, i.e. ovulating.[34] When the male makes his first approach she butts him with raised spines on her forehead. But he persists until accepted by her. Four to five young are born blind and hairless and if the mother is disturbed when the young are very small she will eat them. Otherwise they leave the nest around 22 days old but continue to suckle for about four more weeks. The spines of hedgehogs provide effective protection from most of their potential predators, but they are of little use when crossing the road at night, which is how many come to grief. Hedgehogs make attractive and beneficial garden pets which consume harmful slugs.

Fox

Of all Irish mammals the fox is the most adaptable and successful. All attempts to control its numbers or eliminate it from the countryside have met with total failure. For example, one of the earliest 'bounty' schemes was operated in Co. Antrim in the area of The Manor of Glenarm, stretching over 342 km^2 of countryside between Larne and the River Glendrum. Between 1765 and 1781 a total of 1,462 bounties of 10p for every fox head turned in were paid. There was no perceptible effect on the amount of 'nuisances' wrought by the fox.[35] However, a decrease in numbers in Ireland was noted from about the middle of the eighteenth century for unknown reasons and they were reported to have 'disappeared' from Co. Antrim by the end of that century. Fairley believes they started to reappear again between 1920 and 1930 to such an extent that by 1943 a government bounty scheme was introduced. By 1997 when the scheme was abandoned a total of 290,000 bounties had been paid, again with no noticeable benefit except to those who produced the bodies or heads at local police stations (with tongue excised to thwart repeated submissions). To reduce effectively the numbers of an animal so adaptable, cunning and prolific as the fox a much higher removal rate of adults from the population would have to be achieved. The figure would have to be somewhere in the region of 60–80% adults per annum for several years. The resources and logistics required for such an operation are beyond the means of most agricultural authorities.

The bones of contention between man and fox concern the fox's diet. The fox is an opportunist feeder and a predator on a range of small mammals which are selected on the basis of their ease of catching rather than anything else. It is their predation of lambs, chickens, ducks and geese which causes the most anguish amongst the farming community. Fairley analysed the food remains in the stomachs of 340 adults and 163 cub foxes killed in Northern Ireland between February 1966 and March 1968. While there are many methodological problems about analysing stomach food remains based on the frequency of occurrence of animal remains, the results obtained provided the best information available to date on what the 'northeastern fox' was eating (Table 8.5).

Table 8.5 Percentages of the stomachs of 340 adult and 163 cub foxes containing various food items (data from Fairley[32]).

Food	Adults	Cubs
Rabbit and hare	45	59
Sheep	9	6
Rat	17	16
Wood mouse	6	1
Galliformes (poultry and game birds)	16	15
Passerines (perching birds)	4	10
Other birds	2	1
Unidentified	20	9

Rabbits and hares made up the largest part of the identified food taken, followed by rats and then poultry and game birds. Sheep were a seasonal source of food, mainly in the winter and spring, and it was considered that sheep remains outside the lambing season came from sheep carrion.

Foxes are in all habitats, even urban areas, often to the surprise of those who see a fox gambolling across a lawn or rummaging in a dustbin in full daylight. A pair even established their underground home, or 'earth', beneath one of the temporary cabin-offices at the very busy Radio Telefís Éireann headquarters in Donnybrook, Dublin. But they are probably most common in the agricultural landscape where they dig out their earth in scrubland, woodland and at the base of hedgerows. A favourite habitat is scrubland with large boulders under which they set up home with little trouble. Like the badger they are essentially nocturnal with special elliptical pupils in the eye that assist greater gathering of dim light. During the day the pupil closes down to just a slit, letting in only minute amounts of light.

Stoats

The stoat is another carnivore widely spread throughout the countryside. Sole native Irish representative of the genus *Mustela*, the Irish stoat, *M. erminea hibernica*, received its subspecific recognition in 1895 when the eminent Irish mammalogist Gerald Barrett-Hamilton teamed up with his distinguished English colleague Oldfield Thomas to show that they differed from their English counterparts in both colour and size. The Irish form is slightly smaller and has a deeper brown colour, the white underparts are restricted to a narrow line except between the legs and its upper lip and the margins to its ears are dark. Irish stoats rarely turn white in winter whereas those in the northern parts of its range in Britain do. Stoats resident in the Isle of Man also belong to the Irish subspecies.

The stoat occupies a wide range of habitats throughout Ireland but its preferred general habitat is woodland when available (54% of all recorded occurrences), followed by open countryside (37%). They are considered in this chapter because of their widespread occurrence throughout a broad range of farmland habitats including Foaty Island, Co. Cork (316 ha), which was formerly a large private estate of farmland, woodland and parkland. Their distribution in woodland on the island was studied by Sleeman who fitted radio transmitters onto four individuals which were tracked across the woodland. Most of the records (60%) came from underground where the stoats were sheltering principally in brown rat holes with fewer records from rabbit and wood mouse holes. Some 17% of the records came from animals in cover and a further 8% were of stoats in trees, probably on hunting missions. When two stoats were radio tracked in the open country most of the locations were in trees, followed by pasture, hedges and underground.[36] The home ranges of stoats was also determined on Foaty Island by use of radio tracking and the results for 3 females averaged 11 ha, the same as a single male. These territories were relatively small and probably related to high densities of prey. Other studies from the Continent give results of an average of 34 ha for a male and 7.4 ha for a female (Finland); and 43 ha and 20.5 ha for males and 7.1 ha and 45 ha for females (Russia).[37]

In 1992 Sleeman determined the contents of 89 stoat guts mostly from the southern counties of Ireland. Rabbit was the most frequent prey taken (31%) followed by pigmy shrews (26%), rats (14%), birds (18%), wood mouse (5%), bank vole (3%), stoat (1%) and 2% unaccounted for.[38] The large percentage of small rodents, particularly shrews, came as a surprise as they did not feature in a previous study conducted by Fairley on the food remains of 29 stoats collected in the early 1960s from widespread localities in Northern Ireland.[39]

The stoat has a remarkable repertoire for creative behaviour. When hunting a bird or small group of birds the stoat will sometimes approach its prey and jump up and down, gig or dance in front of the birds in a presumed attempt to mesmerise, hypnotise or simply hold the attention of the prey until the stoat is close enough to strike. Prey is always killed by a bite to the back of the neck. In the autumn small hunting packs of stoats have been recorded and these are probably family parties.

Badgers

The badger, like the stoat, is a member of the order Carnivora. But while it might be endowed with the anatomical attributes of a carnivore it is omnivorous in diet, eating anything from earthworms to fruit, bulbs, grass and nuts. As one of Ireland's commonest larger mammals, it is very much a creature of the agricultural landscape where it occurs more numerously and in greater densities than elsewhere. As a member of the Mustelidae family it is related to the otter, stoat, pine martin and American mink. Its total length, tail to snout, is about 90 cm and its weight ranges from 10–27 kg. Shy of man and nocturnal in habits, it has longitudinal black and white stripes extending backwards from its elongated snout providing easy identification. Its Irish name, *broc*, means 'grey'.

Badgers are highly social, forming small groups, dominated by one male, and abiding underground in a complex system of tunnels and chambers. This subterranean maze or set is occupied by many generations of badgers, for they are traditional in their habits. The set contains headquarters used for breeding and overwintering and smaller satellites, occasionally used for other purposes. Several different groups of badgers will live in on area and occupy neighbouring sets. Sadly most people's only encounter with a badger is a dead one, killed by a motor vehicle at night as the badger slowly lumbered across the road. Many farmers would be happy with more dead badgers as, together with other mammals including deer, they are known carriers of the bacterium *Mycobacterium bovis*, the cause of bovine tuberculosis in cattle.

In order to contribute to a better understanding of the possible role of the badger in the outbreaks of bovine TB amongst cattle an extensive country-wide

survey of badger distribution and numbers was ini-
tiated by the National
Parks and Wildlife Service
in 1989 and undertaken
by Smal.[40] The average
size of badger social
groups was estimated at
close to six adults per
group based on the num-
ber of all animals caught
in a number of different

Badger. From Corbet & Southern[37].

sets. The mean density of badger social groups in Ireland – estimated from a
count of *main* sets in a sample of 729 one km squares, covering about 1% of
Ireland land surface – was estimated at one group (six individuals) per 2 km^2.
This yielded a calculated population of 200,450 badgers for the Republic of
Ireland, a population level similar to that found in Britain and Sweden.

Some uncertainty remains as to its precise role in the transmission of the disease. All in all, badgers are quite harmless and rather endearing quadrupeds.
While their carnivore status confers a whiff of an exciting list of prey, their
main diet in Ireland is earthworms. An occasional 'rogue' badger will sometimes have a go at larger and more illicit fare such as a chicken but such a meal
is a rarity.

The 1989 survey showed that badger distribution throughout the country was
uneven. The highest numbers occurred in Co. Kilkenny and Co. Louth, where
a large proportion of the landscape is occupied by hedgerow, tree lines, arable
land and pastures. Galway, Mayo and Longford had the least animals. In Galway
and Mayo the large amount of unsuitable bogland and upland habitat certainly accounted for this dearth. The most popular habitats for set construction
were hedgerows and tree lines because of the cover and dry, stable earth banks.
The badger survey was aimed only at providing information about badger ecology, distribution and abundance. The question of the badger's role and degree
of culpability in the spread of bovine TB must await further research.

Owls

The barn owl, gliding low over fields and open countryside, hunting for mice
and rats, is very much a bird of the agricultural landscape. Closely associated
with farms, they breed and roost in barns, outhouses and old ruined buildings.
For such an agricultural country as Ireland, where there is no apparent short-
age of roosting or breeding sites, and a plentiful supply of rats and mice, they
are surprisingly scarce. Indeed, many people living on farms or in the countryside have rarely if ever encountered one of these graceful owls. A decrease
in their numbers in parts of Ireland was first noticed around 1950 with more
marked declines from the 1960s onwards.[41] The reasons for this decline are
not understood but may have been associated with an increase in the use of
pesticides and other poisons many of which, although being banned today,
were used with some adverse effect on seed-eating birds. Whatever the reason
their numbers have never fully recovered to their earlier strength. During a
special survey carried out from 1982–5 it was estimated that two or three pairs
of barn owls bred in each of the 10 km squares taken as sample squares. From

this data it was calculated that the breeding population lay somewhere between 600 and 900 pairs.[42] However, since then the population would appear to have declined. A survey conducted with the assistance of the public during 1995–7 revealed only 130 nest/roost sites, most of which were below the 100 m contour. The greatest concentrations of owls were in Counties Kilkenny and Cork. A good few occurred in the southern part of the Shannon basin while they were particularly rare or absent from the drumlin landscapes of the north Midland and from along the northwest coast.[43]

The diet of the barn owl can be quite easily determined by identifying the small bones and other remains contained in the pellets regurgitated by the birds at their traditional roosts. Fairley has carried out extensive analyses of barn owl pellets from many parts of Ireland throughout the four seasons. His collective results show that the owl's principal prey is the wood mouse, followed by the brown rat, house mouse and pigmy shrew.[35] Thus the barn owl is a useful ally of the farmer as biological controller of mice and rats.

Seed-eating birds

Seed-eating finches and buntings are frequently encountered on farmland, particularly in winter flocks.

Of all the seed-eating finches, the goldfinch with its cheerful tumultuous song and attractive plumage was the most eagerly sought after and trapped by bird catchers during the nineteenth century when numbers were significantly reduced. By the 1940s the population had somewhat recovered following the implementation of the *Wild Birds Protection Act, 1930*. Today, goldfinches are widespread breeders throughout the country, occurring in every county but not encountered in the large wintering flocks recorded in the 1940s and 1950s. Post-breeding flocks of usually 10–15 and often up to 30 birds can be seen in August to September, sometimes augmented by immigrants, possibly from Britain, which arrive from the end of September through to November. Large numbers of passage birds have been noted at the bird observatories on Great Saltee, Co. Wexford, and Clear Island, Co. Cork, respectively. Old pasture land with plenty of thistles is the goldfinch's favourite feeding habitat from the autumn into winter. But the extent of this type of pastureland is slowly shrinking due to the increasing amount of improved grasslands, greater extent of silage and rising fertiliser application, all detrimental to weed growth. However, there still remain substantial quantities of thistles in rough grassland pasture, especially in the Midlands. Railway embankments, rough land along many new road developments, and some boglands now provide some of the best feeding habitat. Favourite seeds are from thistles and common knapweed. When these food sources have been exhausted by winter, goldfinches pick up the fallen seeds of teasel and the scarcer burdocks in grass fields.

The linnet is common and widespread throughout the country but was more plentiful in previous years especially in the 1970s and 1980s when quite large flocks could be seen compared with groups of 50 to 150 birds today. From late September to November, especially in coastal areas where flocks of 400–600 have been noted in Wexford and Donegal, there is a pronounced passage movement of birds – possibly Irish birds, reinforced by British immigrants, on their way further south to France and the Continent. Favourite linnet food includes the seeds of shepherd's-purse, charlock and oil-seed rape, while common chickweed is taken throughout the year. Apart from oil-seed rape and flax, both set-a-side crops, their food plants are characteristic of waste places, broken ground, roadside verges, field margins and other untidy and agriculturally unimproved areas. Upwards of 1,000 birds have been noted feeding in oil-seed rape fields near Dublin. They are also plentiful in cultivated lands especially where vegetable are grown such as north County Dublin. West of the Shannon linnets tend to congregate around hay sheds and haggards in search of knapweed seeds. Linnets are most numerous during winter in the eastern and southern parts of Ireland, especially near the coast.

Greenfinches, another common resident seed-eater, are frequently found outside the breeding season generally in small flocks of 20–30 birds but sometimes up to 100, feeding in arable and cultivated ground where they glean wheat, barley and oat seeds. They are most frequently observed in the rich agricultural areas of the northeast, east and southeast. In recent years the oil-seed rape has become a particularly attractive food for them. As with the other seed-eating finches, numbers increase in coastal areas in September to October reflecting possible passage movement of Irish and possibly British immigrants. A few continental birds winter in Ireland.

The chaffinch, a numerous and widely distributed bird, especially in deciduous woodlands, also forms winter flocks some of which can be up to 1,000 birds strong. Largest numbers occur in the east and southeast where there are generally more beech trees to provide their preferred food, beechmast. From mid-October through November large numbers of chaffinches migrate to Ireland from Fenno-Scandinavia and other parts of the Continent. These immigrants, belonging to the sub-species *Fringilla coelebs coelebs*, are larger and paler than Irish residents and feed characteristically in the larger and more open farm fields whist Irish chaffinches keep more to the hedgerows and enclosed landscape. Often accompanying the chaffinches are bramblings, a continental visitor, turning up in varying numbers. Flocks of up to 260 and 420 have been recorded from the east coast and Cork respectively, but such numbers are unusual. Bullfinches generally occur in smaller winter flocks of 10–15 birds and in August seek out birch seeds as well as weed seeds. Blackberries are taken in September while from January to April they feed on the buds of fruit trees often causing considerable damage to the fruit crop.

The siskin is the most volatile and noisy of the seed-eating finches, especially during migration. Up to the mid-nineteenth century, siskins were only winter visitors to Ireland but by 1900 they were known to be breeding in 16 counties. During this century their breeding range and population size has increased dramatically along with the expansion of coniferous plantations throughout the country. The plantations provide excellent breeding habitat. Like many of the other finches they congregate in coastal areas in the autumn, possibly joined by immigrants from Britain and the Continent. Movements of upwards of 100 birds a day have been recorded at Cape Clear Bird Observatory. During the winter they are found principally in the south, especially in river valleys where there their principal food, seeds of alder, occurs. In recent years increasing numbers have been noted feeding at bird tables.

The lesser redpole is a widespread but thinly scattered breeding bird throughout Ireland. In the winter and autumn they come together in small and highly mobile flocks of some 20–30 birds to roam the countryside and farmland particularly in central and northeast Ireland where they seek out their preferred food of birch seeds from late August onwards although they will also take alder seeds when available.

The breeding distribution of the twite in Ireland is not well known but appears to be mainly focused in coastal areas. In the winter twites gather in small flocks in coastal areas, especially estuaries and salt marshes. The seeds of daisies, charlock and dandelion are their favourite foods.

The yellowhammer, another seed-eating bunting, is on the decline in the agricultural landscape, having disappeared from many areas where it was relatively common a decade ago. In a survey of breeding birds in Co. Tipperary during 1997 the breeding density was 0.31 pairs per km^2 compared with 21.8 pairs per km^2 found in farmland with hedgerows in Britain. The Tipperary survey showed that the optimal habitat for almost all yellowhammers was farmland, with a preference for hedgerows with trees. The field types used by the birds were improved grassland (36%), tillage (32%), mixed grass and tillage (23%) and unimproved grassland (7%).[44]

The decline of cereal crops and their associated ecology in Ireland has directly affected the destiny and distribution of three seed-eating game birds while the population size of a fourth has almost certainly been restricted by the contracting amount of land under grain crops. The numbers and the breeding distribution of the native grey partridge, the introduced red-legged or French partridge, the introduced pheasant and the migratory quail have all been influenced by the extent of tillage land under cereal and especially wheat crops.

During the nineteenth century the native grey partridge was numerous and bred in every country but by the turn of the century their numbers and breeding range were seriously contracting as the extent of land under wheat was reduced. The downward trend in numbers continued into the early 1930s but was arrested by the enactment of the *Wild Birds Protection Act, 1930* which introduced shooting seasons. Fresh stocks of birds were introduced to Ireland. However, further decreases were noted from the early 1960s onwards. During the period 1968–72 and 1988–91 there was a marked decline evidenced by only thirty 10 km squares recorded as occupied by breeding birds compared with 253 for the earlier period.[45] Today this small and attractive partridge is now confined to a few Midland counties and one or two locations in eastern and Northern Ireland.[22] In 1997, surveys by Kavanagh revealed only some 70 grey partridges remaining in an area of cutaway bog at Boora, Co. Offaly, and a further 17 at Lullymore, Co. Kildare. Indeed, according to Kavanagh, this species is perilously close to extinction in Ireland. Barley, oats and kale have been sown along dykes in both areas to provide food and cover while there has also been predator control of foxes, hooded crows and stoats.[46]

The closely related red-legged partridge, a native of France, south of the Loire and Jura, has been introduced into Ireland – encouraged by its successful introduction to Britain some 300 years ago – on at least two occasions by sportsmen wishing to boost game stocks. In 1840 a Mr Gildear introduced some to Co. Galway. Their fate is not known but some possibly survived because two birds were shot in Co. Galway and a single bird was shot near Clonmel, Co. Tipperary, on 4 February 1849. Approximately 1,000 young birds were released in 1979–81.[47,48] Some of these survived as testified by 21 broods recorded during 1980–82. More were still believed to be breeding in Dublin, Louth and Tipperary and possibly in Kilkenny and Wexford in 1987.[22] Their fate, like that of the grey partridge, seems bound up with the availability of a cereal agricultural landscape to supply essential nesting habitat for the adults and, most importantly, adequate food for the chicks.

The quail has all but disappeared as a breeding species in Ireland. Several pairs struggle each summer to bring off a successful brood of young in their traditional stronghold of Kildare where there is a relatively high proportion of cereal lands. Elsewhere very small numbers probably attempt to breed most years in the lush pastures of the Shannon callows, and breeding has been recorded in Louth, Antrim and Mayo. The male's unmistakable trisyllabic call, 'whic, whic-ic', reveals the presence of birds in May or June. The warm summer of 1989 was a bumper year for them when they bred more widely than in earlier years. The number of records were back to normal the following summer.[49,50] Quail were almost certainly common breeding birds throughout Ireland during the eighteenth century. Throughout the early part of the century they wintered so regularly that they were considered residents, rather than migrants. They became very numerous during the first part of the nineteenth century up to the time of the Great Famines of 1845–52. Ussher and Warren record in *The Birds of Ireland* that the extensive cultivation of wheat and numerous potato gardens favoured the large numbers of quail. The loss of the many pre-famine smallholdings, coupled with the post-famine shift in agriculture from tillage to grassland reduced quail numbers to presumed extinction as a breeding species by 1880. Numbers recovered in the 1890s but they have been scarce breeders ever since, with probably fewer than 50 pairs in the country today.

The fourth grain-eating game bird is the pheasant, believed to have been introduced to Ireland relatively late, in 1589.[51] A few years later, between 1599 and 1603, Moryson reported that in Ireland there was 'such a plenty of pheasants as I have known sixty served up at one feast, and abound much more with rails, but partridges are somewhat scarce'.[52] There are earlier records of its presence in Britain with fossil records of probably wild pheasants dating from the Roman period, but it was probably not domesticated in Britain until 1059 and subsequently became naturalised in the countryside in the fourteenth or fifteenth century.[53] Two different races of the pheasant have been brought into Ireland. First to be introduced was the Caucasian pheasant – originally from Georgia and Armenia on the southeastern borders of the Black Sea – and later, in the eighteenth century, birds of the Chinese race from eastern China with a characteristic white ring on the neck. They occur throughout most of Ireland but mostly in very low densities. In one of the richer agricultural landscapes at Lyons Estate, Co. Kildare, the average density of breeding males was 2.3 per 40 ha.[54] Approximately 200,000 cock pheasants are shot each year in Ireland compared with about 7 million in Britain.

Cock pheasant displaying.

9

The Coastline

The coastline of Ireland extends slightly over 3,000 km – including estuaries and other sea inlets – but when all the islands are taken into account the figure amounts to double that.[1,2] This places Ireland among the countries with the highest ratio of coastline to land surface, in the same league as Scotland and Norway. As elsewhere in the world, the contours of the coastline are a reflection of the underlying geology. The generally rugged western Atlantic seaboard contrasts sharply with the more gentle and lower, sandy and gravelly east coast, occasionally broken by rocky headlands jutting out into the Irish Sea. However, despite this dichotomy, Ireland is fortunate in that it possesses the whole range of coastal ecosystems.

The contours of the coastline are not fixed. They wax and wane like the moon in the sky. While material is worn away from one section of the coast, it slowly accumulates in another. Whole chunks of cliffs are known to fall into the sea, as testified by abandoned farm houses whose doorsteps are now near the void. Islands, like the Inishkeas in North Mayo, are being split and channels forced through them. Conversely, shallow lagoons, progressively cut off from the ebb and flow of water by the slow emergence of dunes, are drying up and turning into flat pastures, with dead cliffs, formerly headlands, acting as a surrounding frame. Both the advancing and the receding processes happen over relatively short periods of time. A bad winter can change the landscape; a century will revolutionise it. The outline of the west coast today does not match that of the first Admiralty charts prepared in the mid-nineteenth century – surveyor and map maker William Bald, active at the end of the eighteenth century, would not recognise many of the contours of Co. Mayo as he drew them then, although this is due particularly to the inaccuracy of this early survey. [3] Many areas in his time were inundated twice daily by tides – today the same places are seldom licked by the sea. Conversely, dry and sea-secure portions of the land 200 years ago are now bathed by Neptune's waters and have suffered a sea change into something rich and strange.

On the western seaboard the tough Precambrian rocks in Donegal, Mayo and Galway provide the bones for a rugged, bold coastline with some spectacular cliffs mitigated by many low-lying and sandy areas. Where softer rocks such as limestone occur, erosion has created the Bays of Donegal, Sligo, Killala, Clew and Galway, while the harder sandstones of the Cliffs of Moher, Co. Clare, impervious to much of the undermining effort of the sea, stand unblinking at the sea further southwards. The long fingers of the equally resistant Old Red Sandstones that form the Dingle Peninsula and other land extensions in Kerry and Cork, together with their associated drowned river valleys, provide a series of deep inland funnels for the sea. The rocks between the fingers have been eaten away to create a series of sheltered sea inlets, or rias, providing safe anchorage for shipping of all kinds. The southeast coast is much tamer, with some sunken and broad river valleys opening wide arms to the sea. On the east

The coastline of Ireland: some structural elements and morphological features. From Stephens & Glassock[1].

coast, low sandy and gravelly beaches dominate, sometimes interrupted by headlands. North of Belfast the escarpment of the basalt plateau with its stepped cliffs presides grandly over the coastline up to Lough Foyle in Co. Derry where a low and extensive sand dune system takes over to the northwest.

Within the area labelled 'coastline' there are a number of habitats that grade into each other. For the purpose of this chapter seven broad categories have been drawn and size estimates compiled. The data are derived from satellite

The almost horizontal carboniferous rocks of Downpatrick Head, Co. Mayo, have been eroded into a set of dramatic features including overhang cliffs.

imagery provided by the 1991 CORINE Land Cover project (aimed at mapping the territory of the EU according to its ecological characteristics) and adjusted where it was considered that there had been under-registration.[4,5,6]

In the absence of more accurate data the following figures should be regarded as provisional estimates:

inshore waters and sea inlets (estuaries)	6,200 ha
intertidal mud and sand flats	67,100 ha
salt marshes	3,700 ha
coastal lagoons	1,700 ha
shingle and sand (parts of beaches, dunes and sand)	<16,000 ha
machair (parts of beaches, dunes and sand)	< 16,000 ha
sea cliffs and rocky shores (parts of bare rocks and sparsely vegetated areas combined)	< 53,300 ha

Each of the coastal habitats has a characteristic flora and fauna, including species particularly suited to cope with high salinity and extreme wind speeds. The inshore flora and fauna is equally rich and diverse and has assumed greater importance in recent years with the development of shellfish and fin-fish farming. The many bays, estuaries and lagoons constantly replenished by tides provide food and security for large numbers of wintering wildfowl and waders visiting Ireland in internationally important numbers. The seabirds, especially terns, are also generally bound to the coastline and small offshore islands, where they nest and raise their young. As for the low grassy machairs stretching behind sandy beaches, on the other side of dune systems, they play host to communities of flowers and invertebrates as well as a diminishing number of breeding waders such as dunlin, common snipe and lapwing.

This chapter will progress from the wettest to the driest sections of the coastline, i.e. from features that are most exposed or subjected to the sea to the more inland areas and their own typical maritime life. Sea cliffs, with their plants and birds, are kept for discussion in Chapter 10. This chapter starts with a description and analysis of several inshore waters and sea inlets. First, Strangford Lough on the northeast coast – an outstanding example of a sea lough; then the Killary Harbour dividing Co. Mayo from Co. Galway – Ireland's only fjord, whose benthic life has many special characteristics; then the turbulent inshore waters off Carnsore Point, Co. Wexford, which represent a challenging environment for the survival of marine life. Mulroy Bay, Co. Donegal; Lough Hyne, Co. Cork and then Galway Bay follow. They fit in between the extremes of Killary Harbour and Carnsore Point.

The bays and estuaries of Ireland have long been the haunts of mussels and oysters, once common fare for early settlers, now rare and pricey food. The ecology of these molluscs is explored in the chapter. Struggling out of the waters and seeking terrestrial identity are the salt marshes, shingle beaches and sand dunes. They are backed by flat grasslands or machair. Each ecosystem has its own special evolution processes, flora and fauna, including Irish specialities – choughs, natterjack toads and terns. Coastline instability makes life difficult for plants, many of which are endangered species, while others are the progenitors or relations of many vegetables we eat. All these topics are discussed in this chapter.

Strangford Lough, Co. Down

Strangford Lough is one of the largest and most diverse sea loughs in Ireland and Britain. It originated as a fault basin within Silurian rocks some 438–408 million years old, infilled at the north end by a layer of Triassic rocks from about 248–213 million years ago, and later carved out by glaciers. The latter stage left behind a rich legacy of glacial deposition, now occurring in the form of drumlins, or whale-backed islands, along the western side. Along the eastern side, the drumlins have been eroded away and become 'pladdies', i.e. mere piles of pebbles and boulders only exposed at low tides. The Lough is 'fjardic' rather than 'fjordic', meaning that although it is of glacial origin, it remains shallow with many islets and passes, and does not have the structural narrowness of a fjord.

Strangford Lough is almost entirely landlocked. It is bounded on the east side by the Ards peninsula and on the west and north by Co. Down. The connection with the Irish Sea is achieved through a narrow inlet about 8 km long, mostly less than 1 km wide – known as the Narrows – and with a slender underwater lip at the entrance, deep enough to allow the passage of boats. The Lough is over 24 km long and about 8 km wide. Most of it is shallow – less than 20 m deep – and the coastline, stretching over 130 km, is highly indented. The ecology of Strangford Lough is dominated by the fact that about one third of its total area (150 km^2) is intertidal. This natural phenomenon controls, through the sifting and deposition of particulate matter, the Lough's substrata and benthic communities. The currents can reach speeds of up to 9.72 knots near the Narrows where the sea comes into the Lough. Such tidal speeds have profound effects on the algae and marine species trying to gain footholds

East side of Strangford Lough looking south.

here. Further into the Lough conditions are much quieter allowing a broad spectrum of marine life to flourish. About 80% of all the Irish Sea coastal and inshore habitats and 75% of all the marine species recorded from Northern Ireland are found here.[7]

Naturalists and scientists of Northern Ireland have a long tradition of investigations into sublittoral (the zone of water 6–10 m deep) marine biology which started with the first dredgings by John Templeton in 1790. Later, under the aegis of the British Association for the Advancement of Science, more surveys were undertaken, the results of which were compiled by Dickie in a 1857 report on the marine zoology of Strangford Lough.[8] A century later, in 1954, the Royal Irish Academy published a study by Williams together with a summary of previously collected data.[9] More recently, in the 1980s, a study on the marine life of littoral and sublittoral areas of Northern Ireland including Strangford Lough was carried out by Erwin and colleagues.[10] The following information concerning the Lough and its algae and invertebrates is taken from the Erwin report, published in 1990.

At least 12 major invertebrate community types occur in the Lough, ranging from very rich high-energy rock communities in the Narrows – receiving an abundance of food from the rapid current – to the extremely sheltered community of the Norway lobster inhabiting burrows in the finest of muds. The channels between the drumlins and most of the central part of the Lough are characterised by beds of horse mussel (up to 10 cm long), plus the diverse associated fauna, mostly sponges and hydroids attached to the horse mussel shells. To the north of the Long Sheelagh in the northeast of the Lough the variegated clam is co-dominant with horse mussel, a community not known elsewhere in Ireland or Britain. In the mud between the clumps of horse mussels lies a rich infauna – benthic organisms that dig into the sea bed, or construct tubes or burrows beneath the surface of a sediment. They include the queen scallop, worms and burrowing sea-cucumbers such as *Thyone roscovita* and *Thyonidium commune*. In the deeper water in the centre of the Lough where tidal streams are unimpeded and slower the fine mud substrata is dominated by the Norway lobster.

The Strangford Narrows, influenced by strong tidal streams, are almost completely sheltered from wave action. The seabed there mostly consists of boulders, with small areas of bedrock and extensive patches of coarse gravel, pebble and mud fanning out into various bays along the sides. Common species include dead man's fingers, dense colonies of the hydroids *Tubularia indivisa* and *Sertularia argentea*, a few sponges such as *Amphilectus fucorum*, *Haliclona viscosa*, *Myxilla incrustan*s and *Pachymatisma johnstonia*, and the large yellow boring sponge *Cliona celata*. A remarkable total of 306 species of molluscs have been recorded from the Lough.[11]

The open part of the Lough to the north of the Narrows is mainly dominated by dense beds of more echinoderms; a large brittlestar *Ophiothrix fragilis* with much smaller numbers of another brittlestar *Ophioxomina nigra* are present on boulders and coarse gravel. The burrowing sea-cucumber *Neopentadactyla mixta* accompanied by the dog cockle *Glycymeris glycymeris* are found in the coarse sands. In the small pockets of sand on the sides of the main current flow are species of the razor shell while the finer, less coarse sands support a rich *Amphiura* spp. community (brittlestars with five very long and thin arms) including the small coin shell Icelandic cyprine. Hydroids, sponges and

Knot – over 6,400 regularly
winter in Strangford Lough
(J. Barlee).

foliaceous bryozoans grow on the boulders. Some areas are clear of *O. fragilis*, possibly because the tidal streams are too strong, and in these locations the great scallop becomes a characteristic species in the muddy depths.

The diverse and abundant invertebrate fauna in the Lough as well as the extensive intertidal and sublittoral beds of eelgrass and sea lettuce, especially at the northern end, represent vital food resources for large numbers of wintering wildfowl and waders. The mean number of visiting ducks, geese, swans and waders over 5 winters from 1989/90–1993/4 was 58,886, thus making the Lough the most important coastal wetland in Ireland for total numbers of wintering wildfowl. Three species occur in internationally important numbers, meaning that more than 1% of the individuals in the total population occur on average at the site over a five year period. A five year peak mean for each species is derived from the peak counts over the five most recent winters:

Pale-bellied brent goose   11,708
Knot   6,412
Redshank   2,464

A further 25 species occur in nationally important numbers (more than 1% of

Pale-bellied brent geese.
Strangford Lough is the most
important wintering site in
Europe for these geese.

the all-Ireland population occurring 'regularly' – based on a five year's mean peak) including shelduck (2,366), teal (1,429), mallard (1,736), gadwall (99), pintail (197), shoveler (124), goldeneye (383), red-breasted merganser (277), oystercatcher (4,931), golden plover (7,178), lapwing (12,640), dunlin (5,244), bar-tailed godwit (599) and curlew (1,530).[12]

Some 28 years ago Strangford Lough was an internationally important site for wigeon when numbers peaked at about 20,000 birds in the winter of 1971–2. Since then there has been a dramatic decline of about 90% to some 2,000 birds. What has happened? An analysis of the brent and wigeon numbers in the Lough from 1965–89 suggested that competitive interactions between the two species for similar food resources was not the major factor but that the wigeon's decrease was partly related to a decline in the availability of its food in the Lough and partly due to increased human disturbance whether by shooting, boating or other kinds of recreation.[13] Some support for this argument came from a recent study of the quality of food consumed by brent geese and wigeon in the Lough. Mathers & Montgomery found that both species selected their food to maximise nutritional value. They concluded that interspecific differences in food selection and reaction to human disturbance may have contributed to the decline in wigeon numbers in the Lough while numbers of the brent have been maintained.[14]

Strangford Lough is the single most important European site for the pale-bellied brent goose which breeds in arctic Canada. Each October up to 75% of this population comes to Strangford Lough. Together with Lough Foyle, Strangford

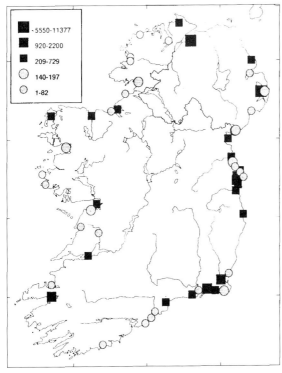

Pale-bellied brent geese. Maximum counts during the winter 1995–6. From Delany[15].

- 5550-11377
920-2200
209-729
140-197
1-82

Lough held most of the Northern Ireland peak total of 16,908 brent recorded in October 1995. After their mass arrival in Northern Ireland the birds disperse southward to other Irish haunts of which the ten most important, with maximum numbers recorded during the winter 1995–6, were Wexford Harbour and Slobs (2,200), Rogerstown Estuary, Co. Dublin (1,804), Malahide Estuary, Co. Dublin (1,200), Castlemaine Harbour and Rossbehy Creek, Co. Kerry (1,062), Bannow Bay, Co. Wexford (920), Baldoyle Bay, Co. Dublin (729), Dungarvan Harbour, Co. Waterford (651), North Wicklow coastal marshes (650), Dublin Bay (650) and Tramore Back Strand, Co. Waterford (561).

Other estuaries important for wildfowl

Apart from Strangford Lough there are 15 other coastal wetlands in the Republic of Ireland that held more than 10,000 wintering wildfowl (highest monthly core count during the winter 1995–6). Unfortunately information for Northern Ireland was not available at the time of writing and therefore data on some important sites cannot be presented. A wetland is deemed of international importance if it regularly supports 20,000 or more waterfowl or if it hosts a species of international importance.

Table 9.1 Maximum numbers (highest 1995–6 monthly core count) of waterfowl counted at the top 15 coastal sites in the Republic of Ireland (data from Delany[15]).

Area	Total number of waterfowl	No. of spp. of international importance	No. of spp. of national importance
Shannon and Fergus Estuaries	51,423	6	17
Wexford Harbour and Slobs	41,097	5	18
Cork Harbour	33,013	2	19
Dundalk Bay, Co. Louth	24,130	2	10
Lough Swilly, Co. Donegal	22,750	3	20
Dungarvan Harbour, Co. Waterford	22,418	3	13
Ballymacoda, Co. Cork	17,212	0	13
Rogerstown Estuary, Co. Dublin	15,170	2	17
Boyne Estuary, Counties Meath/Louth	14,650	1	9
Tramore Back Strand, Co. Waterford	13,480	1	9
Cahore Marshes, Co. Wexford	12,430	0	6
The Cull and Killag, Co. Wexford	12,401	3	7
Malahide Estuary, Co. Dublin	11,194	1	16
Tacumshin Lake, Co. Wexford	11,070	0	16
Bannow Bay, Co. Wexford	10,022	1	10

Townsend's cord-grass

Amongst the many ecological threats to Irish estuaries is the spread of an invasive maritime cord-grass, Townsend's cord-grass, which was introduced to Irish estuaries and intertidal zones from about 1925 onwards with encouragement from the government. It was intended to stabilise deep mobile mud and to assist the reclamation of estuaries. This cord-grass has two types of roots: a few long ones growing down vertically, and extensive horizontal rhizomes from which grow fine, nutrient-absorbing roots. The former secure the necessary

The Shannon Estuary together with the Fergus Estuary host the largest number of wintering waterfowl in Ireland including six species of international importance and 17 of national importance.

anchorage for a plant that sometimes reaches 130 cm in height in an environment of flowing and ebbing water; the latter bind and hold the soft mud together. Because of its remarkable powers of collecting and retaining silt, the cord-grass can build up the level of a marsh in a considerably shorter period of time than the other open mud coloniser, glasswort, which has recorded accretion rates of 6.8 mm per annum under certain conditions. Within a few years of introduction Townsend's cord-grass will convert unstable mud flats into a thick sward – a cord-grass 'meadow'– suitable sometimes for grazing by cattle. This cord-grass is a hybrid that does not produce seed and spreads by its horizontal vegetative roots or from small pieces of root that have broken off and deposited in suitable habitats.

Townsend's cord-grass thrives best in deep soft mud which, under normal circumstances, would host a large biomass of all the living organisms in that particular habitat. In a study carried out at Lindisfarne, Northumberland, on the reduction in overall density and diversity of macro-invertebrates in mud areas colonised by Townsend's cord-grass, it was found that the most affected species were the amphipod *Corophium volutator*, a mollusc the Baltic tellin, and three marine worms, or polychaetes (the blow lug, the lugworm *Scoloplos armiger* and the estuary ragworm), all important food for waders, to which Townsend's cord-grass is, of course, highly detrimental.[16] Other estuarine waterfowl such as pale-bellied brent geese and wigeon which feed on eelgrass, *Zostera* spp., the green algae *Enteromorpha* spp. and sea lettuce, will find areas that were densely covered by their food now taken over by the tall cord-grass. To many ecologists this cord-grass is an evil and dangerous plant, destroying the ecology of many estuaries and responsible for driving away wildfowl such as the pale-bellied brent goose and wigeon.

Despite its adverse impact on the ecology of estuaries there has been little investigation into the spread of Townsend's cord-grass in Ireland. At Rogerstown Estuary, Co. Dublin, it colonised a significant amount of ground between 1950 and 1955, eliminating areas previous dominated by common salt marsh-grass and sea-purslane. At North Bull Island, Dublin, large expanses of glasswort have been obliterated and the cord-grass has been rapidly spreading on the fine silts and muds accreting along the north side of the causeway built in 1963. In an attempt to learn more about the distribution of this grass, Nairn organised a questionnaire survey which he circulated amongst naturalists in 1986. Thirty-nine estuarine sites were examined and the grass was present in 28 of them. The study showed it increasing in 14, and static in the remaining 14. On the credit side the grass provides some benefits to estuarine ecology. It generates organic material through the shedding of its parts and accumulates silt and fine muds by slowing the movement of water down. The generated and trapped organic matter is then broken down into detritus which, in turn, enters the food chains in the estuary. However, in Strangford Lough its spread was considered so detrimental to the waterfowl feeding ecology that its control and elimination in the area of its major growth at Armillan Bay has since been a high priority in the conservation objectives for the Lough.

Killary Harbour, Co. Mayo

If the formation of Strangford Lough was more 'fjardic' than 'fjordic' then the reverse is true of the Killary Harbour.[17] Set on the Atlantic seaboard, this fjord has a southeasterly orientation and is approximately 15 km long by 700 m wide. Its mean depth is about 20 m, the deepest point occurring at 42 m just inside its mouth, or entrance point. Immediately outside the entrance the floor rises rapidly. For a long time geologists maintained that the Killary Harbour was not a true fjord, because it lacked the classical uprising of rocks and glacial materials at its entrance, one of the main characteristics of fjords.[18] As a glacier moves down the valley, from inland towards the sea, the ice acts as a giant excavator, pushing in front of it materials gathered up as it moves along. New information from surveys in the 1980s about the nature of the base of the Harbour obtained by sonar sound – a method used to determine the rock configurations of the Harbour, along its bottom and up the sides – showed a total absence of rock outcrops along its floor from the inland head of the Harbour to Rusheen Point, about 1.7 km before the mouth – a sure sign that a glacier scooped up all the rocks on the harbour's bottom. From Rusheen point to the mouth well-developed rock outcrops diversify the floor while immediately outside the entrance the bottom rises with a gradient of 1 in 130. And despite its fjordic birthing it has inherited the title Harbour, more a reflection of its function rather than an accurate description of its geomorphological origin.

Whittow states that there is little doubt that Killary is the finest fjord in Ireland and comments 'With a depth of 13 fathoms [26 m] over most of its length, a shallowing seawards and an entrance almost closed by islands, it bears all the hallmarks of glacial overdeepening. But in no other Irish fjord are the valley walls so steep and so high, for here the bulk of Mweelrea rises from the sea in one enormous sweep to the summit ridge.'[19]

Since the 1960s the Killary has always been a favourite haunt of divers on account of its sheltered nature. Information about the benthic animals was first collected irregularly by amateurs before a collaborative venture between the Zoology Department, University College, Galway, and a French scientific team from the Roscoff 'Station Biologique' took over in 1974. The scientists' task was to investigate the ecology of the Harbour, under the direction of Keegan.[20] The time could not have been more appropriate as the Killary, which had remained pristine until then, was about to become one of the largest centres for the cultivation of mussels and, to a lesser extent, of caged salmon.

The main sediment type in the Harbour is a very soft, fine-grained mud with an organic content up to 11.6%. Unlike classic fjords where the low salinity water typically rides on top of the main body of saline water, the water in the Killary is not stratified but resembles that of a partially mixed estuary with large variations conditioned by local winds and ingress of fresh water – from the River Erriff entering the Harbour at its head and many small streams cascading off the valley sides. Concentrations of all nutrients were low at the time of survey. The species composition of the phytoplankton (dominated by diatoms) and zooplankton were typical of northern temperate waters. The benthic fauna was poor compared with that of other adjacent coastal areas. One of the major animal phyla, the Cnidaria – jellyfish, sea anemones and corals – was represented by 18 species of sea anemones. The species composition of the benthos most closely resembled an impoverished version of the *Raspailia–Stelligera* association found in other temperate areas. The Killary Harbour benthic communities also shared close similarities in terms of species composition with the benthic communities found in parts of Inner Galway Bay.

The Killary presented high densities of some echinoderms such as starfish. For instance, amongst the brittlestars, the large brittlestar was found locally aggregated on both hard and soft terrain in densities higher than 20,000 individuals per m^2. This was not unique and only confirmed what had been previously noticed of other inshore areas along the Irish west coast. The purple sea-urchin was found during the 1974 survey in the inshore areas of the Killary in densities up to 1,600 per m^2 and the feather star at 1,200 per m^2.[21] What could be the possible advantages of such 'crowded' conditions that approximate some of the most densely populated cities in the world? To assist reproduction, provide shelter for one another, enhance the food supply, or create unknown social benefits? The answers remain unknown.

The common sun starfish reaches up to 350 mm in diameter and has 8–14 narrow arms. It is carnivorous with a preference for other starfish, especially the common starfish.

Scallops. Some of these can
live up to 20 years. Outside
the Killary Harbour they can
be found offshore up to
depths of 100 m.

Apart from the common starfish and the very large spiny starfish (up to 70 cm in diameter), the most conspicuous creature in the Killary was the Norway lobster, found in burrows along the muddy bottom in densities estimated at $c.$ 3 per m^2 outside the entrance to $c.$ 1 per m^2 in the upper and more shallow reaches. The fish Fries' goby, which could be more appropriately called a 'sea cuckoo', was regularly found sharing the lobster's abode. The great scallop was another noticeable species, found mainly on the flanking slopes at depths between 6 m and 20 m. They lie in a horizontal rather than a vertical position. The rounded shell raises the water intake points of the creature a few centimetres above the muddy and silty bottom, thus enabling access to cleaner waters. Scallops do not always stay put and have a remarkable ability for swimming by expulsion of water from their gill cavity inside their shells. Their swimming is driven by the contraction of the large central muscle, which induces a series of jerky movements as water is shot out of the gill cavities and drives the creature through the water. The Killary was also found to be a repository for the common mussel with beds extending well up onto the shore.

One notable feature of several of the Killary benthic organisms is gigantism. This could be a response to enhanced food supplies (which is unlikely as there are low levels of nutrients in the Killary), a side effect of longevity, itself the product of low levels of biological and physical disturbance, or the expression of some genetic aberrations. Instances of gigantism are found in the plumose sea anemone, easily identified by its much divided tentacles forming a feathery mass; the dahlia anemone, whose basal disc should be 10 cm in diameter as opposed to approximately 25 cm in the Killary; the common brittlestar, frequently found with disc diameters greater than 25 mm in the Killary as opposed to the usual 20 mm or less elsewhere; and some of the tunicates (sea squirts), which are up to one third larger in the Killary than elsewhere.

Carnsore Point, Co. Wexford

The macrobenthic fauna of the southeast corner of Ireland off Carnsore Point, Co. Wexford, manifests no signs of gigantism. The marine life here has been well studied in conjunction with proposals, made during the 1970s and now dead, for the establishment of a nuclear power station at Carnsore Point. The benthos off Carnsore Point is not unique in Ireland but representative of fast-moving and sometimes violent water conditions unlike the very sedate waters of Killary Harbour. At Carnsore the sea is turbulent with surface currents moving faster than 1.5 knots and tidal streams at spring tides exceeding 2.4 knots. Investigations into the macrobenthic fauna in 1977–8 found an impoverished community of invertebrates on the relatively mobile sediments.[22] In its most extreme form the community was dominated by a burrowing polychaete annelid *Nephtys cirrosa;* a mysid *Gasterosaccus spinifer* and a burrowing worm *Ophelia borealis* – an invertebrate grouping similar to one found in the eastern English Channel where conditions are comparable. At Carnsore most members of the benthic had upright rather than sessile encrusting forms – a characteristic feature of invertebrates living on hard bottoms subjected to fast-moving currents. Their upright position places them out of the way of debris swept along the bottom and at better level to receive suspended foods flowing past.

Mulroy Bay, Co. Donegal

Mulroy Bay is a complex marine lough on the north coast of Ireland, extending inland about 19 km with a much indented shoreline totalling some 80 km. One of the most diverse sea loughs in the country, its depth ranges from 0–47 m and its current speed from 0–0.5 knots. The substrata embrace solid bedrock to fine muds to marl deposits. Water temperature varies from 4°C (February) to more than 19°C (July–August). Of the 500 or so molluscs recorded in Irish inshore waters 232, or 46%, have been reported from Mulroy Bay[23] – the larger Strangford Lough holds 306 and the marine nature reserve at Lough Hyne, Co. Cork, 209+. Mulroy Bay also has 28 living species not found elsewhere along the northern coastline. Both Lough Hyne and Mulroy Bay share the phenomenon of 'bathymetrical telescoping', a term coined by Praeger when he observed that deepwater animals in Lough Hyne were living close to the surface in the company of species accustomed to the littoral zone. The vertical zonation of the flora and fauna within the Lough is therefore very much condensed. At Mulroy this is also true for the feather star, a crinoid. Most crinoids are fixed to the bottom substrate; they are long-stalked with a crown of moveable arms surrounding a mouth. The feather star is joined by other normally deepwater species – a cup coral *Caryophyllia smithii*, a clamp shell *Crania anomala* and a close, white-coloured relation of the common mussel, a file shell named *Limaria hians*, displaying orange-red contractile tentacles growing outwards from the edge of the mantle (the tissue lining of the shell) and protruding through the gaping shell.

Several members of Mulroy Bay's molluscan fauna are more characteristically found in warmer, more southern or southwestern areas in Ireland and in Europe. Certain of these species occur at their northern limits in the Bay. These are: the small coat-of-mail shell (up to 8 mm long), the sea slug *Cuthona genovae* and a cockle, the warty venus. Their presence here is made possible by the warm waters of the North Atlantic Current flowing past the west coast and allowing these more fragile specimens to survive further north than usual. Mulroy Bay hosts both molluscs requiring warm water and molluscs requiring cold water because offshore, to the west of Malin Head, lies the 'oceanic front', an interface of warm and cold water, marking a biogeographical boundary beyond which many northern and southern molluscan species cannot live because the waters are respectively either too warm or cold for them.

Lough Hyne, Co. Cork

Lough Hyne is a deep, landlocked bay, roughly triangular in shape, of about 60 ha with an average depth of 40 m and a maximum of 65 m. The high salinity (34.6–34.8 parts per thousand compared to about 32 for enclosed coastal areas with freshwater inputs), clarity of the water and greater warmth – summer water is 3–6°C warmer than elsewhere on the open coast – all combine to produce excellent growing conditions for algae. Norton once compared the lough to 'a large culture dish' for algal growth and marine life. [24]

Many explanations have been put forward to account for the origin of this deep sea lough: tectonic subsidence, river erosion, solution and marine erosion. Holland, however, has convincingly argued that the Lough arose by glacial action on the rock basin during the Munsterian cold stage (302,000–132,000 years ago) when the sea level was much lower than at present. Following the glacial scooping out of the lough, the basin was first occupied by fresh water. Then, about 4,000 years ago, marine water gained entry.[25] A narrow, shallow channel, known as 'The Rapids', links the basin to the sea and regulates the flow of water in and out of the Lough. The tidal flow into the Lough lasts about 4 hours and the outflow takes approximately 8.5 hours. In full flow the current surging through the narrows reaches a speed of 5.2 knots. An underwater stone sill in the channel acts as a weir, preventing the Lough from draining out totally at low tide. The tidal range within the Lough is only 1 m compared with 3 m outside in the Barloge Creek, leading to the sea.

Lough Hyne's shores are unique with regard to the vertical distribution of the flora and fauna. Within the Lough the marine invertebrates are extraordinarily abundant and the crustose coralline algae *Lithophyllum incrustans* unusu-

Lough Hyne, Co. Cork. Note the rapid current gushing through 'The Rapids' (A. Walsh).

ally prolific. The purple sea-urchin's main predators are the starfish *Marthasterias glacialis* and various crabs which themselves are forced by *their* predators, the herring gulls, to feed only at night. Therefore the purple sea-urchins stay hidden at night, only daring to venture out during the day in order to graze large areas of soft seaweed.[26] An analysis of the Lough's marine amphipods showed a greater wealth of species per unit area than at any other site studied on the Irish coastline. More interestingly, the amphipods, viewed together, revealed that the Lough shared a closer affinity with the Mediterranean than with other marine sites along the south coast of Ireland or England, and from this it was suggested that Lough Hyne acted as a 'warm' refuge during the interglacial periods, harbouring amphipods unable to survive elsewhere.[27]

As a result of intensive research into the Lough's marine heritage, many rare and startling species have been detected. However, the Lough's reputation as a centre for the rare and exotic is gradually waning with the discovery of an increasing number of its specialities elsewhere around the Irish coastline as marine investigations spread and multiply. Nevertheless, the range of marine habitats, the diversity and abundance of the flora and fauna, as well as the presence of several rare and unusual species, justified the declaration of the Lough as Ireland's first marine nature reserve in 1989. The Lough has been a centre for marine research for over 70 years – largely stimulated by Professors L. Renouf and J. A. Kitching – with three marine laboratories currently on site and more than 250 scientific publications to its credit.

The magical mystery engendered by the Lough's natural attributes inspired Praeger to pen this lyrical description in *The Way That I Went:*

> 'The clear sheltered lake, fed by pure Atlantic water entering at one corner during the upper half of each tide, resembles a gigantic marine aquarium, and the peculiar conditions of life have remarkable repercussions on the fauna and flora. Many forms common on the surrounding shores are absent from or very rare in the lough – or instance, the great brown oar weeds that are so familiar a sight at low water; their place is taken by beds of whitish encrusting coralline seaweeds. On the other hand, many animals and some plants grow to quite remarkable dimensions. The fauna is characterised by a remarkable abundance and variety of species, particularly of sedentary and sessile species: for instance, the beautiful Purple Sea-urchin, *Paracentrotus lividus,* of which twenty adult specimens, besides smaller Marine invertebrates are extraordinarily abundant in it and corals unusually prolific ones may be counted on each square foot over extensive areas, most of them wearing on the top of the spines a parasol, in the shape of an empty Anomia shell; Anomia itself, the Pearly Oyster, is likewise enormously abundant, and innumerable smaller creatures more attractive than these echinoderms, polyzoans, tunicates, coelenterates, sponges, and so on, many of brilliant colour and beautiful form. To lean over the side of a boat and view the bottom with a 'water-telescope' is like peeping into a strange sort of calcareous fairyland.' [28]

Galway Bay, Co. Galway

The benthos of Galway Bay and the adjoining areas has been under scrutiny since the early 1970s. In the period 1975–7 a major survey of the macrofaunal benthic communities and associated sediments took place.[29] Samples were gathered from 2,000 km^2 of the Bay in water less than 100 m deep. Silty and sand substrates covered approximately 65% of the Bay's bottom. The benthic associations on these substrates were a brittlestar *Amphiura filiformis* community in which the eponymous species reached a mean maximum density of *c.* 700 per m^2. The associated species were the bamboo worm *Melinna palmata*; the tower shell; the small wedge shell *Abra nitida*; the razor shell, and the mollusc *Spisula subtruncata*. The other association was a venus shell *Chamelea striatula* community. The benthic communities on the coarse and hard bottom areas were more difficult to classify but included a *Axinella dissimilis–Phakellia ventilabrum* community composed of cup like sponges as well as a population composed of the large (up to 120 mm long) spectacularly coloured purple heart urchin *Spatangus purpureus* and the distinctive subtriangular banded venus shell on the substrates where marl was a common constituent. Most of the benthic communities were related to known equivalent communities from European coastal seas. Numerous other littoral and benthic studies covering a wide range of flora and fauna in Galway Bay and the adjacent areas have been carried out by members of the Zoology Department, University College, Galway, over the past 30 years, so important ecological baseline studies now exist which can be used in the future to evaluate any changes as well as allowing comparison with other benthic communities throughout European waters.[30,31,32]

Oysters

Lurking in the waters below the feeding limits of wading birds is one of the most famous members of Galway Bay's littoral fauna, the oyster, celebrated each September at the Galway Oyster Festival. From time immemorial there have been significant private and public oyster fisheries in the Inner or on the southern shores of the Bay.

The European oyster is a native of Ireland and was historically a most important food, collected from natural, self-maintaining oyster beds, and eaten by men and women in coastal settlements. They were the perfect food, as they required no cultivation, were easy to gather in the shallow sheltered waters, and were seemingly limitless in supply. The many, often large, deposits of oyster shells together with other molluscs in 'kitchen middens' (refuse dumps of Mesolithic, Neolithic, early Christian and later settlers) around the Irish coastline bears testimony to the oyster's importance as a staple food. It was not yet a delicacy to suit gourmets and gourmands – like the bloated Roman Vitellius who is reputed to have consumed 1,000 in one meal.

As the cities and towns of Europe grew in size, so the demand rose for the flat and rounded oyster native of northern Europe as opposed to more irregularly shaped species from the Mediterranean. To meet the large demand, some oysters were lifted from their natural beds, taken some distance and grafted into new beds along the coast, known as parcs, which were not uncommon during the eighteenth and nineteenth centuries. So began the first cultivation of oysters. Young 'seed oysters' were collected from unexploited natural beds wherever they could be found, and laid down to grow on the local shore until they attained a larger and more fleshy body size. In the mid-nineteenth century the demand for oysters was staggering – in 1864 alone almost 500 million went through the Billingsgate fish market in London.

In fact the nineteenth century demand was so prodigious that the natural beds suffered gross over-exploitation until they became exhausted. As the most accessible beds became depleted because of over-cropping, the hunt moved on to deeper waters. In Ireland the once great natural offshore beds on the Wicklow and Wexford sandbanks were extinguished between 1863 and 1892, when a total of 188 million oysters were landed during the 20 years for which data are available. Today there is no oyster fishery on the Wexford and Wicklow sandbanks.

Thriving natural populations of oysters used to exist around the Irish coastline wherever there were sheltered bays, estuaries, sea inlets and lagoons. Unlike the two other economically important shellfish, the common mussel and the common cockle, they prefer deeper waters and are seldom exposed by low tides. During the early nineteenth century many of the better oyster beds in Ireland were held as private property under grants of Royal Charter, some of which originated several hundred years previously. These beds were natural beds on which the owners held exclusive rights. However, under common law, the general public had access to the other oyster beds, those not protected by Royal Charter grants. Enterprising fishermen set up their own ponds and 'rings' on the foreshore and on offshore mud and sand banks for the proliferation and commercial growth of oysters. In order to regulate this new form of farming, Sections 17 to 19 of the *Fisheries Act, 1845* permitted the formation, protection and stocking of artificial oyster beds. This was the first law for the

Clew Bay, Co. Mayo. An important area for oysters. (C. Devany).

regulation of aquaculture within Ireland or Britain.[33] From 1845 a number of private oyster beds were farmed around the coast of Ireland under licences issued by government.

A detailed account of all Irish oyster fisheries was prepared by Browne for the government in 1904.[34] He catalogued 23 public or natural beds of which Carlingford Lough, Tralee Bay, Galway Bay and the Newry River estuary were considered the most important and belonging to the public; ten Royal Chartered oyster beds or layings; 62 licensed oyster beds, and seven unlicensed beds belonging to the public.

The economics of oyster cultivation were attractive because a healthy oyster bed represents one of the densest concentrations of animal life.[35] The farmers had little work to do apart from harvesting and sometimes controlling natural predators of which the starfish, *Asterias* spp., are the most voracious. Only four licences were issued during 1845–9, when the Great Famine was raging, but many followed thereafter. Wilkins lists all the oyster cultivation licences issued for the period 1845–1905. They amounted to a total of 179 covering approximately some 11,665 ha in the bays and estuaries around the whole Irish coast, with 57% of all the beds in the estuaries, bays and lagoons of the highly indented coastline of Galway and Mayo. Of these licences only 71 had not been revoked by 1905; the owners of these had demonstrated that they had undertaken some management of their beds. The state did not look sympathetically upon those who had been negligent.[33]

While native Irish oysters can assume many different forms, all belong to the species *Ostrea edulis*, known on the Continent as the 'flat oyster.' Neither the Portuguese oyster nor the American oyster have acclimatised themselves to Irish waters. Portuguese oysters were introduced to Cork Harbour for fattening in 1877 and three years later to the greater Sligo Bay area. The American oysters were introduced to Sligo for fattening in 1878 (and four years later to Cork Harbour) but neither of these alien cupped oysters bred because the water temperatures required (18–20°C) were never attained and therefore no offspring came from these plantings.[36] The American oyster has also been introduced to Ireland to supplement the high demand for oysters. It was thought that it would be unable to spawn in the cold Irish waters but spat resulting from a natural settlement in 1990 were found during July 1991 in Donegal Bay.[37]

Over the years there has been a great deal of mixing of native oysters from one area to another together with numerous transplantations of stock from France (especially Brittany), England and, to a lesser extent, Norway. The oysters in Norway are all derived from mid-nineteenth century imports from Oosterschelde, Holland which, in turn, originated from France – whose own beds had been reconstituted from English imports! The possibility of the introduction of diseases with foreign imports and the dangers of upsetting the genetics of Irish stocks led the government, in 1972, to prohibit the restocking of Irish oyster beds with non-Irish oysters. In fact, this control came too late to claim that a truly Irish native oyster still exists but is has prevented many problems experienced in other oyster-producing countries.

Today, the main oyster beds are along the southwest, west and northwest coasts with the most productive ones found at Clarinbridge, Galway Bay, and Tralee Bay, Co. Kerry. The genetic variability of three local stocks of oysters – from Clarinbridge in Galway Bay, Belmullet in Co. Mayo and Tralee Bay in Co.

Kerry – has been tested. The results showed some slight genotypic variations between the Irish populations but the divergences were not large enough to support claims that Clarinbridge oysters are a different race or strain from, say, those from Tralee Bay or Belmullet. The findings reinforce the argument that transplanting oysters between different Irish locations is acceptable.[38]

Mussels

The common mussel is another economically and culturally important bivalve mollusc present in most Irish coastal environments. The productivity from some mussel beds can be quite astonishing in comparison with agricultural yields known on terra ferma. For example, Yonge, quoting from an official report relating to the 1930s, states that approximately 0.4 ha of the best mussel bed will produce annually 4,536 kg of mussel meat equivalent to 3,000,000 calories, while the same 0.4 ha of average to rich fattening grassland (under grassland management of the 1930s) will yield 45–86 kg of beef representing 120,000–480,000 calories. Moreover the food supplies to the mussels are free, constantly being carried to molluscs by tidal currents.

Lough Foyle, Co. Derry, is one of the largest estuarine sea loughs with the largest mussel colony of any estuary in Ireland and for this reason a study of the population dynamics of one of the mussel beds was undertaken by Briggs in 1978–9.[39] Salinity levels in the Lough fluctuated between 14 and 25% sodium chloride and water temperatures ranged from 4°C in January to 18°C in July–August. Growth rates of mussels were slow and analysis of meat yield in a sample of intertidal mussels gave cooked meat yields of 8–10% by weight, compared to commercially acceptable levels of 20%. Briggs reported a low level of primary settlement of spat, or baby mussels, at densities of 6,000 per m^2 – reflecting high mortalities of the spat and/or inadequacy of suitable settlement surfaces. The overall arrangement of the mussel bed, in terms of composition and size, was stable. This suggested that mortality inflicted by young crabs and birds was balanced by recruitment. The shore crab occurred at peak densities of 400 per m^2 in October on the edge of the mussel bed. The young crabs were almost certainly feeding on the baby mussels. Other traditional predators such as starfish, *Asterias* spp., were absent but they were replaced by oystercatchers which, no doubt, contributed significantly to mussel mortality. Twelve species of crustaceans – amphipods and isopods – were associated with the mussel bed, the most abundant species being *Corophium volutator*, *Eulimnogammarus obtusatus*, *Gammarus* spp., *Melita palmata* and *Jaera albifrons*. Over 90% of the commercially marketable mussels (shell length >50 mm) were encrusted by barnacles, *Semibalanus balanoides*.

Salt marshes

Salt marshes form the first permanent vegetation zone above the open estuary and, together with sand dunes, they provide a vital defensive 'skin' between the sea and more permanent land. The plants and vegetation growing on sand dunes and shingle beaches are influenced by salt spray but are only very rarely submerged by salt water. The plants of salt marshes are, on the contrary, subjected to regular immersions and thus need to be especially adapted to these halophytic conditions. A salt marsh begins life when fine silts, muds and sands are deposited by local tidal currents in flat, sheltered areas such as sea inlets behind dunes, sand spits and shingle beaches, or in slack water areas in pro-

Mudflats at the forefront of the salt marsh, North Bull Island, Dublin.

tected corners of estuaries, or around the margins of bays. The materials, brought suspended in the water, are dropped and settle down on the bottom in calm water conditions. Over time and with continued deposition the fine grained particles build up to a level where the first colonising plants can gain a toehold and survive a twice daily dunking of sea water.

The salt marsh at North Bull Island, Dublin Bay has been studied more than any other salt marsh in Ireland because of its proximity to many academic institutions. It is a classically structured salt marsh where the sequence of the different vegetation communities from open mud flats to fixed grassland is both clear and easy to study. Moreover, changes are taking place – some species are becoming less frequent and others more frequent. The vegetational sequence at Bull Island is known in technical terms as a *Salicornietum– Salicornio–Glycerietum–Armerio–Plantago–Triglochinetum–Juncetum maritimae*, named after the dominant species in the marsh ranging from the mudflats to the upper salt marsh. The initial detailed analysis was described by O'Reilly & Pantin in 1957.[40] The following description is conveyed in the present tense as the colonisation process is an ongoing one.

Whenever the moment is right the first vegetation to settle on extensive level mud beds in the lagoon between the North Bull Island and the mainland is the flat and leaf-like species of algae – especially the sea lettuce – and up to five different species of the long thin straggly *Enteromorpha* spp. of which gutweed is possibly the best known. These are often accompanied by the dwarf eelgrass and beaked tasselweed, which, together with glasswort, are three of the very few flowering plants that can grow in the sea. The algae and other pioneering species forming green mats are able to survive repeated and long soakings in sea water. Meanwhile the silts accumulate around the vegetation, rising the substrate level and diminishing immersion time. Glasswort, the primary

Well-developed upper
section of a saltmarsh
with drainage channels
(R. Cabot).

coloniser of the soft exposed muds, can then establish itself.

Glasswort occurs at high densities, up to 500 plants per m^2 at North Bull Island where the plants are crowded closely together and stand stiff like small leafless green trees. There are two species: *Salicornia dolichostachya*, the first coloniser, is fitted with a much longer tapering terminal spike and a much bigger root system than the other species, *S. europaea*.[41] Glasswort spreads by producing vast numbers of seeds in the autumn which are then distributed over the mud flats by the swirling water. The alien and invasive Townsend's cordgrass will also take root in this part of the early development of the salt marsh. Both species slow down tidal water movements further thus encouraging deposition of silts and fine particles – over 5 mm of mud deposition per year has been recorded north of the Causeway at North Bull Island. The marsh level rises again, allowing other species that can only tolerate even shorter periods of immersion to become established.

The next zone of the salt marsh, sitting on slightly more elevated land than the lower mud flats is dominated by perennial species such as common salt marsh-grass with lesser amounts of annual sea-blite, glasswort, greater sea-spurrey, sea arrowgrass and lax flowered sea-lavender. If erosion, brought about by wave action and whipped up by winds, affects this zone, sea arrowgrass is the species that will persist with its tough rhizomes spreading through and binding the mud together. The salt marsh-grass spreads by sending out long stolons and gives its name – *Puccinellietum* – to the zone which extends from the mean high water mark to about half way up the salt marsh.

The greater part of the salt marsh is dominated by three species: thrift, sea arrowgrass and sea plantain. Sea aster is abundant in this middle marsh zone with the less frequently occurring species lax-flowered sea-lavender, glasswort, common scurvygrass, sea-milkwort, annual sea-blite, common salt marsh-grass and sea-purslane. Sea channels and pans are frequent in this zone. The pans are bare patches of mud, generally circular and about 10 cm deep, filled with saline water brought in by the tides. Algae, especially gutweed, sea lettuce, spiral wrack and channelled wrack grow in the pans.

The uppermost part of the marsh is dominated by dense growths of sea rush, while in some areas the salt marsh rush predominates. Other species abundant and frequent in the upper salt marsh at North Bull Island are sea-milkwort,

common scurvygrass, thrift, sea arrowgrass, sea plantain, sea aster, common
salt marsh-grass, red fescue and glasswort.

Salt marshes are dynamic plant communities and at North Bull Island there
have been some quite remarkable changes over the years since the marsh first
started developing in the eighteenth century. The last major triggering phenomenon was the building of a causeway in 1963. Since then the glassworts,
Salicornia europaea and *S. dolichostachya*, have spread dramatically on the mud
flats accreting north of this man-made barrier – along with Townsend's cord-
grass, which has obliterated large areas of dense growth of glasswort. Finally,
sea-purslane, which was rare in 1951, had become dominant by 1976 in many
areas of the lower parts of the salt marsh.

Shingle beaches

Shingle beaches are the result of rock material thrown up by the waves. Shingle
varies from small pebbles 2–3 cm in diameter to much larger stones up to 25
cm long often mixed with smaller materials. Most shingle beaches are only
drenched by sea spray but some receive periodic washings from high tides,
especially during storms. On first sight they appear forlorn and barren environments inauspicious to plants. Shingle bank flora in Ireland has seldom
been described apart from the plant communities on the shingle/gravel bar at
Lady's Island Lake, Co. Wexford, where cottonweed occurs (see below). On
the coast of Co. Louth, south of Dundalk, there is an 'inactive' shingle bar (not
any longer being built up, moved around or submerged by tides), or ridge, sitting on a postglacial raised beach and running south of Dunany Point and
then in a more interrupted manner to Clogher Head. The width of this bar
varies from 10–20 m. It is vegetated to varying degrees. White examined it in
1981 and found a recurrent combination of species, dominated in summer by
the tall and vigorously-growing sea radish and curled dock. Cleavers formed
extensive prostrate mats up to 1.5 m in diameter and herb-robert thrived in
places.[42] The vegetation association on the shingle beach fitted the phytosociological class described as *Honkenyo–Elymetea arenarii* – a vegetation communi-

Oystercatcher, a characteristic bird nesting on shingle
beaches. (J. Barlee)

ty dominated by sea sandwort *Honkenya peploides* and lyme-grass, *Leymus* (formerly *Elymus) arenarius*. The other plants characterising this association are sea radish, curled dock, sea beet, tree-mallow, perennial sow-thistle and sea kale.

The little tern is the only tern of the five species breeding in Ireland that shows a strong habitat preference for nesting on shingle beaches. Both common and Arctic terns may also occasionally nest. Two other very characteristic shingle beach nesters are the ringed plover and oystercatcher, both widely distributed around the coastline as well as on many offshore islands.

Sand dunes and machair

Sand dunes, like salt marshes, are one of the very few habitats where the complete range of vegetation succession can be viewed in one sweep. They are initially formed by sand being blown from the beach and arrested by single or groups of small plants growing above the high tide line. As more of fine material is dropped over them the plants never cease to push upwards. Further accretion is met by further vegetational response, which in turn helps to anchor more sand. Thus the dune slowly gathers in size; some can reach heights of up to 60 m and more. Sand dunes represent an extreme and harsh environment as they are generally poor in nutrients – especially if built mostly of quartz sand grains derived from granite and other siliceous rocks – and rain quickly passes through sand leaving behind a generally dry and moisture-free fabric. In hot climates these areas would be deserts. Such quick-draining qualities make sand dunes ideal locations for golf courses.

Before the dunes start to develop, the first contact between sand and vegetation is at the top of the soft-slanted beach where a clutch of hardy annual plants live a fitful existence, appearing and disappearing as conditions dictate,

Well-developed sand dunes, Co. Donegal, with a series of recurved splits.

most starting life from seeds, either washed up or blown along the beach. These pioneers are halophytes. Most of them have a trick of absorbing salt – toxic to most plants as it destroys the cell's protoplasm – and using it to draw fresh water into their cells. They resemble cactuses in that they are vegetable water reservoirs and continue looking fleshy and replete in this arid zone. The most frequent front-line colonisers, forming the foreshore vegetation, are the white- or mauve-flowered and rather bushy sea rocket (commoner on the east coast than in the west), the much branched and spreading prickly saltwort, which has glaucous leaves ending in a sharp prickle, and the spear-leaved orache, a prostrate or spreading plant with mealy or powdery-white leaves. The frosted orache is common on eastern shores but rare elsewhere. Its leaves are narrowly oval or rhombic. The other common foreshore species is sea sand-wort, a creeping perennial with fleshy pointed leaves, about 1.2 cm long. Seedlings are seldom encountered because the fruits, which look like small green peas, are mostly washed away and seldom land in a suitable germination spot. The plant survives by spreading vegetatively, sending out lateral shoots. It is inside the zone of foreshore vegetation that the dunes start to develop.

The sand couch is a specialist, fast-growing grass, thin and straggly, occurring in clumps with the leaves drooping down to the ground. A relation of the common couch or scutch grass, much hated by gardeners as a pestilent weed, it is the key species in the building of the foredunes as it spreads laterally by sending out rhizomes. Another important species in binding together and trapping more sand is lyme-grass which, however, is mostly local and principally confined to the east coast. Higher up the shore and in the dunes proper is marram which unlike sand couch cannot withstand immersion in sea water. As soon as fresh sand is blown the stem has another burst of growth upwards while a new network of lateral fibres is produced to knit into the body of the dune. Marram thus creates internal scaffolding with new roots being extended upwards and sideways as more sand comes down. A single plant can grow upwards for 25 m in response to repeated burials and many thousands of plants will stitch the dune together very effectively. The flowering stems are up to 1 m high and the leaves are long and ridged. The outer margins are rolled protectively inside so as to expose the least surface possible to the wind and prevent unnecessary evaporation of water. Marram never entirely covers the ground. At the back of the dunes further away from the shore marram gives way to a dense continuous mats of red fescue and sand sedge. Both also have extensive rhizomes, running like long cords under the sand surface and sending up tufts of bristle-like leaves at regular intervals.

Some of the most characteristic and striking plants in the early stages of the fixed dunes are sea spurge, which has several stems growing up from a heavy rootstock bearing crowded glaucous thick leaves, and sea bindweed, with its beautiful, pale pink, large (3.5 cm in diameter), trumpet-shaped flowers and prostrate stems. Where the dunes are somewhat unstable, sea-holly can be found growing stiff and erect with bluish-green and very prickly leaves. Its flowers are pale blue and bloom from June to September. The three commonest mosses found growing in the fixed dunes are *Tortula ruraliformis*; *Camptothecium lutescens* and *Entodon concinnus*. On the dunes at Magilligan, Co. Derry, the moss *Rhytidium rugosum* is abundant in its only Irish station. Fixed dunes will develop in time into more stable systems of either grassland, heathland or scrub, depending on the nature of the sand and introduced species. On the

Murlough sand dunes at Dundrum Bay, Co. Down, sea-buckthorn has spread over a large area, forming an impenetrable shrub cover. The same has happened on several other east coast dune systems including those at Courtown, Co. Wexford. Sea-buckthorn was first introduced into Northern Ireland at Murlough sand dunes, Co. Down, about 1884 but never really got going for some unexplained reason until about 45 years ago, when most of the buckthorn established itself on the dunes.

Sand dunes dominated by fixed marram grass present a very restricted breeding habitat to ground-nesting birds. Usually just two, the skylark and meadow pipit are found. Together they may occur at densities of 100 pairs per km^2 or, in the case of 'mobile' dunes, i.e. dunes less bound together by marram, and more subjected to wind movements, at such low densities as 40 pairs per km^2. Where the soils become more acidic, bracken replaces marram, while brambles, burnet rose and patches of gorse are also attracted, thus providing additional nesting opportunities for an increased number of species. The attractiveness of dune systems is considerably enhanced by the dense thickets of sea-buckthorn, together with the combination of heather and bell heather spreading at the back of many dunes in layers up to 1 m thick. When these species are present on the ground the number of birds increases dramatically. At Murlough Nature Reserve, Co. Down, the overall density of breeding birds in a mixed vegetation area of 38.5 ha (comprising a central part of the dune system with marram grass, scattered sea-buckthorn scrub and heathland) surveyed in 1975–7 was just short of 300 pairs per km^2.[43] The community structure of the bird population here was much more diverse than in marram grassland. The key species were skylark (comprising 19.6% of all breeding birds

It is only the sand-binding properties of marram grass that are holding these last few clumps of sand together in this general area of active erosion (F. Guinness).

(pairs) in the mixed dune vegetation), meadow pipit (15.7%), wren (7.8%), linnet (7.4%), chaffinch (7.0%), reed bunting, (6.1%), willow warbler (5.7%), blackbird (5.2%), robin (4.8%) and 12 other species (20.7%).

Most of the west coast sand dunes are highly calcareous. They are made up of small shells, fragments of larger shells and sometimes calcareous algae. The fixed dune community at Dog's Bay, Roundstone, Co. Galway, contains 7% calcium carbonate and has a pH of 8.1. At Castlegregory, Co. Kerry, the partly fixed dunes contain 17.9% calcium carbonate and have a pH of 7.3. Tramore dunes, Dunfanaghy, Co. Donegal, contain 25.4 % calcium carbonate and have a pH of 8.3. Rosapenna dunes, Co. Donegal, contain 48.3% calcium carbonate and have a pH of 8.6.[44] Sand samples from six beaches along the 29 km north Galway Bay coastline from Barna to Cashla Bay, which is set within the Galway granite region, gave an average content of 66% calcium carbonate with a range of 55–69%. The beach material was made up of shell fragments of echinoderms and other pieces of unidentified calcite together with foraminifera tests – often well preserved. Foraminiferans, a group of microscopic amoeboid protozoa whose single cell is protected by a test or shell, are washed up onto the shores in their millions to contribute towards the composition of beach sand. Amongst the non-calcareous materials found during Keary's survey of the Galway Bay beaches quartz was the dominant mineral.[45] The abundance of foraminifera species in Irish waters, and thus their availability as sand material, was confirmed during the Clare Island Survey of 1911–15, when Heron-Allen & Earland found 286 species and 13 varieties including 13 species new to science and 26 new to Irish and British coastal waters.[46]

Further west, along the Connemara coastline, the beaches at the head of Mannin Bay and in Cashla Bay are composed of a bright white material which, on close examination, reveals millions of coral-like fragments. These are parts of the calcareous skeletons of nullipore seaweeds *Lithothamnion corallioides* and *Phymatolithon calcareum* thriving in the shallow offshore waters. These two red algae excrete calcium carbonate, derived from lime in the sea water, to form a sort of exoskeleton over the fronds, which gives rise to the name nullipores – from the Latin *nullus* meaning 'none' and Greek *poros* meaning 'passage' or 'pore'. The commercial potential of using these nullipores as a cheap source of lime for land spread, either by removal from beaches, or by suction pumping from shallow bays, has not been overlooked by entrepreneurs. In the past considerable quantities of *Lithothamnion* have been dredged from Bantry with the use of special sand boats. In view of the difficulties of dredging up *Lithothamnion*, many Irish farmers, living along the western seaboard, have taken an easier route to 'free' sources of lime by removing large quantities of lime-rich sand, when it has been available, from beaches.

Behind many dune systems along the west and northwest coasts are areas of level grassland on calcareous soils called machairs. This word is derived from the Irish *magh* meaning 'plain' or 'level tract'. It is used extensively in local nomenclature and generally appears in the anglicised forms of 'Maghera' and 'Maghery' which are the names of several villages or townlands throughout Ireland. Maghera, the more usual form, is employed as a prefix in about 200 place names which are most frequently found in the province of Ulster. For example Magheralin, Co. Down – *Machaire-linne*, the plain of the *linne* or pool; Magheramayo, Co. Down – *Machaire-muighe-eo*, the (large) plain of the (smaller) plain of the yews; and Magheranagay, Co. Mayo – *Machaire-na-ngédh*, mean-ing the plain of the geese – a goose green,[17] possibly an area visited by migra-tory geese. Irish machairs carry a plant community typical of similar flat areas in the west and northwest coasts of Scotland. However, this was not established until quite recently. Praeger, who visited and commented on areas such as Dooaghtry, Co. Mayo and Ballyconneely, Co. Galway, was unable to see the botanical similarity between these calcareous grasslands and the machair com-munities of western Scotland.[47, 48] Only since Akeroyd & Curtis tested five defining criteria of Scottish machair on a few dune grassland areas in western Ireland has it been possible to conclude that the term 'machair' could be prop-erly applied to some dune grasslands in western Ireland.[49]

The basic characteristics of Scottish machair, found typically along the west-ern seaboards of the Uists, in the Outer Hebrides, are lime-rich sands with a high pH and a vegetation cover somewhat similar to that of other fixed dune pastures except that the sand-binding species are either absent or reduced. The species occurring most often are red fescue, yarrow, lady's bedstraw, rib-wort plantain, eyebrights, daisy and the moss *Rhytidiadelphus squarrosus*.[50]

The five criteria used by Akeroyd & Curtis to assess the compatibility of Irish machair sites with Scottish ones were: (1) a mature coastal sand dune phase, with a more or less level surface; (2) a significant proportion of shell fragments in the sand producing a lime-rich soil (pH >7.0); (3) grassland vegetation with a low frequency of sand-binding species, and a majority of the species listed above; (4) a history of human interference, principally through grazing, dur-ing the recent period and (5) a moist, cool, oceanic climate. It is the windiness of climate (an oceanic feature) which is crucial, spreading the sand out as a low plain behind the seaward fringing dunes.

A total of 26 machair sites have now been identified in northwestern and western Ireland between Malin Head, Co. Donegal, and the Aran Islands, Co. Galway by Bassett and Curtis. The two finest examples were found on the Co. Mayo coastline, at Annagh–Termoncarragh in the northwest and at Dooaghtry in the southwest.[51] An analysis of the vegetation at all Irish sites revealed the presence of nine 'core species', the first six of which had been found in Scotland: red fescue, lady's bedstraw, ribwort plantain, daisy, common bird's-foot-trefoil, white clover, sand sedge, spreading meadow-grass and the moss

In some machair areas, exten-sive patches of wild thyme can develop.

Brachythecium albicans. This moss replaces *Rhytidiadelphus squarrosus* found in Scottish machairs, while the moss *Tortula ruraliformis,* also recorded with a high frequency at Irish sites – though not one of the nine core species – is lacking or occurs in reduced abundance in Scottish sites. A curious feature of Irish machair is the presence of field wood-rush – in Europe this species is normally associated with dry acid soils that are poor in nitrogen.

Sand dunes and machair communities represent a generally hostile environment for insects and other invertebrates because of the sparse vegetational cover, the lack of organic material in the sand and the quick draining of water. Many of the invertebrates, especially insects, that are found on sand dunes and in the machair are either remnants of a once more widespread distribution, or specialist species adapted to survival in these uncompromising habitats. Surprisingly few investigations into the invertebrates of Irish sand dunes and dune grasslands have been carried out apart from two recent reports, both by Speight, relating to North Bull Island, Dublin, and the Raven, Co. Wexford.[52,53]

Two species restricted to coastal locations are found at North Bull Island: the hairy woodlouse *Eluma purpurescens* (present in Co. Dublin despite not occurring further north than France in Europe) and a minute snail *Pupilla muscorum* (generally confined to coastal locations in Ireland). The presence of these invertebrates in the dunes is possibly related to the drier and warmer conditions prevailing there. Within the dune slack at North Bull Island – a wet depression supporting an alder marsh – live two insects typical of damp woodland – a small green-coloured jumping plant louse *Psylla foersteri* and the fine pearly-green lacewing *Chrysopa ventralis,* a delicate, fragile-looking and green-bodied flying insect with large, translucent wings traversed by many veins. Nearby at Portmarnock the dunes host a great rarity, one of the green lacewings *C. abbreviata.* This *Chrysopa* is inexplicably scarce in Ireland, known only here and further south at Magherabeg, Co. Wicklow. Its larvae probably feed on aphids that are specific to marram.[54]

Perhaps the most noticeable invertebrates, because of the general sparse character of the vegetation, are the snails which, after wet weather, seem to emerge from nowhere to populate every square metre of dune grassland. Amongst the commonest is the brown-lipped snail. Also conspicuous on the grassland areas is the menacing-looking big black slug *Arion ater.* Other terrestrial molluscs likely to be encountered are the snails *Helix aspersa, Cochlicella acuta, Helicella itala, Lauria cylindracea* and *Cernuella virgata.* The sand-hill snail, *Cochlicella acuta,* a narrow pointed spire shell with whitish and brown bands, and *Helicella virgata* try to escape the hot dry sands on warm days by climbing up the stems of common ragwort and other tall vegetation in search of cooler breezes.

Within the dune grassland are several moths whose caterpillars are specialist feeders on the dune flora. The coast dart is one of the noctuid moths, characterised by stout bodies and drab brown or grey wings. This moth has a dull brown coat and its caterpillars feed on the sand couch and sea sandwort that grow on the seaward side of the dunes. Another noctuid dwelling in the dunes is the shore wainscot which is totally dependent upon marram – the caterpillars munch the leaves and the adults feed on the bushy flower spikelets from June to August. As to the red and black six-spot burnet moths, their bright markings act as a warning to avian predators and therefore they can feed safely during the day while most other moths can only feed at night. Common bird's-foot-trefoil is the food plant for their black and white striped caterpillars. After many months of feeding the caterpillars move from the trefoil food plants to crawl up the tall stems of the marram and attach their cocoons about half way up, where they look like closed flowerheads. Despite this conspicuous position, birds find it difficult to settle on the thin leaf to pluck the pupa off. Moreover the pupa has an unpleasant taste, adding to its chance of survival.

Many sand dune insects are nocturnal, thus avoiding the desiccating effects of the sun. One of Ireland's rarest crustaceans, the pale dune woodlouse *Armadillidium album*, hides in marram tussocks during the day and roams over the dunes, especially along the strand-line, at night. It is found both at the North Bull Island, Dublin, and on Raven Point, Co. Wexford, and is known only from four other coastal sites in Wexford, Wicklow and north Co. Dublin. It also has a restricted coastal distribution in Britain, where it is confined to about 12 sites, chiefly on the west coast from south Wales northwards. It is a 'human-sensitive' species occurring where recreation pressure is low and needing a good supply of strand-line drift wood amongst which it forages for its food.

Coastal areas with brackish loughs, marshes, streams, sand dunes and machair will host important non-marine mollusca faunas. One such area is Dooaghtry, situated just north of the mouth of the Killary Harbour, some 13 km southwest of Louisburgh, Co. Mayo. Within the 4 km^2 of this sand dune *cum* brackish lough area reside some 59 non-marine mollusca, which led Stelfox to state in his 1909 survey that Dooaghtry 'is perhaps the richest sanctuary for mollusca on the west coast'.[55] During the summer of 1989, the area was re-examined to determine what changes had taken place over the 80 intervening years.[56] Six species were found that had not been recorded by Stelfox, four of which (*Candidula intersecta, Cochlicella acuta, Cernuella virgata* and *Potamopyrgus jenkinsi*) were recent colonists. Eleven species were not found again. In all 70 species have now been recorded from this remarkable site. The rarest mollusc at Dooaghtry is the wetland snail *Catinella arenaria*, which is listed as an endangered species in Britain where it is known only at four sites. In Ireland it occurs at several other west coast sites and one or two lime-rich Midland fens.

Most machairs in Ireland were once held in 'common' by local farmers, who grazed their cattle and sheep together and agreed to respect stocking densities. Regrettably these arrangements have been abandoned and today the natural integrity of most machairs has been badly disrupted at the behest of local farming communities demanding that 'commonage' be divided, apportioned and returned to the shareholders. Upon receiving their stripes of land, farmers erect fences with several layers of barbed wire strung between high concrete posts. Most of these enclosures now carry makeshift cattle sheds and feeding troughs. They exhibit a bewildering variety of grasslands ranging from natural machair to re-seeded pasture, fed on a rich diet of fertilisers, to crops. New alien weeds, such as thistles, have been introduced through silage provender regularly deposited on the ground to supplement an ever dwindling supply of grass. Apart from the ecological aspects of such land restructuring, new, unattractive landscapes are created. Simultaneously, public rights of way to amenity coastline, lakes or rivers, protected under the *Local Government (Planning and Development) Act, 1963* and subsequent Regulations have been ignored and extinguished in a cavalier manner in many areas. Most machair commonages along the western seaboard are now so severely overgrazed by sheep that much of their ecological integrity and value has been greatly diminished and destroyed.

Undisturbed machair grasslands belong to a small and declining group of specialist habitats that are critical for breeding waders. To ascertain their ecological importance Nairn surveyed 51 sites between north Co. Donegal and Galway Bay in 1985.[57] He found nine species totalling a minimum of 604 breeding pairs (Table 9.2). The main difference with Scottish machairs was the virtual absence of oystercatchers and the restricted numbers of ringed plover and redshank.

Table 9.2 Number and area of machair sites surveyed in northwest Ireland, with minimum number of pairs of breeding waders (from Nairn[57]).

	Donegal	Sligo	Mayo	Galway	Total
No. machair sites surveyed	21	3	21	6	51
Total area surveyed (ha)	1,180	208	1,886	526	3,800
No. sites with breeding waders	14	2	18	4	38
Total area sites with breeding waders (ha)	992	140	1,740	440	3,312
Lapwing	112	18	140	42	312
Dunlin	17	4	94	6	121
Redshank	9	3	5	0	17
Common snipe	18	8	27	1	54
Ringed plover	12	1	41	10	64
Oystercatcher	2	0	19	0	21
Common sandpiper	1	0	11	0	12
Red-necked phalarope	0	0	1	0	1
Golden plover	1	0	1	0	2
Total number of waders (pairs)	172	34	339	59	604
% distribution of waders in the counties	28	6	56	10	100

Machair is a particularly important breeding habitat for the dunlin in Ireland. At the time of the survey about half of all the known breeding dunlin were located in this habitat (declining to 20–34% in 1996 as revealed by a repeat survey of 48 sites) whereas in Britain a larger part of the estimated 9,000 pairs are found on wet moorland and upland habitats. If they breed so numerously on these peatlands in Britain, why is this not the case in Ireland? There is no easy answer except that perhaps overgrazing by sheep has rendered Irish wet moorland and upland areas unattractive to the birds.

Another wading bird of the coastal zone, closely related to the dunlin, is the red-necked phalarope, a very rare and endangered intermittent breeder whose traditional haunt in Ireland since 1900 has been at Annagh Marsh, near Belmullet, Co. Mayo. It has also been known to nest spasmodically at other coastal – or sometimes inland – sites mainly along the western seaboard. Its Holarctic and circumpolar breeding distribution takes it mainly to the tundra and sub-arctic zones extending southwards through Iceland, the Faeroes, Fenno-Scandinavia and to local sites in northern Scotland, where up to 19 pairs have been recorded in recent years while Ireland was only hosting one pair. Its breeding site in Co. Mayo is the most southerly in the world.

Table 9.3 Breeding sites of the red-necked phalarope in Ireland 1900–97 (from Whilde[58]).

Year	Annagh, Co. Mayo Pairs (+ non-breeders)	Other sites Site	Pairs
1900	2–3		
1902	breeding proved		
1905	50		
1911–12		Dooaghtry, Co. Mayo	breeding
1919	20	5 km from Annagh	2–3
1919		8 km from Annagh	a few pairs
1923	40–50		
1924		5 km from Annagh	0
1924		Roaninish, Co. Donegal	1
1927		Roaninish	1
1929		Roaninish	1
1929	50*		
1930–34		Murroe, Co. Donegal	1
1932	13	8 km from Annagh	6
1940	6		
1944	5	8 km from Annagh	1
1945	2		
<1950	a few		
1953–66	1–4	Dooaghtry (1953–56)	1
1967	1–2 (+8)	Turloughcor, Co. Galway	1
1968	3–5 (+20)	Lady's Island Lake, Co. Wexford	1 female
1969	3 (+8)	Akeragh Lough, Co. Kerry	2
1970	5 (+20)	Akeragh Lough	1
1970		Glenamaddy, Co. Galway	2–3
1971	3–4 (+12)	Akeragh Lough	1
1971		Lady's Island Lake	nest with 3 eggs
1972	0 (+3)	Akeragh Lough	1 bird
1973–8	0		
1974		Glenamaddy	3 birds
1976		Glenamaddy	1
1979	1 (+3)		
1980	bred		
1981–90	0–2		
1989	1 (no confirmed breeding)		
1990	1 (no confirmed breeding)		
1991	1 bird (no confirmed breeding)		
1992	1 bird (no confirmed breeding)		
1993	1 (no confirmed breeding		
1994–7	no information		

*J. Walpole-Bond[59]

The ecological factors that have drawn the red-necked phalarope to northwest Mayo may also explain the presence of several other sub-arctic and northern boreal species in more southerly latitudes in Ireland than in Britain and other northwestern European countries. Many of these 'northern' species are con-

Annagh Marsh, near
Belmullet, Co. Mayo.
Breeding habitat for
the red necked
phalarope.

fined to Irish coastal areas, especially the western seaboard. They are Leach's
petrel, eider, black guillemot, wild rock dove, Arctic tern, twite, red-throated
diver and goosander. The common gull – essentially a breeding bird of north
and west Britain – flourishes on the west coast of Ireland as far south as Co.
Kerry. The whooper swan is a spasmodic breeder in Co. Donegal – its main
breeding area is Iceland and Fenno-Scandinavia, with occasional pairs breeding in Scotland. The one suspected breeding record of the black-throated
diver has also been from Donegal. The red-throated diver also breeds in small
numbers (5–15 pairs) in Co. Donegal. While most of these are typically coastal
species, Ireland also exercises its southwards pull on several inland breeding
species such as the hooded crow, common scoter and hen harrier.

Greenshank and dotterel have also bred in the west of Ireland. The greenshank has bred at only one known site on Achill Island, Co. Mayo, probably in
1971 and definitely in 1972 and 1974. The dotterel is known to have bred only
once in Ireland when a pair nested in the Nephin Mountain range, Co. Mayo,
in 1975.[60]

The reasons for the breeding range of the sub-arctic and boreal species
being more southerly in Ireland than in Britain are not fully understood but it
is unlikely in view of the number and diversity of species under the spell that
one simple factor is at work. One hypothesis would argue that the position of
Ireland, on the outer edge of the European land mass with an unimpeded
direct line of flight to the Arctic, together with a smaller number of competing
species, would provide encouragement for certain birds to explore more
southerly breeding grounds. If global warming continues it is possible that several of these arctic–boreal species may contract their range northwards. The
red-necked phalarope may already be on its way north for these reasons.

Choughs

While the chough is certainly not an arctic-boreal species, but of a more
Mediterranean–alpine distribution, the reasons why it flourishes so successfully in Ireland, occupying a more southerly breeding range than in Britain, are
better understood. One of the most distinctive birds of the northern, western
and southern coasts of Ireland the chough occurs in greater abundance here
than anywhere else along the European coastline. It is a bird that endears itself

to everyone with its glossy black plumage, long curved red bill and red feet, its buoyant and often tumbling flight during which the widely separated primary feathers spread like fingers on a hand. There is no other call like its high-pitched '*cheeaah*', echoing loudly in the air.

Three national surveys of choughs in Ireland have been carried out. The first was in 1962,[61] followed by more extensive ones in 1982[62] and 1992[63] (Table 9.4). Due to different census methods and various extents of coverage it is not possible to make meaningful comparisons between the results. However, the figures show that the overall population trend is healthy and generally stable with an increase in numbers in some regions. In 1982, Bullock was intrigued to discover choughs breeding at some of the same sites where they were recorded 100 years earlier by Ussher.

It is evident from the chough's distribution and numerical strength that it is attracted to areas with low-intensity farming, such as the northern, western and southern Irish coastal zones, where the survival of rough grassland, some machair and undisturbed maritime pastures has been possible. In these uncultivated quarters the birds are provided with ample supplies of their favourite food, insects – especially the larvae, or leatherjackets, of craneflies. When Bullock surveyed breeding choughs in Ireland in 1982 he found that of 33 detailed feeding observations 60% involved leatherjackets as likely prey items, 24% ants (especially the yellow meadow ant), 12% beetle larvae and 9% spiders.[64] In the 1992 survey choughs were recorded feeding on seven different habitat types during the period from April to July. The habitat they preferred most was rough pasture, followed by maritime turf, improved grassland, cliff, heather communities, sand dunes and machair.

Bullock also recorded further observations on habitats used for feeding. His study area covered a total of 864 km². The most preferred habitat was maritime turf, i.e. short, herb-rich turf on cliff tops and headlands, drenched by spray in winter, with thrift, sea plantain and buck's-horn plantain as key species. Machair was the next preferred habitat followed by rough grass i.e. 'unimproved' grassland, usually unploughed for at least 10 years – typically a mossy, herb-rich turf usually on poorer soils. Then came improved grass, i.e. richer pasture, often on deeper soils, with evidence of recent 'improvement' (fertilisation, ploughing or re-seeding).

Vegetation height was a key factor in the attractiveness of a feeding site. Low vegetation, 1–3 cm high, allows the chough to dig into the soil for its insects, and hence two-thirds of all chough feeding records occurred on land grazed by sheep. Choughs hunt for their food by visual clues. Hence the vegetation has to be short to enable sighting of food before the birds drive their specialist bill, essentially a digging and probing tool, into the ground.[64] They often excavate cowpats and sheep droppings in

Chough.

Tormore Island, northwest of Port Hill, Co. Donegal. The area is typical breeding habitat for choughs (A. Walsh).

search of scarab beetles, *Aphodius* spp., and leatherjackets, a behaviour more common in young birds than in adults. They also forage amongst seaweed on the shoreline in search of maggots of the kelp fly, *Coelopa frigida*.

A more recent study of the foraging behaviour of five breeding pairs of choughs in the Rosguill Peninsula area, Co. Donegal, from March to June showed that, of the seven possible options, machair was the habitat where most time was spent feeding. Despite the generally inhospitable nature of many machairs as habitats for insects, sampling of invertebrates in the Donegal machairs revealed a great range of insects. The machairs were particularly rich in leatherjackets, while good numbers of staphylinid beetles, spiders and adults and larvae of carabid beetles were also found.[65]

Choughs, like other corvids, display a remarkable fidelity to traditional nesting sites, and their 'intelligence' lies in quickly learning the value of a productive site and sticking to it. They even maintain contact with it throughout the year by roosting close by. As the breeding season approaches in early April they feed together in small flocks without territorial disputes, an adaptation thought to allow the birds to feed unimpeded and thus get into good breeding condition for the season. However, if food is in short supply the cosiness of these social arrangements can break down.[64] Most choughs breed successfully in their third year of life with improving breeding success up to the age of ten. Of an average clutch of five eggs two successful fledglings emerge. Successful survival for the choughs may well involve a certain amount of altruistic behaviour amongst relatives during flocking. While in their flocks the individual becomes skilled to compete successfully for the selection of a mate and to acquire a home range with a nest site.[64]

The greatest concentration of choughs occurs in southwest Ireland, especially at the proximities of the long sea peninsulas where densities of 21–45 pairs per 10 km^2 were recorded in 1992.[63] The persistence and success of the birds in these areas is almost certainly related to the lack of farming pressure. With regard to the choice of nest sites the chough is very much a maritime creature, with 92% of the 650 recorded breeding pairs in 1982 nesting along the coast. The favourite nest site (61% of 135 sites examined) was in a crevice in a rock cliff leading to a sizeable cavity for nesting. Fewer pairs (39%) nested in caves. Natural crags were the preferred inland sites while only 5% of inland nesting birds used man-made structures, of which ruined castles were the most popular. The furthest inland breeding site recorded in 1982 was 19 km from the sea, in the Macgillycuddy's Reeks, Co. Kerry.

Table 9.4 Number of pairs and birds in flocks recorded in Ireland during chough surveys of 1962, 1982 and 1992 (1962 data from Cabot[61]– recalculated by Bullock, et al.; 1982 data from Bullock, et al.[62]; and 1992 data from Berrow, et al.[63]).

County	1960–65 Pairs	1982 Pairs	Birds in flocks	1992 Pairs	Birds in flocks
Antrim	21–22	9–10	3	1–2	2
Donegal	104–107	109–112	103	28–101	164
Leitrim	0	0	0	0–4	0
Sligo	4–6	5–6	6	7–14	22
Mayo	49–66	73–75	72	23–65	66
Galway	44–52	38–39	33	20–38	28
Clare	15	31–34	35–37	16–28	17
Kerry	103–135	205–209	131	53–315	122
Cork	48–70	148–153	171	67–282	292
Waterford	12–14	37–46	59–65	4–49	93
Wexford	0	1	2	1–8	15
Totals	**400–477**	**656–685**	**615–623**	**220–906**	**821**

Ireland plays an important role in harbouring nearly three-quarters of the northwest European chough population. The geographical breakdown of the population in 1992 is shown in Table 9.5.

Table 9.5 Numbers of choughs in Ireland, Scotland, Isle of Man and Wales, 1992 (data from Bignal, et al.[64]).

Location	No. breeding pairs	% total population	No. birds in flocks	% in flocks
Ireland	906	74.2	821	73.0
Scotland	88	7.2	62	5.5
Isle of Man	77	6.3	90	8.0
Wales	150	12.3	151	13.5
Totals	**1,221**	**-**	**1,124**	**-**

On the wider European canvas the population (including Ireland and Britain) has been estimated at 16,000 pairs with over three-quarters of these located in

Spain, Greece and Italy.[66] Other elements of the European population reside
in Brittany, southern France, Portugal, Sardinia and Sicily.[67]

Choughs are mainly sedentary, making local feeding movements of seldom
more than 10 km. There is no evidence of bird movements between the Irish,
Scottish, Welsh and Breton populations.

Terns

Of all coastal birds to be seen during the summer months, terns are the most
conspicuous and attractive. Marked out by their swallow-like and graceful
flight, whitish plumage, black caps and forked tails, they hover and plunge into
the sea in pursuit of small fish such as sand eels, *Ammodytes* spp. and herring
sprat. Their breeding colonies are crowded and noisy gatherings, scattered
along the coastline on sandy and shingle beaches, amongst sand dunes and on
small offshore islands. They are also found inland on the islands and peninsulas of many of the larger lakes. They are a vulnerable group of birds, victims to
many predators from gulls to rats, peregrine falcons to mink. Man is a pest too,
disturbing breeding colonies on beaches and islands in his pursuit of recreation. The sudden desertion of a colony halfway through the breeding season

Aerial view of Tern Island,
Wexford Harbour, 1967.
Before it was washed away
during winter storms some
ten years later the island
held the largest breeding
colony of roseate terns in
Europe.

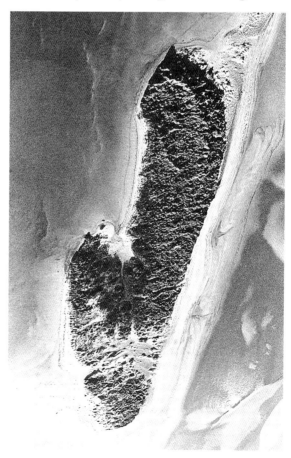

or the shifting of a traditional nesting site to another location are signs of their acute sensitivity to disturbance. However, as long-lived species they can afford to 'miss' a breeding season in order to save themselves to breed again in subsequent years.

Five species of tern regularly breed in Ireland. They are all vulnerable and listed for special protection under the EU Directive on the conservation of wild birds. Ireland is of special significance for the roseate tern, so called because for a short time during the breeding season adults have a roseate or pinkish hue to their chest feathers. In 1968 there were 3,812 nesting pairs in northwest Europe. Thereafter numbers fell almost continuously to reach their lowest level of 561 pairs in 1987. Since then the population started to increase gradually and had recovered to 686 pairs in 1994. Of these some 538, or 78.4%, of the total population bred in Ireland.[68] The numbers of breeding pairs in Ireland rose to 687 pairs in 1996 but declined slightly to 649 in 1997[69] and increased slightly to 660–662 pairs in 1998.

The censusing of breeding terns is notoriously difficult owing to their capricious use of nesting localities, the difficulty in covering all possible sites, and the problems, once at the site, of obtaining accurate counts of nests. The two most recent All Ireland censuses were carried out in 1984 and 1995 (Table 9.6). During the 1995 breeding season colonies were predominantly located on offshore coastal islands (70% of all colonies), islands on inland freshwater lakes (21%), on mainland coastal areas (6%) and on islands in brackish lagoons (3%). There were nine sites each holding 10–15% of the overall Irish population of the following species. *Arctic*: Cockle Island, Co. Down; Rock Island (Aran Islands), Co. Galway; Illaunamid (off Slyne Head), Co. Galway. *Little*: Fox Island, Co. Galway; Illauntannig (Magharees), Co. Kerry; Kilcoole/ Newcastle, Co. Wicklow. *Sandwich*: Ogilby (Co. Down). *Roseate and common*: Rockabill, Co. Dublin. *Roseate* and *sandwich*: Lady's Island Lake, Co. Wexford.[70]

Number of pairs of roseate terns breeding in Ireland and Britain 1960–94. From Cabot[68].

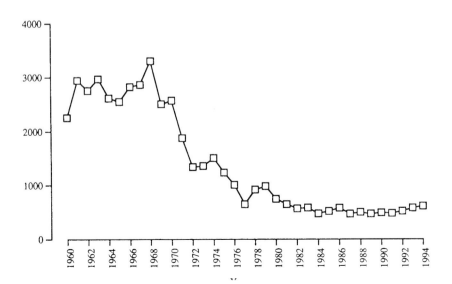

Table 9.6 Numbers of breeding pairs of terns and colonies in Ireland 1984 and 1995 (from Hannon et al.[70]).

Species	Number of pairs and colonies (in brackets)		% Change no. pairs
	1984	1995	
Common tern	2,848 (109)	3,053 (88)	+ 7
Arctic tern	2,460 (97)	3,092 (83)	+ 26
Roseate tern	268 (10)	624 (4)	+ 133
Sandwich tern	3,467 (25)	2,941 (23)	- 15
Little tern	257 (38)	174 (23)	- 32
Total	**9,300 (279)**	**9,884 (221)**	**+ 6.3**

The small overall increase of 6.3% of all terns masks two significant population shifts. Firstly, during the 1984–95 period, roseate tern numbers more than doubled. Studies at the largest and strictly protected colony at Rockabill, Co. Dublin, have shown that the mean productivity of chicks has been fairly constant at 1.37 per nesting pair for 16 years from 1979–94, providing more than enough young to keep the population on the increase. The factor allowing the population to grow has been an apparent reduction in mortality in the African wintering grounds where the recovery rate of pulli ringed in Ireland and Britain has declined from a high of 1.54% during the period of steepest population decline in the years 1967/8–73/4 to a level some two thirds lower at 0.51% for the period 1987–94.[68]

Secondly, little terns are in trouble. There has been a one third decline of the breeding population over the ten year period. Their productivity is far more variable than the roseate and fewer young are fledged per pair of breeding adults. A six-year study from 1985–90 of the principal breeding colony on the east coast of Ireland on the shingle beach at Newcastle, Co. Wicklow, demonstrated a consistently low breeding success.[71] The colony grew from 14 pairs in 1985 to 56 in 1989 but declined to 33 in 1990. The fledging rate ranged from 0–1.21 chicks per breeding pair with a mean of 0.6 young per pair attempting to breed over the six years. Of the 227 breeding attempts during the period,

This roseate tern nest at the base of a small forest of tree mallow on Rockabill, Co. Dublin, is well out of the way from any possible avian predators.

82% were unsuccessful. Predation by mammals – brown rats and foxes – was the main adverse factor. Amongst avian predators, the hooded crow was the most serious. On one occasion a group of 16 crows arranged themselves in linear fashion and walked into the colony picking up eggs as they marched through. Losses due to human disturbance were minimal, contrary to experience at other colonies in Britain where recreational pressure in the coastal zone has undoubtedly been very detrimental. Unless the little tern can breed more successfully its days as a breeding species in Ireland could be numbered.

Despite its precarious position in Ireland the little tern has not been given sufficient conservation support in the way that the roseate tern has. The latter received priority because of its overall small and imperilled European population, whereas the former was deemed less in need of protection in Ireland because its European population was very much healthier: there were some 18,400 pairs in Europe during 1985–7. However, in 1995 there were only 174 pairs left in Ireland.[72] Should we choose to ignore a species in Ireland on the grounds that its survival within Europe is not endangered?

Natterjack toads

The natterjack toad is the only toad in Ireland and the rarest of the three Irish amphibians, the other two being the European frog and smooth newt. The natterjack is restricted to a few coastal sites in Co. Kerry. Some specimens have been translocated to another site in Kerry while others were introduced by Dúchas about eight years ago to two coastal nature reserves in Co. Wexford – the Raven and Ballyteige Burrows – in an effort to ensure the conservation of this species in Ireland. They are now successfully established at the Raven, but failed to survive at Ballyteige.

Distribution of the natterjack toad in Co. Kerry in 1975. From Whilde[58].

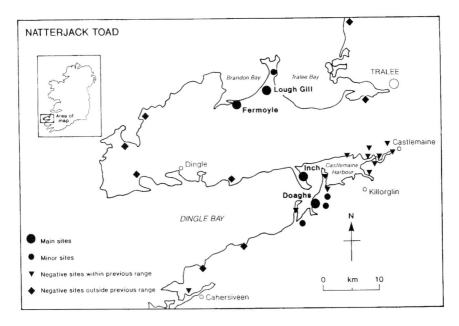

In Ireland the natterjack toad reaches the northwestern limit of its distribution within Europe, where it occurs in 16 countries. Most abundant in the warmer areas of western France (Brittany excepted), Portugal and most regions of Spain, the natterjack toad's range extends northwards through northeast France, up through Belgium, and as far north as southern Sweden and western Russia. Its habitat in Ireland is restricted to coastal sand dunes where the toads breed in shallow pools, lakes and drains in both fresh and brackish water.

Natterjack toads were first reported from Castlemaine Harbour, Dingle Bay, Co. Kerry, in 1805. The first records of the toads outside the relatively enclosed Dingle Harbour were from the northern side of the Dingle peninsula, at Castlegregory and Fermoyle in 1975. [73] By the 1990s natterjacks bred at some 48 sites in Kerry, of which 30 were very circumscribed.[74] The population is now confined in Kerry to the coastal sand dunes at Castlegregory and Fermoyle on the north side of the Dingle peninsula, and to the mouth of Castlemaine Harbour on the south side while they are found on the low-lying Dooaghs area. They also occur on the extensive sand dune system at Inch. In Britain the population has declined by up to 80% since the 1940s to about 20,000 adults remaining in some 40 breeding sites, distributed chiefly in southwest Scotland and northwest England.[75] Cumbria is now their British stronghold with 23 of the 39 native natterjack sites located there.[76] The population in Ireland is small with an estimate of only a few hundred adults, and declining. The natterjack toad is classified as an endangered species in Ireland and vulnerable in Britain.[58]

In behaviour the natterjack is nocturnal, spending the day holed up in small burrows – often two or three huddled together – or buried in the sand, or even in the peat that forms part of their habitat at the Dooaghs. Their skin colour varies from golden to a dark, almost olive tint, and they grow to about to 7 cm in length.[77] In his study of the toads in 1941 Macdougald noted that when several were pursuing an insect the successful one was flicked in the eyes by the tongues of the others, in retribution for its sauciness.

Endangered coastal plants

Not only are certain coastal breeding sea birds endangered but there are many less mobile plants under threat as well. They occur mostly in sand dune areas – probably the most threatened of all the coastal ecosystems because of human pressure – to which they are especially suited.[2] Among the rare and threatened species favouring the sandy, often highly calcareous, well-drained, warm soils, are three classified as 'vulnerable' and found at special coastal sites. A member of the gentian family, the seaside centaury is only reported from one sand dune in Co. Derry. It is an erect plant, reaching 35 cm, which looks somewhat similar to the common centaury but is narrower and shorter with rather leathery three-veined leaves. Its flowers are larger and of a paler pink. The closely related lesser centaury is smaller, seldom higher than 10 cm, and lacks the leaf rosette at the base of the flowers, which are also pink. It is restricted to one or two inland sites and otherwise found on sand dunes or sandy places at several locations in Co. Cork and along the south and east coasts up to Dublin. The third rare coastal species is an orchid, the green-flowered helleborine. It has the typical helleborine leaves, i.e. broad, elliptical and pointed. The flowers, in bloom from July to September, are borne on one side of longish stem that can reach up to 80 cm. They are green, hardly opening, and often tinged with yellow or purple. This helleborine is confined to dune slacks (wet and damp depressions in sand dunes) in Dublin, Wicklow and Wexford as well as to two woodland sites in Derry and Fermanagh.

Less scarce are six plants that are considered 'rare'. Wild asparagus, *Asparagus officinalis* subsp. *prostratus*, a member of the lily family, is a hairless creeping annual producing small red berries as fruits. Its flowers are small and white, blooming from June to August. This is the wild, prostrate asparagus, distinct from the erect garden asparagus, *A. officinalis* subsp. *officinalis*, that was introduced and grown in English gardens during Tudor times. Perhaps because of its reputation of 'increasing seed and stirring up lust', garden asparagus has occasionally escaped to establish itself in the wild as is the case in Co. Dublin and Co. Fermanagh. The leaves of the wild asparagus are in the form of reduced stems, needle-like, and borne in tufts. These modified stems are known as 'cladodes', and are an adaptation for survival in habitats where fresh water is scarce as they discourage, by their small structure, the loss of water vapour. Wild asparagus, the only coastal plant with this type of modified leaf, is apparently declining in its coastal haunts due to increasing human disturbance.

Another rare coastal species is henbane, a somewhat coarse annual or biennial with sticky, hairy leaves and stems. Together with the tomato and small tobacco plant it belongs to the often poisonous nightshade family. Hyoscyamine, a highly dangerous drug, mostly used as a hypnotic and brain sedative, is derived from its green tops and leaves. Henbane grows about 30–60 cm high, has large oval-oblong leaves up to 20 cm long and dull, creamy yellow bell-shaped flowers with purple veins. It grows in sand dunes, open sandy areas, in disturbed ground and often near old buildings. It has a habit of appearing fleetingly or ephemerally. The other rare but less dramatic coastal species are purple milk-vetch, a low and short member of the pea family with purple flowers and white hairy seed pods, found on calcareous or sandy soils, confined to Inishmore and Inishmaan on the Aran Islands; sea knotgrass, with branching prostrate stems from a woody rootstock and pink or white flowers, found only on the sandy seashore at Tramore, Co. Waterford, but possibly extinct now, and wild clary (also known as wild sage) an erect (30–70 cm) aromatic perennial with blue-violet flowers, growing on dry grassy places and sand dunes, mostly confined to coastal areas south of Louth and Galway but probably commoner than formerly thought.

These are followed by a group of 'indeterminately threatened' species. Sporting bright yellow dandelion-like flowers, the smooth cat's-ear is confined to sand dunes on the Ulster coastline. The sea pea, with its distinctive purple flowers and prostrate fleshy form, is recorded from sand dune sites in Kerry (at Rossbehy and recently again at Inch), west Mayo (discovered on Achill Island but washed away in storms in 1985) and west Donegal (status unknown). Another species is the sea stock. It is an erect, shrubby biennial (up to 10 cm high) with hoary downy leaves and purple flowers. It now appears to be extinct, although it was known to have grown at nine sand hill and sea cliff sites in Kerry, Clare, Galway and Wexford.

Shingle and gravel beaches, an even more specialist and fragile habitat for flowering plants, are threatened by both natural erosion and human removal of the shingle and gravel. Being such inhospitable places, they are basically poor in species with no particular plant dominating the habitat, but one would at least expect to find yellow horned poppy. Growing with a deep vertical tap root its leaves are covered by a dense growth of fine hairs which assist the retention of moisture, reflect much of the sun's heat and provide an extra protective layer against sea spray. It is absent from Antrim to Mayo but local elsewhere.

There are also two special plants found in this frequently changing and mobile habitat that are classified as 'rare' and 'endangered' respectively. The first is the oysterplant, named after its leaves, which taste like oyster. This perennial is a mat-forming, prostrate plant with long stems, up to 60 cm, carrying oval, thick, fleshy, blue-greyish, hairless leaves bearing conspicuous horny spots. Its rootstock is black and the many stolons that extend from it are white. The small flowers, 6 mm across, are purplish-pink when they first emerge and then turn blue. The flowering season is from May to August. This colour change is a feature of the borage family of which the oysterplant is a member. A northern species, more characteristic of the bleak Scandinavian and German coastlines, it even flourishes within the Arctic circle. It needs a spell of low temperatures in the winter to stimulate the germination of its seeds and cool summers to preserve the juvenile plants from drought. Its presence in Ireland marks the southwestern limit of its distribution and thus it is confined to the shingle banks of the northern and eastern coastal areas. During the nineteenth and earlier parts of the twentieth centuries it was recorded in twenty-two 10 km squares extending from Wicklow, Dublin, Down, Antrim, Derry and Donegal. Since then its range has contracted and it now only occurs in six of these squares in Donegal (3), Antrim (1) and Down (2).[78] The other species of plants found most frequently associated with the oysterplant on the shingle banks are silverweed, sea campion, curled dock, oraches, *Atriplex* spp., cleavers and sea mayweed.

The second special and endangered plant of shingle and gravel banks is cottonweed. Unlike the oysterplant this is a southern species with its main distribution centre in the Mediterranean region. Belonging to the largest family of flowering plants, the daisies, cottonweed is a low (up to 30 cm high) creeping and sometimes shrubby perennial covered by a thick felt of white hairs. The flowers are yellow, up to 20 mm across, occurring in small clusters at the tops of the stems and appearing late in the season from August to November. It was more widespread in the nineteenth century in both Ireland and Britain. First found in Ireland by G.J. Allman in 1845 it was recorded before the turn of the century from six coastal sites in Ireland: Kerry (1), Waterford (2), Wexford (2) and Wicklow (1). It is now extinct in Britain while in Ireland it only survives at one main major site on the gravel bank at Lady's Island Lake, Co. Wexford, separating the lake from the sea. This is its most northerly location in Europe. There is another very minor site nearby, to the west, on the Tacumshin shingle barrier, where two clumps survive from transplants from Lady's Island Lake dating from the early 1970s.[79] Attempts to grow it in cultivation at the National Botanic Gardens, Dublin, have had mixed success. After the first year growth was poor, after the second very poor and in the third year there were some small flowers.[80] A hundred years ago it was found along some 1,600 m of the Lady's Island Lake shingle barrier but by 1983 it was down to 500 m, then 375 m in 1986. Its habitat is unusual in that the shingle barrier shows signs of recent crestal overwashing and overtopping sedimentation.[81] But these dynamics may, in some way, be an important ecological factor for its continued presence here. Occasional burial under 15 cm of sand and gravel has not impeded its survival.[82]

It is only at the Lady's Island Lake that the correct mix of sediment types, and the mode and magnitude of their deposition appear to favour cotton-weed's survival despite it being reduced today to one fifth of its original extent. And, ironically, the often very considerable human disturbance inflicted by the removal of material from the beach to drain and lower the water level of Lady's Island Lake could also be a positive factor provided the whole colony is not eliminated during one of these operations. The periodic cutting of the barri-er encourages overwash and promotes local sediment transport and instabili-ty. The surface mosaic of gravel and finer sands determines the vegetation pat-terns of the site. The gravels are dominated by a close cover, in patches, of cot-tonweed while a semi-closed community of marram grows on the sandier ground. Where the two communities meet, marram dominates. In the open cottonweed community, sea sandwort and red fescue also feature while the transitional marram/cottonweed areas also contain rock samphire and groundsel. The sand sedge, sea mayweed and occasional lyme-grass occur around and outside the marram swards.

Lady's Island Lake itself is one of the best-studied brackish lagoons in the Republic, recently chronicled by Healy who detailed results from 17 years of monitoring.[83] Analysis of the lagoon's sediments indicate that a freshwater lake formed here about 4,500–5,000 years ago which existed until about 1700, when the sea first entered it. Since at least the seventeenth century the gravel barrier has been periodically cut either artificially to effect drainage or natu-

Cottonweed on the shingle barrier at Lady's Island Lake, Co. Wexford.

rally by sea storms. The periodic ingress of sea water has led to wild fluctuations of salinity within the lagoon, leading to chaotic environmental conditions
for the flora and fauna abiding there but at the same time making it a fascinating place to study. The maximum area of the lagoon in winter is about 450
ha with a maximum depth of 5 m but at the height of summer the height drops
to 1–1.5 m. The dominant macrophytes in the lagoon are beaked tasselweed
and fennel pondweed. Several features make it an area of exceptional ecological interest. First, as said above, the cottonweed has its principal station in
Ireland here. Second, five of the wintering wildfowl occur in nationally important numbers. Third, two 'vulnerable' charophytes, *Lamprothamnium papulosum*
and *Chara canescens*, are in the lagoon.[84] Finally, there is an internationally
important roseate tern colony, together with three other tern species, on the
islands within the lagoon – first recorded and studied here by the author in
1960.[68]

Another rare coastal plant is the Kerry lily which is restricted to one small
coastal area in the Darrynane region, Co. Kerry. Here it grows in a wild, rocky,
furze heath community with a peaty sub-soil. Its leaves are narrow and grass-
like, resembling those of purple moor-grass with which it can be easily confused when not in flower. The flowers appear to have six petals but in fact there
are only three and three very similar sepals. The flowering stem is 23–30 cm
long with a lax panicle of rather few flowers, white and purplish outside,
appearing in May–June. First discovered by the Rev. T. O'Mahony in 1848, it is
a member of the small group of plants with a Lusitanian distribution found in
Ireland. A new site for the plant was discovered a few years ago near Ardgroom,
west Cork, and reported to Scannell of the National Botanic Gardens.[85]
Formerly introduced to Britain, near Bournemouth, in Dorset, and then transplanted to Hampshire, there are no sites in Britain where it is considered
native. On the Continent it occurs from Normandy, France, to Spain and in
the Mediterranean area from Sardinia, Corsica and Italy. At Darrynane it is
locally frequent on the Darrynane side of Lamb's Head, on Abbey Island and
in many places near the shore of Kenmare Bay for about 13–14 km east of
Darrynane. At Darrynane it grows up to 25–30 cm tall and stands 10–15 cm
above the lower heath-type vegetation dominated by purple moor-grass, gorse
and bell heather in a very peaty soil with a pH of around 4.[86]

Coastal plants and their vegetable cousins

A disproportionate number of plants living along the coastline have been put
directly to human use or selectively bred to yield many of our daily vegetables.
Coastal plants are generally fleshy and many have distinctive tastes and aromas
reflecting their saline/maritime existence. One such plant, formerly a rare
species in Ireland, is the sea kale. A crucifer, sea kale grows in large clumps on
shingle banks, on the upper parts of sandy beaches and even on cliffs at 17
locations recorded since 1970 in Kerry, Cork, Waterford, Galway, Dublin and
Louth. It has also been seen, but not recently, in Down and Antrim.[2] In
Donegal it was known colloquially as 'strand cabbage'. Its leaves are large and
glaucous, with curly and crinkly edges. The flowers are pale mauve or white.
The seed pods, distinctively globular in shape and holding only one seed, are
buoyant in water and are washed around the coastline. Formerly quite rare, it
has made a great recovery in recent years probably as a result of a lack of interest from people, who now get their sea kale in the shops. Historically, and

before cultivation began, sea kale was commonly collected and eaten as a popular wild vegetable. It was not, however, apparently appreciated by one French gardening writer of 1807 who, according to Grigson, is reported to have described it as a *chou marin d'Angleterre*. He mistakenly tried the green leaves which are bitter, instead of the blanched and tasty shoots.[87] Sea kale is one of the few non-Mediterranean species of the Irish native flora that has been developed into an important vegetable in northwestern Europe.

Wild cabbage, another crucifer, is found especially on cliffs in western and eastern Cork as well as in Antrim. However, although growing in the wild, these plants are garden escapees and not the genuine wild ones from the Mediterranean region. A close relation of both the wild cabbage and the sea kale is the sea radish, *Raphanus raphanistrum* subsp. *maritimus*. It is a tall (up to 60 cm high), stout, hairy biannual with yellow flowers, found growing infrequently along the drift line of sandy shores and shingle banks in most coastal counties. It is not the ancestor of the garden radish which is an ancient vegetable, a species in its own right, living only in cultivation or sometimes as an escapee, and noted for its edible tuberous root. The sea beet is a sprawling plant with stems spreading up to 60 cm long some of which can also be tall and upright, often tinged with red. The leaves are dark green, leathery, and somewhat shiny. It occurs on rocky and gravely seashores and cliffs generally around the coast. It has been carefully cultivated and genetically selected by man for more than 2,000 years to produce modified vegetable forms such as the red beetroot and the sugar beet. The young leaves can be eaten like spinach and the species grows perfectly well when transplanted into a garden.

The carrot family, Umbelliferae, has several members of interest that inhabit the coastline. The rock samphire, found growing in isolated tufts or groups of tufts on rocks and cliffs, is a small, shrubby and erect perennial with a much divided stem bearing many fleshy, almost cylindrical, rigid and slightly glaucous leaves. These are divided many times into long narrow leaflets that give the plant an almost spiky appearance. Rock samphire can sometimes be quite large, extending up to 30 cm high in sheltered places. Its flowers are greenish-yellow, growing in small umbels, and the fruits are ovoid. It is moderately widespread around the coast, more frequent along the southern than the northern coastlines. The leaves, when boiled in vinegar and spice, make a strong aromatic pickle. It can also be chopped fresh and added to a salad. It was also popular when boiled and eaten on bread or boiled and minced with butter. It was an important stimulatory herb which, according to K'Eogh (1735), 'provoketh urine and menses, opens obstructions of the bowels, the liver, spleen and kidneys, it strengthens the stomach, and creates an appetite, being pickled, and eaten, or a decoction of it in wine drank'.[88] Another coastal herb whose leaves and seeds, according to K'Eogh, 'increase milk in nurses', is fennel, which is very aromatic and grows up to 90 cm high in a straggly form. Found wild on sea cliffs and sometimes in hedgerows and dry banks around the coast, it has almost certainly escaped from cultivated gardens. The leaves are finely divided into feathery hair-like leaflets which, when crushed, smell like liquorice. The flowers are small and yellow.

Wild celery, another strong-smelling biannual growing up to 60 cm high with a grooved hollow stem is locally frequent in many salt marshes and brackish ditches around the coast. Wild celery is the original stock from which our garden celery has been bred. The sea carrot, *Daucus carota* subsp. *gummifer*, grows

Rock samphire.

on sea cliffs in west Cork, and in Waterford, Wicklow and Dublin. It is related to the wild carrot, an inland species, the ancestor of our garden carrot.

Seaweed and kelp

Seaweed was historically an important source of nutrients for coastal farming communities as underscored by the closely guarded legal rights to gather seaweed from the foreshore included in many land ownership titles. It was frequently applied directly onto the land both as a soil conditioner, supplying organic material and assisting with the retention of moisture in often dry and sandy soils, as well as a manure – an average sample of fresh seaweed contains about 0.4% nitrogen, 0.04% phosphorus and 0.6% potassium. The large Laminarian species together with other species were also burnt to produce an ash called kelp which was sold for industrial purposes. Today, these practices are almost extinct. However, there is now a growing Irish seaweed industry worth £5 million annually. Today Irish seaweed production is about 45,000 tonnes per year – approximately half the estimated potential annual yield – employing some 500 people in seasonal harvesting and processing. Most of the gathered seaweed, chiefly knotted wrack and the kelps, *Laminaria* spp, is dried to produce seaweed meal which is then sold to the European alginate indutry to supply alginates essential for the thickening and gelling agents in food and for the pharmaceutical and textile printing industries.

10

Islands

The galaxy of islands riding the sea around the Irish coastline are mere fractals of the larger mainland and, on a grander scale, of Europe. They are environmental microcosms where the flora and fauna is often, but not always, a reduced version of that found on the mainland. Several mammals and birds, sensitive to human disturbance or in need of specialist ecological niches, depend on them for their survival.

The relative abundance of inshore fish and other food together with the availability of suitable nesting habitats are responsible for attracting large breeding colonies of seabirds. Of 22 species found in Ireland, most breed on the offshore islands. As terns have already been discussed in Chapter 9, they will not be considered here. Amongst the remaining 17 seabirds, three occur in internationally important numbers. These three are pelagic, spending the major part of their lives far out to sea. They are the storm petrel (roughly 30% of the total European population is found in Ireland), the gannet (11.1%) and the Manx shearwater (13.1%).[1] Far away from most human intrusion, islands also provide secure sanctuaries for wintering wildfowl, amongst which the barnacle goose is the most consistent and specialist inhabitant. Herds of seals, particularly the grey but also the common, regarded with suspicion by fishermen because of their shared predilection for salmon and cod, are also encountered especially on many western islands.

Scattered along the coast are several islands, such as Achill (the largest island of the country at 147 km^2) and the Mullet, Co. Mayo, that are only disconnected from the mainland by narrow channels of water, whereas others, such as Tory Island, Co. Donegal, are truly Atlantic and remote, often cut off from the mainland by fierce and dangerous seas (by some 14 km from Meenlaragh Pier in the case of Tory). Bills Rocks, Co. Mayo, and Tearaght Island, Co. Kerry, are also amongst the remotest, some 11 and 10.5 km away respectively from the nearest points of the mainland. An interesting observation made by Praeger was that most of the western islands, such as the Blaskets, Co. Kerry, Aran Islands, Co. Galway, Inishbofin, Co. Galway, Inishturk and Inishkea, Co. Mayo and Rathlin O'Birne and Aran Island, Co. Donegal, had lower rainfall than the nearby mainland. As a consequence their surfaces were less overwhelmed by peatland (with the exceptions of Achill Island, Clare Island and Duvillaun More, all Co. Mayo), and a number of plant species no longer found on the nearby mainland had survived on them.[2] In support of his argument Praeger cites the presence of field mouse-ear on the Blaskets, Co. Kerry, purple milk-vetch on Inishmaan and Inishmore (Aran Islands), Co. Galway, wood small-reed on Inishbofin, Co. Galway, and hoary rock-rose on Inishbofin, Co. Galway and Inishturk, Co. Mayo. On Aran Island, Co. Donegal, there are narrow-leaved helleborine, thyme broomrape and several of the mossy saxifrages including Hart's saxifrage. This saxifrage is now considered to be a subspecies *hartii* of the Irish saxifrage, or possibly a relict of a hybrid population between

Hag Island, near Benwee Head, north Mayo cliffs (J. Barlee).

Irish saxifrage and the tufted saxifrage (not present in Ireland and a mainly arctic species) and is found only on Aran Island.[3]

There might be less rain on these western islands but there is plenty of wind. Thus it is seldom that the vegetation on islands has a chance to raise its head to heights found on the mainland. One particular plant community that thrives well in this harsh environment is a low, dense and carpet-like shining *Plantago* sward made up mostly of sea plantain and buck's-horn plantain. Reaching up to only about 1 cm high, this sward occupies large areas of the more exposed western cliffs and parts of many western islands – all subject to high salinity levels, ferocious winds and constant grazing pressure from rabbits, sheep and wild geese.

Island botany

Islands appeal to naturalists because of their biological isolation which can be used to probe the relationships between species and geography. Central to this probing is, of course, the question of the origin of species, and that of their evolution. Islands, then, are outdoor laboratories. Ever since the first Irish island plant record was published by Lhwyd in 1712 – the maidenhair fern from the Aran Islands, Co. Galway[4] – there has been a regular procession of naturalists to most Irish islands. The great triumvirate of Barrington, Hart and More were eagerly exploring island flora from the 1870s onwards, followed by Praeger and others towards the turn of the century. During the past two decades there has been a revival of interest in island flora and fauna, with inquiries focused on the changing status of plants in relation to the withdrawal of human impact, especially apparent in the decline of tillage agriculture. Here a brief sketch of the flora of the twelve larger islands of Ireland is presented.

Twelve larger islands of Ireland

Tory Island, Co. Donegal

One of the remotest islands, Tory possesses a small flora of some 145 species recorded by Barrington in 1877 – to which Praeger added a further 22 in 1910 – spread thinly over this shelf of rock.[5,6] The island is about 4.8 km long by some 0.8 km wide with the highest point 83 m at the east end where there is a large promontory fort, witness to an early human settlement, and spectacular cliffs made of coarse quartzite. Most of the peaty surface of the island has been removed for fuel, thus reducing formerly available habitats for many of the plants. Amongst the interesting species recorded here by Praeger are Scottish scurvygrass (rare on the northern and western coasts), rock sea-spurrey (growing amongst the rocks by the shore), wild privet (possibly a native species here – it has been frequently introduced elsewhere in Ireland), northern dead-nettle (found on waste and abandoned agricultural land) and finally, in and around water ponds, the least bur-weed, floating bur-weed, slender club-rush, long-bracted sedge and quillwort.[6]

Inishmurray, Co. Sligo

Inishmurray is made up of Carboniferous sandstone with a thin covering of peat and some grassland. About 6.5 km off the Sligo coast, it is a low island, extending over approximately 130 ha. The early Christian remains within the Cashel are probably more interesting than the island's botany. The most conspicuous plant is the purple loosestrife which is found in damp places and grows to a height of nearly 1 m. There are also large amounts of the royal fern with some fronds nearly 2 m long. The lesser butterfly-orchid and the heath spotted-orchid are also numerous. The commonest weed on the former tilled ground is the non-native white mustard. The fern sea-spleenwort grows amongst the boulders. When Praeger visited the island, for just one hour in 1896, he found 145 species and made the comment that the island 'offers no special attraction to the botanist.[7]

The Mullet, Co. Mayo

The Mullet peninsula, hanging like a limb from the mainland in northwest Co. Mayo, is one of the most desolate areas in the country. Technically an island, it was linked to the mainland by only a few metres of ancient Dalradian schists – dating from the last part of the Precambrian, some 590 million years ago – that have been cut by man to allow passage of water and small boats between Broad Haven and Blacksod Bay. Geologically most of the Mullet is made up of a complex of Precambrian rocks – quartzite and gneiss – which puts the Mullet in the same age group as the Outer Hebrides, off the west coast of Scotland. These ancient structures form the northern sea cliffs and hills. At the southern end of the peninsula, Termon Hill (103 m) is constructed of ancient granite rocks dating from the late Caledonian period, some 500 million years ago. Strung out between Erris Head and Termon Hill is a relatively flat landscape of peatland, glacial and periglacial drift, sand dunes, machair and blown sand.

Inishmurray, Co. Sligo (A. Walsh).

The latter covers about 15% of the total area of the Mullet and its high calcium carbonate content (34–80%) has a profound influence on the vegetation. In most respects the flora and vegetation of the Mullet – and of offshore islands such as Inishkea North and South and Inishglora – is remarkably similar to the vegetation found on the Outer Hebrides.

Curtis, McGough & Akeroyd surveyed the flora of the Mullet during visits in late June 1979 and added 29 species to the list of 337 recorded by Praeger in 1904 but 83 plants noted by Praeger could not be found. [8,9] A quarter of these were weeds and ruderal species, and it appears that the decrease in tillage on the Mullet and modern agricultural methods including the use of herbicides have contributed to their disappearance. Overall the number of species on the Mullet is extremely poor due to a combination of human activity, exposure to strong winds and lack of shelter.

Clare Island, Co. Mayo

Clare Island, a dramatic hump of an island lying at the entrance of Clew Bay, is one of the most interesting of all Irish insular territories because of its ecological diversity. It covers 1,555 ha, and is inhabited by approximately 160 people. The oldest rocks date from the Dalradian period. These dark sandstones and slate form the northern part of the island and the sea cliffs that rise up to a vertiginous 122 m. The more recent rocks – sandstones, shales and conglomerates from the Lower Carboniferous period, some 300 million years ago – are buried under glacial boulder clay in the eastern quarters. The rest of the island is constructed of older rocks dating from the Silurian period, some 445 million years ago. These grey sandstones and purple shales are the substance of Knockmore (462 m), a bald and domineering hill casting its watchful eye over the whole island.

The most interesting areas botanically are the cliffs on the north side of Knockmore, at a height of about 300–400 m. Here the sure-footed botanist can find a group of alpine and scarce species including moss campion, purple saxifrage, St Patrick's cabbage, kidney saxifrage, Irish saxifrage, roseroot, alpine saw-wort, dwarf willow, brittle bladder-fern (not seen recently) and Wilson's filmy-fern. On the south-facing and sloping land of Knockmore is a thin heather peatland, formerly bushy but now much eaten down by sheep.

The grassland lower down gives way to a remarkable green and shiny *Plantago* sward, especially along the tops of the western and northeastern cliffs. This is a very distinctive dwarf maritime vegetation community, and an Irish speciality, found on many of the windswept western cliffs and islands. It occurs from sea level to about 130 m. The *Plantago* sward on Clare Island consists mainly of sea plantain (about 80% of all species) and buck's-horn plantain, together with ribwort plantain, wild thyme, eyebrights and upwards of 30 other species including, typically, tormentil, English stonecrop, heath bedstraw, sheep's-bit, field wood-rush, early hair-grass and sheep's-fescue. Many species found in the *Plantago* swards such as devil's bit scabious, cat's-ear, allseed, adder's-tongue and bog pimpernel are stunted and prostrate, much more so than in sheltered habitats on the mainland where they attain normal heights.

At Portlea, on the eastern side of Clare, are the remnants of the island's only small and probably ancient woodland. Here sessile oak, hazel, downy birch, holly, rowan, eared willow and grey willow struggle for survival. The wood's future has been secured recently by the erection of a sheep-proof fence. Honeysuckle and bog-myrtle are prolific in the vicinity. In the wet spots below the wood are large examples of the royal fern. Further north, along the coast, is an unusual outlying station of Irish heath. The nearest other sites are at Bellacragher Bay, north of Mallaranny, and the Killary Harbour, Co. Mayo.

North cliffs of Clare Island, Co. Mayo, with a flock of barnacle geese flying off the cliffs.

Questions concerning the origin of island flora and fauna led a pioneering group of Irish biologists, at the turn of the century, to carry out one of the most extensive investigations into the natural history of a specific area ever undertaken in Ireland. Clare Island was selected as the best location; it was large, had a broad range of habitats, was easy to access, inhabited, and with available accommodation for the visiting field workers who came not only from Ireland but from several other European countries. The Clare Island Biological Survey, 1909–11, was masterminded by Praeger, under the aegis of the Royal Irish Academy. Discoveries made during the survey resulted in an addition of 18% to the flora and 24% to the fauna of the country. Three years earlier, in 1905–6, there had been a 'dry run' on Lambay Island, off the coast of Dublin.[10,11]

During the Clare Island Survey, 393 native higher plants were listed together with an additional 20 introduced species. In a re-examination of the island's flora during 1984 Doyle & Foss re-located only 307 species and discovered another 22 (eight introduced plants – the remainder either natives or garden escapes occurring in natural habitats).[12] They concluded that the general reduction of species reflected a fundamental change in the island's vegetation, resulting from changed agricultural practice, with a major shift from arable land to sheep grazing systems. The changes were particularly noticeable in the reduction of weed species associated with both grain and root crops. The former heather community no longer existed and had been almost entirely replaced by a severely grazed and eroded grassland dominated by common bent and sheep's-fescue.

During the New Clare Island Survey 1991–8 some 372 plant species were found by Ryle. The move from tillage to pastoral farming has again been deemed responsible for most of the changes. Gone are the field gentian, the narrow-leaved helleborine and the stone bramble. Amongst the alpine species the holly fern, green spleenwort and brittle bladder-fern have not been rediscovered. The heath cudweed is also missing.

Inishbofin, Co. Galway

Inishbofin, one of the larger and more populated islands, 8.8 km from the nearest point of the mainland, was one of the first to be explored by naturalists. More and Barrington launched the visiting trend in mid-August 1875. They were followed by a succession of others with the most recent published reports from Brodie & Sheehy-Skeffington together with colleagues from University College, Galway.[13,14] The geology of the island is similar to that of the adjacent mainland – mainly a mixture of quartz, feldspar schists and gneisses from the Dalradian period, covered with a thin acid soil supporting a peatland vegetation in some places and rough grassland in others. Windblown sands in the area south and southwest of Cloonamore strand exercise a calcareous influence on the soils there. The island covers about 930 ha, its highest point is 88 m and there are extensive rocks that break through the often thin overburden of soil. Agriculture is low intensity, and tillage has declined markedly since 1967. The most striking feature of the vegetation is the total absence of any native trees or shrubs higher than about 1 m, which means that shade- and shelter-loving plants are deprived of a vital habitat. Fuchsia is the commonest hedge species on the island. The *Plantago* sward on the western cliff is well developed, while most of the island is covered by a low heather and in places by mat-grass community.

On their first visit to Inishbofin, More and Barrington recorded 303 species; Praeger added a further 82 in 1911 but could not locate 11 earlier records.[15] Webb & Hodgson found 367 species of which 36 were new.[16] Brodie and Sheehy-Skeffington found 311 species, including 19 new ones, but failed to locate 80 others of which nearly half were wetland or bog species while the remainder were from grassland and hedgerow habitats. Their loss was ascribed to human activity in the bogs (now nearly all dug out), drainage of the pools, and to the decline in tillage possibly compounded by the impact of herbicides and fertilisers. Similar losses have been noted on other islands. While extinctions are occurring on Inishbofin, new records are also appearing. Whether these are genuine new arrivals or records overlooked by previous workers will never be known. However, despite the comings and goings of some species, Webb noted the overall stability of the island flora and stressed that the great majority of species had shown no change over nearly a century. He singled out the persistence of the native wood small-reed and alien elecampane as examples of endurance.

Aran Islands, Co. Galway

'In other landscapes the rounded might be equated with the natural and the right angle with the human contribution. Here, though, it is as if the ground itself brings forth right angles. Because of the limestone's natural partings along its vertical fissures and horizontal stratifications, the oblong and the cuboid are the first-fruits of the rock.'[17]

Thus Robinson points to the singular angularity of Inishmore, Aran Islands, conditioned by its geology and making it a fit object for intellection and abstract musing. On Inishmore nature thinks along straight lines. The three islands that straddle the mouth of Galway Bay – Inishmore, Inishmaan and Inisheer – are an extension of the Carboniferous limestone of the Burren, and were cut off from it by the rising sea levels some 9,500 years ago. Because they are less folded and faulted than the rocks of the Burren, they look almost flat.[18] Naked and fissured limestone prevails, mitigated by green pastures and fields where the islanders have created a unique plaggen soil made up of sand, seaweed and manure (see p. 273). The Burren flora is largely repeated, with some notable absentees. The rarest plant is a member of the Leguminosae or pea family, the purple milk-vetch – a low-growing, straggly and downy perennial with purple flowers, whose fruit is an elongated hairy pod. Possibly a survivor from warmer times before the final phases of the Ice Age (it has a curious discontinuous distribution within Britain and on the Continent, where it is commoner in eastern than in western areas) it is typically found in chalk grasslands and on calcareous sand dunes. Other special plants of the island – because of their rarity elsewhere – are pyramidal bugle, wood small-reed and the mossy saxifrage. Many of the Burren specialities are represented, including the spring gentian, hoary rock-rose, Irish eyebright and the maidenhair fern.

As a result of the changes in agricultural practices in many areas in western Ireland, it was thought that five species of arable weeds had become extinct in Ireland as they had not been recorded since 1970. They were the corncockle, corn chamomile, cornflower, darnel and shepherd's-needle.[19] However, on further investigation of the Aran islands, Curtis and colleagues not only discovered darnel and cornflower but also two other rare arable weeds, the bristle oat and smooth broom. Certain traditional agricultural practices that persist in at least some areas of the Aran Islands have ensured the survival of these rarities. Darnel was first found growing in six thatched roofs on Inishmaan, the plants having originated from seed heads gathered with the rye as it was harvested for thatching. It was later found growing in ten fields on Inishmaan, two on Inishmore and one on Inisheer. Only two plants of cornflower were found on Inishmore. Smooth brome was also found at only one site while the bristle oat was located on all three islands.[20]

Magharee Islands, Co. Kerry

These islands, also known as The Seven Hogs, lie about 1.5–3 km north of the northern point of the Magharee peninsula. Their botany had not been investigated in any detail until Parnell, Wyse-Jackson & Akeroyd landed on them in June and August, 1982.[21] Formed of low-lying Carboniferous limestone overlain by a thin covering of glacial boulder clay, the islands are mainly less than 30 m above sea level. The largest two, Illauntannig (highest point 15 m) and Illaunimmil (22 m), are about 7.3 ha each, and were inhabited until about 30 and 100 years ago respectively. Both are covered with grass, grazed by sheep, and have remains of early Christian monastic settlements. The other islands are small, especially Gurrig Island which is basically a lump of limestone with jagged and sharp edges to the vertical cliffs. Taken as a whole, the flora of the islands is relatively large and diverse with many more species per unit area of island than on the Blaskets, Co. Kerry, and the Aran Islands.[22] The relative richness of the flora reflects the underlying limestone rocks as well as the former presence of man, most clearly heralded by the common nettle. The absence of bracken and several genera of Compositae are noteworthy.

The most dramatic and showy of the plants is the bushy tree-mallow with its purple-pink flowers. It reaches 3 m in height and grows vigorously on Illaunimmil where shags nest under its shelter. Introduced to many parts of Ireland, it is almost certainly wild here. On the cliff faces below are large clumps of rock samphire.

Associated with the monastic remains on Illauntannig and Illaunimmil is an interesting group of plants some of which were almost certainly part of a garden. Yellow-juiced poppy has orangey-red petals and a latex that turns deep yellow on exposure to air. It was probably introduced to Ireland and these islands by man. Broadleaved dock is not a particularly special species as it occurs on waste ground, roadsides and meadows abundantly throughout the country but on the Magharees it is only found in the monastery ruins. A few dwarf specimens of elder grow on the retaining wall of the monastery ruins (did the monks use them for wine?). The milk thistle is an introduced ruderal species to the islands and Ireland. This purple-flowered thistle is rare with a scattered distribution in the country and when it occurs it is often amongst ancient ruins.

The Blaskets, Co. Kerry

The Blasket Islands, comprising a group of six small islands, are the summits of the mountain range that was the western extension of the Dingle Peninsula. Within the group, Tearaght Island (highest point 200 m) holds the distinction of being the most westerly part of Ireland and Europe at longitude 10°39'W,

Tearaght Island, Co. Kerry, with the most westerly lighthouse in Ireland. In the distance are Great Blasket Island (left) and Inishnabro (right).

although the very small Forze Rock Great is slightly further (2 minutes) west. As for Great Blasket Island, it occupies a special place in Irish culture because of a small but precious library of books produced by the islanders – including *The Islandman* by Thomás Ó Crohan and *Twenty Years A-Growing* by Maurice O'Sullivan[23,24] – containing descriptions of island life at its rawest and most trying. The last of the islanders departed for the mainland in 1953.

Great Blasket Island, rising to 292 m at Croaghmore, resembles a sharp-edged, gigantic whale, riding the Atlantic in a southwest-northeast orientation. The steep, south-facing slopes are covered by grassland dominated by buck's-horn plantain and sea plantain. On the drier northern side towards the summit of the ridge, low dwarf heather occurs. It gives way to a *Plantago* sward lower down and towards the west end. Almost pure stands of thrift are found below the sward while even lower down in the sea spray belt are rock samphire and rock sea-spurrey. The searing impact of the wind together with the lack of ecological diversity provide no opportunity for a large flora on the Blaskets, with the result that the total number of species recorded on Great Blasket Island remains small – 208 – to which must be added another eight mustered up from the rest of this cliffy, jagged wave-spent archipelago. As on the Magharee islands, the tree-mallow occurs almost certainly as a wild species.

Saltee Islands, Co. Wexford

Great and Little Saltee are composed of the typically pink Saltees granite of Silurian age (about 436 million years old) rather than the Precambrian gneisses that outcrop at Kilmore Quay on the mainland opposite. A coating of glacial boulder clay derived from the Munsterian glaciation overlays the rocks. Both islands were formerly cultivated – wheat and early crop potatoes were the last

tillage crops. Great Saltee extends over 87 ha and rises to 58 m while Little
Saltee is low-lying (37 m maximum) and much smaller at 40 ha. Bracken and
brambles cover much of the islands with associated extensive stands of bluebells carpeting large tracts of the land in late spring and early summer. Their
profusion is mysterious because of their close ecological association with
woods of which there are none today on the islands. Does that indicate former
woodland cover or do ecological conditions on the Saltees approximate those
of a woodland? Unfortunately the islands are lacking in any lake sediments
which could be subjected to pollen analysis to provide answers. However, it is
not unlikely that the Saltees were once covered with trees.

The bracken and brambles sometimes reach chest-height, making progression akin to a swim through prickly spiky water. The yellow flowers of wild
turnip, an echo from earlier farming, occupy large tracts of the islands, particularly Little Saltee. The remaining areas of open grassland are dominated by
false oat-grass and Yorkshire-fog. Hogweed is also common in abandoned
arable plots. On the more open ground, near the cliffs on the eastern and
southern parts of both islands, are dense growths of thrift, sea campion, common sorrel, sheep's sorrel and rock sea-spurrey. When Hart visited the Saltees
in 1882 they were under cultivation and he recorded 153 species.[25] Praeger
came in 1913 and added 60 new species but was unable to locate 30 of Hart's.[26]
Changes in the flora were already occurring as a result of agricultural abandonment, and many species associated with tillage such as cornfield annuals,
the nipplewort and chaffweed, have since disappeared. Other absentees are
the toad rush, bog stitchwort and lesser water-parsnip, all water-loving plants.
Two ericaceous species found by Praeger in 1913 – bell heather and heather –
have also disappeared.

Great Saltee Island, Co. Wexford, looking north.

Lambay Island, Co. Dublin

Located near the site of an ancient Ordovician volcano (about 450 million years old), Lambay Island is partly made up of volcanic rocks. Its geology is a complex mixture of sandstones, limestones, slates and andesitic lavas and tuffs. It extends over 250 ha (highest point 162 m), lying some 4.8 km off the Dublin coast, north of Howth. Featuring high cliffs on the eastern side, it is mostly covered by heather and grassland dominated by bracken. The remainder of the island is farmed by the present owner. On the cliffs there are robust growths of rock samphire, golden samphire and sea beet. A somewhat similar flora to that of Great Saltee, Co. Wexford, is found on the cliff tops – dense growth of sea campion, thrift, sea mayweed and various orach species. Also in great profusion on the cliff tops and slopes are primrose, bluebell, lesser celandine and ground-ivy.

Rathlin Island, Co. Antrim

Rathlin Island is a basalt outpost of Co. Antrim with fine precipitous cliffs (rising to 136 m at the west end) revealing, on the landward side, black volcanic rocks sitting on deposits of white chalk. Much of the island's surface was once peatland but is now wet rocky heathland punctured by several shallow lakes. Agriculture, apart from sheep grazing, is low intensity. The flora is similar to that of the nearby mainland and comprises about 350 species. On the low south-side coastline there are good amounts of roseroot, rock sea-spurrey, heath pearlwort, sea radish and tree-mallow which is considered native on the high sea rocks. Growing amongst the rocks are the hawkweed *Hieracium iricum*, thyme broomrape, juniper, mossy saxifrage and aspen, the only native tree on the island. Amongst the non-native species there is a group of medicinal plants most of which must have been brought to the island. They include soapwort, houseleek, hemlock (considered native), sweet cicely, caraway, Alexanders, elecampane, feverfew and green alkanet. In the lakes are long-stalked pondweed, ridged hornwort and the stonewort *Nitella translucens*. About ten years ago pyramidal bugle was found here.

Inishtrahull, Co. Donegal

This most northerly point of Ireland is anchored some 7.2 km off the northernmost point of the Inishowen peninsula, Co. Donegal, and extends over some 46 ha (highest point some 42 m). The island is formed of some of the oldest rocks in Ireland, some 1,700 million years in age. These Precambrian formations, much crumpled and metamorphosed by deep earth movements, bear no relationship to the geology of the Donegal or Derry coasts. They are closely related to those of the Hebrides (Islay and Colonsay) and Greenland. In the long distant past, many millions of years ago, Inishtrahull 'drifted' away from the once common area of Greenland and the Hebrides and came to end its course in Irish waters. A considerable thickness of calcareous glacial drift occupies the centre of the island and this probably accounts for the absence of several calcifuge species such as the heathers and heaths.

Inishtrahull's key position in relation to shipping led to the construction there in 1812 of a lighthouse, first operational on 17 March 1813. It was closed in 1958 when a newly-built lighthouse came into action and became automatic in April 1987 when the last lighthouse keepers departed. Despite its remoteness, the island supported a community of 68 people living in 11 houses in 1851. The islanders were evacuated in 1928.[27]

About half the island – principally the low-lying ground – was once cultivated with rye and vetches (for animal food), barley (for making poteen, an illegal liquor), oats, potatoes and cabbages. There were sheep on the high ground at the east end of the island. One of the former lighthouse keepers, D.J. Sullivan, who was also a naturalist and poet, made an extensive collection of plants and ferns which he sent to Stelfox for identification between 1939 and 1942.[28] The number of flowering plants and ferns collected by Sullivan was 119. This figure is in keeping with the 177 species from Tory Island, Co. Donegal, which, although further isolated from the mainland, is much larger and possesses aquatic habitats absent on Inishtrahull. The two most striking plants on the island are Scots lovage – a celery-scented member of the carrot family (Umbelliferae), rare in Ireland and found on rocky shores only along the northern coastline; and Scottish scurvygrass, less rare in Ireland, found on northern and western rocky coastlines.

What conclusions can be drawn from this review of island botany? Despite fewer plant species on the islands compared with the mainland, several have found refuge away from mainland ecological pressures. One subspecies, Hart's saxifrage, has arisen possibly through its genetic isolation and may evolve further, in the future, into a fully fledged species; many of the sometimes dramatic departures of plants from the islands are related to either the withdrawal of tillage agriculture, or the intensification of sheep grazing. Overall the flora of islands is ecologically interesting because of its dynamic nature.

Island mammals

Zoologists are as fascinated by islands as botanists. A ubiquitous island mammal is the wood mouse, *Apodemus sylvaticus*, which, despite its specific name being derived from its normal habitat – the wood – has been recorded on most islands, however windswept, barren and treeless. To chance upon one of these long-tailed, round-bodied creatures, hopping around in a tundra-like environment is an unusual experience. Most of these furry rodents, inadvertently introduced to the islands by man in sacks of grain or other produce, behave like house mice, nesting in abandoned or secluded buildings if these are available. Otherwise they will nest in stone walls, a good alternative sheltered habitat. They have been recorded on Tory, Cruit, Rutland and Inishkeeragh, Co. Donegal; Inishkea North and South, Achill, Clare and Inishturk, Co. Mayo; Inishbofin, Gorumna, Inishmore, Inishmaan and Inisheer, Co. Galway; Great Blasket Island and Valentia, Co. Kerry; Bear, Sherkin and Clear, Co. Cork; Great and Little Saltee, Co. Wexford; North Bull, Dublin and Lambay, Co. Dublin; and Rathlin Island, Co. Antrim.[29]

For unclear reasons, possibly related to the absence of ground predators such as stoats and foxes, which makes escaping down narrow holes and crevices unnecessary, island wood mice are often larger than their mainland cousins.[30] Fairley showed that those from Rathlin Island, Co. Antrim, and Great Blasket Island, Co. Kerry, were significantly larger that those on the mainland.[31]

Ireland's smallest mammal, the insectivorous pigmy shrew, is another intrepid island dweller and has been noted on Tory and Aran Island, Co. Donegal; Inishkea South, Achill and Clare, Co. Mayo; Inishmore and Inishmaan, Co. Galway; Great Blasket Island, Co. Kerry; Sherkin and Clear, Co. Cork; Great

Saltee, Co. Wexford; North Bull, Dublin, and Rathlin, Co. Antrim.[29]

After the wood mouse, pigmy shrew, and possibly the house mouse, the next most widespread terrestrial mammal on Irish islands is the rabbit, followed by the brown rat and then the Irish hare. Rabbits were almost certainly first brought to Ireland in late Norman and early Plantagenet times. The first references to rabbit warrens, or *cunicularia*, where these lagomorphs were kept and bred for their fur, were in the reign of Edward I, between 1274 and 1307. One early record, dated 1282, refers to 20 skins from Ballysax, Co. Kildare.[29,32]

Rabbits are present on most Irish islands and in some populations there is a relatively high proportion of melanistic individuals. For example, on Duvillaun More, Co. Mayo, black rabbits constitute up to 20% of the population at the western end of the island. Here they are at a selective advantage over the normal coloured individuals because of their cryptic concealment amongst the black banks of peat from predation by the ever present great black-backed gulls.[33]

The Irish hare is generally absent from the islands and where it does occur it has been almost certainly introduced. Hares are found on Inishvickillane, Co. Kerry, Mutton Island, Co. Clare and Clare Island, Co. Mayo. There have been several attempts to introduce them to Rathlin Island, Co. Antrim. They have also been brought to Rabbit Island, west Cork. There is a thriving population in North Bull Island, Dublin, where they are easily observed and fully protected. They are absent from the Saltee Islands, Co. Wexford, Lambay Island, Co. Dublin, and the Aran Islands, Co. Galway.

The brown rat is a relatively recent arrival in Ireland. It arrived on a westward migration from Central Asia and is believed to have reached England in 1728 or 1729. Rutty writes that 'it began to infest these parts about 1722'.[34] By 1729 they were reaching pest proportions in Dublin. A contemporary account spoke of 'a parcel of these outlandish Marramounts which are called Mountain Rats, who are now here, grow very common ... walk in droves and do a great deal of mischief'. The writer then describes how they ate a woman and nurse child in Merrion. In 1744 an Irish statute was passed, offering rewards for the killing of otters, weasels, martens, herons, kites and water rats, commonly called 'Norway rats.'[32] Brown rats are still present on most islands such as the Aran Islands, Co. Galway, Mutton Island, Co. Clare, the Saltees, Co. Wexford, Lambay Island, Co. Dublin, and Rathlin, Co. Antrim. There are none on the Inishkea Islands, Co. Mayo, and they are said to have been banished from Tory Island, Co. Donegal, by St Columkille, as related by Mason.[35] The black rat, once numerous in Ireland, is thought to be extinct as a resident species but occasionally escapes from visiting ships to establish itself on islands. However, it is not known if there are viable self-sustaining populations.

The largest mammal to be found on any Irish island is the red deer. A small herd was established on the remote, grass-covered Inishvickillane (81 ha and highest point 135 m), Co. Kerry, by Charles Haughey in the 1970s. The objective was to protect an isolated population, drawn from the 'native' herd in the Killarney Valley, Co. Kerry, from cross-breeding with Japanese sika deer, and thus to ensure the continuance of the genetic purity. Hares were also brought into the island, and, like the deer, are flourishing today. Not all introductions, however, involve native species. On Lambay Island, Co. Dublin, in August 1906 Cecil Barring, later first Lord Revelstoke, released 12 Hermann's tortoises and two European pond tortoises from Italy, and one slowworm. Mouflon and fallow deer were later added to this motley crew. Only the fallow deer survived.

Bird observatories, bird migration and sea-watching

Islands, together with parts of the coastline that jut out into the sea, have long been known as the best places to observe bird migration during the spring and autumn. Ireland's geographic position ensures its commanding position for migrating birds. The western coastline with its islands dotting the sea like so many beacons is a major flyway for waders migrating between their Iceland–Greenland breeding grounds and their wintering areas in Ireland or further south. Ringed plover, turnstone, sanderling, dunlin, purple sandpiper, whimbrel and golden plover generally follow this coastline and the offshore islands during their migrations. Amongst the passerines following the same pattern are meadow pipits, wheatears, white wagtails, snow and other buntings. Fieldfares, redwings and other thrushes together with skylarks from north and northeastern Europe are often driven southwestwards by hard weather to the milder conditions along the Irish west coast and its islands. Spring migrants from north Africa and southern Europe arrive on the southern and eastern seaboards while in the autumn easterly winds often deflect birds returning south from Europe to the eastern and southern coastlines where they are most conspicuous on the islands and isolated headlands.

Off shore, especially along the northern, western and southern coasts, is another totally different world of birds specialised for life in the ocean environment. During the spring and autumn winged processions of seabirds move past the islands and headlands on their southerly or northerly movements. Substantial numbers, and some great rarities, are often recorded during stormy weather or conditions of poor visibility.

The bird observatories at Great Saltee, Co. Wexford (opened in 1950, closed 1964, but still operating on an *ad hoc* basis),[36] Copeland Islands, Co. Down (opened in 1954 and still operating)[37] and Clear Island, Co. Cork (opened in 1959, still functioning)[38] are well positioned to sample Continental species that have either drifted or been pushed westwards from Britain and the European mainland by easterly winds. Rarities from America, driven across the Atlantic by westerly winds, also occasionally appear at Clear Island and other southwestern coastal locations. To these three observatories must be added others, mostly temporary, that have been manned by dedicated and enthusiastic ornithologists. Among the best known are Tory Island (1958–65)[39] and Malin Head (1961–5),[40] Co. Donegal, and Annagh Head (1964–5)[41] and the Inishkea Islands (1961– and *ad hoc* observations), Co. Mayo.[42]

A remarkable project on migration was launched in the late nineteenth century by Barrington, initially under the aegis of the British Association for the Advancement of Science, but later under his own dedicated patronage. Barrington contacted all the Irish lighthouse keepers and asked them to send records of birds striking the light or found dead beneath. While on migration at night birds are drawn to the light and are often killed hitting the glass. His chain of observers spanned the whole Irish coastline including all islands with a lighthouse on them. Later he asked the keepers to send the body or wing of any birds found dead at the light. These specimens, dutifully forwarded by the keepers, provided valuable measurements of wing length, allowing the separation of geographical races of birds such as Greenland and Irish/British breeding wheatears. Barrington ran his scheme from 1852–98 and he collected over 2,000 records which he analysed and published in 1900 as *The Migration of Birds*

MAP
SHOWING THE POSITIONS OF THE
IRISH LIGHT STATIONS
FROM WHICH
OBSERVATIONS OR SPECIMENS HAVE BEEN RECEIVED.

● Lighthouses
+ Light-Ships.

The Irish lighthouse network used by Barrington in his migration studies. From Barrington[43]. (D. Burke).

as observed at Irish Lighthouses and Lightships.[43] Only 350 copies were printed, subsidised by Barrington himself, and today it is one of the most highly prized of Irish ornithological texts, albeit extremely rare.

Fifteen migratory species including two subspecies previously unknown in Ireland were recorded for the first time through Barrington's lighthouse observer network. They were woodchat shrike, red-breasted flycatcher, lesser whitethroat, yellow-browed warbler, short-toed lark, lapland bunting, mealy redpole, Greenland wheatear, melodious warbler, aquatic warbler, reed warbler, Pallas's grasshopper warbler, Dartford warbler, little bunting and the shore lark. Moreover, many birds that had formerly been thought to be residents in Ireland such as the mistle thrush, song thrush, blackbird, goldcrest, meadow pipit, skylark, chaffinch, greenfinch, rook and the water rail, were shown by their frequent occurrences at the light stations to be migrants – quite a revelation at the time.

Seabirds

The islands of Ireland are crucial breeding locations for 22 species of seabirds, including the five tern species discussed in the previous chapter. Three species – the storm petrel, Manx shearwater and gannet – breed here in internationally important numbers. Ireland also hosted over one-fifth of the total British-Irish breeding population of the cormorant (40%), black-headed gull (28%) and herring gull (22%) for the most recent period for which comparative data is available (1985–7, Table 10.1). When one realises that the length of the British coastline is more than double that of Ireland and the islands twice as numerous, the significance of Ireland as a major west European seabird breeding area is even more striking.

Table 10.1 The approximate total numbers of pairs of 17 seabirds breeding in Europe, Britain and Ireland, 1985–7 (data from Lloyd et al.[1]).

Species	European	Britain & Ireland	Ireland	Irish % of European	Irish % of British/Irish
Fulmar	5,840,000	571,000	31,300	0.54	5.48
Manx shearwater	306,000	275,000	*c.* 40,000	13.07	14.54
Storm petrel	247,000	160,000	*c.* 75,000	30.36	46.87
Leach's petrel	60,600	55,000	*c.* 200	0.36	0.33
Gannet	223,600	187,700	24,700	11.05	13.16
Cormorant*	86,000	11,700	4,700	5.46	40.17
Shag	125,000	47,300	8,820	7.06	18.65
Black-headed gull*	1,200,000	233,000	66,000	5.50	28.33
Common gull*	488,000	71,400	3,600	0.74	5.04
Lesser black-backed gull*	187,000	88,500	5,200	2.78	5.88
Herring gull *	978,000	206,000	44,700	4.57	21.70
Great black-backed gull	83,100	23,400	4,500	5.42	19.23
Kittiwake	1,740,000	544,000	50,200	2.89	9.23
Guillemot	3,000,000	806,100	102,500	3.42	12.72
Razorbill	612,000	122,000	22,900	3.74	18.77
Black guillemot	100,000	20,200	*c.* 1,500	1.50	7.43
Puffin	6,890,000	467,000	20,700	0.30	4.43
Totals	**22,166,300**	**3,888,300**	**506,500**	**2.28**	**13.03**

* includes inland breeding birds. Europe as used here excludes USSR, Svalbard, Jan Mayen, Greenland and Macaronesian islands.

There are nine seabird colonies around the Irish coastline, all islands but one, with more than 10,000 breeding pairs in each. Six of these are on the west coast (Table 10.2). The most important area for breeding storm petrels is the southwest, where the largest colonies (each estimated greater than 10,000 pairs in the 1980s) are on Tearaght Island, Inishvickillane, Inishtooskert and Great Skellig, Co. Kerry. The region also held during the 1980s at least three-quarters of the breeding population of the Manx shearwater in Ireland, with large numbers on Scariff Island, Puffin Island, Great Skellig, Inishvickillane, Tearaght Island, Inishnabro and Inishtooskert, Co. Kerry. The question to be

Razorbills.

asked is why are there so many petrels and shearwaters breeding in this area?

Table 10.2 Seabird colonies holding more than 10,000 pairs (from Hutchinson[44]).

Island	No. species	Ful	Manx shear	Storm petrel	Gan	Corm	Shag	Gu/Ra	Puff	Black guille	Gulls
Saltees, Co. Wexford.	12	•	•		•	•	•	•	•	•	•
Skelligs, Co. Kerry.	11	•	•	•	•		•	•	•		•
Blaskets, Co. Kerry.	14	•	•	•		•	•	•	•	•	•
Puffin Id, Co. Kerry.	12	•	•	•			•	•	•		•
Inishglora, Co. Mayo.	9			•						•	•
Illanmaster, Co. Mayo.	10	•	•	•			•	•	•	•	•
Horn Head, Co. Donegal.	9	•					•	•	•	•	•
Rathlin Id, Co. Antrim.	13	•	•				•	•	•	•	•
Lambay Id, Co. Dublin.	12	•	•			•	•	•	•	•	•

Key: Ful = fulmar; Manx shear = Manx shearwater; Gan = gannet; Corm = cormorant; Gu/Ra = guillemot/razorbill; Puff = puffin; Black guille = black guillemot

Gannets breeding on Little Skellig, Co. Kerry.

The mechanisms controlling the distribution and numbers of seabirds are complex but the availability of food seems a critical factor, important both during and outside the breeding season. Competition becomes more severe with higher densities of seabirds. The availability of breeding sites in a particular area is also a factor. The large numbers of storm petrels and Manx shearwaters present in southwest Ireland seem to indicate a more than adequate supply of food within the feeding range of the breeding colonies. The storm petrel feeds exclusively at sea, snatching its fare from the water's surface in the form of crustaceans, small fish, jellyfish and oily offal floating behind fishing boats. The Manx shearwater does the same, taking fish, cephalopods, crustaceans and floating offal, picked up directly off the surface or immediately below it.[45] Factors such as temperature, current upwelling, the availability of nutrients, tidal flows and the population structure of the marine ecosystems, all contribute to enhancing the biological productivity of the waters off this part of the coast with the result that food is plentiful for the large petrel and shearwater populations.

The abundance and availability of food before and during the breeding season allows adult seabirds to combat the drain of energy resulting from raising a family. It also determines the number (generally one or two per breeding pair), health and subsequent survival of young birds. This good start is all the more important as the young become liable to much greater mortality when fledged – up to 30% of many seabirds, such as the razorbill, die in their first year.[46] However, because razorbills do not become sexually mature for several years, such high mortality rates do not have the serious depressive impact on numbers that one would imagine. When immature birds die the colony does not lose valued breeders. Adult mortality rates, on the other hand, are relatively low – for the razorbill it is only 10% per annum in a stable breeding colony.[46] Should there be a small increase in the adult mortality rate, the impact on numbers can be severe. If, in a breeding colony of 50 pairs of razorbills, an additional five adults die on top of the initial 10% each year (i.e. 15 birds instead of 10) this would represent a 50% increase in mortality that would, in turn, lead to a 5% decline in breeding numbers. An extra 5 immature razorbills dying each year represents an increase of only 17% in mortality because they already have such a high mortality rate. The converse is also true. If adult mortality rates were reduced and remained lower on average over several years then seabird numbers could rise quite significantly. This has been found true for several species such as the guillemot breeding in Scotland and England.

The cormorant

The cormorant belongs to the order of Pelicans, or Pelecaniformes, and has a hooked tip to its bill – a useful adaptation for ripping open fish flesh – as well as totipalmate feet in which all four toes are joined by webs. For the biologist it is a rewarding species, being so big and conspicuous that its breeding colonies are easy to locate and census. Accurate records can therefore be gathered about the rise and fall of the different breeding populations. The immatures, somewhat repulsive and mildly reptilian, are easy to catch while still in their nest. This is the best time to ring or tag them with a numbered metal ring on their tarsus. When they die their large size makes it difficult for them to be overlooked if washed up on the beach, thus increasing the chances of any ringed birds being reported. Cormorants are still shot as predators – some legally under licence, others not – in Ireland, Britain, France, Spain and Portugal. These killings produce more recoveries. Moreover, cormorants are often found entangled and dead in fish nets, or caught in fish traps where they ended up whilst in pursuit of prey. As a result they have one of the highest recovery rates (approximately 13% of the total ringed number) of all seabirds. The high rate of return of their rings can provide a detailed picture of their movements, dispersions, migrations, causes and frequency of death. These findings are based on a much greater amount of information than would be possible for a smaller bird such as a warbler or sparrow for which recovery rates are only about one twentieth to one fortieth that of the cormorant.

One of the several cliff-top colonies of cormorants, Little Saltee, Co. Wexford.

Cormorants breed along the coast, mostly on islands, but also at several inland sites where they nest in trees to escape ground predators including man. More than one third of all the cormorants breeding in Britain and Ireland are found in Ireland where the largest colonies also occur – 380 pairs on Sheep Island, Co. Antrim, and 1,027 pairs on Lambay Island, Co. Dublin. An extensive survey was carried out in 1985–6, when 4,455 pairs were found throughout the country. Of these, 44.5% were in colonies on marine islands, 36.5% on the mainland coast and the remaining 19% on islands in inland freshwater loughs.[47] The increase in the size of the breeding population between the two censuses was 142%, compared with a 5% decline in Britain. The jump in the Irish population was inflated because of the more intensive surveys of the second census. The figures may also have been boosted by a decline in adult mortality following the protection of the cormorant under the *Wildlife Act, 1976*. Prior to the Act a bounty scheme was in operation and large numbers were killed each year – 3,527 bounties were paid in the final years of the scheme between 1973 and 1976.

One of the largest cormorant colonies in Ireland is on Little Saltee Island, Co. Wexford. Here most pairs build their bulky nests perched on top of the old stone walls snaking across the once farmed fields. Detailed censusing of the colony and ringing of young birds started in 1960 and is still in progress today, making it one of the longest continuously studied cormorant colonies in western Europe.[48] The colony has remained remarkably stable over the past 38 years with a mean of 300 breeding pairs.

Unless a cormorant breeding colony is severely disturbed by man approximately 95% of all adults will return to their natal colony to breed.[49] As Little Saltee has not been disrupted there has been no reason for adults to move away to breed elsewhere, therefore any natural increase in the numbers of birds should be reflected in the colony size, providing there are no strong negative factors operating on the population such as excessive mortality by shooting. Food is not a restricting factor either as there is no evidence to suggest that the waters around and near the colony are poorly supplied. A study of regurgitated food in the Little Saltee colony conducted over four summers by West, Cabot & Greer-Walker found that corkwing wrasse, cuckoo wrasse, ballan wrasse and unidentified wrasse comprised 76% of the total weight (21.7 kg) of the food examined from the colony. European eels made up 18%, flat fish comprised 3% and other species made up the 3% balance.[50]

There have been no signs of illness or disease amongst the birds in or near the colony. Levels of pesticide residues and polychlorinated biphenyls (PCBs) were measured in the eggs but were not high enough to affect breeding performance.[48] In the absence of detrimental factors in or around Little Saltee itself it would appear that adult mortality, suffered within Ireland and Britain, but perhaps more importantly in France and Spain where many birds spend time, is still sufficiently high to hold down any significant increase in numbers. Overall annual adult mortality for birds of three years old and upwards has been calculated at 14% (see below).

An extensive analysis by Coulson & Brazendale of 1,842 ringing recoveries of cormorants from breeding colonies in Ireland and Britain (representing 23% of the total number of ringed birds) showed there was no migration *per se* although there was a 'movement' of birds. Cormorants from different breeding areas exhibited different patterns of dispersal which were perhaps related

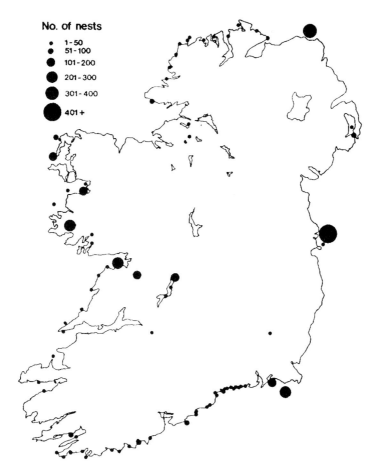

No. of nests

• 1-50
• 51-100
● 101-200
● 201-300
● 301-400
● 401+

Distribution and size of cormorant colonies in 1985 and 1986. From Macdonald[47].

to environmental factors and genetic differences in each colony or group.[51] The results begged questions about the distinction between dispersal and migration. Migration is usually understood to mean a regular and seasonal movement of part or the bulk of an animal population between specific geographic locations. Dispersion is non-directional and not so related to season. However, results from the recovery of Little Saltee cormorants indicate very clearly true migration patterns alongside signs of a more erratic dispersal. There is, in fact, a regular traffic of birds travelling southwards into northern France, Spain and Portugal in the autumn. Other less ambitious groups, made up of both immatures and older birds, move northwards, especially to Northern Ireland, on a regular basis, and to other locations within Ireland. A smaller component of the population moves across the Irish Sea to Wales, northern and southwest England. There have also been two recoveries of older birds from Denmark and Holland (Table 10.3).

Table 10.3 Recovery of cormorants ringed as pulli on Little Saltee 1960–96 (data from Cabot[48]).

Area of recovery	Immatures (12 months from 1 July)		Adults (over 12 months from 1 July)		Totals	
	Number reported	% of all recoveries	Number reported	% of all recoveries	Number reported	% of all recoveries
Co. Wexford	179	15.8	147	13.0	326	28.7
Northern Ireland	113	10.0	44	3.9	157	13.9
Rest of Ireland	134	11.8	45	4.0	179	15.8
Scotland	4	–	1	–	5	0.4
Wales	9	0.8	15	1.3	24	2.1
England	53	4.7	32	2.8	85	7.5
Denmark	0	–	1	–	1	–
Holland	0	–	1	–	1	–
France	182	16.0	65	5.7	245	21.6
Spain	59	5.2	28	2.5	87	7.7
Portugal	16	1.4	6	0.5	24	2.1
Totals	749	66.0	385	34.0	1,134	100

Note: 33 birds, 'controlled' (recaptured on their nests) breeding on Little Saltee are not included in the above table.

While some of these movements clearly fall into the category of dispersal, a large proportion (31%) of all the recoveries each year come from France, Spain and Portugal. Of all the birds recovered in these southern parts, 72.2% are immatures in their first year while older birds make up the remaining 27.8%. The greater proportion of travelling birds in their first year is characteristic of many other seabirds including the gannet. It is not known if these young birds move in family parties with their parents, by themselves, or whether they travel in loose groups. However, both adults and juveniles start moving away from Little Saltee as soon as the breeding season is over which can be any time for the young from early June or much later for adults if they breed later in the season. The regular pattern of recoveries of older cormorants every year from France, Spain and Portugal proves that repeated trips and migrations are made by adult birds breeding on Little Saltee. These movements are a discovery at odds with the earlier theory of dispersal and the generally accepted belief, as stated by Lloyd, Tasker & Partridge, that 'the majority of cormorants breeding in Britain and Ireland are residents or only move locally'.[1]

A total of 9,006 pulli were ringed at Little Saltee 1960–97, generating 1,167 recoveries, or 12.9% of those ringed, as reported to 1 April 1997. The enquiry into the causes of mortality is complicated by the substantial portion of birds being reported 'found dying' or 'found dead', many of which were probably shot. This first difficulty is compounded by the fact that the reports will be biased towards cormorants caught in traps or nets, or shot – and that they will tend to overlook those that died from natural causes such as old age, disease or starvation. The pattern of reported deaths for cormorants ringed as nestlings on Little Saltee show that inexperienced birds in their first year are two and a half times as likely to be shot and three times as likely to drown in fish traps and nets than older and presumably more experienced and 'wiser' birds. In an analysis of recovery rates of ringed cormorants during their first, second and older years from colonies in Britain and Ireland during the period 1976–93, Wernham confirmed the vulnerability of the fledglings. The average survival rate for birds from Ireland in their first year was 32%; it rose to 70% for birds in their second year and increased to 86% for birds in their third year and older.[52] Shooting by man is unquestionably the prime cause of mortality for the cormorant population in Europe (Table 10.4). The report slips for Little Saltee birds are clear about that. They often read 'shot' or 'found shot' – not to mention the euphemistic 'found dead'!

Table 10.4 Reported mortality of cormorants ringed on Little Saltee, Co. Wexford, 1960–96 (data from Cabot[48]).

Reported	Immatures (to 1 July following year)		Adults (older than 12 months		Total	
	Number	% of all deaths	Number	% of all deaths	Number	% of all deaths
Shot/killed	311	27.4	124	10.9	435	38.3
Found dead	261	23.0	156	13.8	417	36.8
Caught in fish nets and traps	141	12.4	48	4.2	189	16.7
Unknown causes	23	2.0	19	1.7	42	3.7
Sick/Injured – broken wing	17	1.5	10	0.9	27	2.4
Oiled	7	0.6	0	–	7	0.6
Collision with overhead wires	5	–	1	–	6	0.5
Taken by wild animals	3	–	1	–	4	0.4
Miscellaneous	3	–	4	–	7	0.6
Totals	**771**	**68.0**	**363**	**32.0**	**1,134**	**100**

The circumstances of death can be most bizarre, as illustrated by the way two Little Saltee cormorants came to grief. Both were young and inexperienced birds. The first, ringed as a nestling on 6 June 1972, was retrieved from the belly of a turbot caught in the Baie d'Audierne, Finistère, France, on 18 August 1972. The second was a nestling ringed 19 June 1966. It drowned in a trammel net at Ares, Coruna, Spain on 23 March 1967. The recovery slip noted that it had 'served as dinner for six'. There was no comment on how it tasted!

The cormorant's claimed predilection for game fish brings it into conflict with anglers and fishery conservators. However, observations by the Salmon Research Trust of Ireland based at Furnace Lough, near Newport, Co. Mayo, have shown that cormorants in some western lakes take up to only 9% of the migrating salmon and trout and that most of the salmon smolt eaten by the cormorants had been released from hatcheries and were not wild.[1] Thus the impact of cormorants on wild salmon stocks during this study was very small. The diet of cormorants feeding in Midland lakes where there are important stocks of brown trout has also been subjected to limited investigation. Their impact was determined by examination of undigested remains in cormorant pellets collected at a roost at Lough Ramor, Co. Cavan, throughout the winter (September 1985 to April 1986). Results were expressed as percentage com-

Nestling cormorants.

position of pellets of identifiable fish remains. Coarse fish, roach and perch were the main species taken, with few or no brown trout, eels or pike record-ed. Roach constituted over 80% of the diet in the period January–February.[47] In fact, the highest concentrations of wintering cormorants in Ireland are found on those lakes holding the biggest populations of roach. The increasing spread and abundance of roach is certainly linked to the growth and expan-sion of parts of the national cormorant population so clearly witnessed at some colonies.

The fulmar

Over the past 200 years the fulmar has undergone one of the most remarkable range and population explosions of any seabird in the Atlantic Ocean. The reasons are not entirely clear. However, Fisher cogently argued the case that their spread was almost certainly related to the availability of extra food in the form of discarded offal, first from the whaling industry and then from trawlers of the expanding fishing fleets.[53] Other less convincing reasons evoked include the emergence of a genetic variation, conferring new vigour to the population and favouring geographic expansion, and the gradual warming of the Eastern Atlantic during the last century.[54,55]

Numbers breeding in Ireland and Britain have increased over the past hun-dred years while the breeding range has gradually extended southwards, not from St Kilda as sometimes stated, but from Foula in the Shetland Isles – which had been colonised by birds from the Faroes in 1878. The annual rate of increase in Britain and Ireland before 1939, leaving out St Kilda, was in the order of 13–19%, falling to 8% for the period 1939–49. It declined further to 4% between 1969–70 and 1985–7, but was still sufficiently high to bring about substantial increases in numbers and breeding range. The first fulmars discov-ered breeding in Ireland were on the north Mayo cliffs in 1911 and in Co. Donegal in 1912. Having gained a foothold they quickly spread to Kerry in 1913, Antrim in 1923, and Clare in 1924. During Operation Seafarer 1969–70 a total of 19,300 pairs were censused and the figure had increased to an esti-mated 31,300 pairs by 1985–7 – representing 5.5% of the total population in Britain and Ireland, distributed mainly in the northwest, southwest and south-

Fulmar (J. Barlee).

ern coastline and islands.[1] On the east coast at Lambay Island, Co. Dublin, numbers increased from 75 to 560 pairs over the same period. The largest colonies found in Ireland during the second census were on the Cliffs of Moher, Co. Clare, (3,100 pairs) and the Blasket Islands, Co. Kerry (2,200 pairs).

The number of fulmars nesting on Little Saltee, Co. Wexford, has been monitored from the time of the first five breeding pairs in 1962. Since then population growth has been rapid, reaching 292 pairs in 1997, despite a somewhat erratic progress, marked by increases some years and declines in others.[56] A similar pattern was noted at the long-studied colony on the Orkney island of Eynhallow. On Little Saltee the low western boulder clay cliffs allow easy access to nest sites for capturing both adults and pulli, leaving only short precipitous sections on the eastern side out of reach. Incubating adults and pulli have been ringed since 1974 while all available adults are caught and checked to see if they bear rings put on them in previous years. The total number of breeding adults ringed between 1974 and 1997 inclusive was 648, in addition to 591 pulli. Each year the population is censused and as many breeding adults as possible are caught. From 1974–97 inclusive a total of 1,285 adults have been examined of which 745 (57.9%) were 'controls' – retraps of birds ringed in previous years on Little Saltee.

To date only five of the ringed pulli have been recovered away from the island, suggesting a low incidence of emigration. One was captured while breeding on the Scilly Isles, aged 13 years; two others, aged seven and 16, were found nesting in Finistère, France; and two, both found dead, aged four and

ten, were reported from Norfolk and Cumbria respectively. Only three individuals ringed as breeding adults have been found away from Little Saltee – all
dead. One had got to Noordholland, ten years after ringing; another to the
Ribble Estuary, Lancashire, a year after ringing and the third to Sweden where
it was a victim of oil pollution 13 years after ringing. Despite large numbers of
fulmars ringed on the nearby Great Saltee only one, marked as a nestling, was
re-trapped at Little Saltee, not breeding but probably just inspecting the
island, when aged three years. So far, the only occurrence of immigrant fulmars was a nestling ringed on Orkney, Scotland, recovered five years later at
Little Saltee but not breeding. In the absence of proven breeding immigrants,
the growth of the Little Saltee colony would appear to be sustained by internal
recruitment.

   The work carried out by Dunnet and colleagues on the Eynhallow colony has
shown that, on average, fulmars breed for the first time at about nine years old
(males at eight, females at ten) and live for another 34–35 years. Those that
survive to breeding age have a total life expectancy of about 44 years.[57] So
when Fisher suggested that fulmars might live as long as 50 years as part of his
explanation for their rapid population increase – arousing general scepticism
amongst ornithologists – he was not far from the truth.[58] Dunnet's work also
showed that each year, on average, only six breeding adults will die out of every
100, that every 100 pairs will rear between 16 and 52 chicks, and that these
have an annual survival of 88–93% up to breeding age. Productivity of young
birds from Little Saltee, measured over 10 seasons from 1976–86, is in general
accordance with the findings from Eynhallow with estimates varying from 0.34
to 0.82 per breeding pair with a mean of 0.51 ± 0.13.

Other island-nesting seabirds

There are many other island breeding seabirds, but here mention is restricted
to three: shags, razorbills and kittiwakes.

   The number of shags breeding in Ireland as a proportion of the combined
Irish/British breeding population (18.6% or 8,820 pairs) is much lower than
the proportion of cormorants (40.2% or 4,700 pairs), with many more and
smaller colonies. Lambay Island, Co. Dublin, is the exception with over 1,000
pairs. Unlike the cormorant, the shag is particularly sensitive to harsh weather
and the availability of food, especially sand eels. For example, in 1979 some
273 breeding pairs were counted on Great Saltee Island, Co. Wexford. The following year the number rose to 434 pairs and the increase was attributed to
particularly good weather in May encouraging shags to nest.[59] Conversely, one
winter of particularly severe weather reduced the breeding popualtion on
nearby Little Saltee from 120 to 27 pairs. Shags are more conservative in their
post-breeding travels than cormorants. Of 1,045 Irish ringed shags reported
recovered up to February 1988 only 66 had travelled away from Ireland, chiefly
to Scotland, and only one made it to France.[44]

   The razorbill and kittiwake are two other characteristic island seabirds with
Ireland hosting 18.8% of the combined Irish/British breeding population of
razorbills (22,900 pairs) and 9.2% of kittiwakes (50,200 pairs). Overall the
numbers of kittiwakes in Ireland increased between 1969–70 and 1985–7 while
there was little change in razorbill numbers despite dramatic decline at some
colonies, especially in amongst the Blasket Islands, Co. Kerry. A remarkable
mainland colony of kittiwakes occurs in the harbour of Dunmore East, Co.

Waterford, where the birds can be observed at close quarters. Large numbers of razorbills, mostly juveniles, and guillemots are trapped and drowned each year in salmon drift nets set off the west coast. In the Galway Fishery District alone, 763 and 109 razorbills and guillemots were recovered and reported trapped in 1977 and 1978 respectively. It was not possible to determine the impact of this mortality on the nearby breeding colonies on the Cliffs of Moher.[60]

Barnacle geese

Despite their protection under the *Wildlife Act, 1976* most barnacle geese still behave the wild way and seek seclusion from man during their wintering period in Ireland. Peace is best provided by inaccessible islands. Of all western Palaearctic geese, the Greenland breeding population of the barnacle goose is most characteristically found wintering on offshore islands along the western and northern coasts from mid-October to the end of April. Their small stubby bills allow them to pluck grasses and herbs too short for sheep or cattle to grasp. On close-cropped swards yielding not a blade of long grass, hungry cattle will follow the birds around and eat droppings of the geese which are extruded at a frequency of about one every three minutes. A grazing flock of 200–300 birds will produce between 4,000 and 6,000 droppings every hour.

Barnacles feed almost incessantly during most of the day and often during the night. Yet they do not make the most of what they eat. The nutritional value – measured by calories – of barnacle goose droppings was investigated by West in a study carried out on the Inishkea Islands, Co. Mayo. He found that only about 30% of the calorific value of the grass had been extracted by the geese – cellulose-digesting bacteria are scarce in goose alimentary tracts – leaving about 70% in the droppings for the cattle.[61] This interesting dependency cannot be called 'symbiosis' or 'mutualism' as the benefits are entirely for the cattle without any apparent advantage conferred to the geese. The former are best described as facultative parasites of the latter, as they can also live independently when grass is more easily available.

The barnacle goose is a small black and white bird that would seem to be colour-adapted to its white (snow) and black (rock) arctic environment where it lives during the summer but not to its wintering areas, the green grass swards

Barnacle geese.

of Ireland and Scotland. Once described by the writer T.H. White as looking like 'prim Victorian spinsters dressed up in white lace', barnacles certainly make a very original sight, a dashing instance of 'pied beauty' to echo the praise of Gerard Manley Hopkins.[62] The numbers of the Greenland breeding population have been increasing but instead of spreading their numbers throughout a large, apparently favourable, habitat from the islands off the Kerry coast to the Shetlands, most are found on the island of Islay, in Scotland, where the feeding ecology is the best and richest within the whole wintering range (Table 10.5).

Table 10.5 Numbers of Greenland barnacle geese found during aerial surveys of Ireland and Scotland 1959–94 (data from Ogilvie et al.[63]).

Year	Ireland	Islay	Rest of Scotland	Total
1994	8,100	25,622	4,633	38,355
1988	7,594	20,292	6,658	34,544
1983	4,432	14,000	6,790	25,222
1978	5,709	21,500	6,556	33,765
1973	4,398	15,000	4,736	24,134
1966	4,719	8,500	6,608	19,827
1962	4,404	4,800	4,766	13,970
1961	4,161	5,500	4,240	13,901
1959	2,771	2,800	2,706	8,277

Meanwhile, despite an increase in the population wintering within Ireland its numbers here as a proportion of the total population in Ireland and Scotland are declining. Such a miserable performance would indicate that the maximum carrying capacity, conditioned by the availability and nutritional value of grass, of most western and northern island haunts has been reached. This is almost certainly the case for the Inishkea Islands, Co. Mayo, where the population dynamics of the barnacle have been the subject of a long-term study by Cabot, West, Cassidy, Viney and other colleagues since 1961.[64, 65] Results from these investigations show that despite a 4.2% annual population growth of the Greenland stock between 1961 and 1983 the numbers on Inishkea remained remarkably stable, fluctuating slightly around a mean of 2,230 birds. These

Inishbofin Island, Co. Donegal, an important wintering site for barnacle geese (A. Walsh).

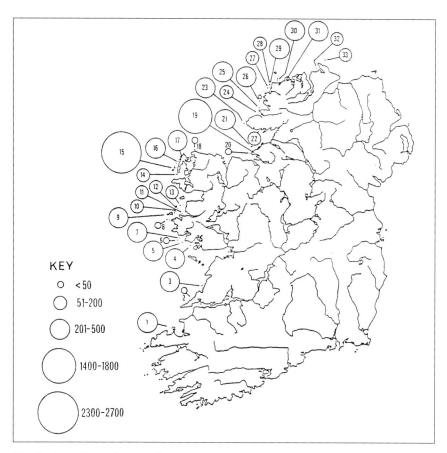

Distribution of barnacle goose flocks in spring 1993 and 1994. From O.J. Merne & A. Walsh (1994). Barnacle geese in Ireland, Spring 1993 and 1994. *Irish Birds* 5: 151–156.

birds are characterised by an almost disproportionate amount of either failed or non-breeding adults, a likely consequence of a low grade feeding habitat, especially towards the end of the winter when little grass remains. Thus, as the winter progresses the successful breeders take their families away from the island to better provided areas where the young can feed on more nutritious grasses – young geese stay with their parents all winter until the next breeding season.

A total of 883 barnacle geese were caught on the Inishkea Islands between 1961 and 1998, mostly in mist nets, and had colour rings or individually inscribed plastic rings (with three alphabetic letters) put on their legs so that the life history of each distinctively-marked goose can be followed from year to year as they return to spend the winter months on the islands. The colour codes and inscribed plastic rings can be read by telescope at a range of up to 350 m so that once ringed the geese need never again endure the trauma of being caught in a net. There have been over 18,000 subsequent sightings of the individually marked geese and the majority of them return to the islands each winter to graze the same fields. Others, particularly the young females, transfer their allegiance to other wintering areas, mainly on Islay. These may have become paired to males with already established wintering grounds on Islay or elsewhere. Such geese are generally lost to Inishkea, seldom reappearing. Other geese are more flexible with a roving life style, dipping into Islay or Lissadell, Co. Sligo, and other west coast island haunts, either within one winter period, or taking a year off Inishkea and then subsequently returning. Once a goose has registered its wintering grounds over two or three winters it is less likely to wander to other haunts.

Barnacle geese are long-lived. Once they have survived to their second year their annual survival rate, calculated for Inishkea ringed birds observed over subsequent winters, is 0.86. In other words only about 14% of the adults die each year. The oldest barnacle goose wintering on the Inishkea Islands recorded so far was 21 years old but the normal life expectancy is in the order of 10–12 years. They pair for life with an extremely low incidence of divorce, but if a mate is lost, its partner finds another for the subsequent breeding season. Being long-lived birds they have delayed sexual maturity, generally not breeding until three years of age. The breeding success, as monitored throughout a lifetime, is highly spasmodic. Some birds never breed successfully, others produce only one successful brood while others can produce several broods, either in subsequent seasons or separated by many years of apparent barrenness. Whether this intermittently successful breeding is because the geese did not attempt to breed in Greenland as they were 'resting' or whether they did breed successfully but then lost all their brood to arctic predators such as the Arctic fox, gyr falcon or glaucous gull is unknown. Certainly predation of nests and mortality of goslings in Greenland can be high. Field studies at one of their cliff nesting sites in Nordmarken (77°33'N), northeast Greenland, in 1987, showed that only 55% of the nests studied were successful and of the 41 gosling hatched only 37% survived predation.[66] In another similar study of other cliff breeding colonies some 650 km south in Ørsted Dal, Jameson Land, the survival rate was slightly higher: 55% of 94 goslings monitored after hatching survived predation by Arctic foxes, gyrfalcons and glaucous gulls.[67]

Whatever the reasons behind their 'patchy' breeding performance, enough young geese endure and enter the breeding population to keep overall numbers steadily rising. The success of the population, especially in recent years, and the rapidly rising numbers on Islay have brought them into conflict with agricultural interests there. Farmers on Islay are currently compensated £9.50 per goose if the birds are deemed to be causing agricultural damage. If the Islay geese are pressurised to leave the island by shooting or other scaring techniques then other Scottish and many Irish islands could be the likely beneficiaries.

Seals

Seals and barnacle geese share one important attribute – both have a fear and distrust of man, sufficient reason for them both generally to inhabit islands. The common seal and grey seal are found in relatively small but increasing numbers on the islands and coastline of Ireland. They are marine carnivores belonging to the order Pinnipedia and are closely related to bears and dogs. They breed on land but spend most of their time in the sea. The fur-seals, sea lions and walruses are also pinnipeds. The latter is an arctic species. The num-

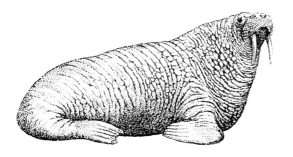

Walrus. There have been a surprising number of recent records in Irish waters. From Corbet & Southern[73].

ber living in the northeastern Atlantic area (mostly in Greenland), belonging to the subspecies *Odobenus r. rosmarus,* has been steadily declining to only 1,000–5,000 in the early 1970s.[68] During the winter there is a southerly movement of young or immature individuals, some wandering as far down as Scotland and Ireland. However, the walrus is a very rare visitor to Irish and British waters with only 24 records between 1815 and 1920. In Ireland, there was one recorded in the Shannon Estuary in 1897, one shot off Darrynane, Co. Kerry, in the 1920s, two seen off Co. Donegal in 1994, one found dead near Sybil Head, Co. Kerry, in 1995 and one observed in the waters at the Blasket Islands, Co. Kerry, in January 1997.[69,70,71,72]

Many people, including naturalists, sometimes find it difficult to distinguish between grey and common seals. The common seal has a more endearing, puppy-like face, different from the longer, more horse-like, or more 'roman' profile of the former. The grey seal is usually larger than the common seal – grey seal males average 2.07 m nose to tail (range 1.95–2.30 m) and females 1.80 m (range 1.65–1.95 m). Common seal males range from 1.30–1.60 m and females from 1.20–1.55 m.[73] The pelt colour can be similar in both but only the grey seal has pure white fur when born. Their habitat preferences are generally different but they do occur together, especially in rich feeding areas and where salmon netting is taking place. Common seals are most often found in sheltered bays and inlets with sand banks which are used as haul-outs. Ballysadare Bay, Co. Sligo, Clew Bay, Co. Mayo, and Strangford Lough, Co. Down, hold some of the largest concentrations of common seals in Ireland. By contrast, grey seals are creatures of the wilder, more exposed and rocky coastline, with haunts on remote, offshore islands. They are quite content to hoist themselves up onto a jagged, stony habitat, and when disturbed they will travel at remarkable speeds across the rough surface as they race to the safety of the sea. However, grey seals will also haul themselves out onto sand banks, sandy beaches or even grass-topped small islands, so it is unwise to assume that seals congregating on sand banks in sheltered bays must always be common seals.

Distribution and breeding

The locations of haul-outs of grey seals around the Irish coastline are not well known. However, two large haul-outs are known on the Inishkea Islands, Co. Mayo and the Blasket Islands, Co. Kerry. To be in close proximity to, say, 1,000 grey seals is a rare experience. The animals form a sea of blubber, a throbbing aggregation of heaving, shifting, grunting, crying, scratching, bickering, biting, snarling creatures. Often seen running amongst those heaps of flesh, in complete contrast to them and quite oblivious of the cacophony, are small, dainty waders such as the turnstone, picking their way in search of minute sandhoppers stirred up by the commotion on the sand.

During the autumn the grey seal cow gives birth to its single pup ashore. She drops it at the top of a sheltered rocky or sandy beach, or sometimes in a more protected and secure site, not so easily reached by the sea, such as the grassy top of a small island. Pups are born anytime from late September to mid-November. Research carried out by Summers on the seals breeding at the Inishkea Islands, Co. Mayo, in 1980 and 1983 found that the mean date of calving was 4 and 5 October respectively, with 95% of all births occurring between 4 September and 3 November and 4 September and 1 November respectively.[74,75] The pupping season at Inishkea is very similar to that in Scotland where, on North Rona for example, the mean date of pupping is 9 October with 95% of the births occurring between 15 September and 1 November. On this evidence Summers argues that the Irish breeding stock is not reproductively isolated from the Scottish stock.

Prior to the breeding season the seals are usually in groups of separate sexes close to the breeding grounds. The bull grey seal then acquires a breeding territory to share with up to 20 cows. The females go ashore and drop their single pup. The females belong to the bull's harem and he copulates with them around 14 days after the pups are born. However, within a week of impregnation the development of the fertilised egg is suspended for approximately 100 days. Thus the cow enjoys a breathing space before the developing embryo recommences its growth. The pups are born about 250 days after implantation. The cows generally moult their fur coats from January to March followed by the bulls from March to May. However, recent research by Kiely provides evidence that some cows at Great Blasket Island, Co. Kerry, start their moult directly after breeding.[76] After the breeding season the bulls and cows disperse and seem to go their separate ways.

Following the abandonment of the pups by their mothers, the mortality amongst the pups is in the order of 10–15% but may, in certain circumstances, rise to over 25%. In normal situations each pup has a 20% chance of surviving to the next moulting stage, some 15 months after birth. High tides and storms can sometimes inflict considerable mortality when newly-born pups are trapped at the top of beaches backed by a cliff wall – an ill-chosen location, often selected by an inexperienced cow.

*Common seals breed earlier in the year, in June and July. The pup is born on a sand bank exposed by the tide but unlike the grey seal, it is often able to swim successfully off the sand bank with the next tide after birth.

Grey seal surveys

In 1964–5 Lockley carried out what could be considered the first survey of grey and common seals in Irish coastal waters.[77] Although his work has been criticised, he was nevertheless the first person to make an informed estimate of the population of grey seals which he put at 2,000 individuals. He did not personally visit many of the breeding sites and failed to distinguish between his own direct observations and those that were sent to him by others. Due to the way seals behave, slipping in and out of the water incessantly, and then when in the water emerging and disappearing with confusing irregularity, it is almost

Bull, cow and pup grey seals. From Corbet & Southern[73].

impossible to count all adults accurately. So the accepted and best method of arriving at an estimate is by censusing the newly-born at all known breeding sites, then applying a multiplier of 3.5–4.5 – a figure obtained after careful research by Harwood & Prime working with *undisturbed* breeding populations of grey seals in Britain. Thus for every pup recorded by Lockley there were assumed to be 3.5 to 4.5 adults.[78] Lockley overlooked many pups, as was revealed by Summers' subsequent work on the west Mayo breeding colonies, so his estimated 2,000 grey seals was considerably below the actual numbers. It would have been more accurate to place the all Ireland all age population in the area of 3,000–3,800 individuals. This adjusted estimate was supported by surveys carried out by Summers in 1980 who arrived at a figure of an all age population of 2,800–3,600. In 1983, when Summers carried out another survey, the population seemed to have gone down with a minimum estimated size of 2,000–2,500 individuals, representing less that 4% of the total stock in Britain and Ireland at that time.[75]

The Scottish population of the grey seal in 1981 was estimated at 82,500 with the largest concentrations in the Outer Hebrides while the Orkneys and Inner Hebrides held smaller numbers. By 1994 the Scottish population had risen to approximately 90,000 out of a total British population of 108,500.[79] There have been seven recoveries, up to 1983, of seals tagged in Scotland in Irish waters – two from the Hebrides, three from the Orkneys and three from North Rona. This suggests that immature Scottish seals move south to Ireland in the summer, reaching the north and northwest coasts when the salmon netting season is in full sway.

An ingenious way of tracking the movements of seals is by photographing their unique facial and head colour patterns. Each photograph is then scanned, digitised and fed into a computerised database. Subsequent photographs of seals taken at the same or other locations are then compared with photographs held in the database in the hope of securing a 'match'. Kiely, who is using this method in Ireland, has had his first 'match' of a totally blind female – this does not seem to impair her fishing or breeding abilities – photographed on the Saltee Islands, Co. Wexford, in August 1996 which then turned up at a north Pembrokeshire breeding site a month later. There have been many recoveries of young seals tagged in Pembrokeshire and recovered in the Wicklow, Wexford, Waterford and Cork coastal areas including one that travelled as far west as Black Head, Co. Clare. Therefore Irish waters do not only play host to Scottish grey seals but also to Welsh visitors.

Interaction with fisheries

But what about the damage caused by seals to commercial fisheries in Irish waters? Salmon fishermen have complained for many years about severe predation by seals on salmon caught in drift nets. In response to these complaints, special inquiries were carried out during 1979–81 by McCarthy of the Department of Fisheries and Forestry's Fisheries Research Centre at Abbotstown, Co. Dublin.[80] Direct observations were made from chartered boats engaged in drift netting in Galway and Sligo Bays (Table 10.6). In addition, salmon landed for sale in Donegal, Mayo, Galway and Kerry were examined for seal damage. A salmon was classified as 'damaged' if the body or head had been partly eaten when the salmon was in the nets. In some cases only heads remained in the nets. Sometimes whole salmon were eaten, as evidenced by a surface mini 'oil slick', arising from the fish when they were being munched by the seal as observed from the boat. This latter category was not included in the damage assessment due to uncertainties as to the numbers taken.

Table 10.6 Observations of damaged salmon extracted from drift nets in Galway and Sligo Bays, 1979–81 (data from McCarthy[80]).

Location and no. boats fishing	Date	Total salmon landed	No. salmon damaged	% damaged
Galway Bay (two boats)	1–28 June, 1979	292	54	18.5
Sligo Bay (five boats)	11–23 July, 1980	439	35*	8.0
Galway Bay (two boats)	16 June–3 July, 1981	229	59	25.8
Sligo Bay (six boats)	June and July, 1981	2,123	209	9.8
Totals		**3,083**	**357**	**11.6**

* a figure of 35 is quoted in McCarthy's text (p.3) while '33' features in his table 1 (p.6)

The seals observed predating netted salmon in both Galway and Sligo Bays were predominately common with fewer greys. McCarthy's limited observations in the Galway and Sligo Bay fisheries in 1979–81 indicated that seals damaged approximately 12% of the salmon *caught* in drift nets. Their impact on the *free-swimming* population of salmon in Irish waters is not known. In this context the International Council for the Exploration of the Sea, an advisory and

Grey seal entangled in fish-ing net.

scientific body, estimated that the impact of grey seals in Britain on salmon stocks could be of the same order as the fishery itself, in other words seals were devouring as much salmon as is caught by the boats engaged in drift netting.[81]

Corbet & Southern quote the mean weight of 25 grey seal bulls as 233 kg (range 170–310 kg) and for the same number of cows as 155 kg (range 105–186 kg). Their daily food requirements have been estimated at 7.7–12.5 kg per day although captive seals have an expected lower intake of 6.8 kg per day as estimated by Steven and quoted by Hewer.[68,73] Thus, taking an average consumption of 7 kg of fish per day – cephalopods and other species are also eaten – a population of 2,250 grey seals, as it roughly stood in 1983, will eat very approximately 15,750 kg of mostly fish per year.

But this could be a minimum. Indeed, observations conducted by the author and Crummey on the Inishkea islands, Co. Mayo, suggest that the relatively small total Irish grey seal population which Charles Summers estimated at between 2,000 and 2,500 in 1983 could be augmented by an ever-increasing number of immigrant Scottish grey seals. A series of 11 counts of seals between 1970 and 1994 at the 'Dock' on Inishkea North, their largest haul-out in Ireland, suggested a 10% annual growth rate in numbers at this site over the 24 year period.[82] In the absence of any increase in the size of the Irish breed-ing population the large and increasing numbers at the 'Dock' are more than likely to be made up mainly of Scottish immigrants. Moreover, photo-identifi-cation of females at the 'Dock' conducted by Kiely suggests that those present in the spring are passing through rather than being members of the local breeding population.

The observed annual rate of increase of seals at the 'Dock' is slightly above, but not out of keeping with, the estimated 7% annual increase in the grey seal population in Britain since 1979.[83] An argument in support of the presence of immigrant Scottish seals on Inishkea comes from the number of pups born in the Mullet assembly in 1994. They were estimated at 101 compared with 197 and 129 in 1980 and 1983 respectively, which suggests that the local breeding population is not increasing numerically.[84]

The 'Dock' (sandy area),
Inishkea North, Co. Mayo
– the largest known haul
out area for grey seals in
Ireland.

Common seal numbers

While conducting his 1964–5 grey seal survey, Lockley reviewed the meagre literature on the numbers of common seals in Irish waters as well as gathering information on the ground. His was the first attempt to arrive at a national figure for common seals, which he estimated to be a minimum of 1,000.[77] A more comprehensive survey, based on direct counts rather than pup counts, was carried out by a team led by Summers during the 1978 breeding season – between 1 and 20 July, when most pups would have been born and before possible dispersal and mortality had reduced the herd sizes. All probable breeding sites, i.e. sheltered intertidal haunts close to deep water such as small rock reefs or skerries exposed at low tides, or estuarine sandbanks, were visited by small inflatable boats. Some counts were made from the shore. Other possible sites were surveyed from the air. A minimum estimate of the population size was 1,248 individuals (Table 10.7).

Table 10.7 Number of common seal adults and pups counted in Irish coastal areas during 1–20 July 1978 (data from Summers, et al.[85]).

Region	Adults	Pups	% Pups
Ballagan Point, Co. Down – Portrush, Co. Antrim	461	124	21.3
Portrush, Co. Antrim – Rossan Point, Co. Donegal	5	1	16.7
Rossan Point, Co. Donegal – Benwee Head, Co. Mayo	167	45	21.6
Benwee Head, Co. Mayo – Killary Harbour, Co. Mayo	122	29	19.2
Killary Harbour, Co. Mayo – Hag's Head, Co. Clare	190	43	18.0
Hag's Head, Co. Clare – Slea Head, Co. Kerry	0	0	0
Slea Head, Co. Kerry – Cape Clear, Co. Cork	48	17	21.6
Cape Clear, Co. Cork – Bannow Bay, Co. Wexford	0	0	0
Carnsore Point, Co. Wexford – Ballagan Point, Co. Down	not surveyed	not surveyed	–
Totals	**989**	**259**	**20.7**

Bull, cow and calf common seals. From Corbet & Southern[73].

Table 10.8 Number of common seals found in breeding sites on the west coast, 1978 and 1979 (data from Warner[86]).

Location	1978		1979	
	Adults	**Pups**	**Adults**	**Pups**
Trawenagh Bay, Co. Donegal	0	0	8	4
Dunglow Bay, Co. Donegal	1	0	54	18
Inner Donegal Bay, Co. Donegal	46	5	22	8
Drumcliff Bay, Co. Sligo	34	15	57	10
Ballysadare Bay, Co. Sligo	78	25	60	15
Achill Sound, Co. Mayo	53	18	42	4
Clew Bay, Co. Mayo	59	11	33	6
Bertraghboy Bay, Co. Galway	27	3	39	7
Mweenish Bay, Co. Galway	10	3	14	0
Kilkieran Bay, Co. Galway	37	11	16	2
Inner Galway Bay, Co. Galway	103	26	143	34
Kenmare Bay, Co. Kerry	18	8	31	1
Glengarriff Harbour, Co. Cork	26	9	59	11
Totals	**492**	**134**	**578**	**120**

An independent check, by the same counting team, using a life table multiplier method based on the number of pups counted, produced a total of 1,200 individuals. Taking into account possible errors such as under-counting during adverse tides and bad weather, the surveyors concluded that there were around 1,500–2,000 individuals in Irish waters in 1978.[85] The stock was about one-tenth of the number occurring in Britain at the time, probably reflecting fewer suitable habitats in Ireland. The number of common seals in Britain in 1994 totalled 28,720.[79]

A repeat survey of many of the west coast sites was carried out by Warner in 1979 to check the 1978 findings and to gather more information on pup productivity.[86] The results revealed a total of 698 adults and pups, compared with 626 the previous year (Table 10.8).

The percentage of pups recorded over the two years for the above survey areas was 21.4% and 17.2% – a figure within the range of 7.4–27.4% reported by Vaughan for common seal herds breeding in the Wash, England.[87]

In conclusion, there is a great void in our basic information on seals such as the size, distribution and breeding performance and movements of both species on our islands and in our coastal waters. That there is an ever-increasing annual southerly movement of the burgeoning Scottish grey seal population into Irish waters is not in doubt. But its seasonality and extent needs urgent clarification. It is only with such information a management strategy can be constructed, if necessary, to address the increasing numbers of grey seals and the need to control these numbers in Irish territorial waters. And we have only barely scratched the surface of the thorny issues concerning seals and their interactions with fishery interests.

Magharee Islands, Co. Kerry.

11

The Sea

The liquid envelope that swaddles the ancient bones of Ireland is a territory where distinctions between the precincts of the Atlantic Ocean, the Irish and the Celtic Seas become blurred. Deciding where one begins and the other finishes is something akin to reading tracks in a desert on a windy day. Despite being surrounded on all sides by water the Irish, as a nation, are more connected to inland affairs – grass, cattle and sheep – paying insufficient homage to the sea, and often being fearful of it.

The sea is the one part of the natural environment which man cannot subjugate or control, and whose resources are never harnessed by him without a considerable amount of toil and frustration. Man is helpless in front of the ferocity of Atlantic storms, conjured up by low pressure systems, tracking more than 4,500 km across a barren seascape before hitting the first land like a wall. In some cases, hurricane-force wind speeds (exceeding 64 knots or 32.7 m per second), recorded numerously along the western seaboard, generate towering waves of up to 35 m in height which are likely to occur in the worst storm in any one 50-year interval.[1] Nevertheless, under less stringent yet windy conditions, heights of Atlantic waves would reach some 13–15 m on many occasions during the winter. These forces however, despite their drama, remain superficial, for underneath the ruffled angry epidermis lies another more quiet world, forever still and smooth, a secret domain only occasionally visited by divers and marine biologists and mostly left to its own devices.

The flora and fauna living attached to or on the bottom sediments of the sea is collectively known as the benthos. Seaweeds of the benthos are restricted to relatively shallow depths where the light they need to manufacture food by photosynthesis can still be captured. At a depth of 2 m in inshore waters half of the light has been absorbed, while at 8 m 90% has been assimilated and the waters at this stage are already almost too dim to support seaweed growth. However, in the open sea, light penetration is almost twice that recorded inshore. Animals there are more flexible, less dependent on luminosity, and form many different kinds of benthic communities, whose nature is largely determined by the type of sediments – rock, sand, gravel, mud, etc. – lining the bottom. Food supply and current speeds are also important factors.

The sea is one of the most biologically productive environments, teeming with a remarkable range of life all dependent upon minute plants that form the phytoplankton. The phytoplankton, confined to a floating, drifting existence in the top 20 m of the sea, is the basis for all marine life. It is made up of diatoms and flagellates which are single-celled organisms. The diatom has a cell wall which forms a siliceous external skeleton often extending into a bizarre range of outward spines ensuring buoyancy. Flagellates have two threads, or flagella, which help them stay at the top of the water column by whipping backwards and forwards. These small plant cells have a much greater surface area in relation to their volume than larger cells and this makes them

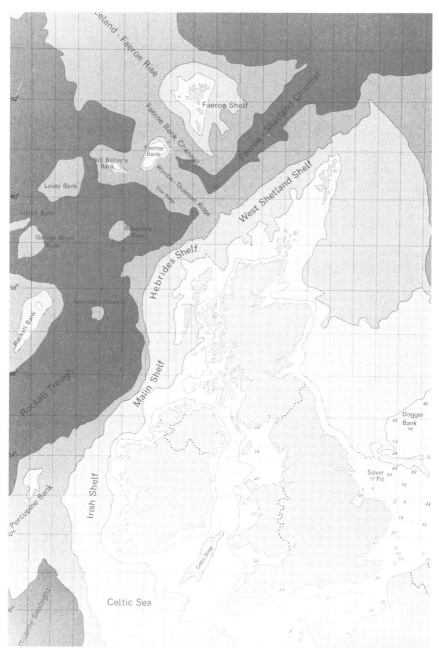

Ireland lies relatively close to the continental shelf (shown here as the Irish shelf) marked by the 200 m isobath and within a few km, depths of more than 1,000 m are met. From Lee & Ramster[3]. Based on Crown Copyright material. (D. Burke).

more efficient in absorbing scarce and essential mineral salts in sea water. Their large surface to volume ratio additionally confers greater frictional resistance to sinking thus assisting them to remain in the upper layers of the water where they benefit from maximum light.

The larger forms of the phytoplankton – the diatoms and dinoflagellates – can be prodigious. They vary numerically according to the time of year, the highest concentrations occurring during spring (stimulated by increasing sunlight) and autumn (encouraged by the upwelling of nitrates and phosphates as the surface waters cool). The amount of phytoplankton in the eastern Irish Sea area was sampled during the first quarter of the century in a classic study involving two plankton tow-nets, each approximately 35 cm diameter, drawn 800 m across Port Erin Bay, Isle of Man, several times a week during April, June, August and October for 14 years. All phytoplankton filtered from an estimated 8 m³ of water was laboriously counted under a microscope. The results showed an average of 727,000 larger diatoms and dinoflagellates per cubic metre of sea water for the most productive month, April. Autumn counts (October) were naturally much lower at an average of 60,625 per cubic metre. Investigations into the zooplankton, carried out over the same times period, produced an average of 4,888 individuals of the zooplankton for their peak month of October.[2]

Zooplankton is comprised of diminutive animals, ranging from single-celled organisms to miniature shrimp-like creatures. The zooplankton feeds or grazes on the phytoplankton and is, in turn, consumed by larger animals such as jellyfish and fish, or by benthic animals living attached to the sea floor. An important ecological function of the benthos is the ingestion and incorporation into their larger bodies of the much smaller, microscopic animals that make up the zooplankton floating and moving around in the sea. In other words, the zooplankton does not remain on top like the phytoplankton but is everywhere in equal amounts. However, not all plankton passes into and through long and complex food chains. Several fish (herring, sprat and mackerel, as well as basking sharks), along with baleen whales, prey directly on the larger animals in the zooplankton by sieving the creatures from the water flowing into their mouths.

The nekton, the animals of the sea that are not floating like the plankton but free-swimming, includes three groups of spectacular marine creatures – the whales, basking sharks and turtles. The whales, together with the dolphins and the porpoises, are cetaceans. These are mammals that hundreds of millions of years ago managed a more successful transition back into the sea than the seals, without the need to return to land for the birth of their young. Many in the whale tribe cruising around Ireland are of interest not only because of their biological features but also because they are scarce, having been hunted close to extinction in the early part of this century.

The North Atlantic Current that reaches Ireland moves northeastwards across the Atlantic after receiving the influx of warmer waters from the Gulf of Mexico and the West Indies. Mean winter surface water temperatures along the western Irish coastline are elevated, allowing some southern garden plants and other temperature sensitive species to thrive. In the coldest month (February), surface water temperatures are 1–2°C higher than in other 'western' areas extending from the Hebrides in Scotland to Cornwall in England.[3]

The North Atlantic Current also transports tropical fruits and seeds – known as disseminules – from the West Indies and America. These are washed up on

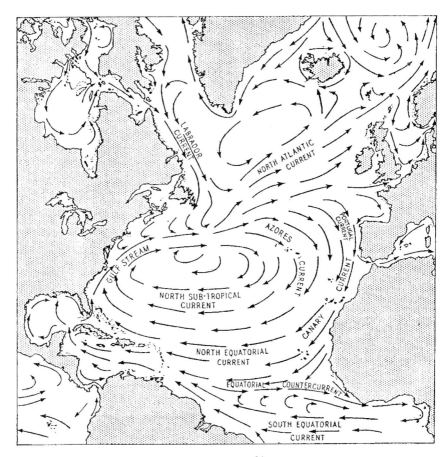

Surface currents of the North Atlantic. From Hardy [14].

Irish shores. Finally, the arrival of various turtles in Irish waters is undoubtedly assisted by the same current. These topics will all be dealt with in detail later
in the chapter, but lack of space precludes treatment of marine fish apart from
sharks.

Seabirds at sea

There are three recognised marine zones off the west coast, separated according to water depth: first, inshore shallow or nertic waters over the continental
shelf less than 200 m deep; second, waters over the continental slope 200–4000
m deep and third, oceanic waters deeper than 4000 m.[4] The distribution and
abundance of seabirds in these offshore areas is patchy and seasonal.
Observations from fishing trawlers between July and January 1994, principally
in southwestern areas around 49°N 14°W but covering all marine zones, found
19 species of seabirds. Eighteen were in the nertic zone, 11 over the continental shelf and 13 in oceanic waters.[5] Manx shearwater, cormorant, guillemot,
black guillemot, great black-backed gull and glaucous gull were only recorded

in nertic waters. The greatest abundance of seabirds observed during limited transects in nertic waters was 6 birds per km (gulls accounted for 63% and petrels 18% of all sightings, with kittiwakes and fulmars the most abundant species). In slope waters, the greatest abundance was 1.1 per km; petrels comprised 79% of sightings, fulmars and great shearwaters were the most abundant species, and lesser black-backed gull was the only gull species recorded. No birds were observed on one transect in oceanic waters. However, another survey along the edge of the continental shelf some 160 km west of Galway in fine weather in August 1973 recorded up to 120 fulmars, 100 kittiwakes, 25 storm petrels, 15 great shearwaters, five sooty shearwaters, three great skuas, three great black-backed gulls, a gannet and one arctic tern.[6]

Oceanographic research indicates that the important feeding areas for seabirds occur where cooler bottom waters rich in nutrients upwell and mix along the boundaries of the three marine zones. The nutrients encourage the growth of plankton which in turn provide food for the fish and cephalopods on which the seabirds feed. Thus tidal mixing occurs off headlands, supporting shoaling fish exploited by gannets, Manx shearwaters, gulls, auks and fulmars as well as by fishermen. Nutrient upwelling with cooler water also occurs further out in the Atlantic along the edge of the continental shelf. Here larger fish and squid are supported by the plankton. This area is attractive to great shearwaters and other petrels. Thermal fronts occur with ocean currents further west in the Atlantic and in the southern areas, more than 250 km off shore, albacore tuna are frequent, along with Cory's shearwaters. Water mixing with upwelling of deeper nutrients are likely to be features of the North Atlantic Current which would explain the occurrence of whales and dolphins together with fulmars, Manx shearwaters, kittiwakes, some skuas and occasional terns far off the western shores in deep oceanic waters.[6]

Whales and dolphins

Twenty-four species of cetaceans have been recorded in Irish waters or stranded on the coast. All known records to the summer of 1972, later updated to 1981, have been documented by O'Riordan.[7,8] A more recent review by Berrow & Rogan lists all cetacean stranding records on the Irish coasts from the beginning of this century to 1995.[9] Most whale records, apart from those caught by Irish whaling stations, are of beached specimens. While these strandings are important they only provide limited information about the real status of cetaceans in Irish waters. The reasons why some live whales become beached are, in most cases, difficult to understand and even more mysterious when mass strandings occur.

Pioneering observations made by ornithologists off Cape Clear, Co. Cork, provided valuable information from the early 1960s onwards on whales in the waters around the island.[10] A new impetus for whale and dolphin recording came with the establishment in December 1990 of the Irish Whale and Dolphin Group, based in the Zoology Department, University College, Cork. The main object of the IWDG was to initiate and coordinate a cetacean stranding and sighting scheme. More recently, ambitious sea-going surveys have been undertaken, of which two examples are given below.

In the summer of 1993 an intensive whale and dolphin survey, employing a towed hydrophone to record cetacean calls and songs, took place in the waters off the Mullet, Co. Mayo, an area previously fished for whales. Twelve days were

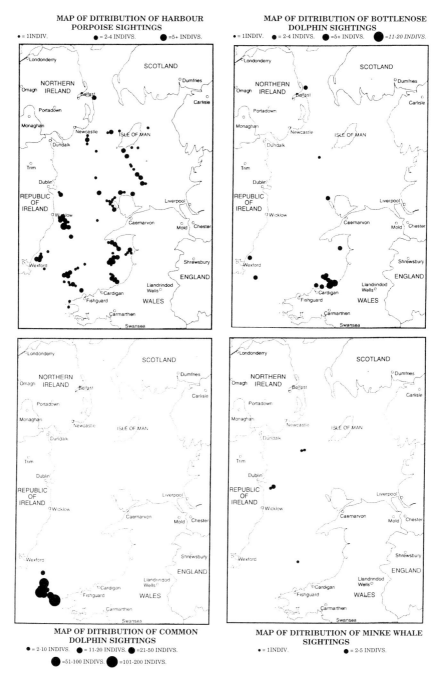

Locations of cetaceans sighted in the Irish sea during the survey of 1995. From Evans[12].

spent in inshore and five in offshore waters as far out as the edge of the continental shelf. Most cetaceans were recorded during the offshore survey. Schools of 10, 7, 4, 14, 12 and 4 pilot whales were recorded. Other sightings included pods of 4, 8, 5 and 15 Atlantic white-sided dolphins, 3 bottle-nosed dolphins and 5 common dolphins. The most westerly recorded cetaceans were 12 pilot whales at 11°N 32°06'W and 15 Atlantic white-sided dolphins at 11°N 31°07'W.[11]

During the summer of 1995 the Sea Watch Foundation and Earthwatch organised a series of line transect surveys of the Irish Sea to determine the densities of cetaceans in the area.[12] Two ten-day surveys were carried out during 10–20 July and 7–17 August. A surprising number of cetaceans were encountered (Table 11.1). Basking sharks and marine turtles were also observed. The greatest number of sightings were of common (or harbour) porpoises, which were also the most widely distributed of all the species recorded, although the common dolphin was the most abundant cetacean. Minke whales were observed in the relatively deep waters southwest of the Isle of Man.

Table 11.1 Number of cetacean individuals and sightings, Irish Sea July/August 1997 (data from Evans[12]).

Species	10–20 July 1995		7–17 August 1995	
	No. individuals	No. sightings	No. individuals	No. sightings
Harbour porpoise	27	37	86	117
Bottle-nosed dolphin	2	6 or 7	17	88
Common dolphin	1	15	9	450
White-beaked dolphin	0	0	1	1
Risso's dolphin	0	0	1	2
Minke whale	2	4	4	4
Humpback whale				
(not confirmed)	0	0	1	1
Totals	**32**	**62 or 63**	**119**	**663**

Cetaceans recorded in Irish fishery waters

The following 24 species of cetaceans have either been killed at sea by whalers in Irish fishery waters – today extending some 322 km westwards into the Atlantic off the west coast of Ireland – or observed at sea with supporting evidence, or stranded on the coastline. Virtually all the reported stranding records have been drawn from the paper by Berrow & Rogan which lists all cetaceans found on the Irish coast, 1901–95.[9]

Baleen whales

1. NORTHERN RIGHT WHALE

Also known by their Dutch name, the nordcapers were 'right' for the whalers because they were slow, lumbering swimmers, easy to catch and, most importantly, floating after death. They also yielded large quantities of valuable oil, meat and whalebone. This whale is usually black all over and distinguished from the rorquals by the absence of a back fin. Adults are 11–18 m long with conspicuous callosities (growths of acorn barnacles) on the head. They seldom occur in groups of more than six and usually spend the winter months in the equatorial waters where they breed and give birth to the young, conceived there the previous winter. The females have their first calves at 7–15 years and

breed every three to four years. In the summer they migrate northwards, passing the Irish and Scottish coasts, to feed in Arctic waters rich in krill. Once
numerous, they are now an endangered species, seldom encountered in the
northeastern Atlantic, and are probably closer to extinction than any other
large whale. It is uncertain whether their populations will ever recover.
Confined to the Northern Hemisphere, they were first fished by the Basques
in the Bay of Biscay in the tenth or eleventh century, then by the Norwegians
and later by British whalers in the seventeenth and eighteenth centuries.
Those remaining were almost exterminated by Scottish and Irish whaling stations before the First World War.

Ironically it was the Irish whale fishery that earlier this century provided
information about their migrations. A total of 18 nordcapers were killed off
the Mullet, Co. Mayo, by the whalers based at Rusheen, Inishkea South, and
Ardelly Point, Blacksod Bay. Most of them were caught in early June as they
travelled northwards. During 1908, the first year of whaling, five were taken
within 15 km of Rusheen but the following year the boats had to go out at least
100 km before they could capture five more.[13] The following summer the last
eight were taken and none was caught during the last season in 1922, suggesting those remaining had moved their migration routes further west into the
Atlantic, or more likely the population had been brought close to extinction,
not only by the Irish whalers but also by those based on the Hebrides where 67
were killed before the First World War. At the more northerly location of the
Hebrides the whales turned up later than off the Mullet, Co. Mayo – 65% of
the total numbers were killed in June and 29% in July.[14,15] During the early
1980s there were an estimated 200–500 in the North Atlantic. There have been
no confirmed strandings of these whales on the Irish coast but two have been
sighted at sea: one in August 1970 off Cape Clear, Co. Cork, and the other in
May 1979 in the north Irish Sea.[11]

2. HUMPBACK WHALE

The humpback is a little smaller than the nordcaper – adults range from
11.5–15 m long – and named 'humpback' because it rounds it back before
sounding (descending down into the water after breaking the surface). Its dorsal fin is low and stubby, set two-thirds of the way along the body. It is blue-black
above and usually partially white below, with very distinctive long, slender flippers, slightly curved backwards, extending nearly a third of the body length.
Humpbacks are playful whales. They often have rows of white acorn barnacles,
up to 8 cm in diameter, growing on the leading edges of the flippers and on
the head. Because these can form distinctive patterns it is sometimes easy to
recognise individual whales. Often attached onto the acorn barnacles are
groups of stalked barnacles, *Conchoderma*, which, as Hardy says, 'add to the
Caliban-effect'.[14] The males at their breeding ground have a long and complex song, reputed to be the most complicated in the whole animal kingdom.

On its northwards migration from the equatorial region the humpback stays
further offshore than the nordcaper, outside the 200 m depth line off Ireland,
the Hebrides and the Faroes.[7] The North Atlantic population is estimated at
about 5,000–6,000 with only a few hundred in the northeast Atlantic. Only six
were caught by whalers off the Mayo coast, the last two in 1913. A total of 70
were caught off Scotland during the period 1903–28. It is now extremely rare
in Irish waters. Two definite strandings have been recorded: a male at Moville,

Co. Donegal, in July 1907 and a female on 31 July 1992, which may have been the one seen in Kinsale Harbour, Co. Cork, at the end of June, four weeks earlier. Nine barnacles, *Coronula reginae*, new to Ireland, were found attached to its throat.[16] A bone thought to have belonged to a humpback whale was found in Galway in 1908. A humpback was spotted off Cape Clear, Co. Cork, in June 1967, and another off Galley Head, Co. Cork on 10 July 1989 .

3. BLUE WHALE
This is the largest whale on earth, ranging from 21–30 m with the record held by a female at 33.6 m. Blue whales are a dark bluish-grey all over and mottled with white spots except on the head. Due to the low numbers, estimated at several hundreds in the North Atlantic, the blue whale is endangered and strictly protected. A total of 124 were harpooned off the west Mayo coastline between 1908 and 1922. Most were found in deep water off the edge of the continental shelf from the later half of June until September.[13] The largest one taken by the Mayo whalers was a female 25.6 m long,[17] some 6.1 m longer than an immature which went aground on a sand bank in Wexford Harbour, Co. Wexford, in March 1891.[7] During this century there has been only one of unknown sex reported stranded, 15.2 m long, at Magilligan, Co. Derry on 26 January 1907. The Scottish based whaling stations killed 396 in the first part of the century.[11] Maximum longevity for these larger whales is 60–80 years. The females of large whale species only breed about every three or four years.

4. FIN WHALE
This is the commonest rorqual whale in Irish waters and the second largest animal in the world. Adults range between 18 and 22 m long, weigh up to 80 tonnes, and are dark grey above and white below. A total of 592 were harpooned by whalers from the stations at Rusheen, Inishkea South, and Ardelly Point, Blacksod Bay, Co. Mayo, making up 66% of all whales caught there. The Scottish whaling stations dispatched another 1,500 between 1904 and 1928. The fin whale is the most frequently observed larger whale in Irish waters. An

Recorded strandings of humpback whales (left) and fin whales (right). Prepared by Rogan (1998).

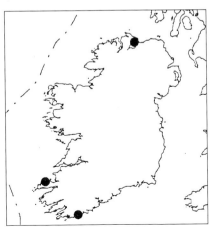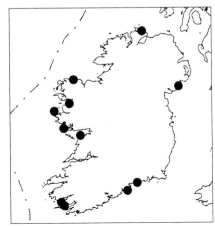

estimated population of over 14,000 individuals cruises in the northeast Atlantic.[18] Captures at the Mayo whaling stations show that it is plentiful from the beginning of May through to September. There have been 12 reported strandings between 1901 and 1995 of which six were from the west coast between Mayo and Kerry and three from the south coast.

5. SEI WHALE

Smaller than the fin whale, with a length between 12 and 16 m, the sei is bluish-grey on its back, grading to white underneath. Unlike the fin whale the under-sides of the flippers are not white. It has a tall sickle-like dorsal fin. Like the other baleen whales it migrates to northern latitudes in the summer and trav-els off the western seaboard of Ireland where it is commonest from May to July. It is listed as a vulnerable species comprising several thousand individuals in the North Atlantic. Their sieving mechanism is much finer than in other baleen whales, thus making it possible for them to retain in their mouths small-er animals contained in the water such as miniature copepods. The total catch made by the Mayo whaling stations was 97 between 1908 and 1922 with a trend towards declining numbers. A further 2,214 were killed, mostly along the con-tinental shelf, by the Scottish whaling stations. There are two recorded strand-ings this century, both before 1914, but five sightings – some possibly involving the same whale – were made from Cape Clear, Co. Cork, between July and September 1991.[11]

6. MINKE WHALE

Sometime called the pike whale or herring hog, the minke is the smallest of the rorquals, seldom exceeding 9 m in length. It is probably the commonest baleen whale in the northeastern Atlantic with population estimates ranging from 37,000–125,000. Like the other species it is bluish-grey on the upper parts and white below. Its distinguishing feature is a distinctive white patch on the outer part of the flippers looking from a distance like a white armband. Although ignored by the early whalers based in Ireland because of its small size, it was hunted until quite recently by about ten Norwegian boats working in the Atlantic some 160 km off the west coast, with quotas set by the International Whaling Commission. This went on for ten years from 1966 until the *Wildlife Act, 1976* put an end to it.[19] There have been 42 records of strand-ings this century with an increase since 1970s and a peak between 1986 and 1990. Most strandings have been along the south (45%) and west coasts (33%). A single adult and an adult with a juvenile were seen feeding off Erris Head on 28 and 29 June 1993 during the whale survey off northwest Mayo. Two others were observed on 4 July 1993 near St John's Point, Donegal Bay and another spotted feeding off the river mouth at Kildowney Point, Donegal Bay. Like other rorquals the minke migrates north-south from equatorial to northern latitudes during the summer months, although some minke whales appear to remain in a relatively small area in temperate or subtropical regions for most of the year. The most likely whale to be seen off the west coast.

Toothed whales

7. SPERM WHALE

This is the largest of the toothed whales, with males reaching up to 18 m, almost twice the size of females. They have an enormous square-fronted head,

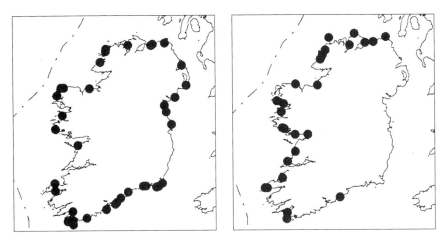

Recorded strandings of minke whales (left) and sperm whales (right). Prepared by Rogan (1998).

comprising about one third of the body length, and a small lower jaw set well back from the front of the head. There are 36–50 conical teeth, up to 20 cm high and 1 kg in weight, set on the lower jaw and fitting into sockets along the toothless upper jaw. The overall body colour is a dark bluish-grey. Despite preferring warm waters, a surprising number have been caught by whalers off Ireland and Scotland. Sixty-three were harpooned off Co. Mayo between 1909 and 1922 with a further 77 taken between 1903 and 1922 in the areas of Rockall and St Kilda by the whalers based on Shetland and the Orkneys. Matthews considered that they did not come much closer to the west coast than the eastern ridge of the warm water lying approximately over the 200 m line.[20] This fits in with the experience of the Mayo whalers who had to go far out into the Atlantic, often up to Rockall some 402 km away, to harpoon these whales. There are 28 Irish strandings this century up to 1995 with an increasing frequency since the 1960s which has been interpreted as representing a real increase in the occurrence of this whale in Irish coastal waters.[21]

The gigantic head provides a reservoir for fatty esters (oil) which are fluid at body temperature but solidify at about 32°C. The liquid resides in a sac and, when cooled below body temperature, separates out into a white wax known as spermaceti, similar to the liquid wax found in other toothed whales (but not in such abundance) and oil. The spermaceti – once erroneously thought to be the whale's spermatozoa – was, in the past, mixed with beeswax to make high quality candles. The function of this massive cranium store – there may be up to one tonne of spermaceti in a fully grown whale – has perplexed zoologists for many years. Is it to facilitate sonar navigation by acting as a gigantic lens, directing sound beams forward (sperm whales can only communicate by ultrasonic clicking sounds)? Is it a supplementary supply of oil to allow extra nitrogen absorption necessitated by the whale's massively deep dives? Is it a hydrostatic organ, assisting buoyancy control as suggested by Hardy in 1959?[14] Clarke has argued that the temperature and hence density of the spermaceti is controlled by regulating the supply of warm blood to it. Thus the whale could control its buoyancy to descend or ascend with little swimming effort.[22]

Sperm whale beached on Trawmore Strand, Achill Island, with Menawn Cliffs in the distance. The whale's lower jaw has been sawn off.

Sperm whales feed principally on giant squids. These squids are usually found in deep waters which might explain the deaths of many sperm whales which, when ploughing through the bottom sediments with their mouths open, sometimes come across submarine cables and become entangled.[23] The stomachs of four sperm whales examined at the Mayo whaling stations in 1914 were found to contain only remains of squid apart from several jawbones of predatory fish.[24] Other stomach examinations of sperm whales caught in the Azores revealed massive squids, the largest being an intact *Architeuthis*, probably *A. harveyi*, measuring 10.5 m from the tip of the tentacles to the tail or 5 m without the tentacles.[25] However, the average length of 112 squids found in sperm stomachs at the Azores was only 2.5 m including tentacles, and 0.9 m for body length only.[26] There have been several occurrences in Irish waters of the giant squid *Architeuthis* which can reach a maximum length of 15 m from the tip of its two longest tentacles (the eight other tentacles are much shorter) to the tail, while the body is only about a quarter of the total length.

Ambergris is a waxy substance sometimes found in the large intestines of these whales and occasionally discovered floating as large lumps in the water or washed up on the shore. Formerly extremely valuable as a chemical fixative or stabiliser in the manufacture of perfumes, it is said that several whaling companies were saved from bankruptcy by the discovery of ambergris. The Irish whaling stations were not so lucky. Of the 63 sperm whales caught in Irish waters only one contained a lump of ambergris weighing 6.8 kg.[27] As ambergris was once worth about £5 per 30 g the amount from this whale would have been worth £1,133 at 1914 prices – a lot of money then. It was once thought that ambergris was only found in large intestines of sick sperm whales, or those close to death. However, it now seems that ambergris is just impacted or hardened faeces. Fairley points out that the Arabs first called ambergris *anbar* meaning the 'great fish' that swallowed Jonah. It then changed to *amber* and to avoid confusion with *amber jaune*, the yellow-coloured petrified pine resin found around the Baltic, it was transformed to *ambergris* or 'grey amber'.[19]

8. PIGMY SPERM WHALE

The first record of this small sperm whale from Irish and British waters was a stranded female at Crag, near Lehinch, Co. Clare, on 24 April 1966.[7] A second specimen was found dead at the top of a beach west of Silver Strand, Barna, Co. Galway, on 6 October 1985.[28] The length of adults ranges between 2.7 and 4 m. Pigmy sperm whales were not recognised as a separate species from the dwarf sperm whale until 1966. They are normally found in warm or tropical waters.

9. NORTHERN BOTTLE-NOSED WHALE

Together with Cuvier's beaked, Sowerby's beaked, True's beaked and Gervais' beaked, the bottle-nosed whale belongs to the beaked whale family, Ziphiidae. The adults are between 7 and 9 m long, have short snouts and lack the notch in the tail fluke. There have been 20 stranding records this century with only a few each decade. Thirty percent of the records have been from the east coast between Louth and Wexford. There have been no strandings from the north-west. The bottle-nosed whale occurs in small pods and shares the same migration pattern as the baleen whales. Autumn is the time when they have been most frequently seen at sea or found stranded ashore, with numerous records off Cape Clear, Co. Cork, mainly in August and September. They can be identified by their pronounced beak and almost hemispherical 'melon' or protuberance in the forehead area which is made up of a mass of fat, oil and liquid wax mixed with tissues.

10. CUVIER'S BEAKED WHALE

In contrast with the bottle-nosed whale, Cuvier's beaked whale is a much more Atlantic species with most strandings (86%) occurring along the western coastline. There have been 21 reported strandings this century. The adults are between 5.5 and 7.5 m long and exhibit a wide range of colouring from pale brown, or cream to blue-grey to white. Old Cuvier's whales can be almost white, leading to confusion with Risso's dolphins and belugas. The males have two distinctive teeth in the lower jaw. There have been sightings off Cape Clear, Co. Cork, in August 1984, Mizen Head in July 1987 and northwest Ireland in August 1987.[11]

11. SOWERBY'S BEAKED WHALE

Little is known about this whale in Irish waters apart from the three positive strandings, all females: two on the west coast (Co. Galway and Co. Sligo) and one in Co. Wexford. It is seldom seen at sea. Adults range in length from 4–5 m. The males have one distinctive tooth, pointing up from the lower jaw halfway between the tip of the beak and the corner of the mouth.

12. TRUE'S BEAKED WHALE

Again, little is known about this species apart from it being a rare whale occurring in the Atlantic Ocean. It has not been observed at sea anywhere. Adults range from 4–5 m in length. Their upper parts are coloured dark grey or bluish-grey while their underparts are mottled grey. Like Cuvier's beaked whale there are two small teeth set at the front of the lower jaw but unlike those in Cuvier's they point forwards rather than upwards. Up to 1988 there were only 30 known standings in the world, including six from the west coast of Ireland – two in Co. Mayo, both from Killadoon, near Louisburgh, one in Co. Clare and three in Co. Kerry.[11]

13. GERVAIS' BEAKED WHALE
The first Irish and only the second European record for this species was a freshly dead specimen found on the rocky shore at Kellystown, Ballysadare Bay, Co. Sligo, on 22 January 1989. The first one had been found floating in the English Channel in 1848. The Sligo specimen was defleshed and minutely examined prior to its transfer to the Ulster Museum, Belfast.[29]

14. BELUGA
This pure white whale was clearly identified in the waters below Clare Island Light House, Co. Mayo, on 9 and 10 September 1948. It was kept under surveillance, through a telescope, by the two lighthouse keepers. It was clean white, without a back fin and estimated at 4.5 m long – a nearby *curragh* providing a yardstick. The beluga surfaced every five minutes, spent half a minute on the surface before lifting down vertically.[30] It was a most unusual occurrence as white whales are normally confined to the Arctic. A second beluga was spotted off the sea front at Cobh, Cork Harbour on 10 June 1988. Its length was estimated to be between 4 and 5 m.[31]

15. FALSE KILLER WHALE
This is a rare whale in Irish waters and some doubt must be cast on the origin of a skull found on a beach in the River Moy estuary, Co. Mayo in 1967 as it is unusual that a fragment of a large whale would be found in isolation from the rest of the body. Part of another skull suspected to be of this species was discovered on Ballybunnion Strand, Co. Kerry, 1971. Neither specimens are listed by Berrow & Rogan.[9]

16. HARBOUR PORPOISE
The common or harbour porpoise, known in Irish as *muc mara* (the sea pig) is the most frequently encountered cetacean in Irish coastal waters. Adults are between 1.4 and 1.9 m long. The young are born in June and July. This porpoise is most regularly noted between September and March when it is thought to be associated with fishing, especially the herring. There has been a large increase in the numbers reported stranded since the mid 1980s with most individuals recorded between December and March. These porpoises were formerly thought to be a coastal species but their presence in offshore waters is shown by the many specimens caught in nets set for fish. In the Celtic Sea alone it is estimated that between 1,825 and 2,050 are caught every year.[32] Stomach analysis of dolphins caught in nets and found stranded found that the most frequent food was cod followed by whiting and herring. Only a few cephalopods were found including the squid *Loligo forbesii* and some cuttlefish.[32]

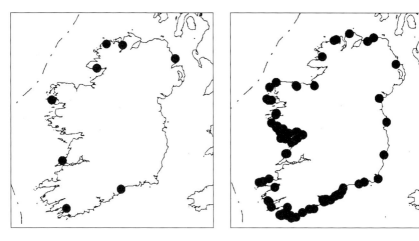

Recorded strandings of killer whales (left) and pilot whales (right). Prepared by Rogan (1998).

17. KILLER WHALE

The killer whale is the largest member of the dolphin family and is identified by its striking black and white colouring. It has a conspicuous white patch above and behind the eye and the body is white underneath from the lower jaw and extending backwards to behind the dorsal fin. Adults range from 5.5–9.8 m in length, with males somewhat larger than females. The dorsal fin stands high in the water – up to 1.8 m tall – and is a good field character. Killer whales are the fastest swimmers of all whales, and they typically travel around in pods. They are also reputedly the fiercest of all toothed whales, and will prey on warm-blooded animals, especially seals and other dolphins. However, they do not harm humans in the wild. Occurring worldwide, the population in the North Atlantic is healthy with an estimated population, based on sightings, of some 3,500–12,500 individuals between Iceland and the Faroes.[11] There are ten records of killer whales stranded in Ireland this century to 1995 – three from Co. Donegal, two from Co. Clare, two from Co. Antrim, one each from Mayo and Cork and a record of three together in Co. Waterford. Two were captured last century off Co. Sligo and Co. Down. Numerous sightings, especially off Cape Clear, Co. Cork, mostly in August and September, are indicative of their sustained presence near Ireland. A school of ten was once seen, but most observations were of three or four, each including a male. They have been reported several times in the area of Ireland's largest haul-out of grey seals at the Inishkea Islands, Co. Mayo.[33] A male and female were seen 3 km southwest of Tory island, Co. Donegal, on 8 July 1992. Three were observed off Great Saltee Island, Co. Wexford, on 1 September 1990.

18. LONG-FINNED PILOT WHALE

This black whale has long flippers, extending about one fifth of the way along the body, and a well pronounced, rounded forehead. Its dorsal fin points backwards. The adults range from about 3.8–6 m in length. They are famous for their mass strandings on the coastline. The largest of these involved 63 individuals on 19 November 1965 in Brandon Bay, Co. Kerry.[34] Why they beach themselves on the shore is not understood. Pilot whales have stranded on the coastline every month of the year except September with most records (73%) during February and March. The most recent mass strandings were of two groups of six in the Rosetellan area of Cork Harbour on 21 September 1995. One group was successfully refloated and the other re-launched themselves.[35]

19. RISSO'S DOLPHIN

Much smaller than the long-finned pilot whale (2.6–3.8 m), Risso's dolphins have no beak and a less conspicuous forehead. They travel around in small herds and are quite common in Irish waters. They are easy to identify in the water by their somewhat battered appearance, their blue-grey bodies being covered by white scars, the results of wounds inflicted by other Risso's dolphins. Off Cape Clear, Co. Cork, they are regular visitors, most common between May and August. There have been several instances of group strandings: five in Blacksod Bay, Co. Mayo in April 1933 and a further nine there in 1978. Most records of strandings have been along the western and southern coasts.

20. BOTTLE-NOSED DOLPHIN

This dolphin is somewhat larger than the common dolphin with a shorter beak and more robust body up to 4 m long. Its white lower beak distinguishes it from all other dolphins. Its back is slate grey. The numerous teeth on both jaws, characteristic of all dolphins, assist the catching of its fish prey. Bottle-nosed dolphins are highly inquisitive, often following and playing around a boat. While travelling through some rough seas between an offshore island and the mainland at the southern extremity of the Mullet, Co. Mayo, the author and Maurice Cassidy were accompanied in their rubber dinghy by a pod of about 12 of these dolphins, like a group of outflanking motorcyclists providing guidance and protection through some dangerous and turbulent waters including large cresting waves.[36]

Found throughout tropical and temperate waters the bottle-nosed dolphin is locally common in the northeast Atlantic where the most important concen-

Recorded strandings of Risso's dolphins (left) and white-beaked dolphins (right). Prepared by Rogan (1998).

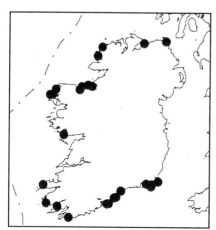
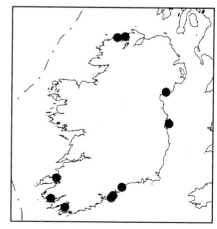

tration in western Europe occurs along the western seaboard of Ireland.[37] Unlike those of the larger whale species, the records of strandings do not reflect accurately the dolphin's abundance in the coastal waters, with only 19 reported strandings this century, most of which have been along the western seaboard. Small parties regularly visit Sligo Bay, Co. Sligo; Clew Bay and Killary Harbour, Co. Mayo; Ballynakill Harbour, Co. Galway, and Galway Bay. Further south they are found in Cork Harbour and the Shannon Estuary. A special survey was conducted in the Estuary in 1993–4 with the objective of developing commercial whale watching there. At least 56–68 dolphins were present with peak sightings three hours before high tide. With the aid of photo identification of individual dolphins, the survey established the first known resident population of this species in Ireland. The presence of recently born baby dolphins suggested that the Shannon Estuary was also a calving area.

21. WHITE-BEAKED DOLPHIN

This dolphin is somewhat larger (up to 3 m) and more robust than other dolphins. The upper and lower parts of the beak are short, although despite its name, the beak is not always white and can be dark or even black. Although regarded as fairly common in Irish waters, there have been only ten strandings recorded this century to 1995. White-beaked dolphins are a North Atlantic species and although recorded southwards to Portugal, Ireland is considered to be at the southern part of their range.

22. ATLANTIC WHITE-SIDED DOLPHIN

Closely related to the white-beaked dolphin, there are 50 stranding records this century, with most from Kerry, Cork and Galway. Most records have been during March and April and are thought to be related to the mackerel fishery active at this time. Like the white-beaked dolphin they are found in the North Atlantic, extending southwards to Co. Sligo and to the north Devon coast in England. The largest mass stranding in Ireland was of a pod of 19 adults and calves in Killala Bay, Co. Mayo on 19 September 1994. Autopsy of the animals found one animal died from congestive heart failure. The others were all healthy. The discovery of the seriously diseased dolphin lends weight to the theory that some mass strandings may result from healthy individuals following a sick and possibly dying animal onto the beach.[38]

23. COMMON DOLPHIN

This is a common visitor and the second most abundant – after the common porpoise – of the small cetaceans in Irish waters. There have been several occurrences of common dolphins being stranded in estuaries by falling tides. Sightings have been made throughout the year but they are most frequent between June and September with August as the peak month. They usually occur in groups of between 10 and 20 individuals. Eighty-four strandings have been recorded this century, with an increase since the mid-1970s. The peak months for strandings are January and February.

24. STRIPED DOLPHIN

This dolphin has a stripe along the side of its body. Its beak is the longest (up to c.13 cm) of all the dolphins, but it has a relatively short body length of up

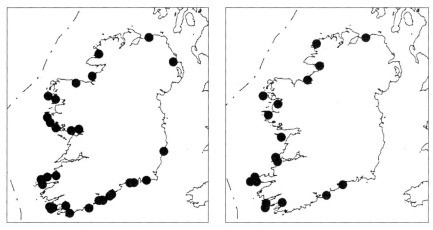

Recorded strandings of Atlantic white-sided dolphins (left) and striped dolphins (right).
Prepared by Rogan (1998)

to only 2.4 m. It has a worldwide distribution in tropical and temperate waters
and within the Atlantic it is normally found off the coasts of Spain, Portugal
and France. Up to 1976 there were only three known strandings in Ireland, all
in the southwest. It is probably more abundant in Irish waters than generally
thought.[39] Until recently the first stranded record was regarded to have been
an individual on 17 September 1984, east of Portstewart, Co. Derry.[40]
However, a re-examination of skulls in the Natural History Museum, Dublin,
showed that there were at least three previous stranding records including two
from last century that had been misidentified as common dolphins. There
have been 36 records of stranded individuals since 1912.

Whaling in Ireland

In 1736, long before the successful twentieth century whaling operations in
Mayo, Samuel Chaplain, a former lieutenant with the British Forces, established a whale fishery in Donegal Bay and caught his first whale the following
year together with a few more before he died in 1739. He was followed by
Thomas and Andrew Nesbitt, brothers from Killybegs, Co. Donegal, who
revived the fishery with moderate success, killing a number of whales in 1760,
including a probable northern right. Several more northern right whales were
possibly taken in subsequent years but precise identification is lacking. In 1762
the Nesbitts caught three whales, two between 18.2 and 21.3 m long, too big
for nordcapers; they were possibly blue or fin whales.[41] Overall the Nesbitts
caught between two or three whales each season. Thomas Nesbitt's claim to
fame was the invention in the 1760s of the first workable harpoon gun.[42] The
next development in weaponry was the design by a Norwegian Svend Foyn in
1865 of a gun that fired a harpoon with an explosive shell in its head.[14]

Having failed to establish a whaling station on Aran Island, Co. Donegal, in
1908 due to local opposition, the Norwegian promoters were facilitated by the
Rev. Spotswood Green, then Chief Inspector of Fisheries. Green, apart from
being a country rector, was an accomplished marine naturalist and adventurer
having explored the fauna of the 200 m depth line off southwest Ireland and

Remains of the Norwegian whaling station, Rusheen, Co. Mayo.

later 2,400 m depth. Soon afterwards in 1890 he left the church for a career in fisheries. He was also a Commissioner on the Congested Districts Board and was concerned with providing employment in congested areas, which was partly why he championed the establishment of the whaling station further down the coast on the islet of Rusheen off the island of Inishkea South, Co. Mayo. The first whales were caught in 1908 and the last catching season was 1913, the station being dismantled in 1914. Another station was constructed on the mainland in 1909 at Ardelly Point, on the west shore of Blacksod Bay, Co. Mayo, and operated until 1914. After serving as a fuel dump for the Admiralty during the war, the station was re-opened in 1920 but burnt down in mysterious circumstances on 21 February 1923. In the face of so much adversity the whalers packed up and left. A total of 899 whales were captured during the operations of the two west Mayo whaling stations between 1908 and 1922.

Table 11.2 Number of whales caught off the west coast of Mayo 1908–22 (data from Fairley[19]).

Species	1908	1909	1910	1911	1912	1913	1914	1920	1922	Totals
Northern Right	5r	5r	4r	0	0	0	0	0	0	**18**
			4a							
Humpback	1r	0	1r	0	0	1r	0	0	0	**5**
			2a							
Blue	19r	27r	5r	4r	6r	5r	13a	9a	18a	**124**
			6a	6a	2a	4a				
Fin	21r	56r	32r	57r	12r	40r	70a	101a	56a	**592**
			20a	53a	26a	48a				
Sei	31r	9r	21r	2a	6r	1a	2a	3a	0	**97**
			18a		4a					
Sperm	0	5r	2r	7r	8r	3r	4a	12a	3a	**63**
			5a	2a	2a	10a				
Totals	**77**	**102**	**120**	**131**	**66**	**112**	**89**	**125**	**77**	**899**

r = Rusheen, Inishkea South, Co. Mayo; a = Ardelly Point, Blacksod Bay, Co. Mayo.

The whales were killed for four products:
1. Oil. This was extracted by placing whale blubber, flensed off the body into

several long strips, chopped up into small blocks and then put into a 'blubber boiler', heated by steam. There were three boilings, each of eight hours. The oil rose to the top and was run off, then loaded into barrels, six of which equalled one ton. Oil from baleen whales was known as 'whale oil' and originally used for lighting, and later in low quality soaps. Treated with chemicals it has a wide range of uses from crayons, candles, glycerine for explosives, medicine, varnishes, inks, linoleum and even perfumes. Oil from the toothed whales was originally known as 'train oil' because of its use as a machinery lubricant. It was also employed for lighting and in clothes production and after transformation by chemicals, as a sophisticated lubricant, for dressings and in cosmetics.

2. Whalebone. This is the horny feeding mechanism from baleen whales. It had wide-ranging uses from springs in the earliest typewriters, to corsets, to strong bristle brushes, to fabric stiffener.

3. Manure, used for spreading on the land.

4. Bone meal and cattle food. Almost every part of the whale, even its teeth, was put to some use. The pigs that were kept by the Inishkea islanders, reputedly wild and ferocious, devoured any scraps that were left on the shore at Rusheen.

Unfortunately the statistics on the products derived from whales available from the Rusheen and Ardelly stations are incomplete but they nevertheless provide some indication of the materials obtained from the whales. The figures for both stations have been combined.

Table 11.3 Recorded production of oil, manure and other products from whales processed at the whaling stations at Rusheen and Ardelly Point, Co. Mayo, 1909–14 (data from Fairley[19]).

Year	Whales processed	Oil (barrels)	Manure (bags)	Manure (bags/whale)	Whale bone (kg)	Bone meal (kg)	Cattle food (kg)
1909	102	2,990	53	0	14,732	121,926	125,990
1910	120	3.365	364	0	8,128	101,605	203,210
1911	131	4,377	5,146	78.8	13,208	0	0
1912	60	2,357	2,562	84.1	2,794	0	0
1913	104	3,900	c.3,100	53.2	4,064	0	0
1914	89	3,304	c.2,260	0a	9,347	0	0
Total	606	20,293	13,485	-	52,273	-	-

Basking sharks

The basking shark is the second largest fish in the world, occurring most frequently in the North Atlantic. It is the largest fish within European waters. The average length of a mature shark, based on measurements taken at the now abandoned Achill Island Shark Fishery, Co. Mayo, is approximately 7.6 m. The dorsal fin extends some 91 cm from its base to its tip while the tail fin span varies from 1.5–2.1 m. The pectoral fins, acting as stabilisers, are up to 1.2 m long. The largest basking shark ever caught by the Achill Island Fishery was 9.9 m long, with a tail span of 2.3 m and a maximum girth measurement of 5.79 m.[43]

Despite the fear they may strike in an observer as they slowly travel through the water, their sharp pointed dorsal and tail fins slicing ominously through the waves, basking sharks are totally harmless and docile creatures. When feed-

Beached basking shark,
Keem Strand, Achill Island,
Co. Mayo.

ing they cruise slowly at about two knots in the top layers of the sea where the plankton is densest, to maximise feeding efficiency. The volume of water filtered has been estimated at least 2,215 m³ per hour.[44] The plankton cocktail washes down the throat and out through a series of five vertical gill slits on either side of the body that are so long – the first set almost extends the whole circumference of the shark – that the head appears almost severed. Along the inner side of the gill openings is a line of comb-like 'rakers' providing an efficient filtering system for the zooplankton, especially small copepods, *Calanus* spp., and other miniature creatures.

Today basking sharks occur in Irish coastal waters generally from April to October with peak numbers in June, which is somewhat later in the year than recorded earlier this century. During the winter months they are thought to move into deeper waters and they emerge in the spring to feed on the bloom of plankton. Specimens caught in winter have no gill rakers which would tend to prove that the sharks enter a quiescence or 'hibernating' period – from October onwards – during which they do not eat. New rakers are then regrown and they are fully developed by February, in preparation for the upcoming plankton feeding season from April onwards.[45] Studies off the Isle of Man in the Irish Sea have shown that the maximum numbers of sharks appeared two months after peak surface concentrations of chlorophyll *a*, the green pigment found in phytoplankton, an indicator of the arrival of zooplankton.[46] Investigations into basking sharks in Irish coastal waters during 1993 showed that surface sightings of the sharks were correlated with sea surface temperatures, first sightings coinciding with a mean sea temperature of 11.5°C.[47]

One extraordinary display performed by the basking shark, which has been observed and reported many times, is its ability to leap completely clear of water.[48] A curious aspect of its biology is the preponderance of females, something also true for another much smaller species, the blue shark, found in Irish waters and fished as game. In a survey of 112 blue sharks caught on long lines off the west coast in 1990 all but two were females.[49] It is thought that the sex imbalance is due to sexually segregated migrations or movements of the sharks.

Basking sharks have been hunted in Irish waters for more than 200 years. Traditionally known as 'sun fish', they were named after their habit of sunning

Blue sharks.

themselves on the surface of the water during calm and warm periods. The real sunfish is a quite different species.

Last century basking sharks used to appear much more frequently along the western seaboard in shallow sheltered bays, often in small groups, especially during warm, calm weather. Further out in the Atlantic, they concentrated in an area known as the 'sun fish bank' west of Inishbofin, Co. Galway, extending from Slyne Head, Co. Galway, in the south to Achill Island, Co. Mayo, in the north. On William Norie's *A new chart of the west coast of Ireland* (1830) the bank is shown at longitude 11°12'W. Various contemporary accounts exist about the 'sun fish bank' such as the following, published in 1836:

> 'Off the coast, about thirty miles, or just within sight of the high land of Achil Island, is the ground called the Sunfish bank; we are on it with Sleavemore, Achil, about E.N.E., per compass, seventy to ninety fathoms. The bank is remarkable for the break of the tide on it, with ebb and flood, and is supposed to be a ridge of land extending from the Blaskets to Erris Head, in about seventy fathoms. Half a mile further off we have fifteen fathoms more water, and the increase of depth is also considerable within it; the water outside deepens quickly to 100 fathoms and upwards; and the probability is, that the bank is near the edge of soundings.' [50]

Basking sharks were hunted historically in the sun fish bank by many boats that travelled out from Galway and the islands. But as numbers of the sharks declined in the second half of the nineteenth century the fishermen found it more profitable to wait until they moved closer towards the coastline before killing them. By 1873 the fishery had ceased, due to the scarcity of sharks.

The harpooner was the most skilled and valued member of the boat crew. Brabazon wrote in 1848: 'These fish are most powerful in the water, and if harpooned in the shoulder they are very hard to kill, often carrying off the whole harpoon line, but experienced harpooners strike them in the body, near the dorsal fin, rather low down, where it will go through into the intestines, or near the vertebrae towards the tail.'[51] Sometimes it was possible to give the harpoon an extra thrust deeper into the animal before the latter took off, downwards to the bottom where it would roll over and over trying to release itself from the weapon. On occasions it would take the full length of harpoon line measuring 400 m before the fish had spent its resistance. An axe was kept handy in the boat's prow to cut the line if the shark went wild. Killing sharks from small boats was a perilous occupation. A powerful shark could struggle up to ten hours before it would be hauled up and killed by thrusting a harpoon into it to sever the cervical vertebrae. Immediately after death the shark was rolled over, belly-up, alongside the boat, the stomach slit open and the liver removed and taken into the boat. The animal was then allowed to sink to the bottom and the livers were brought ashore, chopped up into smaller bits then boiled with water in a vat. The oil floated to the surface, was skimmed off into barrels, then sent to the market in Galway or Westport.

The liver of the basking shark is large, twin-lobed, and can equal roughly one sixth the weight of the shark. Livers weighed at the Achill Island Fishery averaged 356–406 kg with an upper limit of 762 kg.[43] They have a high oil content, average sized livers yielding 182–227 litres. The extracted oil, low in vitamins, was used for a variety of purposes including fuel for lamps, the dressing of wool and the preserving of timber as well as industrial applications such as public lighting and certain manufacturing processes like the hardening of cast steel. It was even reputed to have been burnt in some lighthouse lanterns.

By the time the American film-maker Robert Flaherty arrived on the Aran Islands to shoot his remarkable *Man of Aran* in 1933, the art of hunting basking shark, practised by the islanders in the previous century, had died out. Thus, Flaherty had to 'recreate' the drama of shark fishing for his film. Some years later, in 1947, W.J. Sweeney and Charles Osborne established a fishery on Achill Island, Co. Mayo. They were prompted in their enterprise by the general recognition that sharks were making a nuisance of themselves in the area, impeding the salvage of a sunken ship or damaging valuable salmon nets. A strategy was needed to keep them away. Specially constructed Manilla nets, 48.7 m long by 4.8 m deep made with 9.5 mm diameter twine, were brought to the island and employed to capture and then remove the sharks.

At Keem Bay, at the western end of Achill Island, the sharks arrived regularly in spring, from mid-April until June. The technique for capture for the shark fishery at the Bay was to secure firmly one end of the long net to the cliff or shore, the other being stretched straight out into the water. Once a shark was spotted by the lookout on the cliffs and a signal given, the net was slowly

Keem Bay, Achill island, Co. Mayo.

brought around to 'ring' it. As it became entangled and could not escape, a
curragh was rowed close in whereupon a harpoon was driven down into the
shark's neck, severing the vertebrae. The liver of the dead beast was then
removed and taken for oil extraction by steam rendering at Purteen Harbour.
The fishery thrived initially, boosted by shortages of industrial lubricants after
World War Two. In 1947 the oil was sold at £140 per 1,016 kg. Between 1950
and 1956 the average annual production at Achill was 254,012 kg (worth
£350,000 at 1947 prices) or 196.87 kg per shark. The flesh was also sold to meal
factories while the fins were dried and exported to Hong Kong for shark fin
soup. From 1956 onwards the shark catch started to decline until the operations became uneconomic. By 1975 the fishery had closed.[43]

Table 11.4 Number of sharks caught, their approximate weights, amount of oil produced and
flesh used in manufacturing at the Achill Island Shark Fishery 1947–75 (data from McNally[43]
for columns 1, 3 and 4. data from Went & O'Súilleabháin[52] for column 2).

Year	Number of sharks caught	Approximate weight of sharks landed (kg)	Oil produced (kg)	Flesh used in manufacturing (kg)
1947	6	n/a	n/a	n/a
1948	80	n/a	n/a	n/a
1949	450	n/a	n/a	n/a
1950	905	1,371,667	162,568	1,087,173
1951	1,630	2,863,228	381,019	1,371,667
1952	1,808	3,667,940	345,457	1,747,606
1953	1,068	2,001,618	233,691	1,249,741
1954	1,162	2,357,236	274,333	2,184,507
1955	1,708	n/a	137,167	457,222
1956	977	1,483,433	193,049	894,124
1957	468	711,235	105,669	268,237
1958	500	n/a	111,765	n/a
1959	280	n/a	71,123	n/a
1960	219	n/a	47,754	n/a
1961	258	n/a	59,947	n/a
1962	116	n/a	20,321	n/a
1963	75	n/a	19,305	142,247
1964	39	n/a	10,160	n/a
1965	47	n/a	12,193	n/a
1966	46	n/a	11,685	n/a
1967	41	n/a	11,177	n/a
1968	75	n/a	19,305	n/a
1969	113	n/a	29,465	n/a
1970	42	n/a	11,177	n/a
1971	29	n/a	7,112	n/a
1972	62	n/a	15,241	n/a
1973	85	n/a	19,340	n/a
1974	33*	n/a	8,636	n/a
1975	38*	n/a	c. 9,144	n/a
TOTALS	**12,360**		**2,327,803**	

* including 17 harpooned in 1974 and 36 in 1975, by vessels fishing off Mayo and Galway.

What were the reasons for the dramatic decline in the numbers of sharks appearing at Achill Island? One possible explanation is that there was a relatively large population living in the deeper waters off the west coast during the winter. With the advent of spring the population moved up and eastwards from the deep waters, to feed on the rich concentrations of plankton around Achill Island and off the adjacent coastline. The systematic killing of large numbers of individuals over many years would probably have been sufficient to deplete this population. Moreover the sharks were at the same time being hunted off the west coast during the summer by Norwegian minke whale boats – this additional mortality would also have been detrimental to numbers.[53] Basking sharks are characterised by a long period of maturity and gestation with overall low productivity. Any increase in adult mortality rates would have had damaging effects on recruitment of young sharks. Between 1947 and 1975 over 12,307 sharks were killed at Achill (Table 11.4). The declining trend of numbers taken from 1956–63, assuming a constant catching effort, is characteristic of a population in serious decline. On the other hand it has been postulated that sharks appearing at Achill were part of a much larger herd in the northeastern Atlantic that performs a northwards spring migration along the west coast. However, as the number of coastal sharks declined, Sweeney reintroduced the harpoon gun and persued the sharks in the waters westwards where it was thought there were large numbers. The 1973 and 1974 seasons were generally unsuccessful with one and three boats employed respectively. In all only 18 sharks were taken in 1974.[43]

Sometime before 1974 a new fishing venture, based in Dunmore East, Co. Waterford, started hunting basking shark. Three boats caught 180 in 1974 while in 1995 four boats took 350 in the area between Mine Head, Co. Waterford, and Castletown Bearhaven, Co. Cork. In addition, up to 4,442 individuals were reported to have been caught off southeast Ireland by other boats in 1984 but catches declined to 2,465 by 1986.[54] Kenneth McNally records in his book that Norwegian shark hunters were active in Irish fishery waters for a number of years around the 1970s. Although no records exist of their catches, estimates have put the total kill at several thousand a year.[43] If such numbers were removed from the population living offshore and visiting Achill each spring then the decline of the sharks arriving at Keem Bay would be all the better explained.

A 1993 survey of basking sharks in Irish coastal waters showed that sharks are now scarce in areas where they were formerly fished including the famous sun fish bank off Galway and Mayo, now seemingly bereft of them. They were most frequently observed in the Irish Sea off Co. Dublin and Co. Louth where they had never occurred before. They were also observed off Co. Antrim and off north Kerry. It is difficult to unravel whether these changes in population distribution are related to new patterns of zooplankton availability which, in turn, may be related to global warming, or whether they are an enduring consequence of substantial historical mortality.

North Atlantic drifters

Turtles

Four species of marine turtles from the tropics, belonging to the order Chelonia have been found in Irish waters or washed up along the coastline, after drifting across the Atlantic. The incongruous arrival of these floating and exotic reptiles in Irish waters is due to their involuntary engagement with the North Atlantic Current which transports them and other creatures across the Atlantic from their native habitat in the Gulf of Mexico and adjacent waters to Northern Europe. Once regarded as vagrants in Ireland they have now gained regular visitor status. Indeed, for every turtle seen or reported there are probably several others following suit in the sea. The following species have so far been identified in Irish waters.

1. LEATHERY TURTLE

This is the largest pelagic turtle encountered in Irish waters with a carapace length which can reach 2 m. Adults range in weight from 360–750 kg. The leathery turtle has no outer covering of tortoise-shell, only a soft skin appearing leathery which is thrown up into five or seven prominent longitudinal ridges on its dorsal carapace. Their weight and swimming ability allows them to dive down to depths of 100 m on feeding missions for jellyfish and the pelagic sea squirt *Pyrosoma*. One female found entangled in a lobster pot line off Crookhaven, Co. Cork, on 3 August 1993 had 85 identified prey items in the stomach of which 95% were the jellyfish *Cyanea lamarckii* and the remainder the compass jellyfish. Both species occur in Irish coastal waters during the summer.[55] Another specimen was captured in nets off the coast of Co. Clare in July 1983. On examination it was found to have stalked barnacles *Conchoderma virgatum* attached to the upper side of the left limb. This was the first record of this epizooid in Irish waters.[56] The closely related *C. virgatum* var. *chelonophilus* had previously been found on a sunfish off the west coast.[57] The leathery turtle's breeding sites are restricted to the tropics and those encountered in Irish waters are assumed to come from the Caribbean region.

The leathery turtle is a warm water creature that has been increasingly encountered in Irish waters. Its enormous size, the curiosity it arouses amongst fishermen, as well as its habit of becoming entangled in fishing nets are responsible for most of the records reported so far. In a review of occurrences from 1973–83 King listed 32 further individuals[58] – all captured at sea except seven that were stranded – that should be added to those recorded by O'Riordan.[7] All the capture and stranding records span the period March to October with most records (65%) in July and August. With over 400 sightings of these turtles from Irish and British waters between 1976 and 1996, together with an estimate of about 180 visiting British waters alone each year, the leathery turtle could be considered as a regular visitor to our coastal waters.[59,60]

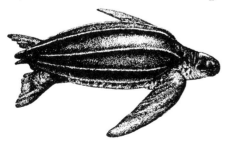

Leathery turtle. From Frazer[62].

2. KEMP'S RIDLEY TURTLE

There are only four well-documented stranding records of this smaller turtle up to 1972 – one from the south coast, one from the east coast and another two from Galway Bay. In December 1982 another was found on Tullavbawn Strand, Co. Mayo by Michael Viney. The carapace length of adults extends up to 70

Kemp's ridley turtle (left) and loggerhead turtle. From Frazer[62].

cm, sometimes more. However, it is the juveniles that are almost invariably found in Irish waters and their carapace length is in the range of 30–50 cm. Their colour is grey or olive-green, and the shell is of equal or greater width than its length. The Kemp's ridley is a native of the Gulf of Mexico and adjacent waters.

3. COMMON LOGGERHEAD
The common loggerhead is also much smaller than the leathery turtle with the adult carapace extending about 150 cm but like the Kemp's ridley it is usually the juveniles, with pointed knobs along the spine of the shell, that are recorded in Irish waters. They are reddish-brown. The common loggerhead was once the most frequently recorded marine turtle in Irish waters while in Scottish waters they comprise only about 10% of all turtle records, the bulk being made up of the leathery (about 60%).[60] There are 19 records from Irish waters to 1972, of which five were captured at sea. Virtually all records have come from the west coast.[7]

4. HAWKSBILL TURTLE
The hawksbill is the smallest turtle – ranging from 90–100 cm in length – to reach our shores. Its hooked bill is diagnostic. Its shell is brown with yellowish markings and is the source of commercial tortoiseshell. The first recorded specimen in Irish waters was caught in a herring net off Cork Harbour in February 1983. It was probably an elderly adult, based on body measurements.[61] The hawksbill is extremely rare in European waters with known breeding grounds in the Gulf of Mexico, the Caribbean, the Bahamas and rarely in Florida. The Cork specimen weighed 76 kg with a carapace length of 91 cm and a maximum width of 82 cm.

Frazer records the occurrence of a green turtle from the west coast of Ireland without providing fu rther details.[62] This was almost certainly the specimen captured in August 1959 near Achill Island, Co. Mayo, and erroniously identified as a green turtle. Later investigations showed it to be a leathery turtle.[7]

Hydrozoans
The origin of the turtles found in Irish coastal waters was not fully understood for a long time until there were coincidental arrivals with common logger-

heads and Kemp's ridley turtles of a giant type of jellyfish, the Portuguese man-of-war. These hydrozoans were also known to emanate from the Caribbean region, with no breeding areas in the eastern Atlantic along the west European coast. The arrival of both species suggested that they had drifted across the ocean with the North Atlantic Current. Clinching evidence was provided by the identification of tufts of a brown seaweed found growing on the carapace of a common loggerhead stranded at Bude, north Cornwall, in August 1945. The alga was *Ectocarpus mitchellae*, a species found in America.[14]

The Portuguese man-of-war is both a wondrous and dangerous creature, belonging to the phylum of animals known as Cnidaria, which includes the sea anemones, jellyfish and corals. Cnidarians have radially symmetrical soft bodies usually fixed at one end to a substrate, and a mouth surrounded by tentacles at the other end – a form known as a polyp. The Portuguese man-of-war belongs to the order Siphonophora, and is a polyp which has been modified for a pelagic, travelling life. It is a floating colony of cells which consists of an oval and flattened disc, known as a pneumatophore, up to 30 m in length, riding the water surface. Rising up from the disc is a structure resembling a sail that catches the wind. The prevailing southwesterly winds, aided by the North Atlantic Current, are responsible for driving the Portuguese man-of-war into Irish waters from the western Atlantic. Hanging down from the disc is a bundle of long straggly tentacles, extending sometimes tens of metres in length, bearing an array of specialised cells which have been especially evolved for stinging, reproduction and feeding. The stinging cells (nematocysts) contain poison powerful enough to kill a fully grown fish before it is consumed. A sting from this jellyfish can also be extremely unpleasant, even dangerous, to humans.

Another North Atlantic Current siphonophore is the by-the-wind-sailor, which appears principally along the western and southern coasts, often in exceptionally large numbers either in inshore waters or washed up on the tideline. Each is like a miniature, deep blue raft measuring up to 10 cm long by nearly 4 cm wide, with a triangular fin set like a sail on top of the raft. Below hang the tentacles, acting as a sort of keel. The central mouth, or siphon, hangs downwards from the underside of the raft. Why these sailors arrive in such large numbers some years and are scarce in others is not fully understood but may be related to a combination of current movements, sea temperature, and wind speed and direction. It is likely that by-the-wind-sailor occurs in Irish waters every year but is not always noticed and therefore when larger invasions occur the phenomenon is exaggerated. Exceptional numbers were recorded in the summer of 1992, when tens of thousands of animals littered the shore at Mweenish Strand and Ballinaleama Bay, Co. Galway, and Trawmore Strand, Achill Island, Co. Mayo. Along the coast at Doonloughaun and Mannin Bays and Errislannain Point, Co. Galway, there were continuous drifts with several million by-the-wind-sailors hitting the beaches.[63]

Tropical seeds and fruit

While most tropical curiosities that arrive on the North Atlantic Current would be unable to survive and reproduce in the low temperatures, there is one category of drifters that are less sensitive, retaining a capacity for establishing bridgehead populations on new continents. These are the tropical seeds and fruits – amongst the highest prizes a beachcomber could encounter. All seeds originating in the topics and warm areas of the western Atlantic are endowed with both

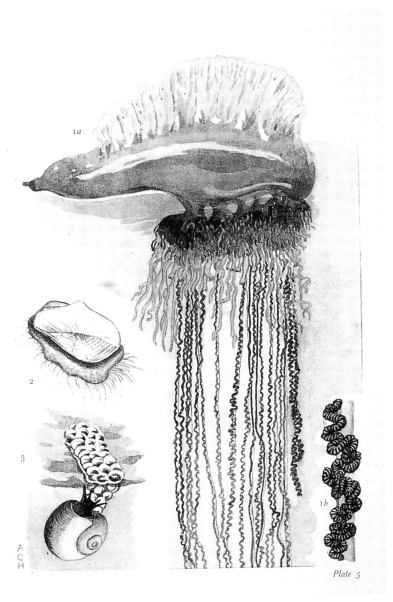

North Atlantic drifters: 1a Portuguese man-of-war; 1b enlarged portion of tentacle; 2 by-the-wind-sailor; 3 violet snail. From Hardy[14].

buoyancy and a tough and water-resistant integument protecting the seed inside. Several tropical seeds washed up along the western coastline have been made to germinate on their removal from salt water. Their ability to travel such long distances while retaining their reproductive capacity raises intriguing biogeographical questions about the dispersal of plant species and the colonisation of new lands. The first record of such a germination involved a seed called a nickar nut from a thorny bush, *Caesalpinia bonduc*, a member of the pea family and native of Jamaica. It was washed up on the west coast of Ireland around the beginning of the nineteenth century, and grown into a plant.[64]

The first published record of tropical beans washed up on either British or Irish shores, almost certainly the sea-heart, a legume also known as the sea-bean and sea-kidney, was in 1570 when these beans were found in 'great plenty on the shores of Cornwall'.[65] Sir Hans Sloane, the famous Irish-born doctor and founder of the British Museum, was the first to record the occurrence of tropical drift seeds on Irish beaches in 1696. He said about the sea-heart, one of the commonest collected drift seeds, 'This, I am told, is cast up on the coast of Kerry in Ireland.'[66] He later noted that the nickar nut, another legume, was 'often cast ashore by the sea on the northwest coast of Ireland and Scotland'.[67] During the intervening period dozens more tropical drift fruits and seeds were found on the west coast of Ireland. An early and unexpected account of four different species of tropical seeds is found in a book about life in western Connemara, *Letters from the Irish Highlands of Cunnemara* (1825):

> 'Our sea nuts are another marine curiosity, having very much the appearance of horse chestnuts, but of various shapes and sizes. They contain a kernel, white and bitter to the taste: some are small and round like marbles [nickar nut]; others oval, with a handsome black or yellow band round the middle [true sea-bean]; others, again, with an impression like a stamp on one side [Virgin Mary's bean], On shewing some of them to a nurseryman near London, he pronounced them to be South American, all diadelphous and siliquosus. The largest, a hypmena, a forest tree, with the fruit enclosed in pods about two feet long and six or eight inches broad [sea-heart] .These pods discharge their fruit every two years with a report like a pistol. The quantity of essential oil which they contain, causes them to float so long in the water, that the seeds would no doubt germinate as hardy store plants. Some of the smaller species were indeed formerly cultivated in England, but have been neglected on account of their rambling unornamental appearance. The unlearned natives of Cunnemara have, however, found a fanciful use for the nuts, by laying them under the pillows of their straw bed, as a charm against the nocturnal visits of the fairies.'[68]

The arrival of tropical seeds and fruits on Irish shore perplexed early naturalists. How did they manage to cross the Atlantic vastness? Was it by currents or by the agency of man? The eminent father of English botany, John Ray opined, in a letter to Hans Sloane in 1696, that 'It is very unlikely to me that they should be brought so far by any current of the sea. I should rather think they came from vessels cast away by shipwreck near these parts.'[69] One problem was that no-one had ever encountered any of the seeds or fruits in the Atlantic at a time when seeing was believing. Moreover there was some evidence to show that the North Atlantic Current petered out at 30°W some 1,300 km from the west coast of Ireland. Despite these impediments it became clear from the arrival of abandoned vessels and materials from shipwrecks, originating in the western Atlantic, that there was an oceanic current eastwards. It was also noted that the seeds and fruits were almost exclusively found on the western rather than eastern shores of Ireland and Scotland.

Experimental bottles and floats released off North America and other western Atlantic sites confirmed the accuracy of the phenomenon. The casting-out and recovery dates allowed Guppy, a pioneering investigator into the North Atlantic Current, to calculate an average rate of travel of 14.8 km per day from the West Indies to the shores of Europe, i.e. a spell of about 14 months was needed to bridge the two continents.[70] In addition, the system of the Atlantic oceanic currents (see p.390) makes it possible for a seed grown on the banks of the Niger or Congo in West Africa to reach European shores by first travelling westwards to northern Brazil, thence northwards to the Caribbean and Gulf of Mexico until entering the North Atlantic Current and moving eastwards to Europe – a journey of some 16,000 km, lasting close to three years, and involving three continents.

It was not until the discovery of a specimen of sea-heart on the shore near Inveran, Galway Bay, was brought to the attention of Colgan in October 1916, that the first review of the occurrence of these drift seeds along Irish shores was published.[71] Colgan established a list of eight species of plants whose disseminules had been thrown up on Irish shores and collected as curiosities. The disseminule of greatest interest to biogeographers is known as peregrine – something foreign, e.g. seeds and fruits, that has been imported or travelled long distances, in these cases on ocean currents. Other kinds of disseminules can originate from local sources or can be of refuse origin, such as material washed off boats, or abandoned cargoes. These are of less interest than the peregrine.

In 1978 Nelson reviewed disseminules recorded in Ireland since Colgan's work.[64] While clarifying Colgan's list of peregrines, Nelson added a new species, the coconut, thought until then to originate from boats or to be of refuse origin. Since 1978 another species has come ashore, *Canavalia nitida,* a legume native of the West Indies. Unusually, it was not found on the west coast but on Ballinesker Beach, north of Curracloe, Co. Wexford, in April 1981.[72]

The seeds of the nine peregrine species that have been so far recorded in Ireland having travelled some 6,450 km eastwards across the ocean from the West Indies are listed below.

1. Nickar nut or grey nickar nut

The parent plant is a thorny bush, widespread in the tropics including the West Indies and Florida. A native of southeastern Asia, this legume is now pancontinental through drifting in oceans. The seed is similar in size to the acorn, light grey, with concentric hair-like cracks, ovoid to spherical and about 2 cm in diameter. There have been four records, one each in Donegal and Mayo, and two in Kerry, one of which was the last Irish record, fished from the sea near Valentia Island in the 1930s. One seed is reputed to have been germinated and to have grown into a small bush. The buoyancy of the seed is due to an internal air-filled cavity.

2. Coconut

A fibrous husk usually surrounds the hard, dark brown seed, about 30 cm long by 20 cm wide. Most of the records originate from refuse sources or have been washed off boats. However, there is good evidence to suggest a transatlantic crossing by at least two Irish specimens, one found in Kerry, the other in Mayo. Their peregrine status was argued on the basis of their long period of immersion in the ocean indicated by the attachment of barnacles and algae together with the presence of the marine mollusc *Psiloteredo megotera* that had bored into the fruit as far as the bony endocarp in the Kerry specimen.

3. SEA-PURSE BEAN

The mother plant is a woody vine with a pantropical distribution. Irish-collected seeds have been dark brown, variable in shape, often circular with sometimes one straight side. The hilum, 1–2 cm, is black. The seeds are about 3 cm in diameter and 1–2 cm thick. This legume can be confused with true sea-bean (see below) which may be the reason why it is so infrequently recorded. Two specimens have been found on the Irish coastline.

4. SEA-HEART, SEA-BEAN, MOLUCCA BEAN, SEA-KIDNEY

The parent plant is a wood vine occurring in central tropical Africa, central and southern tropical America and in the West Indies. The seeds are contained in a pod over 1 m long and are a dark maroon-brown, generally heart-shaped to circular in outline. They are large, about 5 cm in diameter and about 2 cm thick. This legume is the most commonly found species – 73 recorded from Irish shores to 1977 – and one of the most buoyant of all drift seeds to reach Irish shores. One collected in Donegal has been geminated at the National Botanic Gardens, Dublin, and is under cultivation. The seeds have been made into snuffboxes, key rings, used as buttons, and worn by children to keep away the evil eye. Some were even placed under pillows as a charm against night visits by the fairies.[68] They have also been employed, when ground up, as a cure for epilepsy.

5. VIRGIN MARY'S BEAN

From a high-climbing woody liana of wet mixed forests in central tropical America, Cuba and Hispaniola, this species is also found in Africa and Asia. The seeds are black or dark brown, circular and flattened in outline, with a c-shaped hilum on the ventral surface and an impressed cross-mark on the dorsal surface. They are about 3 cm in diameter and about 2 cm thick. There are only three recorded examples from Ireland – two from Mayo and one from Donegal.

6 & 7. TRUE SEA-BEAN, HORSE-EYE BEAN

It is difficult to identify the species of *Mucuna*, and it is likely that several different kinds have arrived on Irish shores over the years such as *M. fawcettii* and *M. urens*. The true sea-bean is produced by a woody pantropical vine. The seeds are in pods which are covered with stinging hairs on the surface and are dark brown, spherical or slightly compressed, with a lighter greyish or reddish-brown band around the hilum and are about 2.5 cm diameter. The hilum is black and 3.5 cm broad. One seed of *M. cf. sloanei*, collected in west Donegal, has been germinated in the National Botanic Gardens, Dublin.

8. *SACCOGLOTTIS AMAZONICA* BEAN

The parent plant of this seed is a tall forest tree of the Amazon and Orinoco

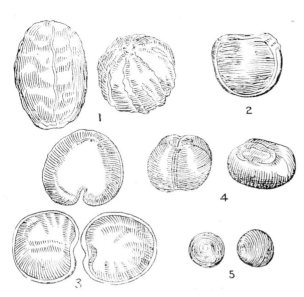

Early drawings of West
Indian Drift Seeds.
1. *Saccoglottis amazonica*
2. Sea-purse bean
3. Sea-heart, sea-bean,
Molucca bean,
sea-kidney
4. *Ipomea tuberosa*
5. Nickar nut or grey
nickar nut
From Colgan[71].

estuaries. The woody endocarp is 2–6 cm long by 2–4 cm diameter and contains two seeds. A number of empty vesicles in the endocarp allows it to float
in the water for up to two years. One example, based only on a description, has
been recorded from Ireland.

9. *CANAVALIA NITIDA* BEAN

The parent is a native of the West Indies. The seed is ellipsoidal, and the specimen from Co. Wexford was 21 mm long by 16 mm in diameter and reddish-
brown with a distinct black linear hilum. Only one other example has been
recorded in Europe and was from the Outer Hebrides around the turn of the
century.

The seeds of three tropical species that have arrived in Irish waters have been
germinated – with encouragement – by first cracking open the tough outer
skin or testa to let water in to trigger off the germination. However, they are
incapable of surviving out-of-doors in Ireland and must remain in the warm
shelter of a glasshouse if they are to survive. The number of registered species
from Irish coasts is disappointing when compared with the fifteen or more
recorded from the beaches in the Outer Hebrides and other Scottish islands.
The most plausible explanation is that despite the seeds being found and collected the information fails to be reported to the National Museum, or the
National Botanic Gardens, Dublin, or to be publicised in scientific literature.
There is the case of one farmer from Clare Island, Co. Mayo, who has collected literally a basket full of seeds of several species, none of which came to the
attention of botanists until recently.[73]

Other North Atlantic Drifters

Apart from the Portuguese man-of-war, the by-the-wind-sailor and the tropical
seeds and fruits, the North Atlantic Current also conveys onto Irish beaches
other exotic pelagic species. They include the violet snail, a mollusc not dis-

similar to the ordinary garden snail, but coloured lavender-blue. It produces a
large 'float' of air bubbles bound together in a mass of gelatinous material that
has a purple tint. The snail hangs upside down from the bubble platform. This
'float' device serves both as a buoyancy aid and as a sail that catches the wind,
driving the snail eastwards towards Ireland when southwesterly winds prevail.
The violet snail feeds on the by-the-wind-sailor, a fellow traveller, apparently by
squirting an anaesthetising violet dye which enables it to browse on the food
caught in the by-the-wind-sailor's tentacles.[14] The floats of the violet snail are
occasionally found on beaches, but are greatly discoloured.

Other Atlantic drifters are sea squirts *Salpa* spp. The adult sea squirt has a
soft body protected by a leathery test or outer skin made of a chemical similar
to the cellulose found in plants. These tunicates sometimes occur in large
numbers washed up along the western coastline. Another wanderer from the
western Atlantic is the Sargassum weed, originating from the Sargasso Sea.
This seaweed floats by means of many small air bladders positioned around the
edges of its fronds. It is reputed to have been found washed up in Valentia
Harbour, Co. Kerry by the famous Delap sisters – Constance and Maud Jane –
who as gifted amateurs contributed a great deal of knowledge to marine biology around the turn of the century.[74] The weeds were found encrusted with a
polyzoan *Membranipora tuberculata*. While most of the pelagic species mentioned turn up in the sea and washed up on the coastline on an almost regular basis, no recent records of the Sargassum weed would appear to have been
reported.[75]

Rowing to the west –
Michael Meenaghan.

12

Conservation of Nature

It is often incorrectly thought that threats to wild nature are recent events of the latter half of this century, but the first attacks on Ireland's natural environment came from the Neolithic farmers who arrived in Ireland some 6,000 years ago with their cattle, pigs and sheep together with cereals including barley, small smelt, emmer and einkorn wheat. Woodlands were cleared to free up fertile lands for crop cultivation and grasslands for cattle to graze were created. The diminution of woodland coverage initially came about by the chopping down of trees, burning them or ring-barking which left them standing dead without foliage, thus allowing penetration of light to the rich soils on the woodland floor during the summer. The last two techniques would have been the easiest and least time and energy consuming options. The impact of an ever increasing number of grazing cattle eating seedlings and preventing natural woodland regeneration was a most powerful and possibly underrated ecological force in the process of Neolithic woodland clearance. The fossil pollen records for this period demonstrate a decline in tree pollen and a rise in grass and herb pollen as the first farmers gradually depleted the woodlands. The onslaught on the woodlands continued as the human population expanded with the need for more grazing lands. Marshes were also drained to facilitate farmland expansion and human settlements. The landscape from these early times has continued to be managed with increasing intensity principally for agricultural purposes.

The rapid rise of the population in the late eighteenth century brought increased pressures on the landscape and wildlife resources. By 1785 the population stood at 4 million and in 1841, just prior to the famine, there were 8.2 million people, a figure way beyond the natural carrying capacity of the land for the time. The remarkable population boom had been fuelled and supported by the potato, a 'wonder' food able to flourish in marginal and other lands unsuitable for virtually all other crops as shown by the presence of potato ridges or 'lazy beds' in many upland areas seemingly unfit for any form of cultivation. The failure, in 1845, of the potato crop from potato blight had devastating social consequences. About 800,000 people died and a further approximately 1.6 million emigrated during the subsequent six years. The population continued in decline to 4 million in 1930. By 1990–91 the population had increased to 5.11 million (3.523 million in the Republic in April 1991 and 1.589 million in Northern Ireland in June 1990). The enormous pre-famine population had a profoundly negative ecological impact on the countryside leaving behind a 'ruined landscape almost destitute of any woody growth'.[1]

From the earliest times man has been responsible for the extinction of many species for flora and fauna in Ireland either though the destruction of essential habitats or by direct persecution. Habitat disturbance was probably responsible for the extinction of the breeding populations of cranes (extinct during the middle ages), capercaillie and greylag goose (eighteenth century), bittern

(1840) and woodlark (1894 with a few subsequent records). Direct persecution by trapping, poisoning and shooting took its toll amongst many raptors once widespread throughout the country: buzzard (1891, but now re-established and expanding), white-tailed eagle (*c.* 1910), golden eagle (1912 but one subsequent breeding pair 1953–60) and marsh harrier (1917). Another three woodland nesting raptors – the goshawk (bone remains at human settlements from Mesolithic to early Bronze Age), red kite (present in Medieval times) and osprey (present in the twelfth century) – bred contemporaneously with man and should be added to the list of species whose extinctions were brought about by him. However, their extinction dates are not certain. Amongst the mammals the wolf (1786) and the red squirrel (*c.*1662 but reintroduced from 1815 onwards) also fell foul to man's persecutions. The variety of charr (also known as the 'whiting') formerly abundant in Lough Neagh until about 1837 became extinct soon afterwards through overfishing. Amongst the vascular plants eight extinctions are known, most of which have been brought about by man's activities. Thus Ireland has endured, in common with other west European countries, a long history of fluctuating fortunes of wild nature. The final onslaught on wild nature commenced some 60 years ago when modern agricultural technology including machinery and agrochemicals quickened the pace of damage to the landscape and its wildlife in a way never experienced before.

Ireland's awakening to an enlightened attitude towards nature conservation is a recent event. Forty years ago anyone calling for the preservation of raised bogs, machair or wetland habitats or arguing the case for the protection of the Greenland white-fronted goose was generally associated with a privileged elite. There was minimal support within government for conservation, an activity regarded as something foreign to the mainstream of Irish life. Moreover government was then preoccupied with sowing the seeds of Ireland's future economic prosperity which commenced in the early 1960s, gathered pace in the 1970s and 1980s and boomed throughout the 1990s, boasting the fastest economic growth recorded in any European country during the present decade. But concomitant with increasing economic development came pressures on the country's fragile ecosystems which led to the destruction of many ecologically valuable habitats and a reduction in the numbers of many plants and animals.

The growth of new attitudes by government and subsequent action was not without pains. Voluntary conservation organisations played important and often critical and nursemaid roles while more recently the Commission of the European Union has provided 'encouragement' through the necessity of all member states to comply with two vital Council Directives on *The Conservation of Wild Birds* and *The Conservation of Natural Habitats and of Wild Fauna and Flora*. Moreover, the Commission, in support of Ireland's efforts of compliance, has provided some limited funding for the identification and designation of important habitats as well as assisting with the purchase of several important sites.

This chapter will consider some of the critical issues, discuss some conservation objectives for Ireland, describe various developments in the history of the conservation of nature in Ireland and present some nature conservation achievements.

Some critical conservation issues

Agriculture

1. DRAINAGE

The most damaging impacts on sites and areas of nature conservation importance have come from agriculture. Arterial and other drainage schemes have physically destroyed countless wetlands, particularly turloughs, many of which were important wildfowl and botanical habitats. River habitats including fish spawning beds and river banks, important for breeding birds and many invertebrates, have also been destroyed or severely disrupted. EU priority species such as the otter, river lamprey, brook lamprey and freshwater pearl mussel have lost important habitats through insensitive drainage schemes in the past. Since the commencement of the *Arterial Drainage Act, 1945*, 37 schemes have been completed. Over a quarter of a million hectares of land were affected, but not all detrimentally. Today the demand for drainage schemes has diminished due to the completion of so many projects. New legal requirements make it mandatory to provide environmental impact assessments, clearly revealing both the benefits and disadvantages of any proposed scheme before the scheme can proceed.

2. OVERGRAZING

The overstocking of sheep, encouraged by EU-funded Sheep Headage Payments and government Ewe Premiums, both provided in good faith to support farm incomes in disadvantaged areas, has devastated many peatland, sand dune and machair habitats, especially in western areas. Sheep numbers in the Republic have nearly trebled from 3.3 million in 1980 to 8.9 million in June 1991. Peatlands in Donegal, Mayo, Galway and Kerry have been particularly badly affected with noticeable loss of valuable heather moorland. The destruc-

Drainage in progress with whooper swans in foreground, Turloughcor, 4.5 km southeast of Headford, Co. Galway.

tion of vegetation cover, and in particular heather, removed essential breeding habitats of red grouse, golden plover, hen harrier, merlin, dunlin, and the wintering habitats for the Greenland white-fronted goose – all listed in the *Irish Red Data Book* as threatened species.[2] Moreover, the accelerated erosion of soil encouraged by overstocking and its runoff into streams and into coastal waters have detrimental effects on the proper functioning of aquatic ecosystems. Fish populations as well as freshwater pearl mussel populations are suffering directly from it.

The Irish Peatland Conservation Council has shown that 50 peatlands of conservation value throughout the Republic, extending over 54,220 ha, have been seriously degraded by overgrazing. Five of the sites have lost their conservation value. A further four sites in Northern Ireland, covering 13,920 ha, have also been seriously degraded.

Upland blanket bogs cannot withstand the grazing impacts at a stocking rate of 1.7 sheep per hectare as recommended by the Department of Agriculture and Food.[3] According to Dúchas – The Heritage Service, appropriate stocking rates on Irish upland wet heaths should be in the range of 0.2 sheep per hectare while the stocking rate can rise to 0.6 sheep per hectare on lowland dry heath with good heather growth. Stocking rates on blanket bog where there is moderate damage (e.g. some bare soil) should be kept between 0.15 and 0.4 sheep per hectare in most cases.[4]

Experimental investigations in Co. Antrim uplands found that common cottongrass and purple moor-grass plant communities resulting from overgrazing of sheep represented a degradation of the heather and bilberry vegetation. The optimal level of grazing to achieve the objectives for conservation and agricultural values was considered to be in the order of three sheep per hectare over the summer months.[5] The overgrazing also led to an expansion of mat-grass on the uplands, which is of poor feeding value to sheep.[6] In the Connemara uplands, overgrazing of sheep has not only resulted in the loss of the heather but has also led to erosion of peat which has adverse impacts on river and coastal fisheries.

Peat silt destroys spawning beds of fish in rivers and lakes by smothering the eggs and cutting off their supply of essential oxygen. It also inhibits algal growth and fish productivity in lakes by reducing the amount of light and oxygen in the waters. Moreover when the rains run off the uplands into coastal waters the extra burden of peat fragments and silt chokes to death many shell fish, including valuable beds of oysters and mussels, which depend on filtering out from the water minute plants and animals that form the phyto- and zooplankton. One does not need scientific studies to establish what the eye can see clearly – degradation of heather moorlands, with unprecedented exposure of bare soil and rocks on many mountain slopes and hillsides in western Ireland. A sanguine view was held by the late Frank Mitchell who wrote (1997) 'The point from which recovery is possible may have already passed, but unless the overgrazing is halted immediately, vast areas of the west will come to resemble areas of the Burren.'[1] In the summer of 1998 the Department of Agriculture and Food announced that there would be a destocking programme of up to 200,000 ewes on the most damaged areas in the west.

Apart from environmental damage caused by overstocking in unsuitable habitats, other kinds of agricultural intensification have already detrimentally affected or threatened some bird species: numbers of corn bunting (probably extinct 1998), yellowhammer and grey partridge have declined (hedgerow removal and decline in mixed and cereal farming), along with the barn owl (general tidying up of farmland and loss of old farm buildings), the corncrake (changes in grassland management) and the dunlin (field drainage). The chough is threatened by intensification of grassland management in coastal areas. However, other species (swans, geese and ducks, as mentioned in Chapter 8) have benefited from feeding on improved grasslands.

3. GRASSLAND IMPROVEMENT AND HEDGEROW REMOVAL

Many ancient grasslands and pasture meadowlands rich in plant and insect species have been destroyed by drainage, ploughing, re-seeding with rye and other grasses, fertilisation and the application of herbicides. Many of the eco-logically valuable and rich limestone grassland pastures in the Burren, Co. Clare, have been irredeemably altered by fertiliser application which has encouraged the growth of grasses at the expense of herbs thus altering the flo-ral structure of the pastures. While there is less of an economic drive for hedgerow removal in Ireland because of the beneficial shelter they provide to grazing animals in generally windier and wetter conditions than in many other European countries, an increasing trend of removal in the richer eastern and southeastern Counties has been noted.

Water pollution

Many important freshwater ecosystems, especially lakes, have had their nutri-ent status significantly enhanced to the detriment of their ecology by pollution originating principally from agricultural diffuse or non-point sources – the leaching of phosphates and nitrates from the application of chemical fertilis-ers and animal slurries. Single-point discharges from municipal and industrial sewage works also contribute to the pollution of the lakes. In an assessment of the trophic status of lake water quality carried out during 1991–4 a total of 104 lakes was examined. On the basis of their annual maximum chlorophyll con-centrations, 24 had such high levels that their beneficial uses as sources for drinking water, recreation and for fish populations were impaired. Moreover, there was an increasing number of lakes between 1987–90 and 1991–4 in the strongly and highly eutrophic and hypertrophic categories.[7] The eutrophica-tion of lakes is thought to have affected several species of birds, classified as threatened breeding populations, such as the common scoter and the black-necked grebe. The Arctic charr, also a threatened species, is susceptible to water pollution.[2]

Forestry

The government is committed to an ambitious afforestation programme with a target planting of 30,000 ha per annum, constituting the greatest land use change taking place in Ireland today. Much of the planting is of coniferous species – sitka spruce and lodgepole pine – on blanket bogland (211,000 ha already planted) and raised bogs (6,400 ha already planted). The afforestation programme is supported by EU and government grants. The grants are no longer available for plantings considered likely to cause damage on proposed Natural Heritage Areas (NHAs). But at present there is nothing to prevent a private investor, such as a pension fund, from establishing commercial planta-tions on designated NHAs. Some ancient semi-natural woodlands (e.g. Slish

Afforestation of lowland blanket bogland, Connemara, Co. Galway. Such developments
have destroyed several blanket bogs of high ecological interest in western Ireland.

Wood, Co. Sligo and Blackstones Bridge Woods, Co. Kerry) have unfortunately been underplanted with or replaced by coniferous species in the past and it
is to be hoped that this will never happen again. The impact of coniferous
plantations on landscape quality is a more intractable and contentious issue.
In an effort to mitigate these and other impacts the state forestry board,
Coillte, has adopted series of environmental guidelines concerning landscape
values, natural heritage areas, archaeological sites and river ecology. In
defence of coniferous afforestation there are some positive wildlife benefits
such as provision of new breeding habitats, albeit often for only a few years, for
some bird species including siskin, hen harrier, sedge warbler, coal tit and jay,
as well as for mammals, including the pine marten.

Peat and mineral extraction

The extraction of peat for burning in power stations or for sale to private consumers is a continuing threat to the conservation of peatlands, especially the
Midland raised bogs. Traditional turbary rights for the cutting of bog peat over
the past 400 years has led to the loss of 68% of the raised bogs and 46% of the
blanket bogs. The mechanical extraction of peat has been far more serious. In
the Midland raised bogs over the past 50 years there has been even more devastation leading to a loss of 22% of the initial resource. In 1984, Ryan & Cross
estimated that 92% of all raised bogland had been man-modified and lost for
conservation purposes.[8] The Midland raised bogs are particularly vulnerable
because they are relatively easy to develop and hold deep deposits of peat in
comparison with the shallower and more topographically challenging blanket
bogs. Moreover the financial return from the exploitation of Midland raised
bogs is much greater than from blanket bogs.
    The quarrying of gravel, especially from esker ridges, has destroyed many
important botanical sites with deciduous woodlands and associated rich herb

Tynagh Mine Co. Galway. A huge lead-zinc-copper-silver deposit was discovered here in 1961. It was first worked as an open cast mine and later by underground methods until 1980. (C. O'Rourke).

ground floras. The mining of minerals has also led to some damage and localised impacts.

Aquaculture

Intensive fin fish aquaculture is a particularly important economic activity, especially along the western seaboard where unemployment and lack of job opportunities are often acute. Initially aquaculture seemed a perfect marriage between the clean waters and sheltered bays of the western coast and the need to provide employment. However, such fish farming has two major environmental impacts. When located in shallow coastal waters with poor dispersal conditions, the wastes falling from the fish enclosures accumulate underneath to form a carpet of organic detritus on the bottom sediments, leading to deoxygenation and loss of some of the benthic species in the impacted zone. Secondly the disastrous decline in sea trout numbers in rivers in Connemara and south Mayo from 1988 onwards has been blamed on an explosion of sea lice linked with the establishment of salmon farms located too close to the sea trout rivers. The collapse of the sea trout populations in several western areas led to a ferocious dispute between sea trout anglers and the salmon farmers.

Research carried out by the Salmon Research Agency at Newport, Co. Mayo, into the causes of the decline showed that the majority of the sea trout returning to the fresh water were thin, emaciated and heavily infested by sea lice. The anglers argued that these trout had received their sea lice burdens from the large numbers attracted to and living on the caged salmon. It was claimed that thousands of the lice had been dislodged from the salmon by chemicals in an attempt to cure the problem and had sought out the sea trout as alternative hosts. Despite considerable research and much contentious argument both the Sea Trout Action Group (STAG) and the Salmon Growers' Association cannot agree on the reasons for the sea trout collapse. STAG concluded in 1992 that 'in the absence of absolute proof, which may never be achievable, the weight of available evidence indicates that the increase in the number of lice emanating from salmon farms was a major contributory factor in the sea trout collapse. No other factor has emerged from STAG's investigations.'[9] The alternative viewpoint of the Salmon Growers' Association was that 'Sea trout populations in the mid-Western region are under pressure because of a long-term climatic and/or environmental factors in the sea and or fresh water which result in osmoregulatory stress in sea trout smoults and causes premature return to fresh water. The effects of these factors were particularly severe from 1989 to spring 1991 and resulted in a predisposition to disease, parasites and lice infestation. Some of the lice may or may not have emanated from salmon farms.'[10] The government appointed a special Sea Trout Task Force to study the problem and it concluded that scientific investigations 'point to infestation of sea trout [by sea lice] in the vicinity of sea farms as the factor most closely associated with the marked incidence of adverse pressure on sea trout stocks in recent years'.[11] The adoption of the precautionary principle of avoiding the location of new fish farms within a radius of 20 km of the entrance of important sea trout rivers would seem prudent until more scientific information becomes available on the decline of sea trout.

Tourism and recreation

The continuing growth of tourism and increasing interest in the natural environment are leading to visitor pressures which, in some places, not only threatens the environment but decreases the enjoyment of others seeking to be at one with nature. In 1994, for the first time ever, the number of overseas tourists, some 3.7 million, exceeded the number of residents in the Republic. Many of these visitors were drawn to Ireland principally on account of its unspoilt natural environment. As result of such a massive influx some of the better known areas such as National Parks and some national monuments are close to reaching their carrying capacities. In 1996 nearly 200,000 visitors were recorded at Killarney National Park, Co. Kerry; 82,000 at Glenveagh National Park, Co. Donegal; 70,000 at Connemara National Park, Co. Galway; approximately 200,000 at Aillwee Caves, Burren, Co. Clare; 42,000 at the Céide Fields Interpretative Centre, Co. Mayo while 30,000 people travelled on the Clonmacnoise Bog Train, Co. Offaly. Visitor numbers at Dún Aonghasa, a late Bronze Age structure perched on the cliff edge on Inishmore, Aran Islands, Co. Galway, some 100,000 annually, are so great that the site is in danger of being damaged.

To cater for visitors, a proliferating infrastructure of interpretative centres, visitor centres, car parks, nature trails and toilet facilities are springing up throughout the countryside. Although often despised by many purists they perform some positive functions. Firstly their location can be used as a management tool ('honey pots') to focus visitors in particular areas while keeping them away from the more sensitive elements of the landscape where wildlife and ecosystems are best left alone and undisturbed. Secondly the state, as manager of protected areas, is under an obligation to provide basic facilities for visitors who have contributed towards the purchase of protected areas through their taxes. Some interpretative facilities are needed to provide information to the many visitors who are less knowledgeable about the natural environment than the specialists or experienced naturalists. However, the location of such centres has resulted in bitter conflicts between environmentalists and the state authority Dúchas with responsibility for National Parks and nature reserves.

The proposed interpretative centres at one of the entrances of the Burren National Park, Co. Clare, and to the Wicklow National Park in the early 1990s generated deep divisions of opinion and philosophy between the opposing factions. The Burren has long been recognised, both nationally and internationally, as one of the natural history jewels of Ireland. It was for this reason that the government has purchased 1,673 ha (to mid 1998) centred on the Mullagh More area to protect the vitally important ecosystems – limestone pavement, ash and hazel woodland, turloughs and calcareous grassland. The thought of locating a visitor centre which would attract thousands of visitors to a particularly outstanding part of the Burren aroused the anger of most environmentalists within and outside Ireland. The dispute was fought mainly over the proximity of the centre to Mullagh More Mountain (some 2.4 km away) considered by many the most sensitive area of the National Park and where one could have uplifting and spiritual experiences – provided not too many people were around. Those opposed to the centre felt that it would open up this part of the Burren to an unacceptable number of visitors leading to harmful impact on the fragile ecology of the area. There were also concerns about traffic generation, littering and pollution threats to underground waters feeding nearby important turloughs. Environmentalists argued that the centre should be located within the existing infrastructure of villages further away from the National Park area. The dispute has had, so far, two important outcomes.

Firstly, development works undertaken by Dúchas, formerly exempt from the need to apply for planning permission, are now subject to the *Planning and*

Mossy moist hazel woodland, Burren Co. Clare. Entering such a woodland and crawling around in search of mosses and lichens is like visiting a botanical fairyland, full of surprises.

Development Acts following a Court decision won by the environmentalists. Secondly, the issues argued during the controversy have engendered a broader debate on questions of access to protected areas and the need for new strategic management planning to cope with increasing numbers of visitors. Certain areas of Ireland will soon be in danger of being engulfed by increasing numbers of tourists each year. For example it has been estimated that upwards of 9 million visitors will come to the Republic of Ireland during 1998, swamping the resident population by almost three to one.

Síle de Valera, Minister for Arts, Heritage, Gaeltacht and the Islands and responsible for Dúchas put forward a compromise to the original plans for the proposed Burren centre. The centre was considerably scaled down and planning permission was sought from Clare County Council. As part of the management plan for the Burren National Park, the Minister also proposed to provide ancillary interpretation facilities in the villages of Corrofin, Kilfenora (the village already has a small interpretative centre, funded by the Carnegie Trust in the early 1970s) and Ballyvaghan, all some way off the Mullagh More area. Clare County Council rejected the revised plans in September 1998 and the Minister has appealed the decision which will now be adjudicated by the Planning Appeals Board.

Some nature conservation objectives for Ireland

A nature conservation strategy for Ireland should aim to protect a representative range of the best habitats from mountain summits to the sea bed, as well as particular species requiring safeguarding. The selection of sites and species should meet both national and European criteria.

The EU Habitats Directive lists 45 priority habitats found throughout the European Community, the majority occurring in southern Europe, scattered around the Mediterranean basin where biological diversity is much greater than in the colder northern lands. Nevertheless, Ireland possesses particularly fine examples of sixteen of these priority habitats – coastal lagoons; fixed dunes with herbaceous vegetation (grey dunes); decalcified fixed dunes with crowberry; Atlantic decalcified fixed dunes; machairs; turloughs; semi-natural dry calcareous grasslands rich in orchids; species-rich mat-grass grasslands on siliceous substrates in mountain areas; actively growing raised bogs; actively growing blanket bogs; calcareous fens with great fen-sedge and the sedge *Carex davalliana* (not present in Ireland); petrifying springs with tufa formation; limestone pavements; bog woodland; residual alluvial forests and yew woods. Amongst the second priority EU habitats the following are particularly well represented in the country: estuaries, large shallow inlets and bays, oligotrophic waters, vegetation on dry calcareous rocky slopes and old oak woodlands with holly and hard fern. The information now available to the National Parks and Wildlife Service (NPWS) of Dúchas arising from many national surveys provides a firm basis on which sites can be selected to fulfil EU priority habitat conservation obligations.

In addition to the NHA database, a fundamental review of the key issues facing the natural environment in Ireland was carried out in 1991–2 by the Green 2000 Advisory Group, established by the then Taioseach Charles Haughey, and charged with 'identifying policies and strategies which should be adopted to protect and enhance the natural environment.'[12] The Group identified eleven major areas of economic activity considered to have significant implications for

The extensive Atlantic lowland blanket bogland north of Roundstone and southeast of Clifden. One of the most important bogland sites in Ireland.

nature and the natural environment. Specific recommendations in the chapters on agriculture, aquaculture, inland fisheries, forestry, nature conservation and landscape protection were directed towards strengthening protective mechanisms for the conservation of the natural environment. Many of the recommendations have since been adopted.

National and European perspectives are also relevant for the conservation of animal and plant species. From the European viewpoint there are three measures demanded from Ireland for the fauna (birds excluded) and flora species listed below. Annex II of the Directive identifies flora and fauna requiring designation of areas of conservation to ensure the survival of the listed species; Annex IV lists species in need of strict protection, and Annex V lists plants and animals that need to have special measures to prevent their deliberate capture or killing, picking, uprooting, etc. (Table 12.1).

In addition to these EU requirements, more specific national priorities for conservation action required for threatened mammals, birds, amphibians and fish in Ireland have been specified the relevant *Red Data Book*.[2] The *Irish Red Data Book* on vascular plants also outlines recommended measures.[13]

All wild vertebrates in the Republic apart from fish species are protected by the *Wildlife Act, 1976* but only three invertebrates have legal protection. The Kerry slug, freshwater pearl mussel and freshwater crayfish receive recognition under the *Protection of Wild Animals Regulations 1990*. Sixty-eight species of flowering plants and ferns and their habitats are protected under the *Flora (Protection) Order, 1987*. The moss *Drepanocladus vernicosus* and the liverwort *Petalophyllum ralfsii* listed for strict conservation measures in EU Habitats Directive are not as yet protected under Irish law.

Table 12.1 List of species requiring designation of conservation areas, in need of strict protection and special measures to prevent deliberate killing, capture etc.

Species	Requiring special areas of conservation (SACs) (Annex II of Directive)	In need of strict protection (Annex IV of Directive)	Exploitation and taking in the wild subject to management measures (Annex V of Directive)
Pine marten			•
Irish hare			•
Lesser horseshoe bat	•	•	
Brown long-eared bat		•	
Common pipistrelle bat		•	
Leisler's bat		•	
Whiskered bat		•	
Daubenton's bat		•	
Natterer's bat		•	
Otter	•	•	
Grey seal	•		•
Common seal	•		•
Bottle-nosed dolphin	•	•	
Harbour porpoise	•	•	
All cetaceans		•	
Brook lamprey	•		
Sea lamprey	•		
River lamprey	•		•
Atlantic salmon (only in fresh water)	•		•
Allis shad	•		•
Twaite shad	•		•
Killarney shad	•		•
Pollan			•
Natterjack toad		•	
European frog			•
Freshwater crayfish	•		•
Marsh fritillary	•		
Kerry slug	•		
The snail *Vertigo angustior*	•		
The snail *V. geyeri*	•		
The snail *V. moulinsiana*	•		
Freshwater pearl mussel	•		•
Margaritifera m. durrovensis	•		•
Killarney fern	•		
Luronium natans	•		
Slender naiad	•		
Marsh saxifrage	•		
The moss *Leucobryum glaucum*			•
The moss *Drepanocladus vernicosus*	•		•
The liverwort *Petalophyllum ralfsii*	•		•
Red alga *Lithothamnion corallioides*			•
Red alga *Phymatolithon calcareum*			•
Sphagnum moss spp.			•
Clubmosses *Lycopodium* spp.			•

With regard to the amount of land that should be reserved for nature conservation it was authoritatively estimated in 1981 by Michael Neff, Head of the Conservation Branch of the Wildlife Service, that a nature conservation network of 150 sites, covering some 107,000 ha, and a further special species network of 60 sites, covering 56,000 ha, was required to provide protection for the full spectrum of native flora and fauna in the Republic.[14] Marine nature reserves were excluded from these estimates. In 1987 the Union of Professional and Technical Civil Servants (advised by the staff of the Wildlife Service and National Parks Service) produced a policy document which estimated that approximately 200 sites, covering some 200,000 ha, but excluding marine reserves, were needed as nature reserves to provide protection for a representative range of habitats in the Republic.[15]

The above estimates would appear to have been too conservative. More recent surveys by the National Parks and Wildlife Service of Dúchas have shown that some 450 sites (designated as Special Areas for Conservation and Special Protection Areas) covering some 750,000 ha in the Republic must be protected to meet the requirements of the EU Wild Birds and Habitats Directives. This network of reserves includes many of the 1,200 Natural Heritage Areas covering some 900,000 ha.

Some historical developments in the conservation of Irish nature

Nathaniel Charles Rothschild (1877–1923) was a London banker with a passion for nature, particularly insects, and a progenitor of the conservation movement in Britain and Ireland. In 1912 he was one of the three founder members, and convenor, of the Society for the Promotion of Nature Reserves (SPNR) in 'Britain and the Empire'. By 1915 the Society had compiled a provisional list of 284 potential nature reserves for both Ireland and Britain. The SPNR believed that 'The only effective method of protecting Nature is to interfere with it as little as possible; and this can only be done by forming a large number of local reserves...to safeguard the varying species and types of scenery on their native ground..'.[16] The list, a milestone in the history of Irish nature conservation, was submitted to the Board of Agriculture in London in hope of government action. While expressing general sympathy, the Board offered no practical support. The SPNR proposals for Ireland lay dormant for many years but they set an important foundation for future developments.

In preparing the Irish inventory the SPNR chose good examples of natural habitats ('typical primeval country') and places where rare species occurred as sites for conservation. 'Areas of Primary Importance' were distinguished by their special character or urgency of the need for protection while 'Areas of Secondary Importance' were lower priority. The SPNR believed that bogs, salt marshes, shingle beaches and sand dunes were the most characteristic types of wild country in Ireland and had no exact counterpart on the Continent. The Irish shopping list of twenty areas was the first compilation of its kind for habitats deemed worthy of conservation (Table 12.2). Although Irish botanists and zoologists of the late eighteenth and early nineteenth centuries knew most of the important areas in Ireland (see Chapter 1) their information was never marshalled and focused towards conservation objectives. The SPNR had very clear conservation aims for their listed sites. Their inventory not only included some of the most important Irish ecosystems but the idea was way ahead of its time. Some sixty years had to elapse before the first statutory Nature Reserves were declared under the *Wildlife Act, 1976* to commence the protection of several of the listed sites. A few of the SPNR sites such as the North Bull Island, Dublin, and the Lakes of Killarney, Co. Kerry, were fortunate in receiving earlier protective status under the *Wild Birds Protection Act, 1930*, and the *Bourn Vincent Memorial Park Act, 1932*. The latter created Ireland's first National Park based on the Muckross Estate which had been donated to the nation by the American Senator Arthur Vincent with his parents-in-law Mr and Mrs Bourn. Six years later in Northern Ireland the Youth Hostel Association together with the Pilgrim Trust bought 72.2 ha of land at White Park Bay, Co. Antrim. Today the area is one of the properties of the National Trust.

Table 12.2 Provisional Schedule of Areas in Ireland as identified by the SPNR and 'considered worthy of preservation and arranged alphabetically according to their names'. 1915.[17]

Reserve No.	Location	6 O.S. map No.
	Areas of Primary Interest	
213	Brandon Mountain, Co. Kerry	34
228	Benbulbin (SW side), Co. Sligo	5,8
210	*Burren, nr. Ballyvaghan, Co. Clare (great botanical interest)	1,2
88	Cloonee, Co. Kerry	101
214	Gap of Dunloe, Co. Kerry	65,73
212	*Errisbeg, nr. Roundstone, Co. Galway	63
215	*Lake of Killarney and surrounding, Co. Kerry (scenery and botanical interest)	74
208	*Shores of Lough Neagh, Co. Antrim (rare plants)	48,49,62
212	*Lough Nagraiguebeg, Co. Galway (Lusitanian flora)	50
211	North Bull, Dublin	19
217	The Raven, Co. Wexford	38
216	Rostonstown Burrow, Lady's Island Lake, Co. Wexford	53, 53A
209	Cliffs at White Park Bay, Co. Antrim	3,4
218	Sand dunes near Wicklow, Co. Wicklow	31
80, 80a, 80b	*Ahascragh Bog, Co. Galway (of general and botanical interest)	61,61A, 73, 74, 74A
83	*Killucan Bog, nr. Mullingar, Co. Westmeath (of general and botanical interest)	20
81	*Mowhill Bog, Co. Leitrim (of general and botanical interest)	32
82a	*Bogs near River Shannon, Co. Galway (of general and botanical interest)	101,109, 109A
	Areas of Secondary Importance	
10	Saltee Islands, Co. Wexford (breeding-place of birds)	51A, 51B
55	Area south of Kenmare River, Co. Kerry	108

* = of especial interest
Note: the original spellings of place names and the OS map references have been retained from the original SPNR document to capture the historical flavour.

Another important early development was the establishment in 1904 of the Dublin based Irish Society for the Protection of Birds (ISPB), some thirteen years after the formation of the British Royal Society for the Protection of Birds

Reafforestation on sand dunes Co. Sligo. Many Irish sand dunes are EU priority habitats. However, afforestation, division of commonage, development of golf courses and severe overgrazing by sheep have destroyed the ecological value of several sites.

(RSPB). The objectives of the ISPB were to protect birds from being killed for their feathers, to stop egg collecting and to prevent the persecution of birds by man. Seventeen years later the Ulster Society for the Protection of Birds (USPB) came to life in Northern Ireland and one of its early important actions was the purchase of Swan Island, Larne Lough, Co. Antrim, in the late 1930s as a nature reserve for breeding terns. The ISPB followed by the acquisition in 1937 of nearly 7 ha of coastal marshland near Annagh, Co, Mayo, the breeding headquarters of the red-necked phalarope in Ireland – some 40–50 pairs had nested there in 1923 but by the early 1930s their numbers were dwindling. Both the ISPB and USPB effectively lobbied their respective governments for the introduction of new bird protection legislation at a time when these issues were not popular with the general public.

Meanwhile the continuous whittling away of Ireland's natural heritage continued apace. Voices of concern were mounting in the late 1940s. Following a public meeting in Dublin in September 1946 An Taisce – the National Trust for Ireland – was established for the 'Preservation of Places of Interest or Beauty in Ireland'. Its first General Meeting followed two years later. The better known members of the first provisional Council included Robert Lloyd Praeger (first President), Frank Mitchell, Thomas Mason, Sean McBride, Rev. P.G. Kennedy, Felix Hackett, Howard Hudson, Joe Haughton, Helen Roe, Tony Farrington, the Earl of Ross and Cearbhall Ó Dálaigh. Over the years An Taisce gathered strength, supported by civic-minded professional people who unselfishly gave their precious time to further the aims and objectives of the organisation. An Taisce has grown constantly since the early 1970s and is now able to pay for a small support staff.[18]

More recent developments

By the early 1960s the most destructive forces in the rural landscape were arterial drainage schemes. Financed by the state these projects destroyed many
wetlands of great ecological importance. In those days anticipated agricultural
benefits were more important than considerations of ecological ruination.
However, many ornithologists feared that the loss of these wetlands imperilled
the large and internationally important wintering wildfowl populations. Also
in the early 1960s one of Ireland's foremost wildfowl habitats – The North
Slob, Co. Wexford – was purchased as an agricultural investment by the Fiske
family. Drainage and other improvements were planned which many naturalists feared would damage the ecological requirements of the large wintering
flocks of the Greenland white-fronted geese, especially surface water pools.
Approximately half the world population of this subspecies wintered on the
Wexford Slobs at the time.

The puchase of the North Slob together with the threats of arterial drainage
to wetlands throughout the country led, in 1963, to the establishment of the
Irish Wildfowl Committee, later Conservancy. The organisation, based in
Galway, was founded by David Cabot with Bill Finlay as Chairman together with
Oscar Merne, Noel Reid, P.J. O'Hare, R.F. Ruttledge, Fergus O'Gorman,
Gerrit van Gelderen, Peter Roche and Liam O'Flynn as initial Committee
members. The IWC had three tasks – research, education and conservation of
wetlands, all undertaken with a sense of urgency. The IWC rapidly gathered
support from more than 1,000 members, drawn from conservation and wild-
fowling interests a curious blend of interests which on first consideration
might seem contradictory. A major achievement was the purchase of a small
part of the North Slob as a joint venture with government, financially assisted
by the World Wide Fund for Nature. Today the North Slob Wildfowl Refuge
jointly owned by the state and BirdWatch Ireland and managed by Dúchas
receives more visitors every year than any other nature reserve in the country.

Five years after its foundation the Irish Wildfowl Conservancy came together with the ISPB and the Irish Ornithologist's Club – formed in Dublin in 1950
– to create a unified ornithological organisation, the Irish Wildbird
Conservancy, to champion the cause of bird conservation in Ireland. The IWC,
now know as BirdWatch Ireland, built upon the success of its components and
is now a respected and professional conservation organisation.

The machinery of government was also beginning to respond to issues
thrown up by mounting development pressures. The *Local Government
(Planning and Development) Act, 1963* was enacted to assist with the orderly
development of the country in the interests of the 'common good'. The preparation of five-year development plans by local authorities was a major obligation of the Act. These plans, *inter alia*, were required to provide for the protection of amenities, including the conservation of habitats, through the
process of development control.

Technical assistance for the implementation of the Act was sought by government from the United Nations Special Development Fund which respond-
ed by providing advice and a loan for the establishment of an integrated environmental research institute, An Foras Forbartha. AFF was established in 1963
with Padraig Ó hUiginn as its highly able managing director. The Institute,
with the assistance of Michael Dower, a UN special advisor on conservation

and amenity, supplied research and advisory services on conservation and amenity issues to local authorities. In 1969 the Institute published *The Protection of the National Heritage*, skilfully assisted by AFF staffer Ken Mawhinney, which called for a single state-aided National Heritage Council to establish policy, objectives, priorities and standards. Another key recommendation in this landmark report was the need for a national heritage inventory of both the natural and man-built environment.[19] Work on the inventory started immediately and all local authorities were soon supplied with detailed information on sites and areas of nature conservation value in their areas of jurisdiction in the hope that they would receive some protection under the Planning Act. It took longer, some 26 years, before the Heritage Council was put on a statutory footing by the *Heritage Act, 1995*.

In 1981 An Foras Forbartha published *Areas of Scientific Interest In Ireland*, a summary of the national heritage inventory of all known nature conservation sites in the Republic. The 'blue book' described and prioritised 1,059 sites, covering some 231,500 ha or roughly 3% of the Republic, including tidal mud flats.[20] The completion and publication of the inventory was hailed by leading environmentalist John Feehan as a 'milestone of the greatest importance in the identification of the Republic's natural heritage…'.[21] Since its production the inventory has been updated and improved by the National Parks and Wildlife Service of Dúchas, the government agency with sole responsibility for nature conservation and National Parks.

In their review and updating Dúchas has re-named the original Areas of Scientific Interest as Natural Heritage Areas (NHAs). The number of sites rose to approximately 1,200 covering about 800,000 ha. At present NHAs have no statutory protection but it is hoped that the *Wildlife Act, 1976* will be soon amended (see below) to provide for their designation and protection. The owners of these areas will be informed of the nature conservation value of their lands and the intention to designate such lands as NHAs. There will be an appeals procedure for objections to the designations. Meanwhile local authorities have been requested to incorporate the proposed NHAs into the County Development Plans and Dúchas will be obliged to comment on any applications for development that may damage an NHA. Most importantly no grants will be provided by the EU or national government for any developments that may damage or impinge on the proposed NHAs. To encourage the conservation of these sites farmers who join the Rural Environment Protection Scheme (REPS) and whose land is a designated NHA and who undertake specified conservation measures are eligible for additional payments under the scheme.

The best NHAs in the Republic of Ireland, including the Special Protection Areas (SPAs – see below), numbering 235, were selected in February 1997 as proposed candidate Special Areas of Conservation (SACs) with the right of landowners to object to the designations but only on scientific grounds.[22] A list of SACs has been submitted to the EU Commission (see p. 442), as demanded by the Habitats Directive as Ireland's contribution to a European network – NATURA 2000. This 'cohesive network' will contain the best European nature conservation sites. A total of 6,584 sites covering 265,149 km^2 in the 15 member states have been proposed to the EU Commission as of 12 May 1998.[23]

In Northern Ireland the *Amenity Lands Act (Northern Ireland) 1965* allowed the Conservation Branch of the Department of the Environment to purchase lands for nature reserves and to enter into nature conservation management agreements with land owners. The Department's conservation powers were strengthened by *The Nature Conservation and Amenity Lands (Northern Ireland) Order 1985* (amended in 1989) allowing the Environment Service of the Department to establish Sites of Special Scientific Interest (SSSIs). The *Wildlife Order (Northern Ireland) 1985* provided for the creation of wildlife refuges and protection of plant and animal species. The Department is advised by the Council for Nature Conservation and the Countryside (CNCC). Most areas of conservation interest in Northern Ireland have been identified as proposed Areas of Special Scientific Interest (ASSIs). By the end of May 1996, 92 ASSIs had been designated covering some 75,816 ha. The largest is Lough Neagh, occupying 39,777 ha which distorts the overall Northern Ireland figure.[24] For the purposes of the EU Wild Birds and Habitat Directives, SPAs and candidate SACs have also been earmarked. Eleven SPAs have been designated to date: Larne Lough including Swan Island, Co. Antrim; Carlingford Lough, Co. Down; Sheep Island, Co. Antrim; Lough Neagh and Lough Beg; Upper Lough Erne, Co. Fermanagh; Rathlin Island Cliffs, Co. Antrim; Belfast Lough; Dundrum Bay (Inner and Outer), Co. Down; Lough Foyle, Co. Derry; Strangford Lough and Islands; Outer Ards Peninsula, Co. Down.

Concerning voluntary conservation organisations, the RSPB first become involved in conservation in Northern Ireland in 1966 while at the same time absorbing the USPB. Both the RSPB and the National Trust have to their credit many conservation achievements. More recently the Ulster Wildlife Trust, founded in 1978, has established a number of local nature reserves, mostly by agreement with the landowners.

Lowland coastal heath, Co. Donegal, an example of a scarce and valuable coastal habitat.

Administrative, legislative and financial issues

In the past, several government departments in the Republic held doggedly onto a multiplicity of nature conservation responsibilities with the result that no single ministry had overall responsibility, making the development of a coherent national conservation policy and programme impossible. An attempt to bring some sense into the system was behind the preparation of the report *The Protection of the National Heritage.*[15] Soon afterwards, in 1970, a seminar was held in Killarney on the future of Irish wildlife, organised by the Department of Lands. The main recommendation that emerged was the need for a centralised wildlife conservation agency.[25] Later that year the Forest and Wildlife Service was formed within the Department of Lands. However, conservation and forestry sat awkwardly together because forestry was an economic activity while conservation was not. There were inevitable land use conflicts, with forestry interests always winning at the expense of nature. At the same time the responsibility for the management of National Parks was being discharged by the Office of Public Works (OPW), itself part of the Ministry of Finance. After much debate about the need to separate conservation and forestry, logic prevailed and the Wildlife Service was split from Forestry and transferred in 1987 to the OPW to create a unified National Parks and Wildlife Service (NPWS). Since then government has been provided with an increasingly competent nature conservation service. Recently the OPW has been reorganised to provide a heritage service, Dúchas, incorporating the NPWS. Its function is to implement government conservation policy as enunciated by the present Minister for Arts, Heritage, Gaeltacht and the Islands Síle de Valera.

The location and relative importance of Ireland's natural heritage is now well known and extensively documented following many years of inventory investigations and research. The EU Directives on the conservation of wild birds, and the conservation of natural habitats and of wild fauna and flora, have been transposed into Irish law. However, the *Wildlife Act, 1976* requires to be amended to provide protection for the proposed network of NHAs as well as some other measures (see below). These reforms were promised for 1991 but because of the sensitivity of all issues concerning land use control and compensation extensive consultation with other interested government departments has been necessary. The new Bill is expected to be introduced to the Dáil in the near future.

Some achievements

One of the most endangered EU priority habitats in Ireland is active peatland (see Chapter 4). Of the original 311,300 ha of raised bog in the Republic, only 19,402 ha or 6.2% were estimated intact in 1985.[7] A more recent estimate (June 1998) was that only 8,000 ha or 2.6% remained intact,[26] the rest having been dug up as a source of fuel or planted (2% of Midland raised bogs) with coniferous trees or drained. Blanket bogs have survived more successfully with 128,646 ha or 16.6% of the original area remaining unscathed; a large proportion (27%) of the rest has been planted with coniferous trees.

In a statement in 1987 on the government's conservation strategy for peatlands, Noel Tracey, T.D., then Junior Minister responsible for nature conservation, committed the state to the protection of 10,000 ha or 52% of the remaining intact raised bog in Ireland. The target for blanket bog was 40,000 ha or 31% of the remaining intact amount. To date 3,176 ha, or 32%, of the raised bog and 27,279 ha, or 68%, of the blanket bog targets have been met – an excellent achievement bearing in mind the commercial pressures to exploit these peatlands. These achievements have been greatly facilitated by Bord na Móna who in 1990 agreed with the NPWS and the European Commission to sell as well as transfer ownership rights of some blanket and raised bogs to the NPWS for conservation. A total of 4,800 ha had been transferred up to the end of 1997.[27] The conservation of fens has been less successful – only 205 ha,[28] or 0.4% of the estimated 54,026 ha considered to be of conservation value have been safeguarded by the state.

In Northern Ireland the government has a clear policy on the conservation of peatlands[29] which has led to the protection of 1,075 ha of raised bog (40% of remaining total), 11,598 ha of blanket bog (63% of remaining total) and 4,105 ha of fen (94% of remaining total).[3]

A total of 76 Statutory Nature Reserves have been declared to December 1997 in the Republic and are listed in Appendix 2, while in Northern Ireland 45 sites have been declared up to July 1992 under the *Nature Conservation and Amenity Lands (Northern Ireland) Order 1985* and listed in Appendix 3.

Other protected areas

In addition to the statutory Nature Reserves declared in both the Republic and in Northern Ireland, six Refuges for Fauna have been declared under the *Wildlife Act, 1976* in the Republic. These are intended to protect rare species and their habitats. All the sites are important sea bird breeding colonies.

Islands in Lady's Island Lake, Co. Wexford
Cliffs of Moher, Co. Clare
Horn Head, Co. Donegal
Rockabill, Co. Dublin
Old Head of Kinsale, Co. Cork
Cow and Bull Rocks, Co. Cork.

The *Wildlife Act, 1976* also contains provisions for the designation of wildfowl sanctuaries where shooting of traditional game birds is forbidden. Some 68 sanctuaries have been created.

As a major contribution to the conservation of whales and dolphins in the Atlantic, the former Taoiseach of the Republic, Charles Haughey, one of the few senior Irish politicians ever to champion environmental issues, declared in 1991 Europe's first whale and dolphin sanctuary within the exclusive Irish fishery limits which extend some 320 km from the coastline. The legal framework for the declaration was provided by the *Whale Fisheries Act, 1937* in conjunction with the *Wildlife Act, 1976*.

National Parks

In addition to protected sites and areas already mentioned, many ecosystems of international scientific importance receive strict protection within the exiting 47,480 ha network of five National Parks in the Republic. These parks are managed in accordance with IUCN Category II criteria which aim to provide strict conservation of the valuable ecosystems within the parks with few concessions to human activities. Habitats within the parks enjoy a higher degree of active protection and management than found in most of the statutory nature reserves. In addition to the five established parks a sixth is currently under formation in one of the last unspoilt wilderness areas in Ireland, the Atlantic blanket bogland centred around the Owenduff-Nephin Beg area in northwest Mayo. The park will encompass some 10,000 ha of state owned land as announced by the Minister for Arts, Heritage, the Gaeltacht and Islands, Síle de Valera in July 1998. The existing and proposed National Parks and their areas are:

Killarney National Park, Co. Kerry	10,389 ha
Glenveagh National Park, Co. Donegal	16,548 ha
Connemara National Park, Co. Galway	2,957 ha
Wicklow National Park, Co. Wicklow	15,913 ha
The Burren National Park, Co. Clare	1,673 ha
Owenduff-Nephin Beg National Park, Co. Mayo	c.10,000 ha.

There are no National Parks in Northern Ireland but there is a series of Countryside Parks.

International Conventions

The Republic has ratified six International Conventions all of which are now in force.

- Ramsar Convention on Wetlands of international importance (21 sites covering 12,500 ha – all Nature Reserves – have been so far designated)
- Bonn Convention on the Conservation of Migratory Species of Wild Animals
- Bern Convention on the Conservation of European Wildlife and Natural Habitats
- International Convention for the Regulation of Whaling
- Convention for the Maintenance of Biodiversity
- Washington Convention on International Trade in Endangered Species of Wild Fauna and Flora (CITES)

Ireland also co-operates with various international organisation which has led in turn to the strengthening of the conservation status of several of the country's important ecosystems. Co-operation with the Council of Europe has brought about the establishment of 14 Biogenetic Reserves which are also statutory Nature Reserves – Lough Hyne, Co. Cork; Pettigo Plateau, Co. Donegal; Uragh Wood, Co. Kerry; Coole-Garryland, Co. Galway; Slieve Bloom, Counties Laois and Offaly; Pollardstown Fen, Co. Kildare; Slievecarran, Co. Clare; Owenboy, Co. Mayo; Knockmoyle/Sheskin, Co. Mayo; the Gearagh, Co. Cork; Mongan Bog, Co. Offaly; Clara Bog, Co. Offaly; Ballyteige sand dunes, Co. Wexford and Raheenmore Bog, Co. Offaly. Collaboration with UNESCO has brought the designation of two World Biosphere Reserves at North Bull Island, Dublin, and the Killarney National Park, Co. Kerry. The WBRs are intended to combine nature conservation with scientific research, environmental monitoring, training and education as well as local participation.

The future

The main driving force for the conservation of nature in both the Republic and in Northern Ireland is coming through the legal obligations to implement the EU Wild Birds and Habitats Directives. In this process it is clear that close co-operation between the nature conservation authorities in both parts of Ireland is an essential prerequisite for the development of a cohesive all Ireland approach to nature conservation. Indeed, the recent political Agreement on Northern Ireland identified environment as one of the areas for collaboration between the Republic and Northern Ireland and this could open up the way to develop a co-ordinated conservation policy between the two parts of the country. For a start species protection legislation could be harmonised. There is also immediate potential for the creation of cross-border nature reserves for four blanket bogs – Cuilcagh Mountains (Fermanagh/Gavan), Pettigo (Donegal/Tyrone), Killeter (Donegal/Tyrone) and Slieve Beagh (Fermanagh/Monaghan) – which have been classified as SPAs in Northern Ireland.

Already 109 SPAs, intended to conserve rare and vulnerable birds, migratory species and wetlands of international importance, covering some 222,500 ha, have been designated to the end of March 1998 in the Republic and submitted to the EU Commission for consideration to be included in the coherent European network – NATURA 2000 – of the best nature conservation areas. Completed area maps for all sites were also submitted but backed up by incomplete or only partially transmitted information. Moreover the classification of the SPAs as of June 1998 was considered incomplete by the Commission. The Republic has also proposed to the EU Commission 207 candidate SACs covering 553,000 ha but without site maps and the required NATURA 2000 forms.[23] In August 1998, the Republic officially submitted an initial list of 39 SACs, covering more than 50,000 ha, for approval by the EU Commission. Another 161 SACs of the original February 1997 list of 237 have been disputed by Irish landowners, and until an appeals advisory board, set up by the Minister, has adjudicated on the validity of these SACs, they cannot be submitted to the EU Commission. In Northern Ireland a total of 11 SPA sites have been designated. The Environment and Heritage Service of the Department of Environment, Northern Ireland, has submitted 17 possible SACs to the UK Joint Nature Conservation Committee for inclusion in the UK list for the EU Commission. Of the 17 sites 14 were included in the UK's first tranche submitted to Brussels.

In addition to the above and in order to achieve the protection of approximately 1,200 NHAs in the Republic, the *Wildlife Act, 1976* requires to be amended. The *Wildlife (Amendment) Bill (1998)* is at an advanced stage of preparation but many complex legal issues remain to be resolved before it can be presented to the Dáil hopefully in the not too distant future. The Bill will improve the protection of wildlife species and their habitats and will *inter alia* provide for:

- the protection of geological and geomorphological sites
- statutory protection for NHAs
- compliance with international agreements and Conventions
- powers for the acquisition of land both by agreement and compulsorily, which are independent of the Forestry Acts to which the present *Wildlife Act, 1976* is linked.

Finally, an appreciation of the values and needs of nature conservation amongst the general public requires to be promoted more successfully than at present if various policies and legislative reforms are to be effectively implemented. The conservation of nature is best acheived through a partnership between government, landowners and the interested public as represented by the various voluntary conservation organisations. The responsibility for bringing together the often divergent interests clearly rests with government. At a personal level the most valuable course of action that an individual can take is to join and financially support a conservation organisation as well as volunteering help and other practical assistance.

APPENDICES

APPENDIX 1

The Notable Oceanic Ferns, Mosses and Liverworts of Ireland

* Indicates species not found in Britain.

Ferns
Killarney fern *Trichomanes speciosum*
Tunbridge filmy-fern *Hymenophyllum tunbrigense*
Wilson's filmy-fern *H. wilsonii*
Hay-scented buckler fern *Dryopteris aemula*
Irish spleenwort *Asplenium onopteris**
Lanceolate spleenwort *A. obovatum*
Maidenhair fern *Adiantum capillus-veneris*

Mosses
Bartramidula wilsonii
Campylopus atrovirens
C. shawii
Dicranodontium uncinatum
F. curnovii
F. serrulatus
Glyphomitrium daviesii
Hypnum callichroum
Myurium hochstetteri
Oxystegus hibernicus
Sematophyllum demissum
Ulota calvescens

Breutelia chrysocoma
C. polytrichoides
Cyclodictyon laetevirens
Dicranum scottianum
F. monguillonii
Grimmia hartmanii
Hedwigia integrifolia
Isothecium holtii
Orthotrichum rivulare
Rhabdoweissia crenulata
S. micans
U. hutchinsiae

Bryum riparium
C. setifolius
Daltonia splachnoides
Fissidens celticus
F. polyphyllus
G. retracta
Hylocomium umbratum
Leptodontium recurvifolium
O. sprucei
Rhynchostegium lusitanicum
Sphagnum strictum

Liverworts
Acrobolbus wilsonii
Anastrepta orcadensis
Bazzania pearsonii
Cephalozia hibernica*
Drepanolejeunea hamatifolia
Frullania microphylla
Gymnomitrion crenulatum
Herbertus aduncus
L. hibernica*
L. mandonii
Leptoscyphus cuneifolius
Mastigophora woodsii
Mylia taylorii
P carringtonii
P. punctata
Porella pinnata
R. holtii*

Adelanthus decipiens
Anastrophyllum hellerianum
B. tricrenata
Cololejeunea minutissima
Dumortiera hirsuta
F. teneriffae
Harpalejeunea ovata
Jubula hutchinsiae
L. holtii
Lepidozia cupressina
Lophocolea fragrans
Metzgeria conjugata
Nowellia curvifolia
P. exigua
P. spinulosa
Radula aquilegia
R. voluta

A. lindenbergianus
Aphanolejeunea microscopica
B. trilobata
Colura calyptrifolia
Fossombronia angulosa
Geocalyx graveolens
Harpanthus scutatus
Lejeunea flava*
L. lamacerina
L. pearsonii
Marchesinia mackaii
M. leptoneura
Plagiochila atlantica
P. killarniensis
Pleurozia purpurea
R. carringtonii
Riccardia chamedryfolia

Saccogyna viticulosa
S. ornithopodioides
Tritomaria exsecta

Scapania gracilis
Sphenolobopsis pearsonii

S. nimbosa
Telaranea nematodes

Nomenclature

Ferns: **Stace, C.** 1991. *New Flora of the British Isles.* Cambridge University Press, Cambridge.

Mosses: **Smith, A.J.E.** 1993. *The Moss Flora of Britain and Ireland.* Cambridge University Press, Cambridge.

Liverworts: **Smith, A.J.E.** 1990. *The Liverworts of Britain and Ireland.* Cambridge University Press, Cambridge.

Reference

Ratcliffe, D.A. 1968. An ecological account of Atlantic bryophytes in the British Isles. *New Phytologist* 55: 365–439.

APPENDIX 2

Statutory Nature Reserves in the Republic of Ireland

The 76 statutory Nature Reserves listed below have been grouped for convenience into broad habitat categories. However, there are many other sites which, although not declared formally as nature reserves, are in the protective custody of Dúchas. Therefore a mere addition of the land in the network of Nature Reserves below should not be taken as the total amount of protected habitat. The locations of all reserves are marked on the Discovery Ireland Ordnance Survey maps.

(a) Woodlands

1. **Derryclare**, Co. Galway (19 ha, of which about 8 ha is woodland). Situated on the northwest shore of Derryclare Lough, Ballynahinch, this reserve is an excellent example of native semi-natural woodland of the hyper-oceanic type. Apart from the woodland, the remainder of the reserve comprises pond, wet moorland and lake-shore ecosystems.

2. **Glen of the Downs**, Co. Wicklow (59 ha). About 8 km south of Bray the reserve is an area of sessile oak. It is a very good example of the drier type of oak woodland characteristic of acid soils in Wicklow. A small section of wet woodland will be lost through the proposed enlargement of the road through the valley, setting a bad precedent for the safeguarding of other state nature reserves.

3. **Ballykeefe**, 6 km north of Callan town, Co. Kilkenny (55.4 ha) and
4. **Garryricken**, 5 km south-southwest of Callan (27.9 ha) and
5. **Kyleadohir**, 5 km west-southwest of Callan (58.7 ha).
These three nature reserves are good examples of young quasi-natural elm/ash/oak woods on fertile soil and constitute some of the largest woods of their kind left in Ireland.

6. **Caher (Murphy)**. Located in the Slieveaughty Mountains, Co. Clare (9 ha), this area of oak wood on a moist fertile soil contains a rich ground flora.

7. **Uragh Wood**, Co. Kerry (87 ha). Situated on the southwest shore of Inchiquin Lough, west of Kenmare, this reserve is an excellent example of hyper-oceanic, semi-natural woodland with sessile oak the dominant species.

8. **Deputy's Pass**, Co. Wicklow (47 ha). Near Glenealy. Although coppice in origin, this woodland is a good example of its type.

9. **Grantstown Wood and Grantstown Lough**, Co. Laois (48.6 ha) and
10. **Coolacurragh Wood** (8.5 ha).
These reserves are situated about 8 km north-west-north of Durrow. They are rare examples of wet woodland on base-rich soils while Grantstown Lough is a classic example of a lake which has gradually infilled through fen to alder carr.

11. **Vale of Clara**, Co. Wicklow (220.57 ha). This is a large area of fragmented oak wood mostly on the eastern side of the Avonmore River. It contains the largest area of semi-natural woodland in Co. Wicklow and is potentially one of the largest stands of native hardwoods in the country. The area has been at least partially under woodland since the Ice Age.

12. **Rosturra/Derrylahan Wood**, Co. Galway (17.68 ha). 3 km east-northeast of Woodford and
13. **Derrycrag Wood**, (110.47 ha). 1 km southeast of Woodford.
These two reserves comprise fragments of a once extensive forest and now contain stands of oak and ash with an understorey of holly and hazel and a rich ground flora.

14. **Ballynastaig Wood**, Co. Galway (9.75 ha) and
15. **Coole-Garryland**, (363.58 ha).
These two reserves near Gort, through their combination of deciduous woods, limestone reefs, lakes and turloughs, constitute one of the most interesting Irish vegetation and fauna complexes. The Coole-Garryland reserve contains a variety of floral habitats including well formed high forest on deep pockets of soil, dwarf woodland on limestone pavement, a turlough complex in the Callows and Coole Lough. A large portion of this reserve was formerly owned by Lady Gregory, co-founder with W.B. Yeats and Edward Martyn of the Abbey Theatre.

16. **Pollnaknockaun Wood**, Co. Galway (38.85 ha). 1 km northeast of Woodford village. A semi-natural woodland which once formed part of the extensive forest referred to under (12) and (13) above.

17. **Old Head Wood**, Co. Mayo (17 ha). 3 km northeast of Louisburgh. This small reserve lies on the east side of two knolls which form a promontory on the southern shore of Clew Bay. It is an example of semi-natural woodland, oak being the dominant species, with birch, rowan, willow and some introduced beech and sycamore.

18. **Dromore**, Co. Clare (370 ha). 10 km north of Ennis. This reserve comprises semi-natural woodland and wetlands.

19. **Richmond Esker**, Co. Galway (15.7 ha). Located 4 km northwest of Moylough and
20. **Timahoe Esker**, Co. Laois (13.5 ha). Located 1 km northeast of Timahoe.
These are two of the few esker ridges left in the country which still carry native wood-

land. Although extensively planted with conifers and other exotic species it is planned to expand the native woodland using appropriate management techniques.

21. **Keelhilla**, Slievecarran, Co. Clare (145.5 ha). Situated in the northeast edge of the Burren plateau, the area is a good example of karst topography containing three distinct vegetation communities i.e. woodland, scrub grassland and pavement.

22. **Duntally Wood**, Co. Donegal (15.3 ha). Situated in a deep valley 0.5 km southeast of Creeslough, the wood is rich in plant species with alder woodland on the valley floor and there is hazel-ash woodland on the valley sides.

23. **Rathmullan Wood**, Co. Donegal (32.73 ha). Situated on the western shore of Lough Swilly, 20 km northeast of Letterkenny, this oak wood has a well-developed structure and is rich in plant species.

24. **Ballyarr Wood**, Co. Donegal (30 ha). Situated 11 km north of Letterkenny and 5 km west of Ramelton on the eastern bank of a low ridge of hills. An oak wood growing on a range of soil types and with a rich flora, it contains areas of old coppice and old field systems reverting to woodland.

25. **Glendalough**, Co. Wicklow (157 ha). Comprises a series of oak woods extending from the upper lake to the lower slopes of Derrybawn Mountain and including some conifer plantations.

26. **Derkmore Wood**. Situated in Gweenbarra Forest, Co. Donegal (7.0 ha), on exposed undulating ground on the southern flank of Cleengort Hill. An area of oak scrub with well-developed bryophyte and lichen flora.

27. **Fiddown Island**, Co. Kilkenny (62.6 ha). A long narrow island of marsh/woodland on the River Suir. It is covered in willow scrub and bordered by reed swamps – the only known site of its type in Ireland.

28. **Knockomagh Wood**, Co. Cork (12.5 ha). Situated on a hillside overlooking and adjoining Lough Hyne Nature Reserve. It consists of a small area of sessile oak and mixed broadleaved woodland.

29. **Derrycunihy Wood**, Co. Kerry (136 ha). Situated in Killarney valley adjoining and surrounding Killarney National Park. It is owned by Coillte and consists of old native oak woodlands with some patches of bog and lakeshore.

30. **Glengarriff Wood**, Co. Cork (301 ha). The Reserve is located approximately 1 km west of Glengarriff village. The woods are situated at the eastern end of a glacially deepened valley in the Old Red Sandstone rock formation of southwest Cork. They are an excellent example of hyper-oceanic semi-natural woodland, a rare vegetation type in both national and international terms.

31. **Knocksink Wood**, Co. Wicklow (52.3 ha). The Reserve is situated in the Glencullen river valley just northwest of Enniskerry. Some of the valley slopes are dominated by sessile oak, while other areas are characterised by mixed woodland. A notable feature of the slopes are the frequent springs and seepage areas within the woodland. These petrifying springs are listed as a priority habitat in the EU Habitats Directive. The site has one of the most diverse woodland invertebrate faunas in Ireland incorporating wet woodland organisms threatened within the EU. There is an educational centre at the site. This building, formerly managed by the Irish Wildlife Federation through the Conservation

Education Trust, by agreement with Dúchas, has now been taken over by the Dublin Institute of Technology.

32. The Gearagh, Co. Cork (300 ha). Situated in the middle reaches of the Lee River, it is the property of the E.S.B. The only extensive alluvial soil forest in Europe west of the Rhine, it is therefore unique to the network of woodland nature reserves. It consists of narrow channels separating islands which are covered in oak, ash and birch.

(b) Wildfowl wetlands

33. The Wexford Wildfowl Reserve, Co. Wexford (194 ha). Situated on the sloblands north of Wexford Harbour, it is owned jointly by Dúchas and BirdWatch Ireland and forms a wintering ground of international importance for a number of migratory waterfowl species including the Greenland white-fronted goose. The reserve was extended by 84 ha in 1989 to 194 ha.

34. Ballygilgan, Lissadell, Co. Sligo (29.5 ha). A large grass field sloping southwestwards from a public road from Carney to Lissadell. It is a site of international importance for barnacle geese due to the number it supports every winter (*c.*1.000 birds).

35. Rogerstown Estuary, Co. Dublin (195.5 ha). A small tidal bay in the north part of the county which is an estuary of several small rivers/streams which flow at the western and northwestern sides. It is a site of international importance for brent geese.

36. North Bull Island, Dublin (118 ha). Privately owned and
37. North Bull Island (1,318 ha). State owned.
These two reserves are situated in the northern part of Dublin Bay within the boundaries of Dublin city and only 8 km from the city centre. The island is covered with dune grassland. An extensive salt marsh lies to the northwest and extreme low tides there are extensive mud flats between the island and mainland. The reserves are of international importance for brent geese and also on botanical, ornithological, zoological and geomorphological grounds.

38. Baldoyle Estuary, Co. Dublin (203 ha). A tidal estuary situated northeast of Dublin city. The reserve is rated as of international importance for brent geese.

39. Tralee Bay, Co. Kerry (754.53 ha). Situated on the north side of the Dingle Peninsula, west of the town of Tralee. It is of international importance for waterfowl, especially the wintering population of brent geese.

40. Castlemaine Harbour, Co. Kerry (923 ha). Situated at the head of Dingle Bay, 18 km west of Castlemaine, 20 km east of Dingle and 23 km southwest of Tralee. The area is of international scientific importance on ecological, ornithological and geomorphological grounds.

41. Kilcolman Bog, Co. Cork (29.287 ha). State owned. and
42. Kilcolman Bog (21.398 ha). Privately owned.
Situated approximately 6.5 km northwest of Doneraile, just off the Charleville to Mitchelstown road, the reserve contains a fen in a glacially eroded limestone hollow, south of the Ballyhoura Mountains in north Cork. It has been a traditional wintering ground for Greenland white-fronted geese and thousands of duck and is also of great botanical importance, harbouring a number of plant species absent or extremely rare elsewhere in Co. Cork.

Part of the reserve is owned by Dúchas. The remainder is owned by Margaret Ridgeway, who managed the area as a wildlife refuge prior to its designation as a Nature Reserve.

(c) Marine

43. **Lough Hyne**, Co. Cork (65 ha). This is a sea lough with a very wide range of important habitats within the lough and its seaward approaches, a range seldom found in more extensive areas elsewhere. These varied habitats support an exceptionally wide spectrum of animal and plant species. It is situated about 6 km southwest of Skibbereen.

(d) Sand dunes

44. **The Raven**, Co. Wexford (589 ha). The reserve is situated 8 km northeast of Wexford town and is a large, well-developed sand dune ecosystem, foreshore and seabed. The area supports a full range of sand dune animals, several of which are of particular interest, and has a rich flora including some rare species. It is one of the best developed sand dune systems on the east coast. Important also as a roosting area for geese and waders.

45. **Ballyteige Burrow**, Co. Wexford (227 ha). The reserve is a 9 km long coarse-sediment barrier running northwest from the coastal village of Kilmore Quay and adjoining foreshore. The main interest is the plant community of the fixed dunes and associated marsh. The flora includes a number of rare plants such as wild asparagus, perennial glasswort, Borrer's saltmarsh-grass, lesser centaury and the yellow lichen *Fulgensia fulgens*, its only known Irish station.

(e) Seabird islands and cliffs

46. **Capel Island and Knockadoon Head**, Co. Cork (126.9 ha). State owned and
47. **Capel Island and Knockadoon Head** (16.1 ha). Privately owned.
These reserves comprise all of Capel Island off the south coast near Youghal, part of Knockadoon headland opposite the island and the intervening sea area. This was the first privately owned statutory nature reserve established in the state.

48. **Puffin Island**, Co. Kerry (32.73 ha). State owned and
49. **Puffin Island** (53.77 ha). Privately owned.
Puffin Island is situated off the Iveragh Peninsula and is well known for its large colonies of breeding seabirds. It is owned by Dúchas and BirdWatch Ireland. A marine reserve has been established on the surrounding area of sea and seashore to ensure the protection of the birds and to control activities that might cause disturbance.

50. **Great Skellig**, Co. Kerry (22.6 ha). This is a small precipitous rocky pinnacle rising from the Atlantic Ocean off the Iveragh Peninsula. It is rated as of international importance for certain seabird species – Manx shearwaters, storm petrels and puffins. It also provides a good example of typical plant communities of a small and remote marine island.

51. **Little Skellig**, Co. Kerry (7.8 ha). An even smaller precipitous rocky pinnacle rising from the Atlantic Ocean. It is of international importance because of the breeding colony of gannets.

52. **Tearaght Island**, Co. Kerry (19.1 ha). State owned and
53. **Tearaght Island** (27.5 ha). Privately owned.

Tearaght Island – one of the Blasket group of islands – is of international importance because of the large colonies of breeding seabirds. A marine reserve has been established on the surrounding area of sea and seashore to ensure the protection of the birds and to control activities that might cause disturbance.

(f) Blanket bogland

54. Pettigoe Plateau, Co Donegal (900 ha). Some 11 km northwest of Pettigoe, this large reserve is an excellent example of Donegal blanket bog and wet heath complete with a head-water lake complex.

55. Slieve Bloom Mountains (2,300 ha). Situated on the borders of Cos. Laois and Offaly this reserve is an excellent example of mountain blanket bog.

56. Knockmoyle, Co. Mayo (1,198 ha). Situated north of the Bord na Móna works at Bellacorick between the Oweniny River on the eastern side and Sheskin Lodge on the western side. An extensive area of lowland blanket bog densely pool-studded and containing interesting mineral flushes. This reserve was extended by 466 ha in 1989 to 1,198 ha.

57. Eirk Bog, Co. Kerry (16 ha). Situated in the Owenreagh valley, Killarney, 1 km north of Moll's Gap, the reserve is part of a very well-developed and little disturbed example of an intermediate bog with associated poor fen and blanket bog/wet heath communities.

58. Owenboy, Co. Mayo (397.1 ha). Situated 10 km west of Crossmolina and 10 km east of Bellacorick on the south side of the Ballina/Belmullet Road at Eskeragh Bridge. An extensive bog of intermediate type lying in a broad basin and utilised by Greenland white-fronted geese. It contains a number of low domes resembling raised bogs and numerous flushes with a rare species of moss.

59. Lough Barra Bog, Co. Donegal (176.4 ha). Situated in the upper part of the Gweebarra River Valley, it is a lowland blanket bog with a characteristic assemblage of plant species. It is also the habitat of the three species of birds given special protection under the EU Wild birds Directive i.e. Greenland white-fronted goose, merlin and golden plover.

60. Glenealo Valley, Co. Wicklow (1,958 ha). Lies above and to the west of Glendalough. It is a broad open valley surrounded by mountains and generally consisting of a large plateau of mixed heathland and peatland.

61. Easkey Bog, Co. Sligo (607 ha). Situated on the northern side of the Ox Mountains, this is one of the few extensive areas of highland blanket bog in the country. It is intermediate between lowland and mountain blanket bog, the area grades into mountain blanket bog to the south while an extensive area of lowland blanket bog occurs about 2 km to the west. One of few places in the country where all three blanket bog types are more or less juxtaposed.

62. Meenachullion, Co. Donegal (194 ha). Situated on the southern edge of the Lough Barra blanket bog complex north of Gubbin Hill, this is an area of lowland blanket bog vegetation grading into wet grassy heath on the slopes of Gubbin Hill and with small but eroded areas of highland blanket bog on the flat top of Gubbin Hill.

63. Leam West Bog, Co. Galway (373.48 ha). Situated 3 km southeast of Maam

Cross, the bog is of international importance as an area of very diverse blanket bog developed over both acid and base-rich rocks at the northeast limit of the Connemara blanket bogs. It forms part of one of the largest areas of intact bog in Connemara and it is one of the few sites containing both lowland and highland bog. A large number of habitats occur including rock outcrops, bog pools, extremely wet quaking areas, streams and relatively nutrient rich flushes.

64. **Cummeragh River Bog**, Co. Kerry (45.55 ha). Situated 8 km northeast of Waterville, the bog is the most southerly intact lowland blanket bog in Ireland and is of international importance. Almost completely encircled by the Cummeragh River and tributary, it is in excellent condition and actively growing. It has a well-developed pattern of hummocks and pools as well as a mature and luxuriant vegetation cover. Now owned by Dúchas, it was originally purchased with donations from the Dutch Foundation for the Conservation of Irish Bogs.

65. **Brandon Mountain**, Co. Kerry (461.74 ha). Situated on the northeast side of the Dingle Peninsula, the reserve consists of part of the Brandon Mountain range of mountains and the foothills. It was acquired to conserve the mountain blanket bog/heath complex and its famed alpine flora.

(g) Raised bogland

66. **Clara Bog**, Co. Offaly (460 ha). The bog is the last large raised Midland bog remaining substantially intact. It contains a wide variety of vegetation types and habitats and a well-developed drainage (or soak) system.

67. **Mongan Bog**, Co. Offaly (119 ha). Situated near Clonmacnoise, this is an excellent example of a Midland raised bog with a well-developed system of pools. It is a valuable addition to the growing network of peatland reserves and is owned by An Taisce.

68. **Raheenmore Bog**, Co. Offaly (162 ha). Situated 6 km northwest of Daingean, this is a well development and an exceptional example of deep Midland raised bog which is regarded as being of national importance.

69. **Sheheree Bog**, Co. Kerry (8.9 ha). The only raised bog in the Killarney district of Kerry. It has a well-developed lagg, or marginal drainage system, a very rare feature in Ireland. It is the habitat of the slender cotton grass protected under the *Wildlife Act, 1976*. The bog is considered to be very valuable for comparative studies with the intermediate and blanket bog of the Killarney and Owenreagh valleys.

70. **Redwood Bog**, Co. Tipperary (132 ha). About 5 km northwest of Rathcabbin, in north Tipperary, this bog was acquired from Bord na Móna for conservation purposes. A raised bog developed on the southern margin of the Little Brosna flood plain at its confluence with the Shannon, it forms part of the Little Brosna River Callows NHA which is of international importance as a wildfowl habitat and as a classical example of a flood plain ecosystem. The reserve includes the last relatively intact bog dome on the flood plain margin plus a dried-out portion of another dome and an area of fen. The intact dome has a typical raised bog flora and in the centre it retains quaking areas and numerous bog pools.

(h) Fen

71. **Pollardstown Fen**, Co. Kildare (130 ha). Situated on the northern margin of

the Curragh approximately 3 km west-northwest of Newbridge this is the largest remaining spring-fed fen in Ireland possessing a large number of characteristic fenland species and communities.

(i) Transition of fen to raised bog

72. Scragh Bog, Co. Westmeath (22.8 ha). This fen/bog transition is about 4.8 km north of Mullingar. It is the best example in Ireland of the transition from alkaline fen to acidic raised bog and one of the few remaining in Europe. Containing a large number of uncommon plants and insects, also rare in Europe, it is rated as being of international importance. The greater part was purchased by the Irish Peatland Conservation Council with funds generously provided by the Dutch Foundation for the Conservation of Irish Bogs. It was then handed over to Dúchas for management as a Nature Reserve.

(j) Freshwater ponds (natterjack toad habitat)

73. Lough Yganavan, Co. Kerry (25.3 ha) and
74. Lough Nambrackdarrig (3.9 ha).
These two reserves are situated south of Cromane, south of Castlemaine Harbour. They consist of freshwater lakes and are important breeding sites for the natterjack toad.

(k) Shingle spit

75. Derrymore Island, Co. Kerry (106.07 ha). Situated in Tralee Bay, the reserve is a compound spit composed of a series of pebble beaches, making it one of the best of its kind in Ireland. It supports many rare plant communities, mainly of a salt marsh type. The eastern side is grazed by wigeon and brent geese while the white top is an important high tide roosting area for shorebirds.

(i) Calcareous grassland

76. Ballyteige, Co. Clare (6.4 ha). Situated 2 km west of Lisdoonvarna, it consists of five parcels of wet meadow heath. These are being managed in the traditional way for hay-making with the objective of maintaining them as examples of wet meadows found on shale soils.

APPENDIX 3

Statutory Nature Reserves in Northern Ireland

A total of 45 statutory national nature reserves were established under the *Nature Conservation and Amenity Lands (Northern Ireland) Order 1985* in Northern Ireland up to the end of July 1992. These are variously owned, leased or held under agreement by the Environment and Heritage Service, an agency of the Department of Environment.[1]

(a) Woodland

1. Banagher Glen, Co. Derry (30 ha). Three deep glens in Dalradian rocks in the damp conditions of which developed mixed woodlands with rich bryophyte communities.

2. Bohill, Co. Down (1 ha). Tiny area of oak, holly, hazel and birch, surrounded by coniferous forestry. An important site for the holly blue butterfly.

3. Breen, Co. Antrim (21 ha). Typical mature oak and birch woodland developed over a diverse range of soils. A series of glacial overflow channels traverse the site.

4. Castle Archdale Islands, Co. Fermanagh (74 ha). Islands in Lower Lough Erne with mixed deciduous woodland, some of it regenerating since clear-felling in the 1939–45 war period. Rich in woodland bird species.

5. Correl Glen, Co. Fermanagh (34 ha). Mixed deciduous woodland and acid heath on a series off small escarpments of Carboniferous limestone and sandstone. Also small gorge and fast-flowing stream.

6. Glenariff Waterfalls, Co. Antrim (8 ha). A deep gorge with many waterfalls and rapids, the humid conditions of which have resulted in the production of luxuriant bryophyte growth.

7. Hanging Rock and Rossea, Co. Fermanagh (15 ha). A vertical limestone cliff on a knoll reef feature. Mature ashwood has developed at the foot of cliff.

8. Hollymount, Co. Down (15 ha). Ancient carr woodland dating from 1745 when a tidal barrage was built across the Quoil estuary. Also fen and reedswamp. Rich lichen growth on trees.

9. Lough Neagh – Randalstown Forest, Co. Antrim (6 ha). Mixed deciduous woodland on alluvium on succession of old shorelines. Adjoins Farr's Bay NNR and the northeast Lough Neagh Wildfowl Refuge.

10. Lough Neagh – Rea's Wood, Co. Antrim (27 ha). Species-rich fen and deciduous woodland on a series of previously exposed Lough Neagh shorelines. Rich in invertebrates.

11. Marble Arch, Co. Fermanagh (24 ha). A fine example of a moist ashwood in which a narrow, steep-sided glen at the head of which is the striking limestone feature of the Marble Arch, where the Cladagh River issues from an underground cavern.

12. Reilly and Gole Woods, Co. Fermanagh (67 ha). Reilly Wood consists of maturing oak wood developed on thick clays. Gole Wood is mixed scrub which has colonised the site since it was clear-felled in the 1939–45 war period.

13. Rostrevor, Co. Down (20 ha). Mature oak wood on a steep southwest facing slope with a Silurian-derived boulder soil.

14. Straidkilly, Co. Antrim (8 ha). Dry facies of hazel wood developed on a very steep north-facing slope.

(b) Coastal

15. Ballymaclary, Co. Derry (227 ha). A relatively unspoilt area of sand dunes with wet slacks. Several rare plants occur. Part of the Ministry of Defence land holding and used as a training area.

16. Ballyquintin Point, Co. Down (16 ha). A rocky shore with much raised beach shingle interspersed with tidal salt marsh. Vegetation is largely dwarf scrub and maritime grassland.

17. Cloghy Rocks, Co. Down (27 ha). Tidal shoreline and offshore rocks at the western side of Strangford Narrows with an interesting marine fauna. Common seals haul out on rocks between high tides.

18. Dorn, Co. Down (790 ha). Outstanding site for marine biology in Strangford Lough where a rock barrier across the mouth of the bay has resulted in provision of fast currents at most states of tide. Extensive foreshore of mixed sediments and rocky pladdies supports large numbers of wintering waders and wildfowl.

19. Giant's Causeway, Co. Antrim (71 ha). Of exceptional geological significance. The extensive and spectacular exposures of basalt larva flows. including columnar structures in vertical coastal cliffs, are of international renown. Maritime cliff grasslands occur throughout the sites with smaller areas of maritime heath, flushes, perched salt marsh and strandline vegetation. A World Heritage Site.

20. Granagh Bay, Co. Down (24 ha). On the eastern side of Strangford Narrows, an area of tidal foreshore and islands. Complex currents cause wide range of sediment types. Extremely rich in marine fauna.

21. Kebble, Co. Antrim (123 ha). An extensive area of grassland and heath with several wetland areas, massive cliffs of basalt and chalk with tens of thousands of breeding gulls and auks.

22. Killard, Co. Down (68 ha). Lime-rich dune grassland on glacial clays overlain by wind-blown sand. Very rich in plant species, including several species of orchid. Varied rocky and sandy shoreline. Low cliff.

23. Magilligan Point, Co. Derry (57 ha). Sand dune system with parallel ridges and interspersed wet slacks. The coastal section is particularly dynamic.

24. Murlough, Co. Down (283 ha). Mature, stable, sand dune system developed over shingle. Dune land, heath and scrub with a wide range of animal and plant species.

25. North Strangford Lough, Co. Down (1,015 ha). This area of Strangford Lough supports one of the most extensive and least altered mud flats in Northern Ireland. The mud flats display a range of habitats supporting a diversity of invertebrate and bird fauna, in particular wildfowl and waders.

26. Portrush, Co. Antrim (1 ha). Coastal site of exposed fossiliferous Liassic shales which were later altered by intruded dolerite. A site of geological significance.

27. Roe Estuary, Co. Derry (474 ha). Tidal estuary within Lough Foyle, including extensive mud flats, sandbanks and saltmarsh. A variety of wildfowl and waders occur in the autumn and winter.

28. Swan Island, Co. Antrim (0.1 ha). A low-lying vegetated island in Larne Lough supporting an important tern colony.

(c) Peatlands

29. Boorin, Co. Tyrone (58 ha). The area is one of glacial deposition features. On the drier morinic soils heath has developed. A wood with birch and oak occurs on the steep, north-facing slope.

30. Brackagh Moss, Co. Armagh (110 ha). An area of cut-over peat bog with the former fen peat layers exposed. The widely varying conditions have resulted in a rich diversity of plants and an extremely rich insect fauna.

31. Killeter, Co. Tyrone (22 ha). Two small plots of ombrogenous peat bog of contrasting type including several *Sphagnum* species.

32. Lough Naman Bog, Co. Fermanagh (41 ha). An ombrogenous peat bog in a large tract of blanket bog. Well-developed hummock-hollow communities.

33. Meenadoan, Co. Tyrone (20 ha). A small ombrogenous peat bog with an unbroken plant succession going back to at least 12,000 years.

34. Mullenakill and Annagarriff, Co. Armagh (99 ha). Significant portions of the Peatland Park, these reserves illustrate aspects of bog development and native woodland. They contain rare plants and are of high entomological value.

35. The Murrins, Co. Tyrone (54 ha). Part of an extensive glacial outwash feature with heath developed on sands and gravels.

36. Slieveanorra, Co. Antrim (49 ha). Four plots illustrating many aspects of peat development and erosion including bog pool complexes and mature peat.

(d) Fen

37. Castlecaldwell, Co. Fermanagh (7 ha). A series of small, sheltered bays at the western end of Lough Erne, with species-rich fen and associated shoreline scrub.

38. Lough Neagh – Farr's Bay, Co. Antrim (6 ha). Unspoilt species-rich fen and carr developed on a series of shorelines exposed by successive lowerings of Lough Neagh.

39. Lough Neagh – Oxford Island, Co. Armagh (68 ha). Lough shoreline with reedswamp communities, grassland and scrub in higher areas. The site is of ornithological importance for wintering wildfowl and breeding birds.

(e) Wetlands

40. Quoile Pondage Basin, Co. Down (195 ha). Formerly the tidal estuary of the River Quoile, this is now a nutrient-rich lake with species-rich wetland margins and developing woodland. An important site for wildfowl in winter.

41. Ross Lough, Co. Fermanagh (9 ha). A small area of open water and ungrazed fen at the east end of Ross Lough. Fen subject to winter inundation, underlying rock is Carboniferous sandstone.

(f) Quarry

42. Belshaw's Quarry, Co. Antrim (1 ha). Small disused quarry which is a microcosm of the geology of South Antrim. Particularly suitable for educational use.

(g) Cliff and grassland

43. Binevenagh, Co. Derry (70 ha). Basalt grassland and cliffs with a number of rare plant species including purple saxifrage and moss campion. Outflow from Banagher Lake cascades through a steep narrow ravine.

(h) Upland grassland

44. Crossmurrin, Co. Fermanagh (96 ha). An area of mixed grassland and hazel scrub on upland limestone. Small area of blanket bog occurs on a knoll.

(i) Lake islands

45. Lough Neagh – islands (6 ha). Most of the small islands in Lough Neagh, important as nesting sites for ducks, terns and gulls.

Bibliography

CHAPTER 1

[1] **Green, D. & O'Connor, F. (eds.).** 1967. *A Golden Treasury of Irish Poetry* AD *600 to 1,200.* Macmillan, London.

[2] **Praeger, R. Ll.** 1949. *Some Irish Naturalists. A Biographical Note-book.* Dundalgan Press, Dundalk.

[3] **O'Meara, J.** 1949. Giraldus Cambrensis in Topographia Hibernie. Text of the first recension. *Proc. R. Ir. Acad.* 52C: 113–178.

[4] **Boate, G.** 1652. *Irelands Naturall History, Being a true description of its situation, greatness, shape and nature.* Samuel Hartlib, London.

[5] **Carney, J.** 1971. Three old Irish poems. *Ériu.* 22: 41–47

[6] **Meyer, K. (trans. & ed.).** 1903. *Four Old-Irish Songs of Summer and Winter.* Nutt, London.

[7] **Jackson, K. H.** 1951. *A Celtic Miscellany: Translations from the Celtic Literature.* Routledge & Kegan Paul, London.

[8] **Cabot, D.** 1997. Animals and plants mentioned in some early Irish nature poetry. Unpublished note.

[9] **Thompson, W.** 1849-56. *The Natural History of Ireland.* Vols 1–3. Reeve, Bentham, and Reeve, London; vol 4 Henry G. Bohn, London.

[10] **Reeves, W.** 1861. On Augustin, an Irish writer of the seventh century. *Proc. R. Ir. Acad.* 7: 514–522.

[11] **St. Augustine of Hippo.** Quoted in: **Thompson, D'Arcy, W.** 1945. *Sesquivolus,* a squirrel: and the *Liber de Mirabilibus S. Scripturae. Hermathena* 65: 1–7.

[12] **Thompson, D'Arcy, W.** 1945. *Op. cit.*

[13] **Fairley, J.** 1984. *An Irish Beast Book: A natural history of Ireland's furred wildlife.* Blackstaff Press, Belfast.

[14] **White, Gilbert** 1789. *The Natural History and Antiquities of Selborne.* B. White & Son, London.

[15] **O' Meara, J.J. (trans)** 1951. *The First Version of The Topography of Ireland by Geraldus Cambrensis.* Dundalgan Press, Dundalk.

[16] **Stanihurst, R.** 1577. A Treatise contayning a playne and perfect description of Irelande ... In: **Holinshed, R.** *The first volume of the Chronicles of England, Scotland and Irelande.* ... London.

[17] **Kennedy, P.G., Ruttledge, R.F., Scroope, C.F. & assisted by Humphries, G.R.** 1954. *The Birds of Ireland.* Oliver & Boyd, London.

[18] **Stelfox, A.W.** 1938. The birds of Lagore about one thousand years ago. *Ir. Nat. J.* 7: 37–43.

[19] *Polychronicon Ranulphi Higden, Monachi Cestrensis.* 9 vols. Vols. 1 & 2 edited by C. Babington; vols. 3–9 edited by J.R. Lumby. 1858. London.

[20] **Newton, E.T.** 1906. In: **Scharff, R.F., Ussher, R.J., Cole, G.A.J., Newton, E.T., Dixon, A.F. & Westropp,. T.J.** The exploration of the caves of County Clare. 53–7. *Trans. R. Ir. Acad.* 33B: 1–76.

[21] **Newton, E.T.** 1923. The common crane fossil in Britain. *Naturalist* 1923: 284–5.

[22] **Mitchell, F. & Ryan, M.** 1997. *Reading the Irish Landscape.* Town House, Dublin.

[23] **Holder, A.** 1904. *Altceltische Sprachschatz* 2: 103. Leipzig.

[24] **Webster, C.** 1974. New light on the Invisible College. The social relations of English science in the mid-seventeenth century. *Trans. Roy. Hist. Soc.* Fifth series. 24: 19–42.

[25] **Brown, H.** 1934. *Scientific Organisations in 17th Century France.* Baltimore, USA.

[26] **Birch, T. (ed.).** 1772. *The Works of the Honourable Robert Boyle.* London.

[27] **Barnard, T.C.** 1972. The Social Policy of the Commonwealth and Protectorate in Ireland. Oxford D.Phil. thesis quoted in: **Webster, C.** 1974. *Op. cit.*

[28] **House of Commons Journals** 1647 V. 17th July 1647, p. 21. Quoted in: **Webster, C.** 1974. *Op. cit.*

[29] **Hartlib, S.** Quoted in: **Webster, C. (ed.).** 1970. *Samuel Hartlib and the Advancement of Learning.* London.

[30] **Mitchell, M.E.** 1975. Irish botany in the seventeenth century. *Proc. R. Ir. Acad.* 75B: 275–284.

[31] **Nelson, E.C.** 1978. The publication date of the first Irish flora. Caleb Threlkeld's *Synopsis stirpium Hibernicarum,* 1726. *Glasra* 2: 37–42.

[32] **Britten, J.** 1915. Gedeon Bonnivert (fl. 1673–1703). *Journal of Botany* 53: 107–112.

[33] **O' Flaherty, R.** [1684]. *A Chorographical Description of West or H-Iar Connaught.* Edited with notes and illustrations by J. Hardiman, 1846. Irish Archaeological Society, Dublin.

[34] **Ussher, J.** 1650. *Annales Verteris Testamenti.* J. Crook, London.

[35] **Davies, G.L.** 1964. From flood and fire to rivers and ice – three hundred years of Irish geomorphology. *Irish Geography* 5: 1–16.

[36] **Hoppen, K.T.** 1964. The Dublin philosophical society and the new learning in Ireland. *Irish Historical Studies* 14: 99–118.

[37] **Lhwyd, E.** 1712. Some farther Observations Relating to the Antiquities and Natural History of Ireland. In a Letter from the late Edw. Lhwyd. to Dr. Tancred Robinson, F.R.S. *Phil. Trans. Roy. Soc. Lond.* 27: 524–526.

[38] **Stringer, A.** 1714. *The Experienc'd Huntsman.* James Blow, Belfast. 2nd edition (1977) ed. J. S. Fairley. Blackstaff Press, Belfast.

[39] **Threlkeld, C.** 1726. *Synopsis stirpium Hibernicarum.* Davys, Norris and Worral, Dublin.

[40] **Ray, J.** 1696. *Synopsis Methodica stirpium Britannicarum ...* 2nd edition. S. Smith & B. Watford, London.

[41] **Colgan, N.** 1904. *Flora of County Dublin.* Hodges, Figgis & Co., Dublin.

[42] **Mitchell, M.E.** 1974. The sources of Threlkeld's *Synopsis stirpium Hibernicarum. Proc. R. Ir. Acad.* **74**B: 1–6.

[43] **Nelson, E.C.** 1979. In the contemplation of vegetables – Caleb Threlkeld (1676–1728), his life, background and contribution to Irish botany. *Jour. Soc. Bibliog. Nat. Hist.* 9: 257–273.

[44] **Doogue, D. & Parnell, J.** 1992. Fragments of an eighteenth-century herbarium, possibly that of Caleb Threlkeld in Trinity College, Dublin (TCD). *Glasra* 1: 99–109.

[45] **Anon.** 1525. *A boke of the propertyes of herbs the whiche is called an herball.* Bancks, London.

[46] **Linnaei, C.** 1735. *Systema Naturae ...* Theodorum Haak, Lugduni Batarorum.

[47] **K'Eogh, J.** 1735. *Botanalogia Universalis Hibernica, or A General Irish Herbal.* George Harrison, Cork.

[48] **K'Eogh, J.** 1739. *Zoologia Medicinalis Hibernica.* S. Powell, Dublin.

[49] **Rutty, J.** 1772. *An Essay Towards a Natural History of the County Dublin.* 2 vols. W. Sleater, Dublin.

[50] **Browne, P.** 1756. *The Civil and Natural History of Jamaica.* Osborne and Shipton, London.

[51] **Browne, P.** 1996. *The Flowers of Mayo.* Edited by Charles Nelson and illustrated by Wendy Walsh. De Burca, Dublin.

[52] **Browne, P.** 1774. A Catalogue of the Birds of Ireland, Whether Natives, Casual Visitors, or Birds of Passage, Taken from Observation; Classified and Disposed According to Linnaeus. *The Gentleman's and London Magazine: or, Monthly Chronologer.* 1774: 385–387.

[53] **Browne, P.** 1774. A Catalogue of Fishes Observed on our Coasts, and in our Lakes and Rivers, Classified and Disposed According to Linneaus. *The Gentleman's and London Magazine: or, Monthly Chronologer.* 1774: 515–516.

[54] **Wade, W.** 1794. *Catalogus systematicus plantarum indigenarum in Comitatu Dublinensis invitorum. Pars Prima.* G. Sleater, Dublin.

[55] **Wade, W.** 1804. *Plantae Rariores in Hibernia.* Graisberry and Campbell, Dublin.

[56] **Turner, D.** 1804. *Muscologiae Hibernicae Spicilegium.* J. Black, Yarmouth; and J. White, London.

[57] **White, J.** 1808. *An Essay on the Indigenous Grasses of Ireland.* Graisberry & Campbell, Dublin.

[58] **Wade, W.** 1808. *Sketch of Lectures on Meadow and Pasture Grasses ...* Graisberry & Campbell, Dublin.

[59] **Wade, W.** 1811. *Salices or an Essay towards a General History of Sallows, Willows & Osiers, their Uses and Best Methods of Propagating and Cultivating Them.* Dublin Society, Dublin.

[60] **Anon. [Katherine Sophia Baily].** 1833. *The Irish Flora Comprising Phaenogamous Plants and Ferns.* Hodges & Smith, Dublin.

[61] **Mackay, J.T.** 1836. *Flora Hibernica... Arranged According to the Natural System with a Synopsis of the Genera According to the Linnaean System.* William Curry Jun., Dublin.

[62] **Allen, D. E.** 1976. *The Naturalist in Britain. A Social History.* Allen Lane, London.

[63] **Harvey, J.R., Humphreys, J.D. & Power, T.** 1845. *Contributions Towards a Fauna and Flora of the County of Cork Read at the Meeting of the British Association Held at Cork in the year 1843.* John van Voorst for the Cuvierian Society of Cork, London.

[64] **Tate, R.** 1863. *Flora Belfastiensis.* G. Phillips, Belfast.

[65] **Dickie, G.** 1864. *A Flora of Ulster and Botanist's Guide to the North of Ireland.* C. Aitchison, Belfast, & Lovell Reeve & Co., London.

[66] **Moore, D. & More, A.G.** 1866. *Contributions towards a Cybele Hibernica.* Hodges, Smith & Co., Dublin and John van Voorst, London.

[67] **Watson, H. C.** 1847-59. *Cybele Britannica; or British Plants and their Geographical*

[68] **Babington, C.C.** 1859. Hints towards a Cybele Hibernica. *Proc. Dub. Univ. Zool. & Bot. Assoc.* 1: 246–250.

[69] **More, A.G.** 1872. *Recent Additions to the Flora of Ireland – a first Supplement to the Cybele Hibernica.* Gill, Dublin.

[70] **Praeger, R.Ll.** 1896. On the botanical subdivision of Ireland. *Irish Naturalist* 5: 29–38.

[71] **Praeger, R. Ll.** 1901. Irish Topographical Botany. *Proc. R. Ir. Acad.* 23, 3rd Series: i-clxxxviii, 1–410.

[72] **Scannell, M.J.P. & Synnott, D.M.** 1987. *Census Catalogue of the Flora of Ireland.* 2nd edition, Stationery Office, Dublin.

[73] **Allin, T.** 1883. *The Flowering Plants and Ferns of the County Cork.* J. Marche, Weston-Super-Mare.

[74] **Stewart, S.A. & Corry, T.H.** 1888. *A Flora of the North-east of Ireland.* Belfast Naturalists' Field Club, Belfast, and Macmillan & Bowes, Cambridge.

[75] **Scannell, M.J.P.** 1990. Henry Chichester Hart – Botanist, Explorer and Philologist. In: **Mollen, C., Davis, W. & Finnucane, B. (eds.).** *More People and Places in Irish Science and Technology.* Royal Irish Academy, Dublin.

[76] **Traynor, M.** 1953. *The English Dialect of Donegal.* Royal Irish Academy, Dublin.

[77] **Hart, H.C.** 1898. *Flora of the County Donegal.* Sealy, Bryers & Walker, Dublin.

[78] **Hart, H.C.** 1887. *Flora of Howth.* Hodges, Figgis & Co., Dublin.

[79] **Thompson, J.V.** 1828–34. *Zoological Researches, and Illustrations; or, Natural History of Nondescript or Imperfectly Known Animals in a Series of Memoirs.* King and Ridings, Cork. Facs. rpt (1968) as *Zoological Researches and Illustrations 1828–1834.* Society for the Bibliography of Natural History, London.

[80] **Maxwell, W. H.** 1832. *Wild Sports of the West, with Legendary Tales, and Local Sketches.* Richard Bentley, London.

[81] **McKelvie, C.L.** 1986. William Hamilton Maxwell – a Biographical and Critical Introduction. In: **Maxwell, W.H.** 1892. *Wild Sports of the West of Ireland; also Legendary Tales, Folk-Lore, Local Customs and Natural History.* vi–xxxiv. 1986 reprint. Ashford Press Publishing, Hampshire.

[82] **Watters, J.** 1853. *The Natural History of the Birds of Ireland.* James McGlashan, Dublin.

[83] **O'Connor, J.P.** 1997. Insects and Entomology. In: **Foster, J.W. & Chesney, H.C.G. (eds.).** *Nature in Ireland: A Scientific and Cultural History.* 219-240. Lilliput Press, Dublin.

[84] **Patterson, R.** 1838. *Letters on the Natural History of Insects Mentioned in Shakespeare's Plays with Incidental Notes on the Insects of Ireland.* W.S. Orr & Co., London.

[85] **Patterson, R.** 1845. *Introduction to Zoology for the Use of Schools.* Simms & McIntyre, London.

[86] **Patterson, R.** 1848. *First Steps in Zoology.* 2nd edition. W. Mullan, Belfast.

[87] **Patterson, R.L.** 1880. *Birds, Fishes and Cetacea commonly frequenting Belfast Lough.* David Bogue, London.

[88] **Payne-Gallwey, R.** 1882. *The Fowler in Ireland.* John van Voorst, London.

[89] **Benson, C.** 1886. *Our Irish Song Birds.* Hodges, Figgis & Co., Dublin.

[90] **Barrington, R.M.** 1900. *The Migration of Birds as Observed at Irish Lighthouses and Lightships.* R.H. Porter, London and Edward Ponsonby, Dublin.

[91] **Ussher, R. J. & Warren, R.** 1900. *The Birds of Ireland.* Gurney & Jackson, London.

[92] **Foster, J.W.** 1990. Natural History, Science and Irish Culture. *The Irish Review* 9: 61–69

[93] **Wyse-Jackson, P.N. & P.S.** 1992. The Irish Naturalist: 33 years of natural history in Ireland 1892–1924. *Ir. Nat. J.* 24: 95–101.

[94] **Collins, T.** 1985. *Floreat Hibernia: A Bio-Bibliography of Robert Lloyd Praeger. 1865–1953.* Royal Dublin Society, Dublin.

[95] **Praeger, R. Ll.** 1906. Irish Topographical Botany: supplement 1901–1905. *Proc. R. Ir. Acad.* 26B: 13–45.

[96] **Praeger, R. Ll.** 1929. Report on recent additions to the flora and fauna of Ireland. *Proc. R. Ir. Acad.* 39B: 1–94.

[97] **Praeger, R. Ll.** 1934. A contribution to the flora of Ireland. *Proc. R. Ir. Acad.* 42B: 55–86.

[98] **Praeger, R.Ll.** 1909. *A Tourist's Flora of the West of Ireland.* Hodges, Figgis & Co., Dublin.

[99] **Praeger, R.Ll.** 1934. *The Botanist in Ireland.* Hodges, Figgis & Co., Dublin.

[100] **Praeger, R.Ll.** 1897. *Open-Air Studies in Botany: Sketches of British Wild-flowers in Their Homes.* Charles Griffin, London.

[101] **Praeger, R.Ll.** 1913. *Weeds: Simple Lessons for Children.* Cambridge University Press, Cambridge.

[102] **Praeger, R.Ll.** 1921. *Aspects of Plant Life with Special Reference to the British Flora.* Nature Lover's Series, SPCK, London.

[103] **Lindsay, T. S.** 1923. *Plant Names.* Nature Lover's Series. The Sheldon Press, London.

[104] **Adams, J.** 1931. *A Students' Illustrated Irish Flora Being a Guide to the Indigenous Seed-plants of Ireland.* L. Reeve & Co. London.

[105] **Scully, R. W.** 1916. *Flora of County Kerry.* Hodges, Figgis & Co., Dublin.

[106] **Brunker, J. P.** 1950. *Flora of the County Wicklow.* Dundalgan Press, Dundalk.

[107] **Longfield, C.** 1937. *Dragonflies of the British Isles.* Warne, London.

[108] **Corbet, P.S., Longfield, C. & Moore, N.W.** 1960. *The New Naturalist: Dragonflies.* Collins, London.

[109] **Lack, D.** 1965. *Enjoying Ornithology.* Methuen & Co., London.

[110] **Armstrong, E.A.** 1955. *The New Naturalist: The Wren.* Collins, London.

[111] **Armstrong, E.A.** 1940. *The Birds of the Grey Wind.* Oxford University Press, London.

[112] **Armstrong, E.A.** 1952. *The New Naturalist: The Folklore of Birds.* Collins, London.

[113] **Deane, C.D.** 1954. *Handbook of the Birds of Northern Ireland.* Belfast Museum and Art Gallery Bulletin 1,6:119-193.

[114] **Praeger, R. Ll.** 1937. *The Way That I Went.* Hodges, Figgis & Co., Dublin and Methuen & Co., London.

[115] **Praeger, R. Ll.** 1930. *Beyond Soundings.* The Talbot Press, Dublin & Cork.

[116] **Praeger, R. Ll.** 1941. *A Populous Solitude.* A. Methuen, London.

[117] **More, A.G.** 1885. *A List of Irish Birds showing the species contained in the Science and Art Museum, Dublin.* Her Majesty's Stationery Office, Dublin.

[118] **Kennedy, P. G.** 1961. *A List of Irish Birds.* National Museum of Ireland, Dublin.

[119] **Kennedy, P.G.** 1953. *An Irish Sanctuary – birds of the North Bull, Dublin.* At the Sign of the Three Candles, Dublin.

[120] **Praeger, R. Ll.** 1950. *Natural History of Ireland: a Sketch of its Flora and Fauna.* Collins, London.

[121] **Kennedy, P.G., Ruttledge, R.F., Scroope, C.F., assisted by Humphreys, G.R.** 1954. *Op. cit.*

[122] **Ruttledge, R. F.** 1966. *Ireland's Birds.* Witherby, London.

[123] **Hutchinson, C. D.** 1989. *Birds in Ireland.* T & A D Poyser, Calton.

[124] **Webb, D.A., Parnell, J. & Doogue, D.** 1996. *An Irish Flora.* 7th revised edition. Dundalgan Press, Dundalk

[125] **Booth, E.** 1979. *The Flora of County Carlow.* Royal Dublin Society, Dublin.

[126] **Webb, D.A. & Scannell, M.J.P.** 1983. *Flora of Connemara and the Burren.* Royal Dublin Society, Dublin, and Cambridge University Press, Cambridge.

[127] **Wyse-Jackson P. & Sheehy-Skeffington, M.** 1984. *The Flora of Inner Dublin.* Royal Dublin Socety & Dublin Naturalists' Field Club, Dublin.

[128] **Harron, J. with the assistance of Rushton, B.S.** 1980. *Flora of Lough Neagh.* Irish Naturalist's Journal Committee, Belfast and University of Ulster, Coleraine.

[129] **Synnott, D.M.** 1970. *County Louth Wildflowers.* Clarks, Dundalk.

[130] **Mitchell, F.** 1986. *The Irish Landscape.* Town House, Dublin.

[131] **Battersby, E.** 1997. Polymath with a Vision. *Irish Times*, 3rd December. Dublin.

[132] **Nelson, C.E.** 1991. *The Burren: a Companion to the Wildflowers of an Irish Landscape.* Boethius Press, Anglesey.

[133] **Hackney, P. (comp. & ed.).** 1992. *Stewart and Corry's Flora of the North-east of Ireland.* 3rd edition. Institute of Irish Studies, Queen's University, Belfast.

[134] **D'Arcy, G. & Hayward, J.** 1992. *The Natural History of the Burren.* Immel Publishing, London.

[135] **Whilde, T.** 1994. *The Natural History of Connemara.* Immel Publishing, London.

[136] **Whilde, A.** 1993. *Threatened Mammals, Birds, Amphibians and Fish in Ireland. Irish Red Data Book 2: Vertebrates.* HMSO, Belfast.

[137] **Nelson, E.C. & Walsh, W.F.** 1993. *Trees of Ireland: Native and Naturalised.* Lilliput Press, Dublin.

[138] **Walsh, W.F.** 1993 & 1997. *An Irish Florilegium.* (With Introduction by R.I. Ross and Notes by C. Nelson). 2 vols. Thames & Hudson, London.

[139] **Cabot, D.** 1995. *Collins Guide to the Birds of Ireland.* HarperCollins, London.

[140] **Feehan, J. & O'Donovan, G.** 1996. *The Bogs of Ireland.* The Environmental Institute, University College, Dublin.

[141] **Aalen, F.H.A., Whelan, K. & Stout, M. (eds.).** 1997. *Atlas of the Irish Rural Landscape.* Cork University Press, Cork.

[142] **Foster, J.W. & Chesney, H.C.G. (eds.).** 1997. *Op. cit.*

CHAPTER 2

[1] **Coxon, P.** 1993. *Irish quaternary biogeography, climate and the interglacial record.* In: **Costello, M.J. & Kelly, K.S. (eds.).** Biogeography of Ireland: past, present and future. *Occ. Publ. Ir. biogeog. Soc.* 2: 5–23.

[2] **Mitchell, F. & Ryan, M.** 1997. *Reading the Irish Landscape.* Town House, Dublin.

[3] **Coxon, P. & Flegg, A.** 1985. A Middle Pleistocene interglacial deposit from Ballyline, Co. Kilkenny. *Proc. R. Ir. Acad.* 85B: 107–120.

[4] **Kinahan, G.H.** 1865. *Explanation to accompany sheets 115 and 116.* Geological Survey of Ireland, Dublin.

[5] **Jessen, K., Anderson, S.T. & Farrington, A.** 1959. The interglacial deposits near Gort, Co. Galway, Ireland. *Proc. R. Ir. Acad.* 60B: 1–77.

[6] **Watts, W.A.** 1985. Quaternary vegetation cycles. In: **Edwards, K.J. & Warren, W.P. (eds.).** *The Quaternary History of Ireland.* 155–185. Academic Press, London.

[7] **Warren, W.P.** 1985. Stratigraphy. In: **Edwards, K.J. & Warren, W.P. (eds.).** *Op. cit.* 39–65.

[8] **Singh, G.** 1970. Late-glacial vegetation history of Lecale, Co. Down. *Proc. R. Ir. Acad.* 69B: 189–216.

[9] **Forbes, E.** 1846. On the connection between the distribution of the existing fauna and flora of the British Isles, and the geological changes which have affected their area, especially during the epoch of the Northern Drift. *Mem. Geol. Surv. Gt. Britain.* 1: 336–432.

[10] **Praeger, R. Ir.** 1932. Recent views bearing on the problem of the Irish flora and fauna. *Proc. R. Ir. Acad.* 41B: 125–145.

[11] **Beirne, B.P.** 1952. *The Origin and History of British Fauna.* Methuen & Co., London.

[12] **Charlesworth, J.K.** 1930. Some geological observations on the origin of the Irish fauna and flora. *Proc. R. Ir. Acad.* 39B: 358–390.

[13] **Godwin, H.** 1975. *The History of the British Flora.* 2nd edition. Cambridge University Press, Cambridge.

[14] **Reid, C.** 1899. *The Origin of the British Flora.* Dulau and Co., London.

[15] **Corbet, G.B.** 1961. Origin of the British insular races of small mammals and of the 'Lusitanian' fauna. *Nature* 191: 1037–1040.

[16] Quoted in **Mitchell, F. & Ryan, M.** 1997. *Op. cit.*

[17] **Sleeman, D.P., Devoy, R.J. & Woodman, P.C. (eds.).** 1986. Proceedings of The Postglacial Colonisation Conference. *Occ. Publ. biogeog. Soc.* 1: 1–88.

[18] **Costello, M.J. & Kelly, K.S. (eds.).** 1993. Biogeography of Ireland: past, present, and future. *Occ. Publ. Ir. biogeog. Soc.* 2: 1–149.

[19] **Mitchell, G.F.** 1965. Littleton Bog, Co. Tipperary: an Irish vegetational record. *Geol. Soc. Amer. Special Paper* 84.

[20] **Praeger, R.Ll.** 1950. *The Natural History of Ireland: A Sketch of its Flora and Fauna.* Collins, London.

[21] **Kelly, D.** 1997. *Pers. comm.*

[22] **Hobson, D.D.** 1993. *Populus nigra* L. in Ireland – an indigenous species? *Ir. Nat. J.* 25: 244–247.

[23] **Bradshaw, R.** 1997. In: **Mitchell, F & Ryan, M.** 1997. *Op. cit.*

[24] **Scharff, R.F., Coffey, G., Cole, G.A.J., Ussher, R.J. & Praeger, R. Ll.** 1903. The exploration of the caves of Kesh, County Sligo. *Trans. R. Ir. Acad.* 32B: 171–214.

[25] **Scharff, R. F., Ussher, R.J., Cole, G.A.J., Newton, E.T., Dixon, A.F. & Westropp, T.J.** 1906. The exploration of the caves of County Clare. *Trans. R. Ir. Acad.* 33B: 1–76.

[26] **Scharff, R. F., Seymour, H.J. & Newton, E.T.** 1918. The exploration of Castlepook Cave, County Cork. *Proc. R. Ir. Acad.* 34B: 33–72.

[27] **Woodman, P.C. & Monaghan, N.** 1993. From mice to mammoths. *Archaeology Ireland* 7 (3): 31–33.

[28] **Stuart, A.J. & van Wijngaarden-Bakker, L.H.** 1985. Quaternary vertebrates. In: **Edwards, K.J. & Warren, W.P. (eds.).** *Op. cit.* 221–249.

[29] **Lynch, J.M. & Hayden, T.J.** 1993. Multivariate morphometrics and biogeography of Irish mustelids. In: **Costello, M.J & Kelly, K.S. (eds.).** *Op. cit.* 25–34.

[30] **Scharff, R.F.** 1918. The Irish Red Deer. *Ir. Nat.* 27: 133–139.

[31] **Moffat, C. B.** 1938. The mammals of Ireland. *Proc. R. Ir. Acad.* 44B: 61–128.

[32] **Whitehead, G.K.** 1964. *The Deer of Great Britain and Ireland: An Account of their History, Status and Distribution.* Routledge & Kegan Paul, London.

[33] **Harrington, R.** 1980. Exotic deer in Ireland. In: **Kernan, R.P., Mooney, O.V. & Went, A.E.J. (eds.).** 1980. *The Introduction of Exotic Species – Advantages and Problems.* Proceedings of a symposium. 4–5 January 1979. 73–81. Royal Irish Academy, Dublin.

[34] **Lever, C.** 1997. *The Naturalised Animals of the British Isles.* Hutchinson, London.

[35] **Fairley, J.** 1984. *An Irish Beast Book. A natural history of Ireland's furred wildlife.* 2nd edition. Blackstaff Press, Belfast.

[36] **Joyce, P.W.** 1869. *The Origin and History of Irish Names of Places.* Facsimile reprint 1995. Edmund Burke, Dublin.

[37] **Harting, J.E.** 1880. *British Animals Extinct within Historic Times.* Trüber & Co., London.

[38] **Heaney, S.** 1972. 'Midnight'. In: *Wintering*

Out. Faber and Faber, London.

[39] **De Burgo, T.** 1762. *Hibernia Dominicana.* J. Stokes, Kilkenny.

[40] **Thompson, W.** 1856. *The Natural History of Ireland.* Vol. 4. Henry G. Bohn, London.

[41] **Trinity College, Dublin.** MS I.I.3. Also published as an appendix In: **McLysaght, E.** 1939. *Irish Life in the Seventeenth Century.* Irish University Press, Cork.

[42] **Scharrff, R.F.** 1893. Is the frog a native of Ireland? *Irish Naturalist* 2: 1–6.

[43] **Cambrensis, Giraldus [Gerald of Wales]** *The History and Topography of Ireland [Topographia Hiberniae].* Here translated from the Latin by John J. O'Meara with a Map and Drawings from a Contemporary Copy *c.*1200 AD. (Revised edition 1982). Dolmen Press, Portlaoise.

[44] **Mackay, J.T.** 1836. The natterjack (*Bufo rubeta*) occurs wild in Ireland. *Mag. Nat. Hist.* 9: 316–317.

[45] **Thompson, W.** 1856. *The Natural History of Ireland.* Vol 4: 66–67. Henry G. Bohn, London.

[46] **Beebee, T.J.C.** 1983. *The Natterjack Toad.* Oxford University Press, Oxford.

[47] **Persson, O. & Persson, E.** 1980. The osteological analysis of the cremated and unburned bone material at a megalithic cemetery at Carrowmore, Co. Sligo, Ireland. In: **Burenhult, G.** *The Archaeological Excavation at Carrowmore, Co. Sligo, Ireland. Excavation Seasons 1977–79.* G. Burenhults Forlag, Sweden; Appendix 1.

[48] **Smith, C.** 1756. *The Ancient and Present State of the County of Kerry, being a Natural, Civil, Ecclesiastical, Historical and Topographical Description thereof.* A. Reilly (for the Author), Dublin.

[49] **Farrington, A.** 1965. Far travelled ballast on beaches in south County Cork. *Ir. Nat. J.* 15: 110.

[50] **Maitland, P.S.** 1996. Threatened fishes of the British Isles, with special reference to Ireland. In: **Reynolds, J.D. (ed.).** *The Conservation of Aquatic Systems.* 84–100. Royal Irish Academy, Dublin.

[51] **Woodman, P.C., Devoy, R.J.N. & Sleeman, D.P.** 1986. Introduction. *Occ. Pub. Ir. Biogeog. Soc.* 1: 1–7.

[52] **Farran, G.P.** 1946. Local Irish names of fishes. *Ir. Nat. J.* 8: 344–347; 370–376; 402–408; 420–433.

[53] **Went, A.E.J.** 1949. Giraldus Cambrensis' notes on Irish fish. *Ir. Nat. J.* 9: 221–224.

[54] **Wright, T. (ed.).** 1863. *The Historical Works of Giraldus Cambrensis.* Bohn, London.

[55] **O' Flaherty, R. [1684].** *A Chorographical Description of West or H-Iar Connaught.* Edited with notes and illustrations by J. Hardiman, 1846. Irish Archaeological Society, Dublin.

[56] **Westropp, T.J.** 1889. History of the abbey and battles Monasternenagh, Croom, Co. Limerick. *J. Roy. Soc. Antiq. Ir.* 19: 235.

[57] *Civil Survey of Ireland.* Irish Manuscript Commission, Dublin. 1942. Vol 4, 94 & 228.

[58] **Young, A.** 1780. *A Tour in Ireland.* George Bell, Dublin.

[59] **Rosell, R.S.** 1994. Changes in fish populations in lower Lough Erne: a comparison of 1972–3 and 1991 gill net survey. *Biology and Environment. Proc. R. Ir. Acad.* 94B: 275–283.

[60] **Ferguson, A., Himberg, K. J. M. & Svardson, G.** 1978. Systematics of the Irish pollan (*Coregonus pollan* Thompson): an electrophoretic comparison with other Holarctic Coregoninae. *J. Fish Biol.* 12: 211–233.

[61] **Whilde, A.** 1993. *Threatened Mammals, Birds, Amphibians and Fish in Ireland. Irish Red Data Book 2: Vertebrates.* HMSO, Belfast.

[62] **Regan, C.T.** 1909. The charr of Ireland. *Irish Naturalist* 18: 3–6.

[63] **Ferguson, A.** 1981. Systematics of Irish charr as indicated by electrophoretic analysis of tissue proteins. *Biochemical Systematics & Ecology* 9: 225–232.

[64] **Lever, C.** 1977. *The Naturalised Animals of the British Isles.* Hutchinson, London

[65] **Maitland, P.S. & Campbell, R.N.** 1992. *The New Naturalist: Freshwater Fishes of the British Isles.* HarperCollins, London.

[66] **Fitzmaurice, P.** 1997. *Pers.comm.*

[67] **Robert Boyle.** Communication to the Royal Society 29th April, 1663. In: **Went, A.J.E.** 1979. Historical natural history notes on some Irish fishes. *The Western Naturalist.* 8:15–26.

[68] **Grosert, A.E.** (ed.). 1886. *Lismore Papers.* Series 1: 4: 44 and 5: 161–162.

[69] **Smith, C.** 1750. *The Ancient and Present State of the County and City of Cork.* A. Reilly, Dublin.

[70] **Fitzmaurice, P.** 1997. *Pers.comm.*

[71] **Went, A.E.J.** 1950. Notes on the Introduction of some Freshwater Fish into Ireland. *J. of Dept. Agriculture, Dublin.* 47: 3–8.

[72] **Fitzmaurice, P.** 1997. *Pers.comm.*

[73] **Eager, A.E., Nelson, E.C. & Scannell, M.J. P.** 1978. *Erica ciliaris* L. in Connemara, 1846–1853. *Ir. Nat. J.* 19: 244–245.

[74] **Curtis, T.G.F. & McGough, H.N.** 1988. *The Irish Red Data Book: 1 Vascular Plants.*

Stationery Office, Dublin.

[75] **Webb, D.A. & Scannell, M.J.P.** 1983. *Flora of Connemara and the Burren.* Royal Dublin Society, Dublin, and Cambridge University Press, Cambridge.

[76] **Jessen, K.** 1949. Studies in late Quaternary deposits and flora-history of Ireland. *Proc. R. Ir. Acad.* 52B: 85–290.

[77] **Watts, W.A.** 1967. Interglacial deposits in Kildromin townland, near Herbertstown, Co. Limerick. *Proc. R. Ir. Acad.* 65B: 339–348.

[78] **Nelson, E. C. (ed.).** 1995. *Flowers of Mayo. Dr. Patrick Brown's Facsiculus Plantarum Hiberniae.* Edmund Burke, Dublin.

[79] **Praeger, R. Ll.** 1934. *The Botanist in Ireland.* Hodges, Figgis & Co., Dublin.

[80] **Foss, P.J. & Doyle, G. J.** 1988. Why has *Erica erigena* (the Irish heather) such a markedly disjunct European distribution? *Plants Today* 9/10: 161–168.

[81] **Praeger, R. Ll.** 1938. The Cornish heath in Ireland. *Ir. Nat. J.* 7: 3–5.

[82] **Webb, D.A.** 1954. Notes on four Irish heaths: part II. *Ir. Nat. J.* 11: 215–219.

[83] **McClintock, D. & Rose, F.** 1970. Cornish heath in Ireland. *Ir. Nat. J.* 16: 387–390.

[84] **Hackney, P. (comp. & ed.).** 1992. *Stewart and Corry's Flora of the North-East of Ireland.* 3rd edition. Institute of Irish Studies, Queens University, Belfast.

[85] **Watts, W.A.** 1959. Interglacial deposits at Kilbeg and Newtown, Co. Waterford. *Proc. R. Ir. Acad.* 60B: 79–134.

[86] **Devoy, J.R.** 1986. Possible landbridges between Ireland and Britain: a geological appraisal. *Occ. Pub. Ir. Biogeog. Soc.* 1: 15–26.

CHAPTER 3

[1] **Raven, J. & Walters, M.** 1956. *The New Naturalist: Mountain Flowers.* Collins, London.

[2] **Colgan, N.** 1900. Botanical notes on the Galway and Mayo highlands. *Irish Naturalist* 9: 111–118.

[3] **Praeger, R. Ll.** 1934. *The Botanist in Ireland.* Hodges, Figgis & Co., Dublin.

[4] **Ryan, S.** 1984. The Mountains. In: **de Buitléar, É. (ed.).** *Wild Ireland.* Amach Faoin Aer Publishers, Dublin.

[5] **Rohan, P.K.** 1986. *The Climate of Ireland.* 2nd edition. The Stationery Office, Dublin.

[6] **Douglas, C.** 1994. Overgrazing in Ireland – some impacts. Unpublished report. 1–7. National Parks and Wildlife Service, Dublin.

[7] **Webb, D.A.** 1983. The flora of Ireland in its European context: The Boyle Medal Discourse 1982. *J. Life Sci. R. Dubl. Soc.* 4: 143–160.

[8] **Hart, H. C.** 1883. Report on the flora of the mountains of Mayo and Galway. *Proc. R. Ir. Acad. (Science)* 3: 694–768.

[9] **Praeger, R. Ll.** 1950. *The Natural History of Ireland. A Sketch of its Flora and Fauna.* Collins, London.

[10] **White, B.F.** 1879. The mountain Lepidoptera of Britain. *Scot. Nat.* 5: 97 and 149.

[11] **Watts, W.A.** 1959. Interglacial deposits at Kilbeg and Newtown, Co. Waterford. *Proc. R. Ir. Acad.* 60B: 79–134.

[12] **Pethybridge, G.H. & Praeger, R. Ll.** 1905. The vegetation of the district lying south of Dublin. *Proc. R. Ir. Acad.* 25B: 124–180.

[13] **White, J.** 1982. A history of Irish vegetation studies. *J. Life Sci. R. Dubl. Soc.* 3: 14–42.

[14] **Clark, S.C.** 1968. The structure of some *Ulex gallii* heaths in eastern Ireland. *Proc. R. Ir. Acad.* 66B: 43–51.

[15] **Winder, F.O.A.** 1995. Has Wicklow lost two of its few alpine plants? *Ir. Nat. J.* 25: 35–36.

[16] **Curtis, T.G.F. & McGough, H.N.** 1988. *The Irish Red Data Book: 1 Vascular Plants.* Stationery Office, Dublin.

[17] **Moore, J.J.** 1960. A re-survey of the vegetation of the district lying south of Dublin (1905–1956). *Proc. R. Ir. Acad.* 61B: 1–36.

[18] **Ratcliffe, D.A.** 1962. The habitat of *Adelanthus unciformis* (Tayl.) Mitt., and *Jamesoniella carringtonii* (Balf.) Spr. in Ireland. *Ir. Nat. J.* 14: 38–40.

[19] **Wade, W.** 1801. Catalogus plantarum rariorum in comitatu Gallovidiae, praecipue Cunnamara inventarum: or, A systematic account of the more rare plants, principally found in the County of Galway but more particularly in that part of it called Cunnamara. *Trans. Roy. Dub. Soc.* 2: 103–127.

[20] **Roden, C.** 1986. A survey of the flora of some mountain ranges in the west of Ireland. *Ir. Nat. J.* 22: 52–59.

[21] **Webb, D.A. & Scannell, M.J.P.** 1983. *Flora of Connemara and the Burren.* Royal Dublin Society, Dublin and Cambridge University Press, Cambridge.

[22] **Ratcliffe, D.A.** 1997. *Pers. comm.*

[23] **Curtis, T.G.F.** 1993. *Polygonum viviparum* L. in Ireland with particular reference to the flora and vegetation of the Mount Brandon Range, Co. Kerry. *Ir. Nat. J.* 24: 274–280.

[24] **Moore, J.J.** 1966. *Minuartia recurva* (All.)

Schinz & Thell. new to the British Isles. *Ir. Nat. J.* 15: 130–132.

[25] **Farrington, A.** 1936. The glaciation of the Bantry Bay district. *Sci. Proc. Roy. Dublin Soc.* 21: 345–361.

[26] **Farrington, A.** 1954. A note on the correlations of the Kerry–Cork glaciations with those of the rest of Ireland. *Irish Geog.* 3: 47–53.

[27] **Mitchell, F. & Ryan, M.** 1997. *Reading the Irish Landscape.* Town House, Dublin.

[28] **Lhwyd, E.** 1712. Some farther Observations relating to the Antiquities and Natural History of Ireland. In a letter from the late Mr Edw. Lhwyd, Keeper of the Ashmolean Museum in Oxford, to Dr Tancred Robinson, F.R.S. *Phil. Trans. Roy. Soc. Lond.* 27: 524–526.

[29] **Ostenfeld C. H. & Dahl, O.** 1917. De nordiske former av kollektivarten *Arenaria ciliata* L. *Nyt Magazin for Natureviden-skaberne.* 30: 215–225.

[30] **Bellamy, D. J.** 1986.*The Wild Boglands.* Country House, Dublin.

[31] **Hart, H.C.** 1898. *Flora of the County Donegal, or List of the Flowering Plants and Ferns with their Localities and Distribution.* Sealy, Bryers and Walker, Dublin.

[32] **Hart, H.C.** 1885. Report on the botany of the south-west Donegal. *Proc. R. Ir. Acad. (Science)* 4: 443–469.

[33] **Birks, H.J.B., Birks, H.H. & Ratcliffe, D.A.** 1969. Mountain plants on Slieve League, Co. Donegal. *Ir. Nat. J.* 16: 203.

[34] **Hackney, P. (comp. & ed.).** 1992. *Stewart & Corry's Flora of the North-east of Ireland.* 3rd edition. Institute of Irish Studies, Queen's University, Belfast.

[35] **Lockhart, N.D.** 1989. Three new localities for *Saxifraga hirculus* L. in Ireland. *Ir. Nat. J.* 23: 65–69.

[36] **Kertland, M.P.H.** 1958. The cloudberry, *Rubus chamaemorus* L., in County Tyrone. *Ir. Nat. J.* 12: 309–314.

[37] **Hart, H.C.** 1881. On the botany of the Galtee mountains, Co. Tipperary. *Proc. R. Ir. Acad. (Science)* 3: 392–402.

[38] **O'Gorman, F. & Mulloy, F.** 1973. The economical and recreational potential of deer in Ireland. In: **O'Gorman F. & Wymes, E. (eds.).** *The future of Irish Wildlife – a blueprint for development.* 55–63. Agricultural Institute, Dublin.

[39] **Delap, P.** 1936. Deer in Wicklow. *Ir. Nat. J.* 6: 82–88.

[40] **Clotworthy, R.G., Lang, R. & Lang, J.T.** 1976. Red deer, *Cervus elaphus*, in Wicklow. *Ir. Nat. J.* 18: 284–285.

[41] **Sherlock, M.G. & Fairley, J.S.** 1993. Seasonal changes in the diet of red deer *Cervus elaphus* in the Connemara National Park. *Biology and Environment: Proc. R. Ir. Acad.* 93B: 85–90.

[42] **Lever, C.** 1997. *The Naturalised Animals of the British Isles.* Hutchinson, London.

[43] **Bonham, F.R.H. & Fairley, J. S.** 1984. Observations on a herd of goats *Capra* (domestic) in the Burren. *Ir. Nat. J.* 21: 208–212.

[44] **Whitehead, G. K.** 1972. *The Wild Goats of Great Britain and Ireland.* David & Charles, Newton Abbot.

[45] **Whelan, J.** 1985. The population and distribution of the mountain hare (*Lepus timidus* L.) on farmland. *Ir. Nat. J.* 21: 532–534.

[46] **Bullock, I.D., Drewett, D. R. & Mickleburgh, S.P.** 1983. The Chough in Ireland. *Irish Birds* 2: 257–271.

[47] **Ratcliffe, D.** 1998. *Pers. comm.*

[48] **Ussher, R.J. & Warren, R.** 1900. *The Birds of Ireland.* Gurney and Jackson, London.

[49] **Whilde, T.** 1994. *The Natural History of Connemara.* Immel Publishing, London.

[50] **Temple Lang, J.** 1970. Peregrine Survey – Fourth Year. Irish Wildbird Conservancy, Dublin. Unpublished report.

[51] **Norriss, D., Wilson, H.J. & Browne, D.** 1982. The breeding population of the Peregrine Falcon in Ireland in 1981. *Irish Birds* 2: 145–152.

[52] **Moore, N., Kelly, P. & Lang, F.** 1992. Quarry-nesting by Peregrine Falcons in Ireland. *Irish Birds* 4: 519–524.

[53] **Noonan, G.** 1989. Quoted in: **Hutchinson, C.D.** *Birds in Ireland.* p. 92. T & A D Poyser, Calton.

[54] **McGrath, D.** 1987. The Peregrine Falcon in south-east Ireland. 1981–1986. *Irish Birds* 3: 377–386.

[55] **Gibbons, D.W., Reid, J.B. & Chapman, R.A.** 1993. *The New Atlas of Breeding Birds in Britain and Ireland 1988–1991.* T & A D Poyser and the British Trust for Ornithology, London.

[56] **Ratcliffe, D.A.** 1997. *The Raven.* T & A D Poyser, London.

[57] **Forbes, T.O. A. & Lance, A. N.** 1976. The contents of fox scats from western blanket bogs. Notes from the Mammal Society – No 32. *J. Zool. Lond.* 179: 224–226.

[58] **Watson, D.** 1977. *The Hen Harrier.* T & A D Poyser, Calton.

[59] **O'Flynn, W.J.** 1983. Population changes of the hen harrier in Ireland. *Irish Birds* 2: 337–343.

[60] **Coveney, J., Merne, O., Wilson, J., Allen, D. & Thomas, G.** 1993. *A Conservation Strategy for Birds in Ireland.* Irish Wildbird Conservancy, Dublin.

[61] **Batten, L.A., Bibby, C.J., Clement, P., Elliott, G. D. & Porter, R.F.** 1900. *Red Data Birds in Britain.* T & A D Poyser, London.

[62] **Norris, D.W.** 1991. The status of the buzzard as a breeding species in the Republic of Ireland, 1977–91. *Irish Birds* 4: 291–298.

[63] **Hutchinson, C.D.** 1989. *Op. cit.*

[64] **Baynes, E.S.A.** 1964. *A Revised Catalogue of Irish Macrolepidoptera (Butterflies and Moths).* E.W. Classey, Middlesex.

[65] **Hicken, N.** 1992. *The Butterflies of Ireland: a field guide.* Roberts Rinehart, Cork.

[66] **O'Connor, J.** 1997. *Pers. comm.*

[67] **Walton, G.A.** 1967. A site of particular zoological interest – Doughruagh Mountain, Kylemore, Co. Galway. *Ir. Nat. J.* 15: 309–312.

[68] **McCarthy, T.K.** 1975. Some records of the glacial relict water boatman *Glaenocorisa propinqua* (Fieber) (Hemiptera, Corixidae) in Ireland. *Entomologist's Gaz.* 26: 65–66.

[69] **O'Connor, J. P.** 1978. The stonefly *Capnia atra* Morton (Plectoptera, Capniidae) confirmed as an Irish species. *Entomologist's Gaz.* 29: 156–158.

[70] **O'Connor, J.P. & Good, J.A.** 1984. *Tinodes dives* (Pictet): A caddisfly new to Ireland from Ben Bulben. *Entomologist's Record* 96: 108–109.

CHAPTER 4

[1] **Taylor, J.A.** 1983. The Peatlands of Great Britain and Ireland. In: **Gore, A.J.P. (ed.).** *Ecosystems of the World. Vol. 4B: Mires: Swamp, Bog, Fen & Moor.* 1–46. Elsevier Scientific Publishing Company, Oxford.

[2] **Boate, G.** 1652. *Irelands Naturall History, Being a true description of its situation, greatness, shape and nature.* Samuel Hartlib, London.

[3] **King, W.** 1685. Of the bogs and loughs of Ireland. *Phil. Trans. Roy. Soc Lond.* 15: 948–960.

[4] **Heaney, S.** 1984. 'Feeling into words'. In: *Preoccupations: Selected Prose 1968–1978.* Faber and Faber, London.

[5] **Walsh, T. & Barry, T.A.** 1958. The chemical composition of some Irish peats. *Proc. R. Ir. Acad.* 59B: 305–328.

[6] **Foss, P.J. & O'Connell, C.A.** 1996. *Irish Peatland Conservation Plan 2000.* Irish Peatland Conservation Council, Dublin.

[7] **British Government** 1810–1814. *Reports of the Commissioners appointed to enquire into the nature and extent of the several bogs in Ireland; and the practicability of draining and cultivating them.* Volumes I–IV. House of Commons, London.

[8] **White, J.** 1982. A history of Irish vegetation studies. *J. Life Sci. R. Dubl. Soc.* 3: 15–42.

[9] **Hammond, R.F.** 1979. The Peatlands of Ireland. *Soil Survey Bulletin No. 35,* An Foras Talúntais, Dublin.

[10] **Anon.** 1921. *Commission of Enquiry into the Industries and Resources of Ireland: Report on Peat.* Government Publications, Dublin.

[11] **Jessen, K.** 1949. Studies in late Quaternary deposits and flora-history of Ireland. *Proc. R. Ir. Acad.* 52B: 85–290.

[12] **Smith A.** 1997. Quoted in **Mitchell, F. & Ryan, M.** 1997. *Reading the Irish Landscape.* p. 146. Town House, Dublin.

[13] **Feehan, J. & O'Donovan, G.** 1996. *The Bogs of Ireland.* The Environmental Institute, University College, Dublin.

[14] **Osvald, H.** 1923. Die vegetation des hochmoores komosse. *Svensk. Vaxtsoc. Sallsk. Handl.* 1.

[15] **Casparie, W.A.** 1969. Bult-und schlenkenbildung in hochmoor-torf. *Vegetatio* XIX, fasc. 1–6, 146–180.

[16] **Speight, M.C.D.** 1985.The extinction of indigenous *Pinus sylvestris* in Ireland: relevant faunal data. *Ir. Nat. J.* 21: 449–453.

[17] **Schouten, M.G.C.** 1981. *Some Notes on the Preservation of Irish Ombrotropic Bogs.* Catholic University, Nijmegen.

[18] **Moore, J.J.** 1955. The distribution and ecology of *Scheuchzeria palustris* on a raised bog in Offaly. *Ir. Nat. J.* 11: 321–329.

[19] **Curtis, T.G.F. & McGough, H.N.** 1988. *The Irish Red Data Book: 1 Vascular Plants.* Stationery Office, Dublin.

[20] **Morrison, M.E.S.** 1959. The ecology of a raised bog in Tyrone, Northern Ireland. *Proc. R. Ir. Acad.* 60B: 291–308.

[21] **Praeger, R. Ll.** 1937. *The Way that I Went.* Hodges, Figgis & Co., Dublin and Methuen & Co., London.

[22] **Praeger, R. Ll. & Sollas, W.J.** 1897. Report of the Committee.......to investigate the recent Bog-flow in Kerry. *Proc. Roy. Dublin Soc.* New Series 8: 475–508.

[23] **Kertland, M.P.H.** 1968. *Sarracenia purpurea* as an introduced plant in Ireland. *Ir. Nat. J.* 16: 50–51.

[24] **Nelson, E.C. & de Vesci, S.** 1981. *Sarracenia purpurea* L. naturalised in County Laois (H14). *Ir. Nat. J.* 20: 253.

[25] **Foss, P.J. & O'Connell, C.A.** 1985. Notes on the ecology of *Sarracenia purpurea* on

Irish peatlands. *Ir. Nat. J.* 21: 440–443.

[26] Mitchell, F. & Ryan, M. 1997. *Reading the Irish Landscape*. Town House, Dublin.

[27] Mitchell, F.J.G. & Conboy, P. 1993. Early blanket bog development in the Wicklow mountains. *Ir. Nat. J.* 24: 229.

[28] Ratcliffe, D. A. 1997. *Pers. comm.*

[29] Gorham, E. 1953. A note on the acidity and base status of raised and blanket bogs. *J. Ecol.* 41: 153–156.

[30] Boatman, D.J. 1972. The growth of *Schoenus nigricans* on blanket bog peats. II Growth on Irish and Scottish peats. *J. Ecol.* 60: 469–477.

[31] Doyle, G.J. 1982. The vegetation, ecology and productivity of Atlantic blanket bog in Mayo and Galway, Western Ireland. *Journ. Life Sci. Roy. Dubln Soc.* 3: 147–164.

[32] Doyle, G.J., O'Connell, C.A. & Foss, P. J. 1987. The vegetation of peat islands in bog lakes in County Mayo, western Ireland. *Glasra* 10: 23–35.

[33] Scannell, M.J.P. 1997. *Pers. comm.*

[34] Whilde, T. 1994. *The Natural History of Connemara*. Immel Publishing, London.

[35] Warner, S. T. 1967. *T.H.White: a biography*. Jonathan Cape with Chatto & Windus, London.

[36] White, T.H. 1959. *The Godstone and the Blackymore*. Jonathan Cape, London.

[37] Maxwell, W.H. 1832. *Wild Sports of the West*. Richard Bentley, London.

[38] Scannell, M.J.P. 1958. *Saxifraga hirculus* in Co. Mayo. *Ir. Nat. J.* 12: 248.

[39] Lockhart, N.D. 1989. Three new localities for *Saxifraga hirculus* L. in Ireland. *Ir. Nat. J.* 23: 65–69.

[40] King, A.L.K. 1958. *Camptothecium nitens* (Hedw.) Schp. in Ireland. *Ir. Nat. J.* 12: 247–247.

[41] King, A.L.K. 1958. *Meesia tristicha* Bruch & Schimp. in Ireland. *Ir. Nat. J.* 12: 332.

[42] King, A.L.K & Scannell, M.J.P. 1960. Notes on the vegetation of a mineral flush in Co. Mayo. *Ir. Nat. J.* 13: 137–140.

[43] Synnott, D.M. 1970. *Thelypteris palustris* and *Malaxis paludosa* in N-W Mayo. *Ir. Nat. J.* 16: 282.

[44] Duff, M. 1930. The ecology of the Moss Lane region, Lough Neagh. *Proc. R. Ir. Acad.* 39B: 477–496.

[45] White, J.M. 1932. The fens of north Armagh. *Proc. R. Ir. Acad.* 40B: 233–383.

[46] Tansley, A. G. 1965. *The British Islands and their Vegetation*. 4th Impression. Cambridge University Press, Cambridge.

[47] Praeger, R. Ll. 1934. *The Botanist in Ireland*. Hodges, Figgis & Co., Dublin.

[48] O'Connor, J.P., Liston, A.D. & Speight, M.C.D. 1997. A review of the Irish sawflies (Hymenoptera: Symphyta) including a checklist of species. *Bull. Ir. biogeog. Soc.* 20: 2–29.

[49] Cramp, S. & Simmons, K.E.L. (eds.) 1979. *The Birds of the Western Palearctic*, Vol. 2. Oxford University Press, Oxford.

[50] Witherby, H.F., Jourdain, F.C.R., Ticehurst, N.F. & Tucker, B.W. 1945. *The Handbook of British Birds*. Vol 5. H. F. & G. Witherby, London.

[51] Gibbons, D. W., Reid, J. B. & Chapman, R. A .1993. *The New Atlas of Breeding Birds in Britain and Ireland: 1988–1991*. T & A D Poyser and the British Trust for Ornithology, London.

[52] Coveney, J., Merne, O., Wilson, J., Allen, D. & Thomas, G. 1993. *A Conservation Strategy for Birds in Ireland*. Irish Wildbird Conservancy, Dublin.

[53] Watson, A. & O'Hare, P.J. 1979. Red Grouse populations on experimentally treated and untreated Irish bog. *J. Appl. Ecol.* 16: 433–452.

[54] Forbes, T.O.A. & Lance, A.N. 1976. The contents of fox scats from western Irish blanket bogs. *J. Zool. Lond.* 179: 224–226.

[55] Whilde, A. 1993. *Threatened Mammals, Birds, Amphibians and Fish in Ireland. Irish Red Data Book 2: Vertebrates*. HSMO, Belfast.

[56] Lack, D. 1935. The breeding bird populations of British heaths and moorlands. *J. Anim. Ecol.* 4: 43–51.

[57] Madden, B. 1987. The birds of Mongan Bog, Co. Offaly. *Irish Birds* 3: 441–448.

[58] Watson, A. & O'Hare, P.J. 1979. Bird and mammal numbers on untreated and experimentally treated Irish bog. *Oikos* 33: 97–105.

[59] Mayes, E. 1985. The diet of the Greenland white-fronted Goose in Ireland. Internal Report to the Wildlife Service, Dublin.

[60] Ussher, R.J. & Warren, R. 1900. *The Birds of Ireland*. Gurney and Jackson, London.

[61] Hutchinson, C.D. 1989. *Birds in Ireland*. T & A D Poyser, Calton.

[62] Walker, J. & Fairley, J.S. 1968. Food of Irish hares in Co. Antrim, Ireland. *J. Mammal* 49: 783–785.

[63] Smiddy, P. 1994. Hare species in Co. Cork. *Ir. Nat. J.* 24: 417–418.

[64] Lance, A.N. 1971. Numbers of woodmice *Apodemus sylvaticus* on improved and unimproved blanket bog. *J. Zool. Lond.* 171: 471–473.

[65] Fairley, J.S. 1984. Otters feeding on

breeding frogs. *Ir. Nat. J.* 21: 372.

[66] **Smal, C.** 1995. *The Badger and Habitat Survey of Ireland.* Stationery Office, Dublin.

[67] **Speight, M & Madden, B.** 1987. Insects of peatlands. In: **O'Connell, C. (ed.)** *The IPCC Guide to Irish Peatlands.* IPCC, Dublin.

[68] **Bond, K.G.M.** 1989. Clonmacnoise heritage zone, Co. Offaly, Ireland. Assessment of conservation value based on lepidoptera recorded from 1983 to 1987. *Bull. Ir. biogeog. Soc.* 12: 63–89.

[69] **Good, J.A.** 1985. Invertebrates of Irish Midland raised bogs: part IV. Notes on terrestrial insects. *Bull. Ir. biogeog. Soc.* 9: 2–9.

[70] **Higgins, D.G.** 1984. Invertebrates of Irish Midland raised bogs: part I Araneae, Opiliones, Chilopda. *Bull. Ir. biogeog. Soc.* 8: 91–93.

[71] **Bond, K.G.M.** 1991. A preliminary survey of the Lepidoptera of Pollardstown fen, Co. Kildare, including a record of *Cosmopterix lienigiella* (Lienig and Zeller, 1839) (Cosmopterigidae), a species new to Ireland. *Bull. Ir. biogeog. Soc.* 14: 24–47.

[72] **Speight, M.C.D. & Vockeroth, J.R.** 1988. *Platycheirus amplus:* an insect new to Ireland not previously recorded from Europe (Diptera: Syrphidae). *Ir. Nat. J.* 22: 518–521.

[73] **van Helsdingen, P.J.** 1997. The spiders (Araneida) of Pollardstown fen, Co. Kildare, Ireland. *Ir. Nat. J.* 25: 396–404.

[74] **Buchanan, K.** 1978. Dragonflies at Brackagh Bog, Co. Armagh. *Ir. Nat. J.* 19: 287.

[75] **Anon.** 1971. I.B.P. Secondary production working party; Leningrad, February 1971: an account of the Irish contribution. 12 p.

[76] **Withers, P. & O'Connor, J.P.** 1992. A preliminary account of some Irish species of moth fly (Diptera: Psychodidae). *Proc. R. Ir. Acad.* 92B: 61–77.

[77] **Bilton, D.T.** 1988. A survey of aquatic Coleoptera in central Ireland and the Burren. *Bull. Ir. biogeog. Soc.* 11: 77–94.

CHAPTER 5

[1] **Went, A.E.J.** 1947. Notes on Irish pearls. *Ir. Nat. J.* 9: 41–45.

[2] **Charlesworth, J.K.** 1963. The bathymetry and origin of the larger lakes of Ireland. *Proc. R. Ir. Acad.* 63B: 61–69.

[3] **Kennedy, M. & Fitzmaurice, P.** 1971. Growth and food of brown trout *Salmo trutta* (L.) in Irish waters. *Proc. R. Ir. Acad.* 71B: 269–352.

[4] **Stewart, N.F. & Church, J.M.** 1992. *Red Data Books of Britain and Ireland: Stoneworts.* The Joint Nature Conservation Committee, Peterborough.

[5] **Dooge, J.C.I.** 1991. The flow of Irish rivers. In: **Steer, M.W. (ed.).** *Irish Rivers: Biology and Management.* 5–26. Royal Irish Academy, Dublin.

[6] **Joyce, P.W.** 1869. *The Origin and History of Irish Names of Places.* Facsimile reprint 1995. Edmund Burke, Dublin.

[7] **Cambrensis, Giraldus** [Gerald of Wales]. *The History and Topography of Ireland [Topographia Hiberniae].* Here translated from the Latin by John J. O'Meara with a Map and Drawings from a Contemporary Copy *c.* 1200 AD. (Revised edition 1982). Dolmen Press, Portlaoise.

[8] **Whittow, J.B.** 1974. *Geology and Scenery of Ireland.* Penguin Books, Middlesex.

[9] **Jessen, K.** 1936. Palaeobotanical report on the stone age site at Newferry, Co. Londonderry. In: **Movius, H.L.** A Neolithic site on the River Bann. *Proc. R. Ir. Acad.* 44C: 31–37.

[10] **Harris, W. & Smith, C.** 1744. *The Ancient and Present State of The County of Down ... with the Natural and Civic History of the Same.* A. Reilly, Dublin.

[11] **Barton, R.** 1751. *Lectures in Natural Philosophy...* George and Alexander Ewing, Dublin.

[12] **Harron, J. with the assistance of Rushton, B.S.** 1986. *Flora of Lough Neagh.* Irish Naturalists' Journal Committee, Belfast, and the University of Ulster, Coleraine.

[13] **Praeger, R. Ll.** 1934. *The Botanist in Ireland.* Hodges, Figgis & Co., Dublin

[14] **Curtis, T.G.F. & McGough, H.N.** 1988. *The Irish Red Data Book: 1 Vascular Plants.* Stationery Office, Dublin.

[15] **Mitchell, F. & Ryan, M.** 1997. *Reading the Irish Landscape.* Town House, Dublin.

[16] **Charlesworth, G.K.** 1939. Some observations on the glaciation of north-east Ireland, *Proc. R. Ir. Acad.* 45B: 255–295.

[17] **Thompson, W.** 1849–56. *The Natural History of Ireland.* 4 vols. Vols 1–3 Reeve and Bentham, vol. 4 Henry G. Bohn, London.

[18] **Wilson, J.P.F.** 1984. A review of the biology of the pollan *Coregonus autumnalis pollan* Thompson – an endemic Irish salmonid subspecies. *Proc. R. Ir. Acad.* 84B: 111–127.

[19] **Twomey, E.** 1956. Pollan of Lough Erne. *Ir. Nat. J.* 12: 14–17.

[20] **Beirne, B.P.** 1944. The origin of the maritime Lepidoptera of Lough Neagh. *Ir. Nat. J.* 8: 167–171.

[21] **Moriarty, C.** 1978. *Eels – A Natural and Unnatural History.* David and Charles, Newton Abbot.

[22] **Maitland, P.S. & Campbell, R.N.** 1992. *The New Naturalist: Freshwater Fishes of the British Isles.* HarperCollins, London.

[23] **Heaney, S.** 1972. 'A Lough Neagh Sequence'. In: *Door into the Dark.* Faber and Faber, London.

[24] **Crozier, W.W.** 1985. Observations on the food of two sympatric populations of brown trout (*Salmo trutta*) in Lough Neagh, Northern Ireland. *Proc. R. Ir. Acad.* 85B: 57–71.

[25] **Carter, C.E.** 1976. A population study of the Chironomidae (Diptera) of Lough Neagh. *Oikos* 27: 346–354.

[26] **Kennedy, M. & Fitzmaurice, P.** 1971. *Op. cit.*

[27] **Wilson, J.P.F.** 1984. The food of the pollan *Coregonus autumnalis pollan* Thompson of Lough Neagh, Northern Ireland. *J. Fish. Biol.* 24: 253–261.

[28] **Holmes, J.M.C.** 1978 *Gammarus duebeni* (Crustacea: Amphipoda) in Ireland. *Bull. Ir. biogeog. Soc.* 2: 45–48.

[29] **Dick, J.T.A.** 1996. Post-invasion amphipod communities of Lough Neagh, Northern Ireland: influences of habitat selection and mutual predation. *J. Anim. Ecol.* 65: 756–767.

[30] **O'Grady, M.F. & Holmes. J.M.C.** 1983. A new Irish location for *Gammarus tigrinus* Sexton. *Ir. Nat. J.* 21: 44.

[31] **Holmes, J.M.C.** 1975. *Crangonyx psudogracilis* Bousfield, a freshwater amphipod new to Ireland *Ir. Nat. J.* 18: 225–226.

[32] **Lynch, J.M.** 1994. Two new lotic locations for *Crangonyx pseudogracilis* Bousfield, 1958 (Crustacea: Amphipoda). *Ir. Nat. J.* 24: 462–463.

[33] **Strange, C.D. & Glass, G.B.** 1979. The distribution of freshwater gammarids in Northern Ireland. *Proc. R. Ir. Acad.* 79B: 145–153.

[34] **Cranswick, P.A., Walker, R.J., Evans, J. & Pollit, M.S.** 1995. *The Wetland Bird Survey 1993–94: Wildfowl and wader counts.* BTO/WWT/RSPB/JNCC.

[35] **Perry, K.** 1997. *Pers. comm.*

[36] **Mooney, E.P. & O'Connell, M.** 1990. The phytosociology and ecology of the aquatic and wetland plant communities of the lower Corrib basin, County Galway. *Proc. R. Ir. Acad.* 90B: 57–97.

[37] **Delany, S.** 1997. *I-WeBS Report 1995–96.* BirdWatch Ireland, Dublin.

[38] **Cabot, D.** 1967. Personal observations.

[39] **Cabot, D.** 1964. Personal observations.

[40] **Whilde, A.** 1993. Some aspects of the ecology of common gulls. *Irish Birds* 2: 466–481.

[41] **Whilde, A., Cotton, D.C.F. & Sheppard, J.R.** 1993. A repeat survey of gulls breeding inland in Counties Donegal, Sligo, Mayo and Galway, with recent counts from Leitrim and Fermanagh. *Irish Birds* 5: 67–72.

[42] **Harris, J.R.** 1952. *The New Naturalist: An Angler's Entomology.* Collins, London.

[43] **Walton, G.A.** 1936. A new species of Corixidae, *Sigara pearcei* (Hemipt.) from Ireland; together with descriptions of its closely related species. *Trans Soc. Brit. Ent.* 3: 33–47.

[44] **O'Connor, J.P. & Norton, M.A.** 1977. Athlone field meeting: preliminary notes on the aquatic invertebrate fauna of Hare Island and environs. *Bull. Ir. biogeog. Soc.* 1: 20–25.

[45] **O'Connor, J.P. & Wise, E.J.** 1980. The larva of *Tinodes maculicornis* (Trichoptera: Psychomyiidae), with notes on the species' distribution and habitat in Ireland. *Freshwater Biology* 10: 367– 370.

[46] **O'Connor, J.P. & Wise, E.J.** 1984. Observations on the Trichoptera of the Killarney Lakes, Co. Kerry. *Irish Fish. Invest. Ser. A.* 24: 1–15.

[47] **Humphreys, G.R.** 1978. Ireland's former premier breeding haunt of aquatic birds. *Irish Birds* 1: 171-181.

[48] **Cotton, D.C.F. & Hillis, J.P.** 1989. Black-necked grebes breeding in Ireland. *Irish Birds* 4: 72.

[49] **Batten, L. A., Bibby, C.J., Clement, P., Elliott, G. D. & Porter, R. F. (eds.).** 1990. *Red Data Birds in Britain.* T & A D Poyser, London.

[50] **Anon.** 1998. *Wings* 9: 13.

[51] **Whilde, A.** 1993. *Threatened Mammals, Birds, Amphibians and Fish in Ireland. Irish Red Data Book 2: Vertebrates.* HMSO, Belfast.

[52] **Partridge, J. K.** 1989. Lower Lough Erne's common scoters. *RSPB Conservation Review* 3: 25-28.

[53] **Gittins S. & Delany, S.** 1995. A pre-breeding census of Common Scoters in Ireland in 1995. *Irish Birds* 5: 413-422.

[54] **Hutchinson, C.D.** 1989. *Birds in Ireland.* T & A D Poyser, Calton.

[55] **Hannon, C., Berrow, S.D. & Newton, S.F.** 1998. The status and distribution of breeding Sandwich *Sterna sandvicensis*, Roseate *S. dougallii*, Common *S. hirundo*, Arctic *S. paradisaea* and Little Terns *S. alb-*

ifrons in Ireland in 1995. *Irish Birds* 6: 1-22.

[56] **Fitzmaurice, P.** 1997. *Pers.comm.*

[57] **Maitland, P. S.** 1996. Threatened fishes of the British Isles, with special reference to Ireland. In: **Reynolds, J.D. (ed.).** *The Conservation of Aquatic Systems.* 84–100. Royal Irish Academy, Dublin.

[58] **Fahy, E.** 1982. A commercial net fishery taking twaite shad *Alosa fallax* (Lacepede) in the estuary of the river Slaney. *Ir. Nat. J.* 20: 498–500.

[59] **Fitzmaurice, P.** 1997. *Pers.comm.*

[60] **Quigley, D.T.G. & Flannery, K.** 1997. Arctic charr *Salvelinus alpinus* L.: first record from Lough Anscaul, Co. Kerry; further records from Loughs Bunaveela, Kindrum and Coomasaharn; and notice of an introduction to Lough Owel, Co. Westmeath. *Ir. Nat. J.* 25: 435–439.

[61] **Quigley, D.T.G.** 1996. First record of smelt *Osmerus eperlanus* L. from the river Suir, together with a review of Irish records. *Bull. Ir. biogeog. Soc.* 19: 189–194.

[62] **Went, A.E.J.** 1978. The zoogeography of some fishes in Irish waters. *Fishery Leaflet* 93. Department of Fisheries, Dublin.

[63] **Kennedy, M.** 1993. In: **Whilde, A.** *Threatened Mammals, Birds, Amphibians and Fish in Ireland. Irish Red data Book 2: Vertebrates.* HMSO, Belfast.

[64] **Kurz, I. & Costello, M.J.** 1996. Current knowledge on the distribution of lampreys, and some other freshwater fish species listed in the Habitats Directive, in Ireland. Unpublished report commissioned by the National Parks and Wildlife Service, Dublin.

[65] **Lucey, J & McGarrigle, M.L.** 1987. The distribution of the crayfish *Austropotamobius pallipes* (Lereboullet) in Ireland. *Ir. Fish. Invest.* Series A 29: 3–13.

[66] **Reynolds, J.D.** 1982. Notes on the Irish distribution of the freshwater crayfish. *Bull. Ir. biogeog. Soc.* 6: 18–24.

[67] **Moriarty, C.** 1973. A study of *Austropotamobius pallipes* in Ireland. *Freshwater Crayfish* 1: 57–67.

[68] **Matthews, M.A. & Reynolds, J.D.** 1995. A population study of the white-clawed crayfish *Austropotamobius pallipes* (Lereboullet) in an Irish reservoir. *Biology and Environment: Proc. R. Ir. Acad.* 95B: 99–109.

[69] **McFadden, Y.M.T. & Fairley, J.S.** 1984. The food of otters *Lutra lutra* (L) in an Irish limestone river system with special reference to the crayfish *Austropotamobius pallipes* (Lereboullet). *J. Life Sci. R. Dubl. Soc.* 5: 65–74.

[70] **Matthews, M & Reynolds, J.D.** 1990. Laboratory investigations of the pathology of *Aphanomyces astacis* for Irish freshwater crayfish. *Hydrobiologia* 203: 121–126.

[71] **O'Connor, J.P.** 1997. *Pers. comm.*

[72] **Anon.** (nd). *Cal. pat. rolls Chas. I.* p.620.

[73] **Redding, R.** 1693. A letter from Sir Robert Redding, late fellow of the R.S. concerning pearl-fishing in the North of Ireland; communicated to the Publisher by Dr. Lister. R.S.S. *Phil. Trans. R. Soc.* 17: 659–664.

[74] **Government Publications Office.** 1990. Statutory Instrument No. 112 of 1990.

[75] **Fitter, R. & Manuel, R.** 1986. *Collins Field Guide to Freshwater Life of Britain and North-West Europe.* Collins, London.

[76] **Moorkens, E.A., Costello, M.J. & Speight, M. C.D.** 1992. Status of the freshwater pearl mussels *Margaritifera margaritifera* and *M. m. durrovensis* in the Nore, Barrow and Suir river tributaries, South-east Ireland. *Ir. Nat. J.* 24: 127–131.

[77] **Lucey, J.** 1995. The distribution of *Anodonta cygnea* (L.) and *Anodonta anatina* (L.) (Mollusca: Bivalva) in south Irish rivers and streams with records from other areas. *Ir. Nat. J.* 25:1–8.

[78] **Piers, H.** 1682. *A Chorographical Description of the County of West-Meath.* Published for Charles Vallencey in 1786 by Luke White, Dublin.

[79] **Lucey, J.** 1995. The distribution of *Margaritifera margaritifera* (L.) in southern Irish rivers and streams. *J. Conch. Lond.* 34: 301–310.

[80] **Ross, H.C.G.** 1992. The reproductive biology of the freshwater pearl mussel *Margaritifera margaritifera* (L.) in Co. Donegal. *Ir. Nat. J.* 24: 43–50.

[81] **Houghton, W.** 1864. The swan mussel and its anatomy. *Intellectual Observer* 6: 67–75.

[82] **Went, A.E.J.** 1964. The pursuit of salmon in Ireland. *Proc. R. Ir. Acad.* 63C: 191–244.

[83] **Carruthers, T.D.** 1986. Waterways bird survey on the River Flesk, Co. Kerry. *Irish Birds* 3: 229–236.

[84] **Perry, K. W.** 1986. *The Irish Dipper.* Published for the author, Derry.

[85] **Ormerod, S.J., Allinson, N., Hudson, D. & Tyler, S.J.** 1986. Factors influencing the abundance of breeding dippers (*Cinclus cinclus*) in the catchment of River Wye, mid-Wales. *Ibis* 127: 332–340.

[86] **Perry, K.W. & Agnew, P.** 1993. Breeding dipper populations in north-west Ireland, 1972–1992. *Irish Birds* 5: 45–48.

[87] **Coveney, J., Merne, O., Wilson, J., Allen, D. & Thomas, G.** 1993. *A Conservation*

Strategy for Birds in Ireland. Irish Wildbird Conservancy, Dublin.

88 **Agnew, P. & Perry, K.W.** 1993. The diet of breeding dippers in north-west Ireland during the period of incubation. *Irish Birds* 5: 49–54.

89 **Ormerod, S.J. & Perry, K.W.** 1985. The diet and breeding of dippers and their nestlings in north-west Ireland. *Irish Birds* 3: 90–95.

90 **Ruttledge, R.F.** 1968. The kingfisher population. *Irish Bird Report* 15: 11–14.

91 **Chapman, P.J. & Chapman, L.L.** 1982. *Otter Survey of Ireland, 1980–81.* Vincent Wildlife Trust, London.

92 **King, C. M.** 1977. Otter. In: **Corbet, G.B. & Southern, H.N**. *The Handbook of British Mammals*. 367–375. 2nd edition. Blackwells, Oxford.

93 **Ogilby, W.** 1834. Notice of a new species of the otter from the north of Ireland. *Proc. zool. Soc. Lond.* (1834) 110–111.

94 **Dadd, M.N.** 1970. Overlap of variation in British and European mammal populations. *Symp. Zool. Soc. Lond.* 26: 117–125.

95 **Erling, S.** 1967. The home range of the otter *Lutra lutra* L. in Southern Sweden. *Oikos* 18: 186–209.

96 **O'Sullivan, W.M.** 1994. Summer diet of otters on part of the river Blackwater catchment. *Ir. Nat. J.* 24: 349–354.

97 **Fairley, J.S.** 1982. The muskrat in Ireland. *Ir. Nat. J.* 20: 405–411.

98 **Deane, C.D. & O'Gorman, F.** 1969. The spread of feral mink in Ireland. *Ir. Nat. J.* 16: 198–202.

99 **Fairley, J.S.** 1980. Observations on a collection of feral Irish mink *Mustella vison* Schreber. *Proc. R. Ir. Acad.* 80B: 79–90.

100 **Ward, D.P., Smal, C.M. & Fairley, J.S.** 1986. The food of mink *Mustela vison* in the Irish Midlands. *Proc. R. Ir. Acad.* 86B: 169–182.

101 **Kyne, M.J., Smal, C.M. & Fairley, J.S.** 1989. The food of otters *Lutra lutra* in the Irish Midlands and a comparison with that of mink *Mustela vison* in the same region. *Proc. R. Ir. Acad.* 89B: 33–46.

CHAPTER 6

1 **Firth, C.H. (ed.).** 1894. *The Memoirs of Edmund Ludlow*. 2 vols. Clarendon Press, Oxford.

2 **Foot, F.J.** 1864. On the distribution of plants in Burren, County Clare. *Trans. R. Ir. Acad.* 24 (Science): 143–160.

3 **O'Connor, J.P. & O'Connor, M.A.** 1982. *Tinodes unicolor* (Pictet) and *Metalype frag-*

ilis (Picet) (Trichoptera: Psychomyidae) discovered in the Burren, Co. Clare. *Entomologist's Gaz.* 33: 192–194.

4 **Corbel, J.** 1959. Erosion en terrain calcaire – Vitesse d'erosion et morphologie. *Annales de Geogr.* 1959: 97–120.

5 **Williams, P.W.** 1963. An initial estimate of the speed of limestone solution in County Clare. *Irish Geography* 4: 432–441.

6 **Farrington, A**. 1965. The last glaciation in the Burren, Co. Clare. *Proc. R. Ir. Acad.* 64B: 33–39.

7 **Tratman, E.T (ed.).** 1969. *The Caves of North-West Clare*. David and Charles, Newton Abbott.

8 **Chapman, P.** 1993. *The New Naturalist: Caves and Cave Life*. HarperCollins, London.

9 **Finch, T.F.** 1966. Slieve Elva, Co. Clare – a nunatak? *Ir. Nat J.* 15: 133–136.

10 **Watts, W.A.** 1983. The vegetation since the last glaciation. In: **Webb, D.A. & Scannell, M.J.P.** *Flora of Connemara and the Burren*. xxxvi–xl. Royal Dublin Society, Dublin and Cambridge University Press, Cambridge.

11 **Scharff, R.F., Ussher, R.J., Cole, G.A.J., Newton, E.T., Dixon, A.F. & Westropp, T.J.** 1906. The exploration of the caves of County Clare. *Trans. R. Ir. Acad.* 33B: 1–76.

12 **Wade, W.** 1804. Plantae Rariorcs in Hibernia inventae. *Transactions of the Dublin Society*. 4: 1–214.

13 **O'Mahony, T.** 1860. Notes of a botanical excursion in Clare. *Proceeding of the Dublin Natural History Society* 1: 30–34.

14 **Corry, T. H.** 1880. Notes on a botanical ramble in the County of Clare, Ireland, in 1879. *Proc. Belfast. Nat. Hist. Phil. Soc.,* 1879–80: 167–194.

15 **Ivimey-Cook, R.B. & Proctor, M.C.F.** 1966. The plant communities of the Burren, Co. Clare. *Proc. R. Ir. Acad.* 64B: 211–301.

16 **Lousley, J.E.** 1950. *The New Naturalist: Wildflowers of Chalk and Limestone*. Collins, London.

17 **Webb, D.A.** 1962. Noteworthy plants of the Burren: a catalogue raisonné. *Proc. R. Ir. Acad.* 62B: 117–34.

18 **Keane, M.** 1986. *The Burren, County Clare*. Irish Heritage Series: 30. Eason, Dublin.

19 **O'Connell, J.W. & Korff, A. (eds.).** 1991. *The Book of the Burren*. Tír Eolas, Kinvarra.

20 **D'Arcy, G. & Hayward, J.** 1992. *The Natural History of the Burren*. Immel Publishing, London.

21 **Nelson, C.E. & Walsh, W.** 1991. *The*

Burren: A Companion to the Wildflowers of an Irish Limestone Wilderness. Boethius Press, Aberystwyth & Kilkenny and the Conservancy of the Burren.

22 **Webb, D.A. & Scannell, M.J.P**. 1983. *Flora of Connemara and the Burren.* Royal Dublin Society, Dublin, and Cambridge University Press, Cambridge.

23 **O'Neill Hencken, H.** 1938. *Cahercommaun: a stone fort in County Clare.* Royal Society of Antiquities of Ireland, Dublin.

24 **Praeger, R. Ll.** 1934. *The Botanist in Ireland.* Hodges, Figgis & Co., Dublin.

25 **Webb, D.A. & Gornall, R.J.** 1989. *Saxifrages of Europe.* Christopher Helm, London.

26 **Johnson, G.W.** 1864. *The British Ferns Popularly Described.* 4th edition. London.

27 **Dickinson, C.H., Pearson, M.C. & Webb, D.A.** 1964. Some micro-habitats of the Burren, their micro-environments and vegetation. *Proc. R. Ir. Acad.* 63B: 291–302.

28 **Ratcliffe, D.A.** 1998. *Pers. comm* .

29 **Perry, A.R.** 1983. Mosses and liverworts. In **Webb, D.A. & Scannell M. J. P.** 1983. *Op. cit.* 279–284.

30 **Mitchell, M.E.** 1983. Lichens. In **Webb, D.A. & Scannell, M.J.P.** 1983. *Op. cit.* 284–286.

31 **Baynes, E.S.A.** 1964. *A Revised Catalogue of Irish Macrolepidoptera (Butterflies and Moths).* Classey, Middlesex.

32 **Classey, E.W., Robinson, H.S. & Goater, B.** 1951. Burren – 1950. *Ent. Gaz.* 2: 87–99.

33 **Bretherton, R.F., Goater, B. & Lorimer, R.I.** 1983. Noctuidae (Continued). In: **Heath, J & Emmet, A. M. (eds.)** *The Moths and Butterflies of Great Britain and Ireland.* Volume 10. Harley Books, Colchester.

34 **Bradley, J.D.** 1953. Microlepidoptera collected in the Burren, Co. Clare, Ireland, in 1952, including a plume moth new to the British list. *Ent. Gaz.* 4: 135–140.

35 **Harding, P.T.** 1968. A list of woodlice (Crustacea: Isopoda: Oniscoidea) from the Burren, Co. Clare. *Ir. Nat. J.* 16: 16–17.

36 **O'Connor, M.A. & De Courcy Williams, M.** 1988. Notes on *Berytinus montivagus* (Meyer) and *Metatropsis rufescens* (Herrich-Schaffer) (Hemiptera) in Ireland. *Entomologist's Rec. J. Var.* 81–84.

37 **Richards, O.W.** 1961. The fauna of an area of limestone pavement on the Burren, Co. Clare. *Proc. R. Ir. Acad.* 62B: 1–7.

38 **Blackith, R.M., Blackith R.E. & O'Connor, J.P.** 1994. A check list of Irish flesh-flies (Diptera: Sarcophagidae: Sarcophagini) and their known distribution. *Ir. Nat. J.* 24: 427–434.

39 **Ashe, P. O'Connor, J.P. & Casey, R.J.** 1991. Irish mosquitoes (Diptera: Culicidae): a checklist of the species and their known distribution. *Proc. R. Ir. Acad.* 91B: 21–36.

40 **Morris, M.G.** 1967. Weevils (Coleoptera, Curculionoidea) and other insects collected in north west Clare, with special reference to the Burren region. *Proc. R. Ir. Acad.* 65B: 349–371.

41 **Cabot, D.** 1963. Breeding birds of the Burren, Co. Clare. Unpublished report.

42 **Moles, R.** 1982. A study of some bird communities of the Burren, Co. Clare. *Ir. Nat. J.* 20: 419–423.

43 **Gallagher, R.N. & Fairley, J.S.** 1979. A population study of the fieldmice *Apodemus sylvaticus* in the Burren. *Proc. R. Ir. Acad.* 79B:123–127.

44 **Fairley, J.S.** 1984. *An Irish Beast Book: A natural history of Ireland's furred wildlife.* Blackstaff Press, Belfast.

45 **O'Sullivan, P. J.** 1983. The distribution of the pine martin (*Martes martes*) in the Republic of Ireland. *Mammal Review* 13: 39–44.

46 **Warner, P. & O'Sullivan, P.** 1982. The food of the pine marten in Co. Clare. *Trans. inter. Congr. game Biol.* 14: 323–330.

47 **Fairley, J.S.** 1974. Food of pine martens in the Burren. *Ir. Nat. J.* 18: 125.

48 **Fairley, J.S.** 1975. Summer food of pine martens in Co. Clare. *Ir. Nat. J.* 18: 257–258.

49 **Cabot, D.** 1965. The green lizard, *Lacerta viridis*, in Ireland. *Ir. Nat. J.* 15: 111.

50 **McCarthy, T.K.** 1977. The slow-worm, *Anguis fragilis* L.: a reptile new to the Irish fauna. *Ir. Nat. J.* 19: 49.

51 **King, W.** 1685. Of the Bogs and Loughs of Ireland. *Phil. Trans. Roy. Soc.* 15: 948–960.

52 **Webb, D. A.** 1963. *Pers. comm.* to D. Cabot.

53 **Coxon, C.E.** 1987. The spatial distribution of turloughs. *Irish Geography* 20: 11–23.

54 **Mellanby, K.** 1983. *The New Naturalist: Farming and Wildlife.* Collins, London.

55 **Praeger, R. Ll.** 1932. The flora of the turloughs: a preliminary note. *Proc. R. Ir. Acad.* 41B: 37–45.

56 **Sheehy-Skeffington, M.J.** 1985. Vegetation productivity in Rahasane turlough, County Galway. *British Ecological Society Bulletin* 16: 20–23.

57 **Scannell, M.J.P.** 1972. Algal paper of *Oedogonium* sp., its occurrence in the

Burren, Co. Clare. *Ir. Nat. J.* 17: 147–182.

[58] **McNcNeill, I. & Hackney, P.** 1996 *Rorippa islandica* (Oeder ex Murray) Borbas in some Northern Ireland Counties. *Ir. Nat. J.* 25:293–294.

[59] **McGowran, B.** 1979. *Rorippa islandica* (Oeder ex Murray) Borbas in turloughs of south east Galway. *Ir. Nat. J.* 19: 326–327.

[60] **Scannell, M.J.P.** 1973. *Rorippa islandica* (Oeder ex Murray) Borbas in Ireland. *Ir. Nat. J.* 17: 348–349.

[61] **Goodwillie, R.** 1995. Additions to the range of *Rorippa islandica* (Oeder ex Murray) Borbas. *Ir. Nat. J.* 25: 57–59.

[62] **Bilton, D.T.** 1988. A survey of aquatic Coleoptera in central Ireland and the Burren. *Bull. Ir. biogeog. Soc.* 11: 77–94.

[63] **Young, R.** 1976. *Tanymastix stagnalis* (Linn.) in County Galway, new to Britain and Ireland. *Proc. R. Ir. Acad.* 76B: 369–378.

[64] **Grainger, J.N.R.** 1976. Further records for the fairy shrimp *Tanymastix stagnalis* (L.). *Ir. Nat. J.* 18: 326.

[65] **Ali, T.H., Holmes, J.M.C. & Grainger, J.N.R.** 1987. *Diaptomus cyaneus* Gurney, a freshwater copepod new to Britain and Ireland. *Ir. Nat. J.* 22: 240–241.

[66] **Reynolds, J.D.** 1996. Turloughs, their significance and possibilities for conservation. In: **Reynolds, J.D. (ed.).** *The Conservation of Aquatic Systems.* 38–46. Royal Irish Academy, Dublin.

[67] **Grainger, J.N.R** 1991. The biology of *Tanymastix stagnalis* (L.) and its survival in large and small temporary water bodies in Ireland. *Hydrobiologia* 212: 77–82.

[68] **Donaldson, F. & F. & McMillan, N.F.** 1979. A note on the Mollusca of three turloughs. *Ir. Nat. J.* 19: 400–401.

[69] **Byrne, R.A. & Reynolds, J.D.** 1982. Preliminary notes on a doline in Lough Gealain, the Burren, County Clare. *Ir. Nat. J.* 20: 375–377.

[70] **O'Connor, J.P** 1987. A review of the Irish Trichoptera. In: **Bournaud & Tachet, H (eds.)** Proc. 5th Int. Symp. on Trichoptera. Junk, Dordrecht.

[71] **Cabot, D.** 1966. The wildfowl and waders of Rahasane Turlough, Co. Galway, 1964–66. Unpublished report.

[72] **Sheppard, R.** 1993. *Ireland's Wetland Wealth.* IWC, Dublin.

[73] **Scott, D.A.** 1980. *A preliminary inventory of Wetlands of International Importance for Waterfowl in West Europe and Northwest Africa.* IWRB Special Publication No. 2.

International Waterfowl Research Bureau, Slimbridge.

[74] **Buckley, P. & McCarthy, T.K.** 1987. Bird communities in the Dunkellin/Lavally catchments: a pre-drainage survey and environmental impact assessment. Report to the Wildlife Service of the Office of Public Works, Dublin. Unpublished report.

[75] **Delany, S.** 1997. *I-WeBS Report 1995–96.* BirdWatch Ireland, Dublin.

CHAPTER 7

[1] **Rackham, O.** 1995. *Trees and Woodland in the British Landscape.* Weidenfeld & Nicholson, London.

[2] **Kelly, D.L.** 1984. Trees and woodland. In: **de Buitléar, É. (ed.).** *Wild Ireland.* Amach Faoin Aer Publishing, Dublin.

[3] **Forbes, A.C.** 1932. Some legendary and historical references to Irish woods, and their significance. *Proc. R. Ir. Acad.* 41B: 15–36.

[4] **Edwards, K. J.** 1985. The anthropogenic factor in vegetational history. In: **Edwards, K.J. & Warren W.P. (eds.).** *The Quaternary History of Ireland.* Academic Press, London.

[5] **McCracken, E.** 1971. *The Irish Woods Since Tudor Times.* David and Charles, Newton Abbott.

[6] **Tomlinson, R.** 1997 Forests and Woodlands. In: **Aalen, F.H.A., Whelan, K. & Stout, M. (eds.).** *Atlas of the Irish Rural Landscape.* 122–133. Cork University Press, Cork.

[7] **Purcell, T.J.** 1979. *Inventory of private woodlands – 1973.* Forest and Wildlife Service, Dublin.

[8] **Peterken, G.F.** 1981. *Woodland Conservation and Management.* Chapman and Hall, London.

[9] **McEvoy, T.** 1944. Irish native woodlands: their present condition. *Irish Forestry* 1: 27–35.

[10] **Joyce, P.W.** 1869. *The Origin and History of Irish Names of Places.* Facsimile reprint 1995. Edmund Burke, Dublin.

[11] **Kelly, F.S.** 1984. Source of reference In: **Kelly, D.L.** 1984. *Op. cit.*

[12] **Aalen, F.H.A.** 1970. In: **Stephens, N & Classcock, R.E. (eds.).** *Irish Geographical Studies in honour of E. Estyn Evans.* 209–223. The Queen's University, Belfast.

[13] **Condon, F.A. & Jarvis, P.J.** 1989. Trees and shrubs in the hedgerows of Knock, Co. Mayo, western Ireland. *Ir. Nat. J.* 23: 12–16.

[14] **Synnott, D.** 1973. Hedge dating in

Duleek. *Annala Dhamhliag* 3: 12–13.

15 **Hegarty, C.A. & Cooper, A.** 1994. Regional variation of hedge structure and composition in Northern Ireland in relation to management and land use. *Biology and Environment. Proc. R. Ir. Acad.* 94B: 223–236.

16 **Webb, D.A.** 1952. The flora and vegetation of Ireland. In: **Ludi, R. von W. (ed.).** *Die Pflanzenwelt Irlands. Veröfentliehugen des Geobotanischen Institutes Rübel in Zürich* 25: 46–78. Verlag Hans Huber, Bern und Stuttgart.

17 **Praeger, R. L.** 1934. *The Botanist in Ireland.* Hodges, Figgis & Co., Dublin.

18 **Boatman, D.J.** 1966. *Mercurialis perennis* L. in Ireland. *J. Ecol.* 44: 587–596.

19 **Curtis, T.G.F.** 1981. A further station for *Mercurialis perennis* L. in the Burren with comments on its status there. *Ir. Nat. J.* 20: 184–185.

20 **Hackney, P. (comp. & ed.).** 1992. *Stewart and Corry's Flora of the North-East of Ireland.* 3rd edition. Institute of Irish Studies, Queen's University, Belfast.

21 **Mueller-Dombois, D. & Ellenberg, H.** 1974. *Aims and Methods of Vegetation Ecology.* Wiley, London.

22 **Kelly, D.L.** 1981. The native forest vegetation of Killarney, south-west Ireland: An ecological account. *Journal of Ecology* 69: 437–472.

23 **Doyle, G.J.** 1987. A new station for the Killarney fern (*Trichomanes speciosum* Willd.) in Killarney oakwoods (Blechnoquercetum). *Ir. Nat. J.* 22: 353–356.

24 **Watts, W.A.** 1984. Contemporary accounts of the Killarney woods 1580–1870. *Irish Geography* 17: 1–13.

25 **Kelly, F.S.** 1976. The old Irish tree-list. *Celtica* 11: 107–124.

26 **Mitchell, F.J.G.** 1993. The biogeographical implications of the distribution and history of the strawberry tree, *Arbutus unedo*, in Ireland. In: **Costello, M.J. & Kelly, K.S. (eds.).** *Occ. Publ. Ir. biogeog. Soc.* 2: 35–44.

27 **Kelly, F.S.** 1997. Per Daniel Kelly. *Pers. comm.*

28 **Mitchell, F & Ryan, M.** 1997. *Reading the Irish Landscape.* Town House, Dublin.

29 **Webb, D.A.** 1983. The flora of Ireland in its European context. *J. Life Sci. R. Dubl. Soc.* 4:143–160.

30 **Watts, W.**A. 1959. Interglacial deposits at Kilbeg and Newtown, Co. Waterford. *Proc. R. Ir. Acad.* 60B: 79–134.

31 **Watts, W.A**. 1967. Interglacial deposits in Kildromin townland, near Herbertstown, Co. Limerick. *Proc. R. Ir. Acad.* 65B: 339–348.

32 **Richards, P. W.** 1938. The bryophyte communities of a Killarney oakwood. *Annales Bryol.* 11: 108–130.

33 **Tansley, A.G.** 1965. *The British Islands and their Vegetation.* 4th Impression. Cambridge University Press, Cambridge.

34 **Scully, R.W.** 1916. *Flora of County Kerry.* Hodges, Figgis & Co., Dublin.

35 **Mills, S.** 1987. *Nature in its Place.* The Bodley Head, London.

36 **O'Connor, J.P., Schonrogge, K., Ashe, P., O'Connor, M.A., Walker, P. & Wiston, S.** 1995. The distribution of gall-causing cynipids (Hymenoptera) on oak (*Quercus*) in Ireland. *Bull Ir. biogeog. Soc.* 18: 37–65.

37 **O'Connor, J.P. , Ashe, P., O'Connor, M.A. & Wistow, S.** 1995. *Andricus nudus* (Hym:Cynipidae) and *Taxomyia taxi* (Dipt: Cecidomyiidae): insects new to Ireland. *Entomologist's Rec. J. Var.* 107: 105–106.

38 **McCuster, P.** 1990. *The Butterflies of Killarney National Park.* Stationery Office, Dublin.

39 **Chinery, M**. 1989. *Collins New Generation Guide to the Butterflies and Day-flying Moths of Britain and Europe.* Collins, London.

40 **Platts, E.A. & Speight, M.C.D.** 1988. The taxonomy and distribution of the Kerry slug *Geomalacus maculosus* Allman, 1843 (Mollusca: Arionaidae) with a discussion of its status as a threatened species. *Ir. Nat. J.* 22: 417–429.

41 **Smal, C.M. & Fairley, J.S.** 1982. The dynamics and regulation of small rodent populations in the woodland ecosystems of Killarney, Ireland. *J. Zool. Lond.* 196: 1–30.

42 **Kelly, D.** 1997. *Pers. comm.*

43 **Larner, J.** 1992. *The Oakwoods of Killarney.* Stationery Office, Dublin.

44 **Batten, L.A.** 1976. Bird communities of some Killarney woods. *Proc. R. Ir. Acad.* 76B: 285–313.

45 **Wilson, J.** 1977. Some breeding bird communities of sessile oak woodlands in Ireland. *Pol. ecol. Stud.* 3: 245–256.

46 **Simms, E.** 1971. *The New Naturalist: Woodland Birds.* Collins, London.

47 **Fuller, R.J.** 1995. *Bird life of Woodland and Forest.* Cambridge University Press, Cambridge.

48 **Moore N.W. & Hooper, M.D.** 1975. On the number of bird species in British

woods. *Biological Conservation* 8: 239–250.

[49] **Neff, M.J.** 1975. Woodland conservation in the Republic of Ireland: In: **Gehu, J.-M. (ed.).** *La Vegetation des Forets Caducifoliees Aciophiles.* 275–285. J. Cramer, Vaduz.

[50] **Wilson, J.** 1982. Wintering site fidelity of woodcock *Scolopax rusticola* in Ireland. *Trans. Intern. Congr. Game Biol.* 14: 219–231.

[51] **Bishop, M.J.** 1977. The mollusca of acid woodland in west Cork and Kerry. *Proc. R. Ir. Acad.* 77B: 227–244.

[52] Author's data.

[53] **O'Connor, J.P. & O'Connor, M.A.** 1987. A second Irish record of *Melais buprestoides* (L.) (Col., Eucnemidae). *Entomologist's Mon. Mag.* 123: 228.

[54] **Legg, G. & O'Connor, J.P.** 1997. A review of the Irish pseudoscorpions (Arachnida: Pseudoscorpiones). *Bull. Ir. biogeog. Soc.* 20: 105–126.

[55] **Webb, D.A. & Glanville. E.V.** 1962. The vegetation and flora of some islands in the Connemara lakes. *Proc. R. Ir. Acad.* 62B: 31–54.

[56] **Roden, C.** 1979. The vascular flora and vegetation of some islands of Lough Corrib. *Proc. R. Ir. Acad.* 79B: 223–234.

[57] **Ferguson, D.K. & Westhoff, V.** 1987 An account of the flora and vegetation of Derryclare Wood, Connemara (Co. Galway), Western Ireland. *Proc. Kon. Ned. Akad. van Wet.* C 90: 139–172.

[58] **Folan, A.C.M. & Mitchell, M.F.** 1970. The lichens and parasites of Derryclare Wood, Connemara. *Proc. R. Ir. Acad.* 70B: 163–170.

[59] **Gorham, E.** 1954. The soils and vegetation of a western Irish relict woodland. *J. Ecol.* 42: 497–504.

[60] **Praeger, R. Ll.** 1932. Some noteworthy plants found in, or reported from Ireland. *Proc. R. Ir. Acad.* 41B: 95–124.

[61] **Dobson, J.R. & Bradshaw, R.H.W.** 1987. A history of vegetation and fire, 6,000 B.P. to present, County Sligo, western Ireland. *Boreas* 16: 113–123.

[62] **Kelly, D. & Moore, J.J.** 1975. A preliminary sketch of the Irish acidophilous oakwoods. *Colloques Phytosociologiques. Les forets acidiphiles* 3: 375–387.

[63] **Kelly, D.L. & Kirby, E.N.** 1982. Irish native woodlands over limestone. *J. Life Sci. R. Dubl. Soc.* 3: 181–198.

[64] **Warner, D.** 1996. A tale of two squirrels. *Walking World Ireland.* 15: 33–35.

[65] **Anderson, R. & Hughes, D.** 1995. Recent spread of the grey squirrel, *Sciurus carolinensis* Gmelin, into Cos. Down and Londonderry. *Ir. Nat. J.* 25: 118.

[66] **Moffat, C.B.** 1938. The mammals of Ireland. *Proc. R. Ir. Acad.* 44B: 61–128.

[67] **Fairley, J.S.** 1983. Exports of wild mammal skins from Ireland in the eighteenth century. *Ir. Nat. J.* 21: 75–79.

[68] Statutes 14 and 15 Charles II, cap. 9.

[69] **Barrington, R.M.** 1880. On the introduction of the squirrel into Ireland. *Sci. Proc. R. Dubl. Soc.* 2: 615–631.

[70] **Nelson, E.C.** 1977. Summer feeding of red squirrels, *Sciurus vulgaris*, in County Derry. *Ir. Nat. J.* 19: 46–47.

[71] **Cross, J. R.** 1992. The distribution, character and conservation of woodlands on esker ridges in Ireland. *Proc. R. Ir. Acad.* 92B: 1–19.

[72] **Breen, C., Curtis, T.G.F. & Scannell, M.J.P.** 1984. *Cardamine impatiens* L. in Co. Westmeath (H23) – an addition to the Irish flora. *Ir. Nat. J.* 21:344.

[73] **Ivimey-Cook, R.B. & Proctor, M.C.F.** 1966. The plant communities of the Burren, Co. Clare. *Proc. R. Ir. Acad* 64B: 211–301.

[74] **Carruthers, T.D. & Gosler, A.G.** 1995. The breeding bird community of the Muckross yew wood, Killarney. *Irish Birds* 5: 308–318.

[75] **Nelson, E. C. & Walsh, W.F.** 1993. *Trees of Ireland: Native and Naturalised.* Lilliput Press, Dublin.

[76] **Kelly, D.L. & Iremonger, S.F.** 1997. Irish wetland woods: the plant communities and their ecology. *Biology and Environment. Proc. R. Ir. Acad.* 97B 1–32.

[77] **O'Reilly, H.J.** 1954. Survey of the Gearagh, an area of wet woodland on the river Lee, near Macroom, Co. Cork. *Ir. Nat. J.* 11: 279–286.

[78] **White, J.** 1985. The Gearagh woodlands, Co. Cork. *Ir. Nat. J.* 21: 391–396.

[79] **Hewetson, A. & O'Rourke, F.J.** 1960. The dragonflies of the Gearagh, West Cork. *Proc. R. Ir. Acad.* 61 B: 177–185.

[80] **Wallace, I.D., Wallace, B. & O'Connor, J.P.** 1983. *Phacopteryx brevipennis* new to Ireland with notes on *Oxyethira simplex* and *Beraedes minutus* (Insecta: Trichoptera). *Ir. Nat. J.* 21: 168–169.

[81] **Webb, D.A., Parnell, J & Doogue, D.** 1996. *An Irish Flora.* 7th revised edition. Dundalgan Press, Dundalk.

[82] **Cross, J.R.** 1987. Unusual stands of birch on bogs. *Ir.Nat.J.* 22: 305–310.

[83] **O'Connor, J.P. & Speight, M.C.D.** 1987. *Macrosiphum albifrons, Dictenidia bimaculata, Callaspidia defonscolombei* and *Xylapsis*

petiolata: Insects new to Ireland. *Ir.Nat.J.* 22: 199–210.

CHAPTER 8

[1] **CEC** 1992. *The Agricultural Situation in the Community. 1991 Report.* Commission of the European Communities, Brussels/ Luxembourg.

[2] **Gillmor, D.A.** 1994. *Irish land use in the twentieth century.* In: **Fenton, A. & Gillmor, D.A. (eds.).** *Rural Land Use on the Atlantic Periphery of Europe: Scotland and Ireland.* 55–73. Royal Irish Academy, Dublin.

[3] **Keating, T., O'Kiely, P. & Keane, G.P.** 1995. Production from permanent and reseeded swards. In: **Jeffrey, D.W., Jones, M.B. & McAdam, J. H. (eds.).** *Irish Grasslands – their biology and management.* 32–40. Royal Irish Academy, Dublin.

[4] **Feehan, J. & McHugh, R.** 1992. The Curragh of Kildare as a *Hygrocybe* grassland. *Ir. Nat. J.* 24: 13–17.

[5] **Monk, T.** 1682. Descriptive account of the County of Kildare in 1682. *Journal of the County Kildare Archaeological Society* 6: (1909–11): 339–346.

[6] **Delany, S.** 1997 *I-WeBS Report. 1995–96.* BirdWatch Ireland, Dublin

[7] **Nitare, J.** 1988. Jordtungor en svampgrupp pa tillbakagang i naturliga fodermarker. *Svensk. Bot. Tidskr.* 82: 341–368.

[8] **Good, J.A. & Butler, F.T.** 1996. Ancient pasture as a habitat for staphylinidae (Coleoptera) at the Curragh, Co. Kildare, Ireland. *Bull. Ir. biogeog. Soc.* 19: 151– 158.

[9] **Lever, C.** 1906. *Jack Hinton, the Guardsman.* Macmillan & Co., London.

[10] **Heery, S.** 1991. The plant communities of the grazed and mown grasslands of the river Shannon callows. *Proc. R. Ir. Acad.* 91B:1–19.

[11] **Ratcliffe, D.A.** 1977. *A Nature Conservation Review.* 2 vols. Cambridge University Press, Cambridge.

[12] **Thomas, G.J.** 1982. Autumn and winter feeding ecology of waterfowl on the Ouse Washes, England. *J. Zool. Lond.* 197: 131–172.

[13] **Nairn, R.G.W., Herbert, I.J. & Heery, S.** 1988. Breeding waders and other wet grassland birds of the River Shannon callows, Ireland. *Irish Birds* 3: 521–537.

[14] **Fuller, R.M** 1987. The changing extent and conservation interest of lowland grasslands in England and Wales: a review of grassland surveys 1930–1984. *Biological Conservation* 40: 281–300.

[15] **Heery, S.** 1993. *The Shannon Floodlands. A Natural History.* Tír Eolas, Kinvara.

[16] **McGowran, B.A.** 1984. Phytosociological and ecological studies on turloughs in the west of Ireland. Unpublished Ph.D. Quoted in: **Heery, S.** 1991. *Op. cit.*

[17] **Curtis, T.G.F. & McGough, H.N.** 1988. *Irish Red Data Book 1. Vascular Plants.* Stationery Office, Dublin.

[18] **Praeger, R. Ll.** 1950. *The Natural History of Ireland: a Sketch of its Flora and Fauna.* Collins, London.

[19] **Heery, S.** 1996. *Birds in Central Ireland. Mid Shannon Bird Report 1992–1995.* Ballinasloe, Galway. For the author.

[20] **Heery, S.** 1997. *Pers. comm.*

[21] **Smiddy, P & O'Sullivan, O.** 1996. Forty third Irish bird report. *Irish birds* 5: 445–474.

[22] **Hutchinson, C.D.** 1989. *Birds in Ireland.* T & A D Poyser. Calton.

[23] **Cabot, D.** 1967. Results of an aerial survey of Irish wildfowl and their wetlands. Publication No. 8. Irish Wildbird Conservancy, Dublin.

[24] **Sheppard, R.** 1993. *Ireland's Wetland Wealth.* IWC, Dublin.

[25] **Norris, D.W. & Walsh, A.** 1998. *Greenland white-fronted geese in Ireland 1995–6 and 1996–7.* National Parks and Wildlife. Dúchas, the Heritage Sevice, Dublin.

[26] **Gibbons, M.H. & McCarthy, T.K.** 1986. Growth, maturation, and survival of frogs *Rana temporaria.* *J. Zool. Lond.* 209: 579–593.

[27] **Blackith, R.M. & Speight, M.C.D.** 1974. Food and feeding habits of the frog *Rana temporaria* in bogland habitats in the west of Ireland. *J. Zool. Lond.* 172: 67–79.

[28] **Marnell, F. & Reynolds, J.** 1995. The distribution and habitat of the smooth newt *Triturus vulgaris* L. in Ireland: the results of an all–Ireland survey. *Biology and Environment. Proc. R. Ir. Acad.* 95B:129.

[29] **Frazer, D.** 1983. *The New Naturalist: Reptiles and Amphibians in Britain.* Collins, London.

[30] **O'Sullivan, P.** 1994. Bats in Ireland. *Ir. Nat. J. Spec. Zool. Suppl. 1994:* 1–21.

[31] **Stebbings, R.E.** 1977. In: **Corbet, G.B & Southern H.N.** *The Handbook of British Mammals.* 2nd edition. Blackwells, Oxford.

[32] **Fairley, J.** 1970. The food, reproduction, form, growth and development of the fox *Vulpes vulpes* (L.) in north-east Ireland. *Proc. R. Ir. Acad.* 69B:103–137.

[33] **Kruuk, H.** 1964. Predators and anti-predator behaviour of the black headed

gull (*Larus ridibundus* L.). *Behaviour* suppl. 11.

34 **Matthews, H.** 1982. *The New Naturalist: Mammals in the British Isles*. Collins, London.

35 **Fairley, J.** 1984. *An Irish Beast Book. A natural history of Ireland's furred wildlife*. Blackstaff Press, Belfast.

36 **Sleeman, D. P.** 1993. Habitats of the Irish stoat. *Ir. Nat. J.* 24: 218–321.

37 **Corbet, G. B. & Southern, H.N.** 1977. *Op. cit.*

38 **Sleeman, D. P.** 1992. Diet of Irish stoats. *Ir. Nat. J.* 24: 151–153.

39 **Fairley, J. S.** 1971. New data on the Irish stoat. *Ir. Nat. J.* 17: 49–57.

40 **Smal, C.** 1995. *The Badger and Habitat Survey of Ireland*. Summary Report. Stationery Office, Dublin.

41 **Ruttledge, R. F.** 1966. *Ireland's Birds*. Witherby, London.

42 **Shawyer, C. R.** 1987. *The Barn Owl in the British Isles. Its past, present and future*. The Hawk Trust, London.

43 **Berridge, D.** 1998. Barn Owls now very scarce. *Wings* 9:13.

44 **Collins, K.** 1997. Habitat selection and population size of yellowhammers breeding in Co. Tipperary in 1997. *Irish Birds* 6: 118–9.

45 **O'Sullivan, O. & Smiddy, P.** 1992. Thirty-ninth Irish Bird Report, 1991. *Irish Birds* 4: 571–610.

46 **MacConnell, S.** 1998. *Irish Times*, 8 January. Dublin.

47 **Marchington, J.** 1984. *The Natural History of Game*. Boydell Press, Suffolk.

48 **Lever, C.** 1977. *The Naturalised Animals of the British Isles*. Hutchinson, London.

49 **O'Sullivan, O. & Smiddy, P.** 1990. Thirty-seventh Irish Bird Report, 1989. *Irish Birds* 4: 231–257.

50 **O'Sullivan, O. & Smiddy, P.** 1991. Thirty-eighth Irish Bird Report, 1990. *Irish Birds* 4: 423–462.

51 **Kennedy, P.G., Ruttledge, R.F. & Scroope, C.F., assisted by Humphreys, G.R.** 1954. *The Birds of Ireland*. Oliver and Boyd, London.

52 **Moryson, F.** 1617 *An Itinerary...Containing his Ten Yeers Travell...*London.

53 **Fisher, J.** 1966. *The Shell Bird Book*. Ebury Press and Michael Joseph, London.

54 **Robertson, P.A. & Whelan, J.** 1987. The ecology and management of wild and hand reared pheasants in Ireland. *Irish Birds* 3: 427–440.

CHAPTER 9

1 **Stephens, N.** 1970. The coastline of Ireland. In: **Stephens, N. & Glasscock, R.R. (eds.).** *Irish Geographical Studies in honour of E. Estyn Evans*. 125–145. Queen's University, Belfast.

2 **Curtis, T.G.F. & McGough, H.N.** 1988. *The Irish Red Data Book: 1 Vascular Plants*. Stationery Office, Dublin.

3 **Bald, W.** 1830. *Map of the maritime County of Mayo in Ireland*. Executed by the Order of the Grand Jury. Reprinted 1989 by Phoenix Maps, Dublin.

4 **Eurpean Commission.** 1991. *The CORINE Biotopes Project*. Commission of the European Communities, Luxembourg.

5 **Coveney, J., Merne, O., Wilson, J., Allen, D. & Thomas, G.** 1993. *A Conservation Strategy for Birds in Ireland*. Irish Wildbird Conservancy, Dublin.

6 **Cabot, D. (ed.).** 1993. *Report of the Green 2000 Advisory Group to the Taoiseach*. Stationery Office, Dublin.

7 **Boaden, P.J.S.** 1966. Strangford Lough – conservation constrained. In: **Reynods, J. (ed.).** *The Conservation of Aquatic Systems*. 56–67. Royal Irish Academy, Dublin.

8 **Dickie, G.** 1857. Report on the Marine Zoology of Strangford Lough, County Down, and corresponding part of the Irish Channel. *Rep. Brit. Ass. Advmt. Sci.* 1857: 104–112.

9 **Williams, G.** 1954. Fauna of Strangford Lough and neighbouring coasts. *Proc. R. Ir. Acad.* 56B: 29–133.

10 **Erwin, D.G., Picton, B.E., Connor, D.W., Howson, C.M., Gilleece P. & Bogues, M.J.** 1990. *Inshore Marine Life of Northern Ireland*. HSMO, Belfast.

11 **Nunn, J.D.** 1994. The marine mollusca of Ireland. *Bull. Ir. biogeog. Soc.* 17: 23–214.

12 **Sheppard, R.** 1993. *Ireland's Wetland Wealth*. IWC, Dublin.

13 **Fox, A.D., Bell, M.C., Brown, R.A., Mackie, P & Madsen, J.** 1994. An analysis of the abundance and distribution of brent geese and wigeon at Strangford Lough, 1965/6–1988/9. *Irish Birds* 5: 139–150.

14 **Mathers, R.G. & Montgomery, W.I.** 1997. Quality of food consumed by over wintering pale-bellied brent geese *Branta bernicla hrota* and wigeon *Anas penelope*. *Biology and Environment. Proc. R. Ir. Acad.* 97B: 81–89.

15 **Delany, S.** 1997. *I-WeBS Report 1995–96*. BirdWatch Ireland, Dublin.

16 **Millard, A.V. & Evans, P.R.** 1984.

Colonisation of mudflats by *Spartina angli-
ca*: some effects on invertebrates and
shorebird populations at Lindisfarne. In:
Doody, P. (ed.). *Spartina angelica in Great
Britain.* 41–48. Nature Conservancy
Council, Huntingdon.

[17] **Joyce, P.W.** 1869. *The Origin and History of
Irish Names of Places.* Facsimile reprint
1995. Edmund Burke, Dublin.

[18] **Lewis, C.** 1971. Coastal landforms of
Ireland. *Geographical Viewpoint* 2: 155–174.

[19] **Whittow, J.B.** 1974. *Geology and Scenery in
Ireland.* Penguin Books, London.

[20] **Keegan, B.F. & Mercer, J.P.** 1986. An
oceanographic survey of Killary Harbour
on the west coast of Ireland. *Proc. R. Ir.
Acad.* 86B: 1–70.

[21] **Keegan, B.F., O'Connor, B.D.S. &
Könnecker, G.F.** 1985. Littoral and benth-
ic investigations on the west coast of
Ireland – XX. Echinoderm aggregations.
Proc. R. Ir. Acad. 85B: 91–99.

[22] **Keegan, B.F., O'Connor, B.D.S.,
McGrath, D., Könnecker, G & O Foighil,
D.** 1987. Littoral and benthic investiga-
tions on the south coast of Ireland – II.
The macrobenthic fauna off Carnsore
Point. *Proc. R. Ir. Acad.* 87B: 1–14.

[23] **Nunn, J.D.** 1994. The marine Mollusca of
Ireland 2. Mulroy Bay, Co. Donegal. *Bull.
Ir. biogeog. Soc.* 19: 15–138.

[24] **Norton, T.A.** 1991. The algal vegetation.
In: **Myers, A.A., Little, C., Costello, M.J.
& Partridge, J.C. (eds.).** The Ecology of
Lough Hyne. Proceedings of a confer-
ence, 4–5 September 1990. 1–175. Royal
Irish Academy, Dublin.

[25] **Holland, C. H.** 1991. The origin of Lough
Hyne. In: **Myers, A.A., et. al. (eds.).** *Op. cit.*
19–23.

[26] **Kitching, J.A.** 1991. Introduction. In:
Myers, A.A., et. al. (eds.). *Op. cit.* 13–16.

[27] **Costello, M.J. & Myers, A.A.** 1991. The
biogeographic richness of the
Amphipoda. In: **Myers, A.A., et. al. (eds.).**
Op. cit. 157–162.

[28] **Praeger, R. Ll.** 1937. *The Way That I Went.*
Hodges, Figgis & Co., Dublin and
Methuen & Co., London.

[29] **O'Connor, B., McGrath, D., Könnecker,
G. & Keegan, B.F.** 1993. Benthic macrofaunal assemblages of greater Galway Bay.
Biology and Environment: Proc. R. Ir. Acad.
93B: 127–136.

[30] **Keegan, B.F.** 1974. Littoral and benthic
investigations on the west coast of
Ireland. – III (section A: faunistic and
ecological studies). *Proc. R. Ir. Acad.* 74B:

85–123.

[31] **O'Connell, M., Fives, J.M. & Céidigh,
P.Ó.** 1992. Ecological studies of littoral
fauna and flora on Inishmore, Aran
Islands, Co. Galway. *Proc. R. Ir. Acad.* 92B:
91–107.

[32] **O'Connell, M., Fives, J.M. & Céidigh,
P.Ó.** 1992. Littoral fishes on Inishmore,
Aran Islands, Co. Galway. *Proc. R. Ir. Acad.*
92B: 109–131.

[33] **Wilkins, N.P.** 1989. *Ponds, Passes and
Parcs: Aquaculture in Victorian Ireland.* The
Glendale Press, Sandycove, Dublin.

[34] **Browne, T.J.** 1904. *Report on the Shellfish
Layings on the Coast of Ireland.* Government
Publications, Dublin

[35] **Yonge, C.M.** 1961. *The New Naturalist: The
Sea Shore.* Collins, London.

[36] **Went, A.E.J.** 1962. Historical notes on the
oyster fisheries of Ireland. *Proc. R. Ir. Acad.*
62C: 195–223.

[37] **Minchin, D.** 1993. Possible influence of
increases in mean sea temperature on Irish
marine fauna and fisheries. In: **Costello,
M.J. & Kelly, K.S. (eds.).** Biography of
Ireland: Past, Present and Future.
113–125. *Occ. Publ. Ir. biogeog. Soc.* 2.

[38] **Magennis, B.A., Gosling, E. & Wilkins,
N.P.** 1983. Irish oyster populations: a historical and genetic study. *Proc. R. Ir. Acad.*
83B: 291–299.

[39] **Briggs, R.R.** 1982. Community structure
and growth of *Mytilus edulis* L. in Lough
Foyle. *Proc. R. Ir. Acad.* 82B: 245–259.

[40] **O'Reilly, H. & Pantin, G.** 1957. Some
observations on the salt marsh formation
in Co. Dublin. *Proc. R. Ir. Acad.* 58B:
80–128.

[41] **Moore, J.J. & O'Reilly, H.** 1977.
Saltmarsh: vegetation pattern and trends:
In **Jeffrey, D.W. (General ed.).** *North Bull
Island – Dublin Bay – a modern coastal nat-
ural history.* 83–87. Royal Dublin Society,
Dublin.

[42] **White, J.** 1981. Notes on the Irish vegetation: No.1. The vegetation of shingle in
Co. Louth. *Bull. Ir. biogeog. Soc.* 5: 1–4.

[43] **Nairn, R.G.W. & Whatmough, J.A.** 1978.
Breeding bird communities of a sand
dune system in north-east Ireland. *Irish
Birds* 1: 160–170.

[44] **Tansley, A.G.** 1965. *The British Islands and
Their Vegetation.* 4th impression.
Cambridge University Press, Cambridge.

[45] **Keary, R.** 1965. A note on the beach
sands of the Cois Fharraige coast. *Ir. Nat.
J.* 15: 40–43

[46] **Heron-Allen, E. & Earland, A.** 1913.

Foraminifera [Clare Island Survey]. *Proc. R. Ir. Acad.* 31: (part 64) 1–188.

47 **Praeger, R. Ll.** 1911. A note on Dooaghtry. *Irish Naturalist* 20: 193–194.

48 **Praeger, R. Ll.**1934. *The Botanist in Ireland.* Hodges, Figgis & Co., Dublin.

49 **Akeroyd, J.R. & Curtis, T.G.F.** 1980. Some observations on the occurrence of machair in western Ireland. *Bull. Ir. biogeog. Soc.* 4: 1–11.

50 **Gimingham, C.H.** 1974. Plant communities of the machair and floristic relationships with non-dune vegetation. In: **Ranwell, D.S. (ed.).** *Sand Dune Machair, 19.* National Environment Research Council, London.

51 **Bassett, J.A. & Curtis, T.G.F.** 1985. The nature and occurrence of sand-dune machair in Ireland. *Proc. R. Ir. Acad.* 85B: 1–20.

52 **Speight, M.C.D.** 1977. Invertebrates of the dunes and grassland. In: **Jeffrey, D.W. (General ed.).** *Op. cit.* 107–111.

53 **Speight, M.C.D.** 1980. The fauna of the Raven: Invertebrates. In: An Foras Forbartha and Forest and Wildlife Service. *A Study of the Raven, Co. Wexford.* 33–42. An Foras Forbartha, Dublin.

54 **O'Connor, J.P.** 1983. *Chrysopa abbreviata* (Neuroptera) confirmed as an Irish insect. *Ir. Nat. J.* 21: 140.

55 **Stelfox, A.W.** 1912. Mollusca – Land and Freshwater [The Clare Island Survey] *Proc. R. Ir. Acad.* 31: (part 23): 38–40.

56 **Tatterfield, P.** 1993. The non-marine mollusca of Dooaghtry, Co. Mayo: changes in the fauna since 1910. *Ir. Nat. J.* 24: 183–192.

57 **Nairn, R.G.W.** 1985. Breeding waders of sand dune machair in north-west Ireland. *Irish Birds* 3: 53–70.

58 **Whilde, A.** 1993. *Threatened Mammals, Birds, Amphibians and Fish in Ireland. Irish Red data Book 2: Vertebrates.* HSMO, Belfast.

59 **Walpole-Bond, J.** 1929. Manuscript diary. Information *per* D. Ratcliffe, 1998.

60 **Hutchinson, C. D.** 1989. *Birds in Ireland.* T & A D Poyser, Calton.

61 **Cabot, D.** 1965. The status and distribution of the chough *Pyrrhocorax pyrrhocorax* (L.) in Ireland, 1960–65. *Ir. Nat. J.* 15: 95–100.

62 **Bullock, I.D., Drewett, D. R. & Mickleburgh, S.P.** 1983. The chough in Ireland. *Irish Birds* 2: 257–271.

63 **Berrow, S.D., Mackie, K.L., O'Sullivan, O., Shepherd, K.B., Mellon, C. & Coveney, J.A.** 1993. The second international chough survey in Ireland, 1992. *Irish Birds* 5: 1–10.

64 **Bignal, E., Bignal, S. & McCracken, D.** 1997. The social life of the chough. *British Wildlife* 9: 373–383

65 **Robertson, A., Jarvis, A.M. & Day, K.R.** 1995. Habitat selection and foraging behaviour of breeding choughs *Pyrrhocorax pyrrhocorax* L. in County Donegal. *Biology and Environment: Proc. R. Ir. Acad.* 95B: 69–74.

66 **Tucker, G.M., Heath, M.F., Tomialojc, L. & Grimmet, R.F.A.** 1994. *Birds in Europe: Their Conservation Status.* BirdLife International, Cambridge.

67 **Bignal, E. & Curtis, D.J** (eds.). 1989. *Choughs and Land Use in Europe.* Scottish Chough Study Group, Tarbert, Scotland.

68 **Cabot, D.** 1996. Performance of the roseate tern population breeding in north-west Europe – Ireland, Britain and France, 1960–1994. *Biology and Environment: Proc. R. Ir. Acad.* 96B: 55–68.

69 **Newton, S.** 1997. Ireland–Wales teamwork projects Irish Sea terns. *Wings* 7: 12.

70 **Hannon, C., Berrow, S.D. & Newton, S.F.** 1998 The status and distribution of breeding Sandwich *Sterna sandvicensis,* Roseate *S. dougallii,* Common *S. hirundo,* Arctic *S. paradisa* and Little Terns *S. albifrons* in Ireland 1995. *Irish Birds* 6: 1–22.

71 **O'Briain, M. & Farrelly, P.** 1990. Breeding biology of little terns at Newcastle, Co. Wicklow and the impact of conservation action, 1985–90. *Irish Birds.* 4: 149–168.

72 **Lloyd, C., Tasker, M.L. & Partridge, K.** 1991. *The Status of Seabirds in Britain and Ireland.* T & A D Poyser, London.

73 **Gresson, R.A.R. & O'Dubhda, S.** 1971. Natterjack toads *Bufo calamita* Laur. at Castlegregory and Fermoyle, Co. Kerry. *Ir. Nat. J.* 17: 9–11.

74 **Gibbons, M.** 1993. Quoted in: **Whilde, A.** 1993 *Op.cit.*

75 **Beebee, T.J.C.** 1983. *The Natterjack Toad.* Oxford University Press, Oxford.

76 **Banks, B.** 1997. Cumbria – stronghold of the British natterjack. *British Wildlife* 9: 1–6.

77 **Macdougald, T.J.** 1942. Notes on the habits of the natterjack toad. *Ir. Nat. J.* 8: 21–24.

78 **Farrell, L. & Randall, R.E.** 1992. The distribution of *Mertensia maritima* (L.) Gray, oyster plant, in Ireland. *Ir. Nat. J.* 24:135–140.

79 **Hurley, J.** 1997. *Water Level at Lady's Island*

Lake, 1984–1996. SWC Promotions, Kilmore.

[80] **Scannell, M.** 1997. *Pers. comm.*

[81] **Carter, R.W.G., Hamilton, A.C. & Lowry, P.** 1981. The ecology and present status of *Otanthus maritimus* on the gravel barrier at Lady's Island, Co. Wexford. *Ir. Nat. J.* 20: 329–331.

[82] **Wallace, E.** *pers. com.* In: **Hurley, J.** 1997. *Op. cit.*

[83] **Healy, B.** 1997. Long-term changes in a brackish lagoon, Lady's Island Lake, south-east Ireland. *Biology and Environment: Proc. R. Ir. Acad.* 97B 33–51.

[84] **Stewart, N.F. & Church, J.M.** 1992. *Red Data Books of Britain and Ireland: Stoneworts.* Joint Nature Conservation Committee, Peterborough.

[85] **Scannell, M.** 1997. *Pers. comm.*

[86] **Wyse-Jackson, P.S.** 1984. Comments on the status and ecology of *Simethis planifolia* (L.) Gren. in Co. Kerry. *Bull. Ir. biogeog. Soc.* 8: 13–18.

[87] **Grigson, G.** 1960. *The Englishman's Flora.* Phoenix House, London.

[88] **K'Eogh, J.** 1735. *Botanalogia Universalis Hibernica, or, a General Irish Herbal.* George Harrison, Cork.

CHAPTER 10

[1] **Lloyd, C., Tasker, M.L. & Partridge, K.** 1991. *The Status of Seabirds in Britain and Ireland.* T & A D Poyser, London.

[2] **Praeger, R. Ll.** 1950. *The Natural History of Ireland: A Sketch of its Flora and Fauna.* Collins, London.

[3] **Webb, D.A., Parnell, J. & Doogue, D.** 1996. *An Irish Flora.* 7th edition. Dundalgan Press, Dundalk.

[4] **Lhwyd, E.** 1712. Some farther Observations relating to the Antiquities and Natural History of Ireland. In a letter from the late Mr. Edw. Lhwyd, Keeper of the Ashmolean Museum in Oxford, to Dr Tancred Robinson, F.R.S. *Phil. Trans. Roy. Soc. Lond.* 27 (1710–1712): 524–526.

[5] **Barrington, R.M.** 1877. The plants of Tory Island, Co. Donegal. *Journal of Botany* 17: 263–270.

[6] **Praeger, R. Ll.** 1910. Phanerogams and vascular cryptogams: notes on the flora of Tory. *Irish Naturalist* 19: 189–192.

[7] **Praeger, R. Ll.** 1896. The plants of Inishmurray, Co. Sligo. *Irish Naturalist* 5: 177–178.

[8] **Praeger, R. Ll.** 1905. The flora of the Mullet and Inishkea. *Irish Naturalist.* 14: 229–244.

[9] **Curtis, T.G.F., McGough, H.N. & Akeroyd, J.R.** 1981. The flora of the Mullet Peninsula, West Mayo (H 27). *Bull. Ir. biogeog. Soc.* 5: 38–46.

[10] **Praeger, R. Ll. (ed.).** 1911–15. Biological Survey of Clare Island in the County of Mayo, Ireland, and of the adjoining district. *Proc. R. Ir. Acad.* 31B: sections I, II and III.

[11] **Praeger, R. Ll. (ed.).** 1907. Contributions to the Natural History of Lambay, County Dublin. *Irish Naturalist* 16: 1–112.

[12] **Doyle, G.J. & Foss, P.J.** 1986. A resurvey of the Clare Island Flora. *Ir. Nat. J.* 22: 85–89.

[13] **More, A.G.** 1876. Report on the Flora of Inishbofin, Galway. *Proc. R. Ir. Acad.* 2: 663–578.

[14] **Brodie, J. & Sheehy-Skeffington, M.** 1990. Inishbofin: a re-survey of the Flora. *Ir. Nat. Jour.* 23: 293–298.

[15] **Praeger, R. Ll.** 1911. Notes on the flora of Inishbofin. *Irish Naturalist.* 20: 165–172

[16] **Webb, D.A. & Hodgson, J.** 1968. The flora of Inishbofin and Inishark. *Proc. Bot. Soc. Br. Isl.* 7: 345–363.

[17] **Robinson, T.** 1986. *Stones of Aran. Pilgrimage.* Lilliput Press, Dublin.

[18] **Whittow, J.B.** 1974. *Geology and Scenery in Ireland.* Penguin Books, London.

[19] **Curtis, T.G.F. & McGough, M.N.** 1988. *The Irish Red Data Book: 1 Vascular Plants.* Stationery Office, Dublin.

[20] **Curtis, T.G.F., McGough, H.N. & Wymer, E.D.** 1988. The discovery and ecology of rare and threatened arable weeds, previously considered extinct in Ireland, on the Aran Islands, Co. Galway. *Ir. Nat. J.* 22: 505–512.

[21] **Parnell, J.A.N., Wyse-Jackson, P.S. & Akeroyd, J.R.** 1983. The flora of the Magharee Islands, Co. Kerry (H1). *Bull. Ir. biogeog. Soc.* 7: 45–53.

[22] **Barrington, R.M.** 1881. Report on the Flora of the Blasket Islands, Co. Kerry. *Proc. R. Ir. Acad.* (Series 2) 3: 368–391.

[23] **Ó Crohan, T.** 1934. *The Islandman.* Translated from the Irish, with an introduction by Robin Flower. Talbot Press, Dublin and Cork.

[24] **O'Sullivan, M.** 1933. *Twenty Years A-Growing.* Rendered from the original Irish by Moya Llewelyn Davies and George Thomson. Chatto & Windus, London.

[25] **Hart, H.C.** 1883. Report on the flora of the Wexford and Waterford Coasts. *Sci. Proc. Roy. Dublin Soc.* 4: 117–146.

[26] **Praeger, R.Ll.** 1913. Notes on the flora of

the Saltees. *Irish Naturalist* 22: 181–191.

[27] **Beattie, S.** 1992. *The Book of Inishtrahull.* The Foyle Press, Carndonagh.

[28] **Selfox, A.W.** 1943. Survey of Inishtrahull: part 4 (by light-keeper D.J. Sullivan). A list of the flowering plants, ferns, etc. *Ir. Nat. J.* 8: 116–123.

[29] **Fairley, J.** 1984. *An Irish Beast Book: A natural history of Ireland's furred wildlife.* Blackstaff Press, Belfast.

[30] **Fairley, J.** 1964. A collection of fieldmice from Rathlin Island, Northern Ireland. *Ann. Mag. nat. Hist.* 7: 27–31.

[31] **Fairley, J. S., McCarthy, T.K. & Andrews, J.F.** 1978. Notes on the fieldmice of Inishkea North and a large race of fieldmice from Great Blasket Island. *Ir. Nat. J.* 19: 270–271.

[32] **Moffat, C.B.** 1938. The mammals of Ireland. *Proc. R. Ir. Acad.* 44B: 61–128.

[33] **Cabot, D.** 1967. The birds of Duvillaun Mor, Co. Mayo. *Ir. Nat. J.* 15: 357–359.

[34] **Rutty, J.** 1772. *An Essay Towards a Natural History of the County Dublin.* 2 vols. W. Sleator, Dublin.

[35] **Mason, T.H.** 1936. *The Islands of Ireland.* Batsford, London.

[36] **Ruttledge, R.F. & Weaving, J. (eds.).** 1950–63. Annual reports from Saltee Bird Observatory. In: **Ruttledge, R.F. (ed.).** *Irish Bird Reports 1-11.* Irish Ornithologists' Club, Dublin.

[37] Copeland Bird Observatory Reports 1955–1997.

[38] **Sharrock, T.J.** 1973. *The Natural History of Cape Clear Island.* T & A D Poyser, Berkhamsted.

[39] **Pettitt, R.G. (ed.).** 1958–1965. Tory Island Bird Observatory. First Report (1958 and 1959), second (1960), third (1961), fourth (1962), fifth (1963 and 1964) and sixth (1965). Cyclostyled. Privately published.

[40] **Merne, O.J. & Devlin, D.** Malin Head Bird Observatory Reports 1961–1965. Privately published.

[41] **Ferguson, A. (ed.).** Mullet Bird Observatory. First report (1966). Published jointly with sixth report from Tory Island Bird Observatory.

[42] **Cabot, D.** 1962. Inishkea Ornithological Expedition 1961. 1–19. Cyclostyled Report. Privately published.

[43] **Barrington, R.M.** 1900. *The Migration of Birds as observed at Irish Lighthouses and Lightships.* R.H. Porter, London, and Edward Ponsonby, Dublin.

[44] **Hutchinson, C. D.** 1989. *Birds in Ireland.* T & A D Poyser, Calton.

[45] **Cramp, S. & Simmons, K.E.L. (eds.).** 1977. *Birds of the Western Palaearctic.* Vol.1. Oxford University Press, Oxford.

[46] **Lloyd, C.S & Perrins, C.M.** 1977. The survival and age at first breeding in the razorbill (*Alca torda*). *Bird Banding* 48: 239–252.

[47] **Macdonald, R.A.** 1987. The breeding population and distribution of the Cormorant in Ireland. *Irish Birds* 3: 405–416.

[48] **Cabot, D.** 1998. Population dynamics of the cormorant, *Phalacrocorax carbo*, breeding on Little Saltee, Co. Wexford 1960–1998. Unpublished report.

[49] **Sellers, R. M.** In: **Lloyd, C., Tasker, M.L. & Partridge, K.** 1991. *Op. cit.* 89.

[50] **West, B., Cabot, D. & Greer-Walker, M.** 1975. The food of the cormorant *Phalacrocorax carbo* at some breeding colonies in Ireland. *Proc. R. Ir. Acad.* 75B: 285–304.

[51] **Coulson, J. C. & Brazendale, M.G.** 1968. Movements of cormorants ringed in the British Isles, and evidence of colony-specific dispersal. *British Birds* 61: 1–21.

[52] **Wernham, C.** 1997. *Pers. comm.*

[53] **Fisher, J.** 1952. A history of the fulmar *Fulmarus glacialis* and its population problems. *Ibis* 94: 334–354.

[54] **Wynne-Edwards, V.C.** 1962. *Animal Dispersion in Relation to Social Behaviour.* Oliver and Boyd, Edinburgh.

[55] **Salomonsen, F.** 1965. Geographic variation of the Fulmar (*Fulmarus glacialis*) and zones of the marine environment in the North Atlantic. *Auk* 85: 327–355.

[56] **Cabot, D.** 1997. A population study of the fulmar, *Fulmarus glacialis*, on Little Saltee, Co. Wexford, 1960–1997. Unpublished report.

[57] **Dunnet, G.M., Ollason, J.C. & Anderson, A.** 1979. A 28-year study of breeding Fulmars *Fulmarus glacialis* in Orkney. *Ibis* 121: 293–300.

[58] **Fisher, J.** 1952. *The New Naturalist: The Fulmar.* Collins, London.

[59] **Lloyd, C. S.** The seabirds of Great Saltee. *Irish Birds* 2: 1–37.

[60] **Whilde, A.** 1979. Auks trapped in salmon drift nets. *Irish Birds* 1: 370–376.

[61] **West, A.B.** 1972. Observations on the resting metabolic rate of barnacle geese and on their daily energy flux during winter. A preliminary report. Unpublished report, Dublin.

[62] **White, T. H.** 1959. *The Godstone and the Blackymore.* Jonathan Cape, London.

[63] **Ogilvie, M.A, Boertmann, D., Cabot, D., Merne, O., Percival, S.M. & Sigfusson, A**. 1998. In press. Barnacle goose *Branta leucopsis:* Greenland. In: **Madsen, J., Cracknell, G.S. & Fox, A.D. (eds.).** *Goose populations of the Western Palearctic: A review of status and distribution.* Wetlands International, Wageningen, and NERI, Roende.

[64] **Cabot, D. & West, B.** 1973. Population dynamics of barnacle geese, *Branta leucopsis,* in Ireland. *Proc. R. Ir. Acad.* 73B:415–443.

[65] **Cabot, D. & West, B.** 1983. Studies on the population of barnacle geese *Branta leucopsis* wintering on the Inishkea Islands, Co. Mayo. 1. Population dynamics 1961–1983. *Irish Birds* 2: 318–336.

[66] **Cabot, D., Goodwillie, R. & Viney, M.** 1988. *Irish Expedition to North-East Greenland 1987.* Barnacle Books, Dublin.

[67] **Cabot, D., Nairn, R., Newton, S. & Viney, M.** 1984. *Biological Expedition to Jameson Land, Greenland. 1984.* Barnacle Books, Dublin.

[68] **Hewer, H.R.** 1974. *The New Naturalist: British Seals.* Collins, London.

[69] **Ritchie, J.** 1921. The Walrus in British Waters. *Scot. Nat.* 1921. 5–9; 77–86.

[70] **Anon.** 1994. Unusual sightings of marine life around Britain. *Marine Conservation* 3 (3): 14.

[71] **Viney, M. & Berrow, S.** 1995. Walrus *Odobenus rosmarus* (L.) in Co. Kerry. *Ir. Nat. J.* 25:150.

[72] **Kiely, O.** 1997. *Pers. comm.*

[73] **Corbet, G.B. & Southern, H.N. (eds.).** 1977. *The Handbook of British Mammals.* 2nd edition. Blackwell Scientific Publications, Oxford.

[74] **Summers, C.F.** 1980. The Grey Seal, *Halichoerus grypus,* in NW Ireland. A report to the Minister for Fisheries, Forestry and Wildlife. Unpublished manuscript, Dublin.

[75] **Summers, C.F.** 1983. The Grey Seal, *Halichoerus grypus,* in Ireland. Report to the Minister for Fisheries, Forestry and Wildlife. Unpublished manuscript, Dublin.

[76] **Kiely, O.** 1997. *Pers. comm.*

[77] **Lockley, R.M.** 1966. The distribution of grey and common seals on the coast of Ireland. *Ir. Nat. J.* 15: 136–143.

[78] **Harwood, J. & Prime, J.H.** 1980. Some factors affecting the size of British grey seal populations. *J. Appl. Ecol.* **15**: 401–411.

[79] **Hiby, A., Duck, C., Hall, A. & Harwood, J.** 1996. Seal stocks in Great Britain. *NERC News.* January: 20–22.

[80] **McCarthy, D.T.** 1985. *Interaction between seals and salmon drift net fisheries in the west of Ireland.* Fisheries Leaflet No. 126. Department of Fisheries and Forestry, Dublin.

[81] **International Council for the Exploration of the Sea** 1979. Ad hoc working group on the interaction between Grey seal population and fish species. ICES CM 1979 N/:5.

[82] **Cabot, D. & Crummey, C.** 1997. Numbers of grey seals hauled out at the Dock, Inishkea North, Co. Mayo. Observations by D. Cabot 1970–1986 and C. Crummey, 1993–1997. Unpublished data.

[83] **Anderson, S.** 1990. *Seals.* Whitten Books, London.

[84] **Crummey, C.** 1997. *Pers. comm.*

[85] **Summers, C.F., Warner, P.J., Nairn, R.G.W., Curry, M.G. & Flynn, L.** 1980. An assessment of the status of the common seal *Phoca vitulina vitulina* in Ireland. *Biol. Conserv.* 17: 115–123.

[86] **Warner, P.** 1983. An assessment of the breeding population of common seals (*Phoca vitulina vitulina* L.) in the Republic of Ireland during 1979. *Ir. Nat. J.* 21: 24–26.

[87] **Vaughan, R.W.** 1978. A study of common seals in the Wash. *Mammal Rev.* 8: 25–34.

CHAPTER 11

[1] **Draper, L.** In: **Lee, A.J. & Ramster, J. W. (eds.).** 1981. *Atlas of the Seas around the British Isles.* 2.19. Ministry of Agriculture, Fisheries and Food, HMSO, London.

[2] **Johnstone, J., Scott, A. & Chadwick, H.C.** 1924. *The Marine Plankton.* Hodder and Stoughton, London.

[3] **Lee, A.J. & Ramster, J.W. (eds.).** 1981. *Op. cit.*

[4] **Wynne-Edwards, W.C.** 1935. The habits and distribution of birds on the North Atlantic. *Proc. Boston Soc. Nat. Hist.* 40: 233–346.

[5] **Pollock, C.M.** 1994. Observations on the distribution of seabirds off south-west Ireland. *Irish Birds* 5: 173–182.

[6] **Bourne, W.R.P.** 1986. Late summer seabird distribution off the west coast of Europe. *Irish Birds* 3:175–198.

[7] **O'Riordan, C.E.** 1972. Provisional list of Cetacea and turtles stranded or captured on the Irish coast. *Proc. R. Ir. Acad.* 72B: 253–274.

[8] **O'Riordan, C.E.** 1981. A review of the provisional list of Cetacea stranded or captured on the Irish coast. *Ir. Nat. J.* 20:

203–204.

[9] **Berrow, S.D. & Rogan, E.** 1997. Review of cetaceans stranded on the Irish coast, 1901–95. *Mammal Rev.* 27: 51–76.

[10] **Sharrock, J.T.R. (ed.).** 1973. *The Natural History of Cape Clear Island.* T & A D Poyser, Berkhamsted.

[11] **Fennelly, S.** 1993. Mayo Whale and Dolphin Survey. 1993 Report. Unpublished manuscript.

[12] **Evans, P.** 1997. Irish Sea Survey, 1995. *Newsletter for the Sea Watch Foundation* 2 (6): 7–9.

[13] **Lille, D.G.** 1910. Observations on the anatomy and general biology of some members of the larger Cetacea. *Proc. zool. Soc. Lond.* (1910): 769–792.

[14] **Hardy, A.** 1959. *The New Naturalist: The Open Sea: Fish and Fisheries.* Collins, London.

[15] **Thompson, D'A. W.** 1928. On whales landed at the Scottish whaling stations during the years 1908–1914 and 1920–1927. *Scientific Investigations of the Fishery Board of Scotland.*(1929) (3): 1–40.

[16] **Smiddy, P. & Berrow, S.** 1992. Humpback whale *Megaptera novaeangliae* (Borowski). *Ir. Nat. J.* 24: 162.

[17] **Burfield, S.T.** 1913. Belmullet whaling station. Report of the committee. *Report of the British Association for the Advancement of Science* (Dundee:1912): 148–186.

[18] **Evans, P.G.H.** 1992. *Status Review of Cetaceans in British and Irish Waters.* Department of Environment, London.

[19] **Fairley, J.** 1981. *Irish Whales and Whaling.* Blackstaff Press, Belfast.

[20] **Matthews, L.H.** 1952. *The New Naturalist: British Mammals.* Collins, London.

[21] **Berrow, S.D., Evans, P.G.H. & Sheldrick, M.C.** 1993. An analysis of Sperm whale *Physeter macrocephalus* (L.) stranding and sighting data from Britain and Ireland. *J. Zool. Lond.* 230: 333–337

[22] **Clarke, M.R.** 1978. Buoyancy control as a function of the spermaceti organ in the sperm whale. *Journal of the Marine Biological Association of the United Kingdom* 58: 27–71.

[23] **Heezen, B.C.** 1957. Whales caught in deep-sea cables. *Deep-Sea Research* 4: 105–115.

[24] **Hamilton, J.E.** 1915. Belmullet whaling station. Report of the committee. *Report of the British Association for the Advancement of Science* (Australia:1914) 125–161.

[25] **Clarke, R.** 1956. A giant squid swallowed by a sperm whale. *Challenger Society.*

Abstracts 3: VIII. 31.

[26] **Clarke, R.** 1959. Quoted in: **Hardy, A.** 1959. *Op. cit.*

[27] **Hamilton, J.E.** 1916. Belmullet whaling station. Report of the committee. *Report of the British Association for the Advancement of Science* (Manchester:1915) 124–146.

[28] **Fairley, J.S. & Mooney, E.P.** 1989. Pygmy sperm whale *Kogia breviceps* (Blainville). *Ir. Nat. J.* 22: 164.

[29] **Bruton, T., Cotton, D. & Enright, M.** 1989. Gulf stream beaked whale *Mesoplodon europaeus* (Gervais). *Ir. Nat. J.* 23: 156.

[30] **Stendall, J.A.S.** 1948. A white whale off Clare Island, Co. Mayo. *Ir. Nat. J.* 9: 215.

[31] **Carmody, M.** 1988. White whale *Delphinapterus leucas* (Pallas). *Ir. Nat. J.* 22: 540.

[32] **Rogan, E. & Berrow, S.D.** 1996. A review of harbour porpoises, *Phocoena phocoena*, in Irish waters. *Report of the International Whaling Commission* 46: 595–605.

[33] **Crummey, C.** 1997. *Pers. comm.*

[34] **Gresson, R.A.R.** 1966. Pilot whales, *Globiocephala melaena* (Traill) stranded at Cloghane, Co. Kerry. *Ir. Nat. J.* 15: 163–165.

[35] **Smiddy, P.** 1996. Pilot whale *Globicephala melaena* (Traill). *Ir. Nat. J.* 25: 295.

[36] **Cabot. D. & Cassidy, M.** 1997. Personal observations.

[37] **Berrow, S.D., Holmes, B. & Kiely, O.R.** 1996. Distribution and abundance of bottle-nosed dolphins *Tursiops truncatus* (Montague) in the Shannon Estuary. *Biology and Environment. Proc. R. Ir. Acad.* 96B: 1–9.

[38] **Rogan, E., Baker, J.R., Jepson, P.D., Berrow, S. & Kiely, O.** 1997. A mass stranding of white-sided dolphins (*Lagenorhynchus acutus*) in Ireland: biological and pathological studies. *J. Zool., Lond.* 242: 217–227.

[39] **Rogan, E.** 1997. *Pers. comm.*

[40] **Bruton, T. & Greer, J.** 1985. Euphrosyne dolphin *Stenella coeruleoalba* (Meyen). *Ir. Nat. J.* 12: 538–540.

[41] **Anon.** 1768. An account of the whale fishing on the coasts of Ireland. *Scots Magazine* 30: 509–510.

[42] **Fairley, J.** 1981. *Op. cit.*

[43] **McNally, K.** 1976. *The Sun-Fish Hunt.* Blackstaff Press, Belfast.

[44] **Matthews, L.H. & Parker, H.W.** 1950. Notes on the anatomy and biology of the basking shark. *Proc. zool. Soc. Lond.* 120: 535–576.

[45] **Parker, H.W. & Boeseman, M.** 1954. The

basking shark, *Cetorhinus maximus*, in winter. *Proc. zool. Soc. Lond.* 124: 185–194.

[46] **Earll, R.C. & Turner, J.R.** 1992. A review of methods and results from a sighting scheme and field research on the basking shark in 1987–92. Prepared for a Basking Shark Workshop at the University of North Wales. School of Marine Sciences, 15th December 1992.

[47] **Berrow, S.D. & Heardman, C.** 1994. The basking shark *Cetorhinus maximus* (Gunnerus) in Irish waters – patterns of distribution and abundance. *Biology and Environment: Proc. R. Ir. Acad.* 94B: 101–107.

[48] **Matthews, L.H. & Parker, H.W.** 1951. Basking sharks leaping. *Proc. zool. Soc. Lond.* 121: 461–462.

[49] **Crummey, C., Ronan, M. & Fahy, E.** 1991. Blue shark *Prionace glauca* (L.) in Irish Waters. *Ir. Nat. J.* 23: 454–456.

[59] **Anon.** 1836. *First Report of the Commissioners of Inquiry into the State of the Irish Fisheries.* Dublin. Appendix XVII.

[51] **Brabazon, W.** 1848. *The Deep Sea and Coast Fisheries of Ireland.* James McGlacken, Dublin.

[52] **Went, A.E. & Ó Suilleabháin, S.** 1967. Fishing for the sun-fish or basking shark in Irish waters. *Proc. R. Ir. Acad.* 65C: 91–115.

[53] **Crummey, C.** 1997. *Pers. comm.*

[54] **Horsman, P.V.** 1987. The basking shark, *Cetorhinus maximus* – a species under threat? Marine Conservation Society, Ross-on-Wye.

[55] **Berrow, S. & Rogan, E.** 1995. Stomach contents of a leathery turtle *Dermochelys coriacea* L caught off southwest Ireland. *Ir. Nat. J.* 25: 36 – 37.

[56] **O'Connor, B & Bowmer, T.** 1985. First record of *Conchoderma virgatum* (Spengler) (Crustacea: Cirripedia) on a leathery turtle *Dermochelys coriacea* (L.) in Irish waters. *I. Nat. J.* 21: 409–410.

[57] **Cooper, T., McGrath, D. & O'Connor, B.** 1982. Species associated with a sunfish *Mola mola* (L.) from the west coast of Ireland. *I. Nat. J.* 20: 382–383.

[58] **King, G.** 1983. Provisional List of the Leathery Turtle (*Dermochelys coriacea* L.) Recorded in Irish Coastal Waters from 1973 – 1983. Unpublished manuscript, Dublin.

[59] **King, G.** 1996: quoted In: **Langton, T.E.S., Beckett, C.L., King, G.L. & Gaywood, M.J.** *Distribution and status of marine turtles in Scottish waters.* Scottish Natural Heritage Research, Survey and Monitoring Report No. 8. Perth, Scotland.

[60] **Langton, T.E.S., Beckett, C.L. & Dunmore, I.** 1993. U.K. Herpetofauna. A review of British Herpetofauna populations in a wider context. Unpublished report to JNCC by H. C. I.

[61] **O'Riordan, C.E. & Holmes, J.M.C.** 1984. First recorded occurrence of the hawksbill turtle (*Eretmochelys imbricata*)(L.) in Irish waters. *Ir. Nat. J.* 21: 274–275.

[62] **Frazer, D.** 1983. *The New Naturalist: Reptiles and Amphibians in Britain.* Collins, London.

[63] **McGrath, D., Mitchen, D. & Cotton, D.** 1994. Extraordinary occurrence of the by-the-wind sailor *Velella velella* (L.) (Cnidaria) in Irish waters in 1992. *Ir. Nat. J.* 24: 383–388.

[64] **Nelson, E.C.** 1978. Tropical drift fruits and seeds on coasts in the British Isles and western Europe, 1. Irish beaches. *Watsonia.* 12: 103–112.

[65] **L'Obel, Matthias de Pena.** 1570. *Stirpium Adversaria Nova.* London.

[66] **Sloane, H.** 1696. An account of four sorts of strange beans frequently cast on shore on the Orkney Isles. *Phil. Trans.* 19: 298–300.

[67] **Sloane, H.** 1725. *The Natural History of Jamaica.* London.

[68] **[Blake, H., M., L., et alia.].** 1825. *Letters from the Irish Highlands of Cunnemara.* Longmans, London.

[69] **Lankaster, E (ed.).** 1848. *The Correspondence of John Ray.* The Ray Society, London.

[70] **Guppy, H.B.** 1917. *Plants, Seeds and Currents in the West Indies and the Azores.* Williams of Norgate, London.

[71] **Colgan, N.** 1919. On the occurrence of tropical drift seeds on the Irish Atlantic coasts. *Proc. R. Ir. Acad.* 35B: 29–54.

[72] **Nelson, E.C.** 1982. Tropical drift fruits and seeds – a new Irish species. *Ir. Nat. J.* 20: 452.

[73] Seeds seen by the author 1996 in the collection of Bernie Winters, Clare Island, Co. Mayo.

[74] **Praeger, R. Ll.** 1950. *The Natural History of Ireland : A Sketch of its Flora and Fauna.* Collins, London.

[75] **Scannell M.J.P.** 1977. Personal communication to Nelson, E.C. 1978. *Op. cit.*

CHAPTER 12

[1] **Mitchell, F. & Ryan, M.** 1997. *Reading the Irish Landscape.* Town House, Dublin.

[2] **Whilde, A.** 1993. *Threatened Mammals, Birds, Amphibians and Fish in Ireland. Irish Red Data Book 2: Vertebrates.* HMSO, Belfast.

[3] **Foss, Peter J. & O'Connell, Catherine A.** 1996. *Irish Peatland Conservation Plan 2000.* Irish Peatland Council, Dublin.

[4] **Dúchas, The Heritage Service. nd** [1998]. *Nature on the Farm.* Advisory Booklet No 1. Environmentally Friendly Farming. Dúchas, Dublin.

[5] **McAdam, J.H.** 1995. Sheep density and vegetation change in *Eriophorum/Mollinia* upland grassland. In: **Jeffrey, D.W., Jones, M.B. & McAdam, J.H. (eds.).** *Irish Grasslands – Their Biology and Management.* 59–66. Royal Irish Academy, Dublin.

[6] **Bleasdale, A. & Sheehy-Skeffington, M.** 1995. The upland vegetation of north-east Connemara in relation to sheep grazing. In: **Jeffrey, D.W., Jones, M.B. & McAdam, J.H. (eds.).** *Op. cit.* 110–124.

[7] **Stapleton, L. (ed.).** 1996. *State of the Environment.* Environmental Protection Agency, Wexford.

[8] **Ryan, J. B. & Cross, J. C.** 1984. Conservation of Peatlands. In: *Proceedings of the 7th International Congress, Dublin.*

[9] **Sea Trout Action Group** 1992. *1991 Report.*

[10] **Irish Salmon Growers Association** 1992. *Preliminary Review of Sea Trout Problems and Research to December 1991.* Irish Salmon Growers' Association, Dublin.

[11] **Anon.** 1994. *Report of the Sea Trout Task Force.* Department of the Marine, Dublin.

[12] **Cabot, D. (ed.)** 1993. *Report of the Green 2000 Advisory Group to the Taoiseach.* Stationery Office, Dublin.

[13] **Curtis, T.G.F & McGough, H.N.** 1988. *The Irish Red Data Book. 1. Vascular Plants.* Stationery Office, Dublin.

[14] **Neff, M.J.** 1984. The future of nature reserves in the Republic of Ireland – a personal view. In: **Jeffrey, D.W. (ed.).** *Nature Conservation in Ireland: Progress and Problems.* 151–160. Royal Irish Academy, Dublin.

[15] **Union of Professional & Technical Civil Servants.** 1987. *Our Natural Heritage: A Policy for Nature Conservation in Ireland.* Union of Professional and Technical Civil Servants, Dublin.

[16] **Rothschild, M & Marren, P.** 1997. *Rothschild's Reserves: Time and Fragile Nature.* Balaban Publishers, Israel.

[17] **Society for the Promotion of Nature Reserves.** 1915. *Provisional Schedule of Areas in Ireland considered worthy of preservation arranged in alphabetical lists according to their names and according to the Counties in which they are situated, with separate sections for areas of primary and those of secondary importance.* Privately printed, SPNR, London. 1–6.

[18] **Walsh, G. (ed.).** 1997. *Living Heritage* 14: 1–88.

[19] **An Foras Forbartha.** 1969. *The Protection of the National Heritage.* An Foras Forbartha, Dublin.

[20] **Cabot, D. (ed.).** 1981. *Areas of Scientific Interest in Ireland.* An Foras Forbartha, Dublin.

[21] **Feehan, J.** 1997. Attitudes to Nature in Ireland. In: **Foster, J.W. & Chesney, H.C.G. (eds.).** *Nature in Ireland: A Scientific and Cultural History.* 573–596. Lilliput Press, Dublin

[22] **National Parks and Wildlfe Service.** 1997. *Proposed Candidate Special Areas of Conservation.* Department of Arts, Culture and the Gaeltacht, Dublin.

[23] **European Commission DG XI.** 1998. *Natura 2000* Newsletter 6: 6.

[24] **The Council for Nature Conservation & the Countryside.**1997. *Fourth Report 1994–1996.* Stationery Office, Belfast.

[25] **O'Gorman, F. & Wymes, E.(eds.).** 1973. *The Future of Irish Wildlife– A Blueprint for Development.* An Foras Talúntais, Dublin.

[26] **Dúchas – The Heritage Service.** 1998. *Pers comm.*

[27] **Dúchas – The Heritage Service.** 1998. *Pers comm.*

[28] **Dúchas – The Heritage Service.** 1998. *Pers comm.*

[29] **Environment and Heritage Service, Department of the Environment.** 1993. *Conserving Peatland in Northern Ireland. A Statement of Policy.* Environment Service, Belfast.

APPENDIX

[1] **Council for Nature Conservation & the Countryside.** *Second Report 1991–1992.* Stationery Office, Belfast.

Index